Sargent's
American Premium Guide To
POCKET KNIVES
Identifications and Values

By
Jim Sargent

ISBN 0-89689-067-8

BOOKS AMERICANA
INC

DEDICATION

To Jim W. Sargent, Senior
1910-1988

In Memorium

J. P. Huddleston - Rare Case
Fred Rascoe - Western States

ACKNOWLEDGEMENTS

It is never possible to acknowledge all who contribute to works of this sort. There are as always so many helpful and cooperative people in an endeavor such as this that to thank them all in print would be impractical. To those of you who worked so hard on my behalf, my heartfelt thanks. I hope the finished work meets with your approval.

Without photographs the book would be unfinished at best, so many thanks to the following for their cordial hospitality and permission to photograph their collections: Joe Chance, Paul Davis, Barney Hightower, John Lussier, Norma and Herman Williams. A special thanks to Sherry Alexander, Jean Sargent, Jace Sargent and Gina Sargent for their contribution. Other contributors who made this update possible: George White, Dr. Steve Kiltau, Fred Marziotto, Steve Cary, Larry Robertson, J.P. Huddleston, Fred Rascoe, Rich Kupillas, Tony Foster, Ralph Scruton, Cricket Sargent Cooke and Harry King.

WE NEED YOUR HELP!

Should you come across a knife that you feel should be included in our next book, please send us a clear, black and white photograph along with the pattern number (if there is one), handle material, length (closed), and stamping.

TABLE OF CONTENTS

A WORD FROM THE AUTHOR

In considering my approach to this guide, there were several things that I wished to bring to the collector. First and foremost was to have the most realistic values available, next was to photograph as many knives possible and to have them so distinct that the reader could see the smallest details. Last but certainly not least, was to produce a guide for the novice as well as the expert knife fancier.

The reader will also see that emphasis was placed on older knives such as Case's "older knives and Tested XX through 1970 (10 Dot)," anything after that usually carries the suggested retail price anyway. However, beginning on page 144 we do list 9 Dots down through 6 Dot.

There are still a lot of old knives out there that haven't been discovered or just haven't been brought forward. Hopefully we can encourage the folks who possess those Remington Bullets and other rarities to join us in the camaraderie of knife collecting.

This 2nd edition now includes two more U.S. made knives – Keen Kutter and Western States. It also includes a very comprehensive Case Razor section. As this book goes to press, we are researching other U.S. knife manufacturers in order to include them in subsequent editions.

A Word About Limited Editions

Each limited edition knife or set will be given careful consideration as to whether it warrants inclusion into further editions of the "American Premium Guide to Pocket Knives." Those with themes based on National historical events will be given highest priority. Others such as NKCA events, Factory Anniversaries and Conservation themes will follow.

Pricing

Prices in this book are for knives in mint condition only. Deduct value for the following grades: Excellent - 40%, Good - 60%, Poor - 75%.

Remember, when approaching a dealer in order to sell a collection or one knife, you will most likely be offered 40% to 50% of these listed values. Dealers are businessmen and must pay overhead, salaries, etc. and make enough profit to buy the groceries.

THE HISTORY OF KNIVES

A crude cutting tool, or knife, was probably one of the first tools used by primitive man. From the first moment he used a sharp rock to crack a pterodactyl egg, man has never stopped looking for ways to improve on the knife. In reality, it has not been a man's search for a better mouse trap that helped shape society, but rather his search for a better knife.

175,000 years ago, give or take a century, man dropped down out of the trees, stood on his own two feet, picked up a sharp stone and went out to search for dinner. He moved to a cave for warmth and protection. Then, he discovered fire.

The discovery of fire followed by the innovation of cooked foods, created a need for more refined tools (knives). To coin a phrase, "Necessity is the mother of invention." And so, the flint knife was born. Flint was a more pliable medium than stone and man found he could shape and fashion a more efficient tool. He also found that by heating this tool in a fire it became tougher and more durable.

During this period, the family or tribal unit was coming into its own. Man had begun to settle down. He had his cave and his fire, he hunted food and prepared it with his greatly improved knife. Yet, instinctively he knew things had just begun.

Metal was the next great step toward a more durable and pliable resource with which to ease his daily chores. With the introduction of iron around 3000 B.C. man had truly reached a "Golden Age" that would revolutionize his life.

Once iron was a routine part of the tool maker's materials, steel was not far away. Steel was truly the one material that revolutionized our lives. The steel industry, as we know it today, which is actually the basis for all modern day industry, came about because of man's search for the "Better Knife."

By the 14th century advances in the steel industry, and therefore in the cutlery industry, caused a great deal of romance and fantasy to spring up around certain forges. The skill of some steelmakers was cloaked in more secrecy than surrounded the invention of the atom bomb. Mythology speaks of King Arthur's Excalibur, The Singing Sword. It tells us of Balmung, the knife with which Sigfried split the anvil with one stroke.

Metals for the famous Damascus weapons were forged in India. Damascus weapons were produced by laminating high carbon steel with milder steel in layers. This process is still in use today.

During the early Christian era, production of the dagger, or sheath knife, was a forge's major product. The dagger was not just a form of protection, but a utensil important to good table manners.

By the 15th century, England emerged as the center for fine steel and cutlery. London, Hallamshire and Sheffield were known then, as they are today, for their knowledge of the cutler's art. The cutlery guilds began here, and formed the basic models for our present day trade unions.

CARING FOR YOUR KNIVES

Rust is as old as iron and finding a cure for rust is like finding a cure for the common cold. There are some precautions that should be taken so your collection of knives will not diminish in value.

Cleaning

Use a soft, all cotton cloth or chamois to clean your knives, then apply a coat of Simichrome Polish - put on and wipe off (leaves protective film) on the entire knife. Vaseline should never be used because it allows moisture to seep beneath its coat and cause rust. It is a good idea to check your knives often for possible trouble spots.

Storage and Handling

The most recommended method of storing knives is in vinyl rolls with a cloth interior. These rolls are also a very convenient way to transport knives. Leather rolls have a small degree of tanning acid in them and this can cause rust. If it is possible, leave your knives unrolled during storage; this allows air movement and cuts down on moisture.

Display cases with felt interiors are another way to store knives and also allows a collection to be exhibited easily. Some collectors use elastic bands to attach their knives to the display while others choose to use wire. Elastic makes it easier to slip knives in and out for closer inspection while wires must be cut and replaced each time. A plexiglass top will also cut down on dust and possible theft.

Transporting your knives from cold to warmth will cause condensation which will result in rust. In other words, don't leave your collection in your car trunk over night during the cold season and then bring it into the show the next day without expecting some condensation. Keep your knives at a constant temperature or at least within a few degrees at all times.

A word about celluloid. . .celluloid was made from a petroleum base and does give off fumes; these fumes will cause rust. Keep celluloids stored separately.

A word about sunlight. . .direct sunlight fades anything!

Knife handles are fragile especially Bones, Stags, Pearls, so don't toss around carelessly and DON'T DROP. Broken or cracked handles reduce value.

WHAT TO COLLECT

There are some who collect everything as long as it is of excellent quality and brand. Then there are other schools of thought such as collecting by:

Pattern. . .Trappers, Peanuts, Gunstocks, etc.

Handle Materials. . .Goldstone, Pearl, Rogers bone, etc.

Manufacturer. . .Cases, Queens, Schrade-Waldens, etc.

Specialties. . .advertising knives.

It would be wise for a beginner to come to a decision before too much is invested in his or her collection.

KNIVES AS INVESTMENTS

There are knife dealers and there are knife collectors and it is most important to choose your direction before jumping in with both feet. Some people are both but they know when to turn their hat around when it comes to dealing. So, if your main interest is turning a profit in knife marketing there are a few things that affect the pricing structure and you must learn to recognize these.

General economic conditions. . .when times are bad, individuals and dealers are willing to take less than they would during the previous "good times" in order to obtain some badly needed ready cash. As a dealer this may be the best time to pick up some collections at a depressed price but you also know that your own inventory isn't selling at the previous higher prices. If you have the staying power, your purchases at this time can reap benefits when times are better.

Sudden increases in numbers of knives available. . .sometimes large collections are broken up and introduced back into the knife market. A company will announce that it will no longer produce knives with a certain handle material, in turn driving up that particular handle material; however, several years later you may find that the company that stopped producing with that material is going to release another several thousand limited edition with the same material and this may tend to level off prices. There have been warehouse discoveries of large numbers of certain patterns with these being dumped into the market. You can imagine what this will do to prices.

Remember, not all knives continually go up in value. In short, playing the knife market is like playing the stock market; keep your finger on the pulse and stay up with it on a daily basis by reading newsletters, monthly knife publications and by keeping your ears open.

Then there is the investor that purely enjoys his or her collection and the price is inconsequential if that certain Peanut will finally fill out that treasured display. The collection is then thought of as part of the family and no one thinks of selling their children, right?

3

NKCA CLUB KNIFE

YEAR	NO. UNITS	COMPANY	COST	HIGH VALUE	INCREASE	PRESENT VALUE	% INCREASE
1975	1,200	Robert Klass	$12.00	$650.00	5,300%	$425.00	3,400%
1976	3,000	Case	15.00	165.00	1,000%	125.00	740%
1977	5,000	Robert Klass	17.50	100.00	470%	65.00	270%
1978	6,000	Schrade	18.25	75.00	310%	45.00	150%
1979	10,000	Case	22.00	60.00	175%	45.00	105%
1980	12,000	Robert Klass	21.75	50.00	130%	40.00	84%
1981	12,000	Queen	24.50	45.00	84%	35.00	43%
1982	10,000	Schrade	25.50	45.00	76%	35.00	37%
1983	6,000	Case	45.00	110.00	244%	95.00	211%
1984	7,500	Hen & Rooster	38.00	75.00	197%	75.00	197%
1985	7,000	Case 6240SP S.S.	40.00			85.00	
1986	6,200	Gerber 1 blade LB	39.00			75.00	
1987	7,000	Case G6345½SS	42.95			75.00	

FINDING POCKET KNIVES

The days of wandering the backroads in search of general stores and hardware stores in order to relieve the owner of his outdated and overburdened knife displays are over. Some of the reasons that these fertile hunting grounds are a thing of the past are that the owners of these emporiums grew wise to the fact that they themselves already had a decent start on their own collections, another reason is that as knife collecting grew in popularity it didn't take long for the collectors to clean these sources out, and still another is the sad fact that so many of these popular gathering places have been pushed aside for more modern convenient stores, discount stores and malls.

Don't be disheartened though, there are still excellent sources for a would-be serious collector.

Join a nearby club and become a student of knives. Get your hands on as many knife publications as possible and **learn**. (Many knife clubs have swap meets.) Attend Knife Shows. These are excellent places to find knives, and the prices are usually very reasonable due to very competitiveness of the dealers. Several other sources are antique shows, flea markets, estate auctions and dealers' direct mail lists.

Also, don't forget that there are still those mystical, dark, cluttered corners of attics, barns, garages and workshops. One never knows what lurks in the bottom of that tattered old cardboard box.

4

CONDITION

Mint...never been carried or sharpened, straight from the factory and sometimes in the original box.
Excellent...handles are in good shape, blades still close with a snap and also blades show only slight wear.
Very Good...blades show approximately 25% wear, handles in good condition, one blade may snap weakly, blades can't have been repaired or changed, stamp can still be seen clearly with the naked eye.
Fair...blades how 50% wear, blade closing is mushy, cracked handles, replaced handles, blades repaired or changed, stamp is weak.
Poor...these are used mostly as parts knives and will have well worn or broken blades, handles are broken or completely missing, the stamp is barely visible, if at all.

RESTORATION

There is absolutely nothing wrong with restoring a knife by using original parts that are available. Most of the time it makes the knife even more desirable than one in worn condition.

We can draw a parallel here with the restorations of antique and classic automobiles. When one of these is restored with original parts you can be sure it is more valuable so don't worry whether a knife has been restored. Of course, if you find an old knife and you are positive that it is in original mint condition and it's still in the original box you are better off.

COUNTERFEITING

COUNTERFEIT.."something made to imitate another thing with a view to defraud." With the explosion in popularity of knife collecting, there came the unscrupulous individual that preys on the uninformed and novice collector. Some of these individuals have the equipment and skills to produce nearly perfect copies of existing patterns while others do jobs that stick out like a sore thumb.

The following are some obvious things to look for, plus photos that will point out a few of the counterfeiter's tricks:
•handle materials that don't match up with the proper number in the factory numbering system.
•knowing dates and when materials were no longer used, for instance, Christmas Tree, Gold Stone, Candy Stripe and Multi-colored Celluloid were only used prior to 1940...Yellow Celluloid with a white liner was used by Case until mid 50's prior to 1940 while the compositions are still being used today, such as, Yellow, Black, and White.
It will take a little "schooling" to become knowledgeable in this.
•stampings that have been altered either by completely grinding off the old stamp and new ones applied, this is also time to discuss that the tangs and backsprings should be of the same thickness because grinding will make the tang thinner...look for numbers that are of different size than the factory numbers, they will probably be of poorer quality and spaced differently than the other numbers...the black within a factory stamp is hard to come off while it is easier to remove from a counterfeit.
•there should be no protruding rivets inside of liner.
•some shields are obviously amateurishly made and are glued on.

Counterfeits that show up are usually over $100.00 so it is a good idea to ask for a bill of sale or an invoice. Reputable dealers are always happy to supply these. If you find yourself with a counterfeit knife and can't locate the seller, don't put it back in the market but have it displayed somewhere so it may save someone else a loss.

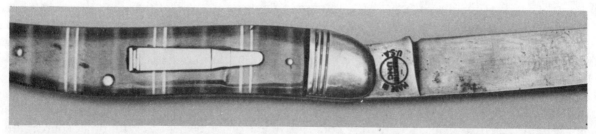

**REMINGTON, wrong number R1615L, bullet shield on a candy-stripe handle, stamp is etched.
REMINGTON CAMMILLIUS.**

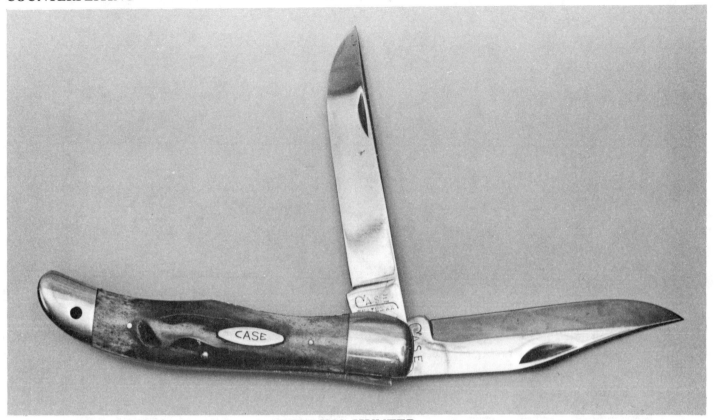

FOLDING HUNTER
5265 SAB TESTED XX, handles have been installed, cold stamp, blade ground to fit backspring, pull in wrong place, drilled for lanyard. Lanyard holes were not drilled until 1964.

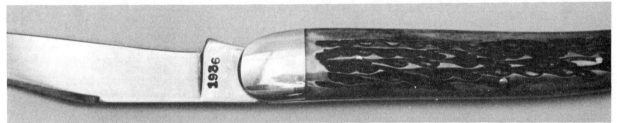

WINCHESTER 1936
Handles put on, cold stamp, 6 is longer than other numbers.

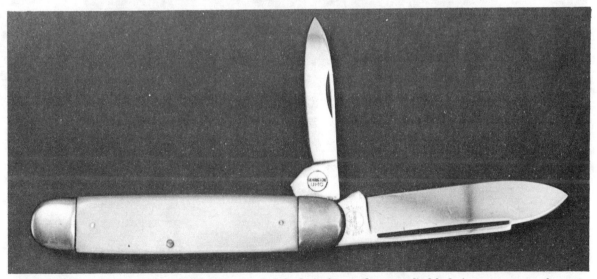

Remington stamp put on with elec. pencil, (circle is fuzzy & ragged), blade is too narrow for backspring.

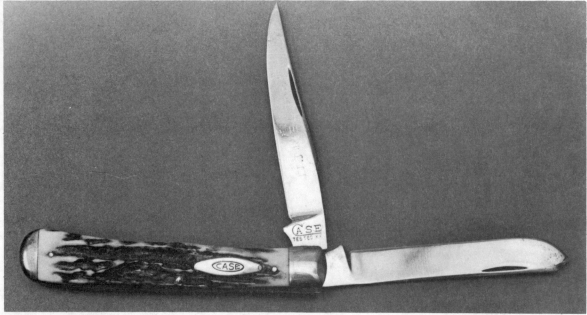

CASE TRAPPER
Stag handle, stag has been installed, master blade milled & too narrow, stamp cold stamped, appears to be on a K-Bar Frame.

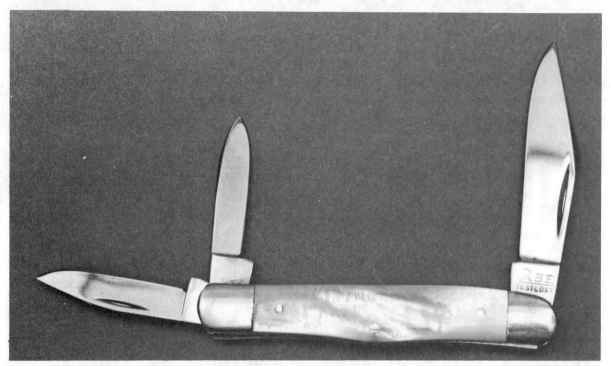

8308 PEARL WHITTLER
New pearl, cold stamped, blade is concave ground made out of a new 08 Pattern Whittler.

AROUND THE SHOWS

Gil and Linda Hibben (center and right) exhibiting at one of the many national shows held in Chicago area.

Tony Matorina, member of the Northern Illinois Knife Club, proudly shows his "obsession" over 200 large and small Barlows.

Jim Sargent with Mr. and Mrs. J. T. Becker who are proudly showing their Case Knife book. The book's cover is leather bound with gold inlay lettering. If all 642 knives displayed were laid end to end, they would extend 280 feet.

HANDLE MATERIALS AND DESCRIPTIONS

Appaloosa — brown and light colored spots (smooth bone)
Black Bone — smooth bone dyed black
Birdseye — not a handle material but refers to large rivets on handle.
Bone — shin bone of cattle
Bone Stag — Same as bone with different jigging
Brass — brass metal
Brown Bone — dyed bone
Buffalo Horn — can be horn from any animal
Burnt Orange — brownish orange delrin
Buttermilk — 2 color cream celluloid
Candy Stripe — red & white stripe celluloid
Celluloid — man made material (transluscent appearance)
Christmas Tree — celluloid of mingled red, green and black
Cocobolo — hard wood
Composition — man made material, dull (solid appearance)
Cracked Ice — off color white (appearance of frosted window)
Delrin — man made plastic, petro base
Ebony — ebony wood
Engine turned silver — metal with uniform knurl lines
Genuine Pearl — mother of pearl shell
Genuine Stag — antlers of deer
Gold — self explanatory, 14K, 12K, 10K & plated
Gold Stone — gold glitter celluloid
Green Bone — bone dyed shades of green
High Art — photos under clear celluloid
Horn — horn from various animals
Imitation Ivory — composition resembling ivory
Imitation Onyx — yellowish marble appearance
Imitation Pearl — man made white composition
Ivory — animal tusk
Jigged Bone — machine notched bone
Laminated Wood — layers of wood pressed together
Marine Pearl — imitation pearl
Mother Of Pearl — same as genuine pearl
Mottled - mingled colors
Multi-Color — many colors in stripes or mingled, comp.

Nickel Silver — self explanatory, also known as German Silver
Pakkawood — man made, pressed wood appearance
Peachseed — jigging on bone appears pitted as peachseed
Pyralin — man made, petro base such as celluloids
Pyremite — same as Pyralin
Red Bone — bone dyed various shades of red
Red Stag — stag dyed various shades of red
Redwood — wood from redwood tree
Rogers Bone — bone processed by the Rogers Co. - dark to brilliant red, also green, brown, heavier than most bones
Rough Black — man made plastic "PLASTAG" -1940
Saw Cut — bone or comp. has been sawn & left marks
Scales — anything used as handle materials
Second Cut Stag — pieces of stag with little or no character or grooves that have been specially jigged and dyed to give the material a stronger stag appearance
Slick Black — man made composition
Smoked Pearl — dark bluish gray in either genunine pearl or imitation pearl
Smooth Bone - self explanatory
Stag — same as genuine stag
Staglon - imitation stag
Stained Bone — dyed bone
Stainless Steel — self explanatory
Sterling Silver — self explanatory
Tortoise — actual tortoise shell - illegal to use now
Tortoise (Celluloid) — imitation of actual tortoise shell
Walnut — wood of walnut tree
Waterfall — transluscent material that resembles waterfall as knife is rotated
Winterbottom Bone — bone processed by Winterbottom Co.
Wire — knife frames made from #9 wire
Wood — various wood, walnut, ebony, redwood, maple, etc.

GLOSSARY

Bail (shackle) — metal ring attached to the bolster so the knife can be put on a key ring or tied to a belt
Drilled — hole drilled in bolster in order to put a lanyard through
Jigging — machine notching
Lanyard — cord or line (usually braided)
Pull — thumbnail groove on blade for opening (regular pull or long pull - see page 11).

Rockwell Hardness Test — a diamond cone being impressed into metal. The deeper the penetration, the softer the metal.
Scale — another term for manmade handle materials
Serrated — saw toothed edge
Shackle — see bail
Shadow — no bolsters
Springer — spring operated (switchblade)
Zipper — switchblade with square release button set into handle

PATTERN NAMES ENCOUNTERED THROUGHOUT THIS GUIDE

Baby Copperhead
Banana
Bark Loosener
Barlow
Bartender's
Birdseye — large rivets on handle
Bowtie
Butterbean
Canoe
Carpenter's
Cattle
Citrus - melon tester
Coke Bottle
Congress
Copperhead
Daddy Barlow
Doctor's (Phys.)
Dog Leg Jack
Easy Opener
Elephant's Toe - also SunFish
Equal End
Fish Scaler
Fisherman's
Florist's Knife

Folding Hunter
Grafting
Greenskeeper
Gunboat
Gunstock
Half Hawkbill
Half Whittler
Hammerhead
Hawkbill
Hobo
Humpback
Jack
Leg
Lineman's
Lobster
Maize
Mako
Moose
Muskrat
Navy
Office
One Arm Man
Peanut
Press Button - switch blade

Pruner
Riggers
Rope
Senator
Serpentine
Shark's Tooth
Shroud Cutter (Paratrooper's)
Sleeveboard
Sod Buster
Sowbelly
Stabber
Stockman
Sun Fish - also Elephant Toe, Toenail
Swell Center
Swell End Jack
Timberscribe
Toledo Scale
Toothpick
Trapper
Utility - Camp or Scout
Whaler
Wharncliffe
Whittler - master blade folds between two
    other blades

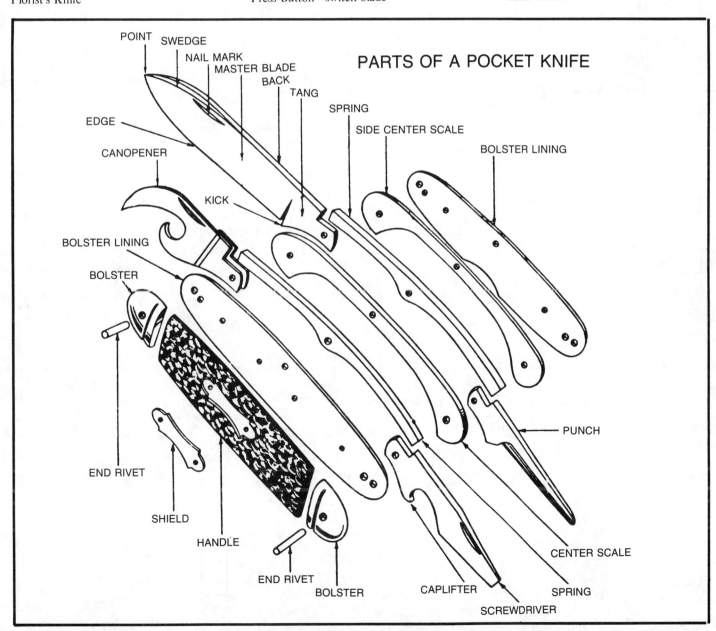

PARTS OF A POCKET KNIFE

BLADE STYLES

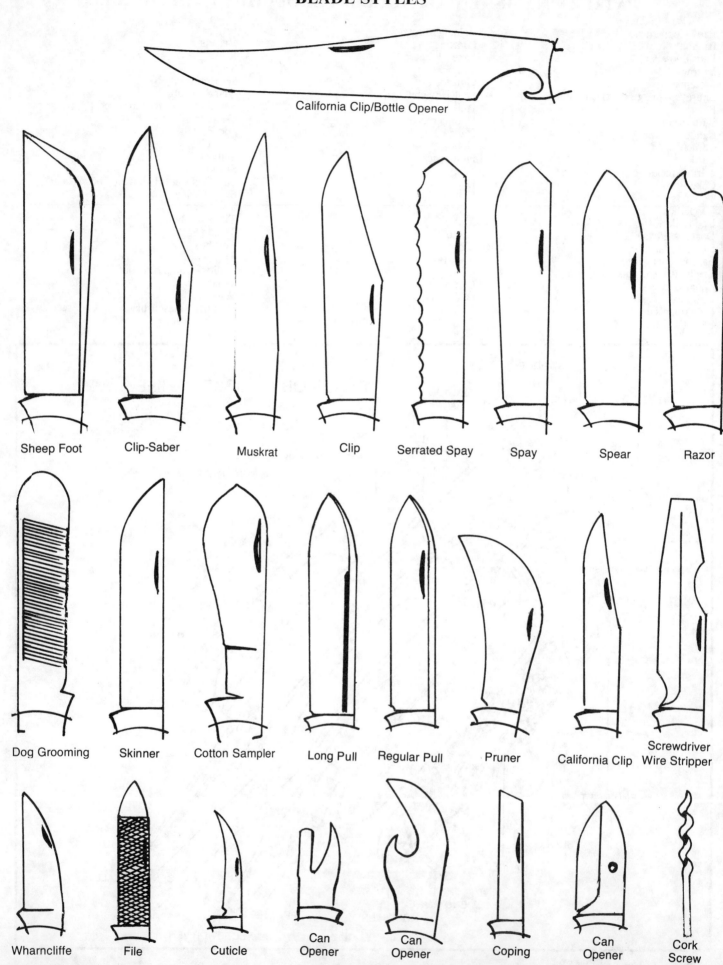

California Clip/Bottle Opener

Sheep Foot   Clip-Saber   Muskrat   Clip   Serrated Spay   Spay   Spear   Razor

Dog Grooming   Skinner   Cotton Sampler   Long Pull   Regular Pull   Pruner   California Clip   Screwdriver Wire Stripper

Wharncliffe   File   Cuticle   Can Opener   Can Opener   Coping   Can Opener   Cork Screw

BLADE STYLES

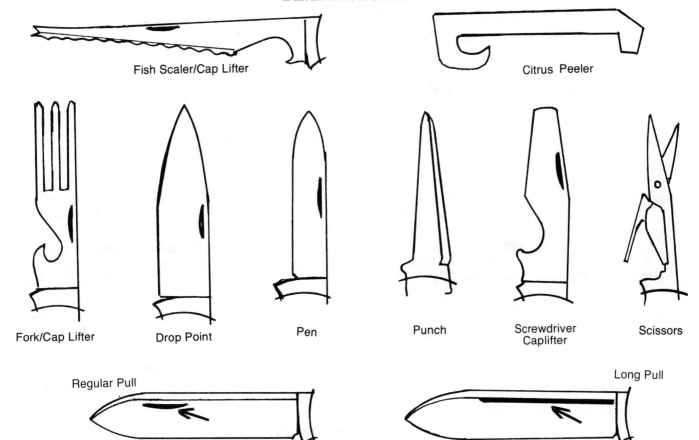

Fish Scaler/Cap Lifter   Citrus Peeler

Fork/Cap Lifter   Drop Point   Pen   Punch   Screwdriver Caplifter   Scissors

Regular Pull   Long Pull

COMMON ABBREVIATIONS & SYMBOLS

½ ..... master blade is clip blade	P .... pakkawood	SCI .... scissors
B .... budding	PEN .... pen blade	SH .... sheepfoot blade
B&G .... budding & grafting	PU .... punch blade	SHAC .... shackle (bail)
EO .... easy opener	R ...... bail in handle (shackle)	SHAD .... no bolsters
F .... file	R .... candy stripe	SP .... spay blade
J .... long spay blade	RAZ .... razor blade	SSP .... stainless steel,
K .... corkscrew	(one arm man)	polished blade edge
L .... lock back	RM .... red mottled	SS .... stainless steel
LR .... electrician's knife	S .... sterling silver	T .... tip bolsters
M .... metal	SAB .... Saber blade	

CASE NUMBERING SYSTEM

First digit denotes handle material.
Second digit tells number of blades.
Last two digits are the factory pattern numbers.
A "O" at the first or the third digit indicates a variation in that particular knife.
Ex. 06263S.S. or 62048SP

Number and Letters of Handle Material

1 .... Walnut	A .... Appaloosa
2 .... Black Composition (slick black)	B .... Imitation Onyx, Waterfall,
3 .... Yellow Composition	Christmas Tree
4 .... White Composition	BM&H .... Brown Mottled
5 .... Genuine Stag, 2nd Cut Stag	C I .... Cracked Ice (Imitation Pearl)
Red Stag, White Stag	G .... Green Bone, Green Delrin
6 .... Bone, Green Bone, Red Bone,	GS .... Gold Stone Celluloid
Delrin, Laminated Wood, Rough Black	HA .... High Art
Rogers Bone, Appaloosa	I .... Imitation Ivory
7 .... Tortoise, Imi. tortoise, Curly Maple	SS .... Stainless Steel
(1970s)	W .... Wire
8 .... Genuine Pearl	GPY .... Variety of Celluloid colors
9 .... Imitation Pearl (Cracked Ice)	SR .... Smooth Rose Bone
	SG .... Smooth Green Bone

CASE BLADE TYPES

PEN .... Pen Blade	B&G . Budding & Grafting Blade	K Cap Lifter or Bartender's Knife
RAZ . Razor (one arm man blade)	SH .... Sheep Foot Blade	SCIS or SC .... Scissors
K .... Cork Screw	½ .... Master Blade is Clip Style	LP .... Long Pull
PU .... Punch Blade	F .... File Blade	DG .... Dog Grooming
CC .... Concave Ground	J .... Long Spay Blade	SKW .... Skate Wrench
SAB .... Saber Ground	L .... Locks Open	SER .... Serrated Edge
SP .... Spay Blade	EO .... Easy Open	FK .... Fork

MISCELLANEOUS ABBREVIATIONS

BOLS .... Bolsters	T .... Tip Bolsters	SB .... Spring Blade
R .... Bail in Handle	SHAD or S .... No Bolster	
DR .... Bolsters Drilled	SSP . Stainless Blades and Springs	
	with Polished Blade Edge	

Stamping Positions Help Date Bulldogs

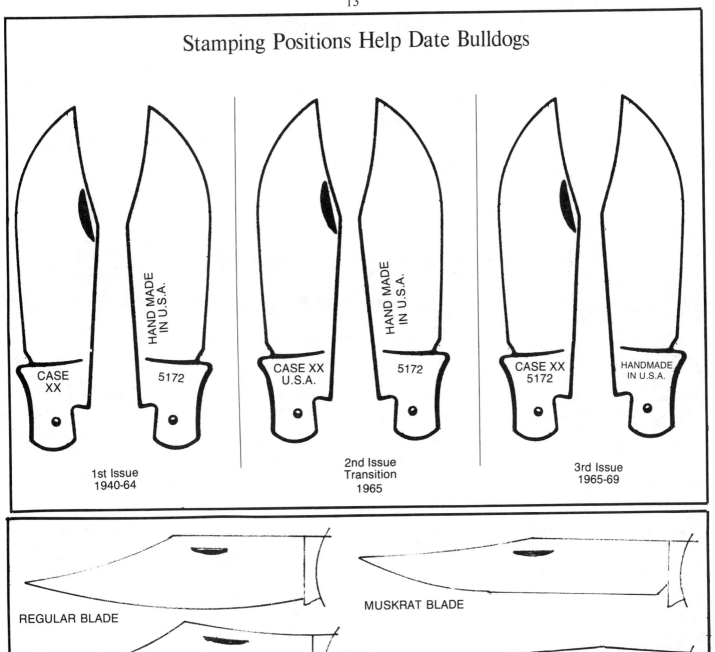

1st Issue
1940-64

2nd Issue
Transition
1965

3rd Issue
1965-69

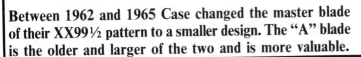

REGULAR BLADE

"A" BLADE

MUSKRAT BLADE

REGULAR BLADE

Between 1962 and 1965 Case changed the master blade of their XX99½ pattern to a smaller design. The "A" blade is the older and larger of the two and is more valuable.

Between 1963 and 1967 both the Muskrat and the regular blade was used in the trapper. The narrower Muskrat blade is more valuable.

XX FRAME

USA FRAME

1965 brought a change in the Folding Hunter. The XX frame has a larger front bolster that has a more pronounced curve where it joins the handle on top. The XX frame was last used in 1964 and the lower bolster was drilled for a lanyard in only the 1964 knife. The USA frame took over in 1965 and the drilling for a lanyard is standard. (See page 61 for more illustrations.)

CASE STAMPINGS

Used until 1915

Used until 1915

CASE'S BRADFORD

Used until 1920

W.R. CASE & SONS CUTLERY CO BRADFORD, PA

Used until 1920

CASE & SON'S BRADFORD PA

Used until 1920

CASE XX

Used until 1920

CASE BRADFORD PA.

Used until 1920

STANDARD KNIFE CO

1920-23

CASE TESTED XX

1920-40

Case

1920-40

CASE

1920-40

CASE TESTED XX

1920-40

Case 25¢

1935-40

Case 50¢

1935-40

CASE XX METAL STAMPINGS LT.D.

1942-45

CASE'S STAINLESS

1947-52

CASE'S TESTED XX

1940-50

CASE XX

1940-64

CASE XX STAINLESS

1950-64

CASE XX U.S.A.

1965-69

CASE XX STAINLESS U.S.A.

1965-69

CASE XX U.S.A.
. . . .

1970-79

CASE XX STAINLESS U.S.A.
. . . .

1970-79

Used from 1980
(Lightning S)

Used from 1980
(Lightning S Stainless)

EXPLANATION OF CASE "DOT" SYSTEM

In 1970 Case began stamping the tang with 10 Dots underneath the U.S.A. and for each year thereafter, a dot was eliminated until 1979 had only 1 Dot. In 1980 they went back to 10 Dots but with the "lightning S". The Dots are between "Case XX and U.S.A." Again, a Dot is omitted for each new year.

W.R. CASE & SONS CUTLERY CO.
ALGONGUIN
BRADFORD, PA. U.S.A.
(Clippers Stamp)

CASE BROS. & CO.
GOWANDA N.Y.

Ca. 1896

W.R. CASE & SONS
GERMANY
1900-1915

W R CASE
&
SONS
MADE IN U.S.A.
1900-1910

CASE
XX
1940-1946

W. R. CASE
& SON
BRADFORD PA
1902-1905

W R CASE & SON
CUTLERY
CO
1902-1905

KANE CUTLERY
CO.
1909

W R CASE
&
SONS
MADE IN USA

KANE CUTLERY
CO.
KANE, PA
1907-1909

C. PLATTS & SONS
ELDRED, PA.
1904

CASE MFG. CO.
LITTLE VALLEY
N.Y.

J. D. CASE
CO.
KANE, PA

CASE
KANE, PA.
1907-1909

L. V. KNIFE ASSN.
LITTLE VALLEY
N.Y.
1900

W.R. CASE
& SON
LITTLE VALLEY
N.Y.
1902-1905

W R CASE
& SONS
BRADFORD, PA

1916-1920
Military Stamp Used WWI

CASE BROS.
CUT.
CO.
1912

CASE HISTORY

Any research of the Case family must go back to the late 1800's when six of the nine children of Job Russell Case, who was a horse trader and farmer, became connected with the cutlery business either by marriage or forming partnerships with in-laws.

It is believed that a daughter of Job's, Theresa, was the first connection to the cutlery business when she married a cutlery salesman by the name of J.B.F. Champlin. They had a son who later came into the company and J.B.F. Champlin & Sons Cutlery Co. was formed in Little Valley, New York. In approximately 1886 the four Case brothers, Jean, John, Andrew and William Russell (W.R.), joined with J.B.F. Champlin & Sons and formed the Cattaraugus Cutlery Co.

One of the daughters, Emma, married John W. Brown and their son, Wallace, and grandson, Dansforth, were associated with Union Cutlery and later with the Kabar.

One of the brothers who originally joined with J.B.F. Champlin & Sons to found Cattaraugus Cutlery Co. was W.R. Case. W.R. had three children, J. Russell, Debbie and Theresa, of which J. Russell and Debbie went with Cattaraugus and Theresa married Herbert Crandall who founded Crandall Cutlery Co. in Bradford, PA at the turn of the century. (See color section for Crandall display.)

While working at Cattaraugus, Debbie married H.N. Platts who along with Debbie and other Platts family members founded C. Platts & Sons Cutlery Co. in 1896 in Gowanda NY. It was also in 1896 when Andrew, Jean and John left Cattaraugus and formed Case Brothers Cutlery Co. in Little Valley, NY. Soon after this, W.R.'s son, J. Russell left Cattaraugus and joined his uncles as a salesman.

In approximately 1903, J. Russell left Case Brothers Cutlery Co. and with his father formed W.R. Case & Son Cutlery Co. in Little Valley, NY. After several years, W.R. Case & Son Cutlery Co. moved from their Little Valley location to Bradford, PA and merged with C. Platts & Sons Cutlery Co. The new company became W.R. Case & Sons Cutlery Co.

In 1911, H.N. Platts left W.R. Case & Sons and upon his leaving, the Crandall Cutlery Co. joined W.R. Case & Sons so the son-in-law of W.R. was back in the fold.

Approximately 1911 W.R. Case & Sons acquired the trademarks and equipment of Case Brothers in Little Valley because a fire had earlier destroyed the Case Brother's facilities and they never overcame the tragedy.

You should also note here that in 1911, Jean Case, one of the three brothers of the burned out Case Brothers, formed his own Jean Case Cutlery Company in Kane, PA and after several years sold out.

In 1929 W.R. Case & Sons Cutlery Co. outgrew their old Bank Street location in Bradford and moved to their present location on Russell Blvd.

J. Russell died in 1953 and his niece's husband, John O'Kain took over.

John O'Kain retired in 1972 and American Brands Inc. purchased W.R. Case & Sons Cutlery Co.

CHRONOLOGY

The "Case" name has been a standard bearer in the cutlery industry for more than 90 years. Although there are many cutlery related businesses to carry the "Case" name, Case Brothers and W.R. Case and Sons are the pivotal corporation and all others seem to revolve around them. A popular misconception among collectors of both knives and razors is that "Case Brothers" was the parent company of W.R. Case and Sons. In truth, they were two competing cutlery manufacturers, and for periods of time unfriendly rivals.

CASE BROTHERS CUTLER CO.

c. 1881-86 John D. Case Co. Little Valley, N.Y. John D. Case awarded patent for his butterfly razor on Feb. 8, 1881.

c. 1886-87 Jean, John and Andrew Case were involved with Cattaraugus Cutlery Co., Little Valley, N.Y.

c. 1890-1900 Case Bros.; Wholesalers of Cutlery, Spring Green, CO.

c. 1896 John, Jean and Andrew Case form Case Brothers Cut. Co. in Little Valley, N.Y. (jobbers)

1900 Case Brothers Cutlery Co. incorporated in Little Valley, N.Y. (manufacturing company)

1901 Elliot and Dean Case left Case Brothers to form Standard Knife Co., Little Valley, N.Y.

1902 J. Russell Case leaves Case Brothers

1903 Standard Knife Company went out of business

1907 Case Brothers open a second factory in Kane, PA

1909 Andrew J. Case leaves Case Brothers to join Union Cutlery Co.
Case Brothers purchased the Smethport Cutlery Company in Smethport, PA
Case Brothers Kane, PA reorganized under the name Kane Cutlery Co.
Smethport factory burns to the ground in June 1909

1910-11 Case Brothers build new factory in Warren, PA to replace Smethport works.

1912 Case Brothers Cutlery Co., Little Valley, NY burns to the ground
On March 27, 1912 Case Brothers Cutlery Co. reach an agreement to rebuild in Springville, NY

1913 Case Brothers, Springville, NY goes into operation

1914 Late 1914 Case Brothers Cutlery Co. unable to recover from two devastating fires (Smethport, PA & Little Valley, NY) goes out of business. Oct. 21, 1914 Case Brothers Cutlery Co. sold their trademark "Tested XX" to W.R. Case and Sons

W.R. CASE AND SONS

1900 Little Valley Knife Ass'n. incopoated in Little Valley, NY. (H. Crandall, jobber)

1902 J. Russell Case forms W.R. Case and Son in Little Valley, NY (jobber)

1904 Late 1904 H.N. Platts in an agreement to form merger with W.R. Case & Son.
H.N. Platts purchases his brothers' shares of C. Platts Sons Cutlery Co., Eldred, PA

1905 C. Platt's Sons and W.R. Case and Son are merged to form W.R. Case and Sons, Bradford, PA Crandall Cutlery Co. incorporated as a manufacturing company in Bradford, PA (formerly Little Valley Knife Association)

1907-09 Platts Brothers Cutlery Co., Andover, NY (in operation for less than 2 years)

1911 H.N. Platts leaves W.R. Case and Sons to form Western States Cutlery Co., Boulder, CO. The actual separation of the two companies took several years to complete (1911-1914)

1912 W.R. Case and Sons acquire Crandall Cutlery Co. of Bradford, PA

1914 W.R. Case and Sons first acquire "Tested XX" trademark from Case Brothers Cutlery Co.

1915 W.R. Case and Sons first use of "Tested XX" trademark. During this period (1914-20) W.R. Case and Sons reorganize their entire product line due to World War I and the departure of H.N. Platts

1917 Start of World War I

1920 W.R. Case and Sons "Tested XX" line in full production
Case introduces a second (less expensive) line under the Standard Knife Co., Bradford, PA mark

1923 W.R. Case end use of Standard Knife mark

1926 Kinfolks incorporated in Little Valley, NY (Kinfolks razors are manufactured by W.R. Case and Sons)

1936 W.R. Case and Sons acquire razor stocks and trademark of Genco corporation

1940 W.R. Case change their line stamping to "Case XX" (full implementation is delayed for several years due to World War II)

1941 Start of World War II

1942 Although Case has been cutting back on razor production since the mid 1930's, in Jan. 1942, W.R. Case effectively ended razor production (relying on existing stocks and razors acquired from Genco) and begin tooling up for the war effort

1945 World War II ends

1955 Case introduces a new line of razors to replace exhausted stocks (marked "Made in USA by Case") (approx. 1955-60) Kinfolks Incorporated, Little Valley, NY goes out of business

1962 W.R. Case manufactures the genuine mother-of-pearl "CASE ACE" as momentos for its officers and salesmen
   W.R. Case and Sons formally ended 57 years of straight razor production
1965 W.R. Case changes product line marking to "Case XX USA"
1970 Case changes product line marking to the dot system
1972 W.R. Case and Sons sold to American Brands Inc.
1980 Case changes product line marking to lightning SS with dots system

Case Cutlery Works, Bradford, PA

Cutlery Works, Springville, NY

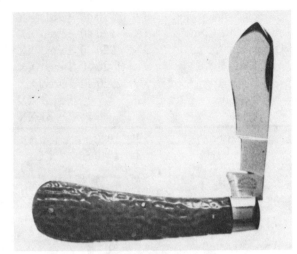

COTTON SAMPLER

| Green bone | W.R. Case & Sons Cutlery, Bradford, |
| PA. Rare | Photo courtesy Jack Shipley |

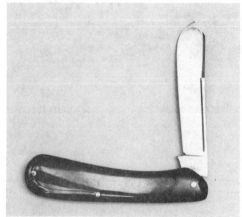

SPAY BLADE

Slick black, LP   3⅝" $160

CASE BROTHERS, Little Valley, NY

| Black composition | | | |
| (castrating knife) | 3½" | | $200 |

Nr.	Handle	Lgth.	Stamp	Mint
B100	Imi. Onyx		1920-40 Tested XX	160
B100	Christmas Tree		1920-40 Tested XX	235
G100	Celluloid		1920-40 Tested XX	160

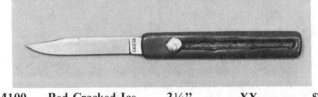

| M100 | Red Cracked Ice | 3¼" | XX | $120 |

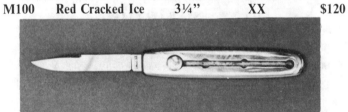

| M100 | All Metal | 3¼" | XX | $110 |

M100	Metal	3¼	1920-40 Tested XX	130
M100	Blue Celluloid	3¼	1920-40 Tested XX	160
M100	Cracked Ice	3¼	1920-40 Tested XX	140
M100	Green Bone	3¼	1920-40 Tested XX	175
M100	Gold	3¼	1940-64 XX	160
P100	Asst. Celluloid		1920-40 Tested XX	175
M101	Metal	2⅞	1920-40 Tested XX	135

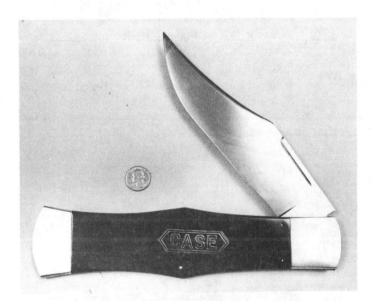

DISPLAY KNIFE

Approx. 500 made (note size in relation to quarter) $900

**Older Case Knives
Begin Page 91**

CASE

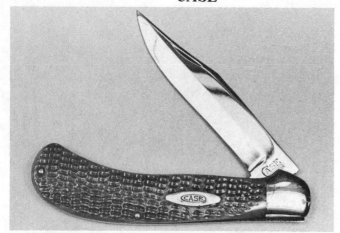

6100SAB Green bone   **4½"**   **Tested XX**   **$550**

Nr.	Handle	Lgth.		Stamp	Mint
3100	Yellow Comp.	4½	1920-40	Tested XX	500
31100	Yellow Comp.		1920-40	Tested XX	500
61100	Bone		1920-40	Tested XX	550

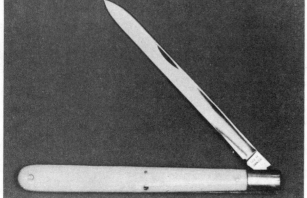

Has both small stamp and large stamp each $45

MELON TESTER OR CITRUS

4100SS	**White Comp**	**5½"**		**XX**	**$45**
4100SS	White Comp.	5½	1965-69	USA	40
4100SS	White Comp.	5½	1965-69	USA	
Serrated Edge					150
4100SS	White Comp.	5½	1970	10 Dot	45
4100SS	White Comp.	5½	1970	10 Dot	
Serrated Edge, Rare					145

6001   **Green bone**   **4¾"**   **$600**
W.R. Case & Sons, Bradford, PA

Nr.	Handle	Lgth.	Stamp	Mint
2103SP	Slick Black	3¼	1920-40 Tested XX	260
3103SP	Yellow Comp.	3¼	1920-40 Tested XX	290
4103B&G	White Comp.	3¼	1920-40 Tested XX	175
5103SP	Stag	3¼	1920-40 Tested XX	315
6103B&G	Bone	3¼	1920-40 Tested XX	200
7103SP	Tortoise	3¼	Tested XX	350
8103SP	Pearl	3¼	Tested XX	400
6104B	Green bone	3⅜	1920-40 Tested XX	240
6104B	Bone	3⅜	1940-55 XX	185

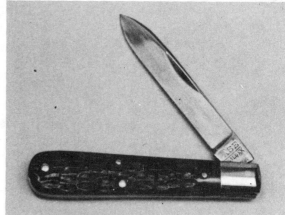

6106	**Green bone**	**2⅝"**	**Tested XX**	**$175**
7106	Tortoise Shell		1920-40 Tested XX	260

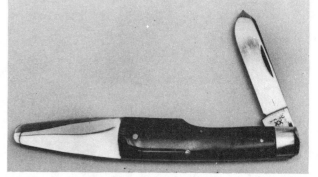

GUNSTOCK, Budding Knife

2109	**Slick black**	**3¼"**	**XX**	**$100**
2109B	Slick Black	3¼	1920-40 Tested XX	160
6109B	Bone	3¼	1920-40 Tested XX	260
2109B	Slick Black	3¼	1965-69 USA	100
2209B	Slick Black	3¼	XX	$250

Folding budding blade, rare

CASE TESTED XX
6109   **Bud, All bone**   **4"**   **$250**

Nr.	Handle	Lgth.		Stamp	Mint
11011	Walnut	4	1920-40	Tested XX	100
61011	Green Bone	4	1920-40	Tested XX	135
61011	Rogers Bone	4	1920-40	Tested XX	210
11011	Walnut	4	1940-64	XX	35
61011	Green Bone	4	1940-55	XX	100
61011̄	Red Bone	4	1940-64	XX	70

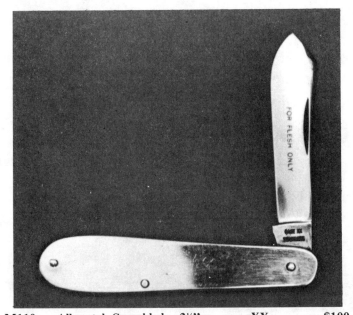

M110   All metal, Spay blade 3⅛"   XX $100

Nr.	Handle		Lgth.	Stamp	Mint
M110	Metal	Spay	3⅛	1920-40 Tested XX	135

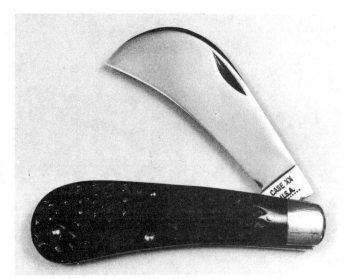

HAWKBILL

61011	Jigged Wood Scales	4"		10 Dot	$22
61011	Rogers Bone		1940-55	XX	150
61011	Laminated Wood		1940-64	XX	33
61011	Bone Stag		1940-64	XX	50
61011	Laminated Wood		1965-69	USA	25
61011	Bone Stag		1965-69	USA	90
11011	Walnut		1970	10 Dot	30

H1211½	Mottled Comp.	4	1920-40 Tested XX	
Switch Blade				500
31211½	Yellow Comp.	4	1920-40 Tested XX	
Switch Blade				500

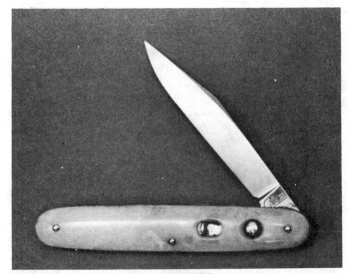

SWITCHBLADE

91210½	Onyx	3⅜"	Tested XX	$400
91210½	Cracked Ice	3⅜"	1920-40 Tested XX	400

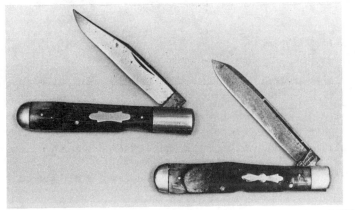

5111½	Stag	4⅜"		$600
Case Bros., Little Valley				
5111L	Stag, long pull	4⅜"		$550
W.R. Case & Son, Bradford, PA				
3111½	Yellow Comp, rare		1920-40 Tested XX	500

11011   Walnut Hawkbill   4"   USA $25

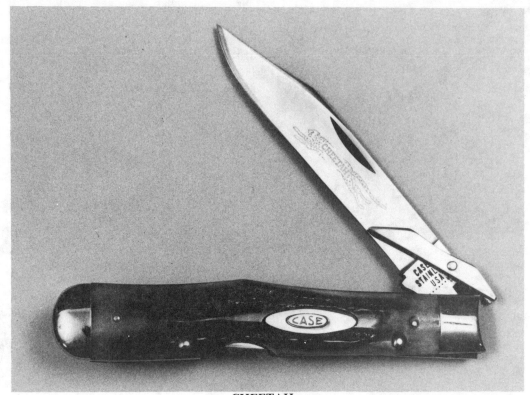

CHEETAH

| 5111½ | LSSP Lockback, | Genuine stag | 4⁷⁄₁₆" | Large stamp | $140 |

| 6111½L | Green bone | 4⅜" | Tested XX | $425 |

W.R. Case & Sons, Bradford, PA

| 6111½ | Green bone, LP | 4⅜" | Case's Bradford, Pa | $450 |

Nr.	Handle	Lgth.	Stamp	Mint
6111½	Green Bone, Long Pull	1920-40	Tested XX	500
6111½	Green Bone	1940-55	XX	400
6111½L	Green Bone Long Pull	1940-55	XX	450
6111½L	Bone	1940-64	XX	75
61111½	Bone	1965-69	USA	175

Extra 1 was a factory error, see photo this page.

| 6111½L | Bone | 1965-69 | USA | 50 |
| 6111½L | Bone | 1970 | 10 Dot | 50 |

6111½ with error knife showing extra 1

SWITCHBLADE

| R1212½ | Candy Stripe Switch Blade | 4 | 1920-40 | Tested XX | 550 |
| 31212½ | Yellow Comp. Switch Blade | 4 | 1920-40 | Tested XX | 500 |

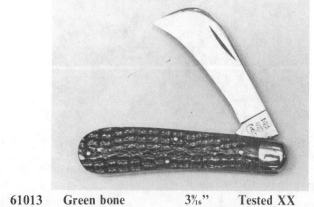

| 61013 | Green bone | 3⁹⁄₁₆" | Tested XX | $200 |

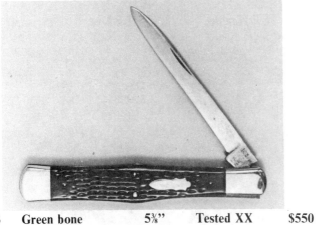

61213   Green bone   5⅜"   Tested XX $550

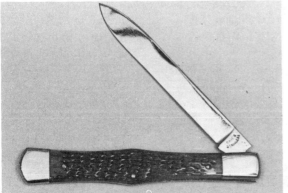

61213   Green bone   Case's Stainless $600

Nr.	Handle	Lgth.	Stamp	Mint
31213	Yellow Comp. Spear	5⅜"	1920-40 Tested XX	500
61213	Green Bone	5⅜"	1920-40 Tested XX	550
31113	Yellow Comp.	4	1920-40 Tested XX	425
61113	Green Bone	4	1920-40 Tested XX	425

61213½   Rogers bone S/B   4"   Tested XX $500

61214½	Bone Switch Blade	4⅛	1920-40 Tested XX	600
51215½F	Stag Switch Blade	5	1920-40 Tested XX	775
51215½G	Stag Switch Blade	5	1920-40 Tested XX	825

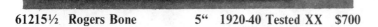

61215½   Rogers Bone   5"   1920-40 Tested XX $700

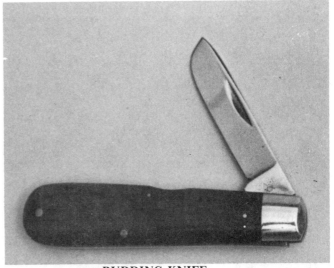

BUDDING KNIFE

1116SP   Walnut   3½"   XX $35

Nr.	Handle	Lgth.		Stamp	Mint
1116SP	Bud Walnut	3½	1965-69	USA	30
1116SP	Bud Walnut	3½	1970	10 Dot	35

WIRE HANDLE/EO

W1216	Wire	3⅛	1920-40	Tested XX	150
W1216K	Wire	3⅛	1920-40	Tested XX	150
W1216 Pruner	Wire	3⅛	1920-40	Tested XX	150
6116	Green Bone	3⅜	1920-40	Tested XX	160
6116 Spear	Green Bone	3⅜	1920-40	Tested XX	185
6116SH	Green Bone	3⅜	1920-40	Tested XX	185

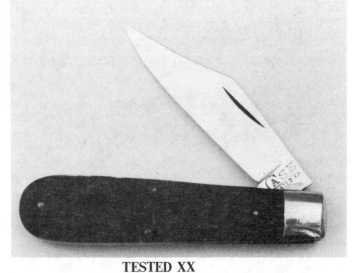

TESTED XX

6116½   CP Green bone   3½"   Tested XX $150

ABBREVIATIONS

½	master blade is clip blade	PU	Punch Blade
B	Budding	R	Bail in handle
EO	Easy Opener	RAZ	Razor Blade
F	File	SAB	Sabor Blade
J	Long Spay Blade	SC/SCI	Scissors
K	Corkscrew	SH	Sheepfoot blade
LR	Electrician's Knife	SP	Spay Blade
M	Metal	SS	Stainless Steel
PEN	Pen Blade	T	Tip Bolsters
SSP	Stainless Steel, Polished Blade Edge		

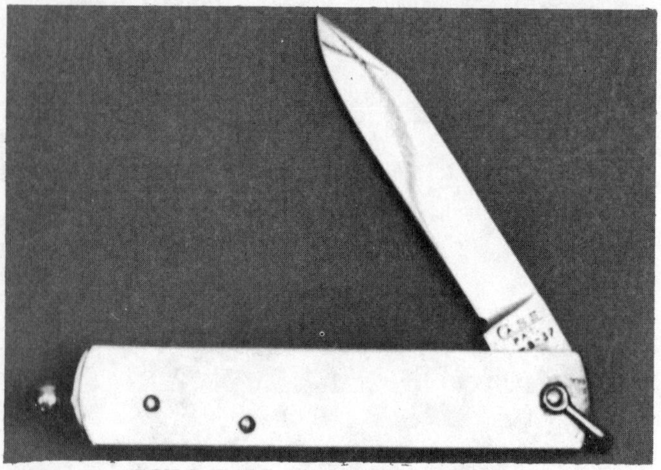

PULL BALL/SWITCHBLADE

M1217	**All Metal**	**2⅞"**	**Tested XX**	**$175**

Made for Case by Schrade

Nr.	Handle	Lgth.	Stamp	Mint
1117SHR	Walnut		1920-40 Tested XX	100
M1218K	Metal	3	1920-40 Tested XX	135

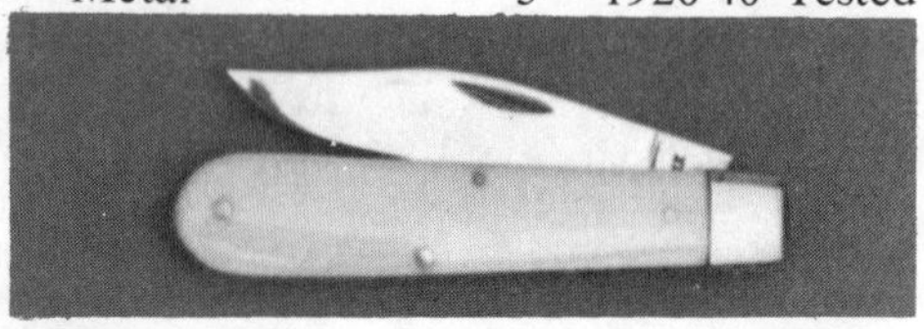

31024½	**Yellow**	**3"**	**XX**	**$45**
3124	Yellow Comp.	3	1920-40 Tested XX	110
3124½	Yellow Comp.	3	1920-40 Tested XX	110
6124	Green Bone	3	1920-40 Tested XX	110
6124½	Green Bone	3	1920-40 Tested XX	110
61024	Green Bone	3	1920-40 Tested XX	110
31024	Yellow Comp.	3	1920-40 Tested XX	110

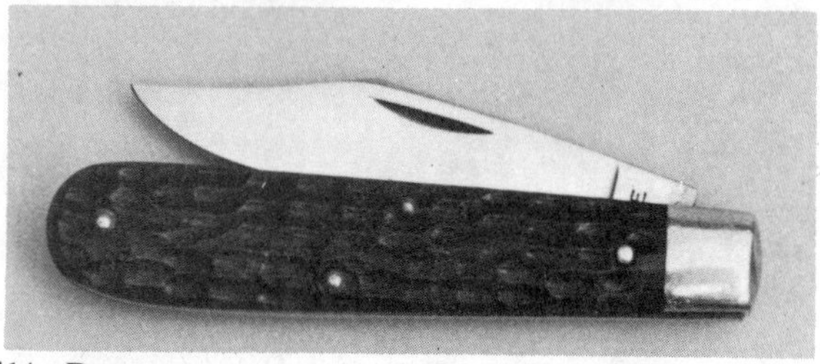

61024½	**Bone**	**3"**	**XX**	**$30**
61024½	Bone	3	1965-69 USA	30
7129½	Tortoise Shell		1920-40 Tested XX	210

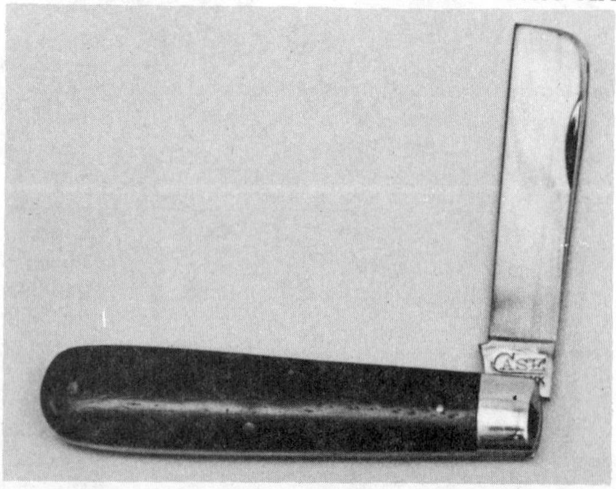

1131SH	**Walnut**	**3¾"**	**Tested XX**	**$80**

Nr.	Handle	Lgth.	Stamp	Mint
1131EO	SH Walnut	3$\frac{1}{16}$	1920-40 Tested XX	135

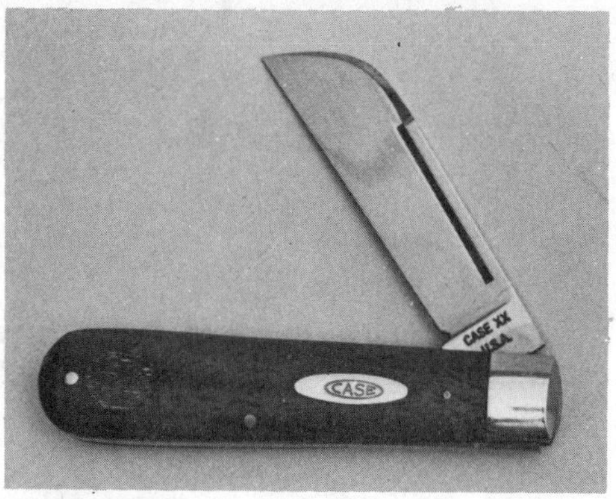

11031SH	**Walnut, LP**	**3¾"**	**USA**	**$20**
11031SH	Walnut	3$\frac{1}{16}$	1920-40 Tested XX	110
11031SH	Walnut	3$\frac{1}{16}$	1920-40 Tested XX	
Concave Ground Blade				120
11031SH	Walnut	3$\frac{1}{16}$	1940-64 XX	25
11031SH	Walnut	3$\frac{1}{16}$	1940-64 XX	
Concave Ground Blade				45
11031SH	Walnut	3$\frac{1}{16}$	1970 10 Dot	18

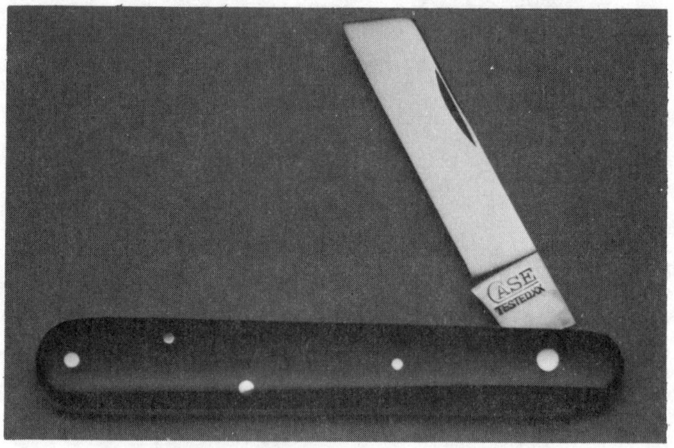

2136	**Black Composition**	**4⅛"**	**Case Tested XX**	**$140**
2136B	Slick Black	4⅛	1940-64 XX	150

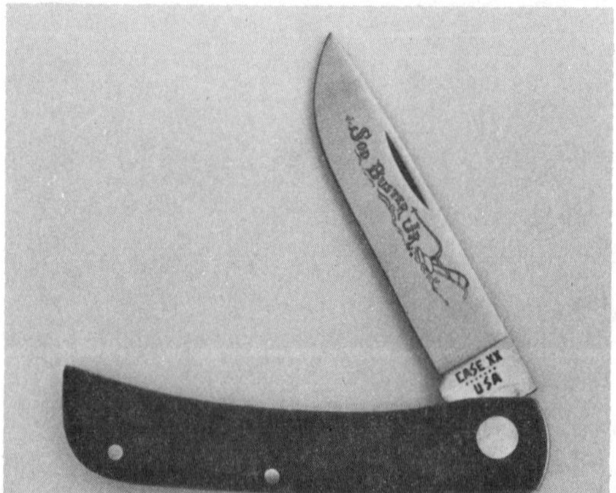

SOD BUSTER JR.

2137	**Black comp.**	**3⅝"**	**7 Dot 1983**	**$12**
2137SS	Black Comp	3⅝	1970 10 Dot	35
2137	Black Comp	3⅝"	10 Dot	75

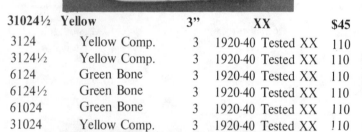

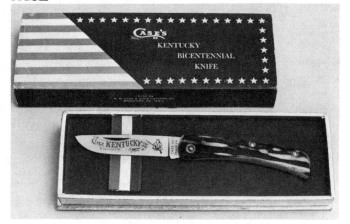

KY. BI-CENTENNIAL

5137SS	Stag	3½"	'Stainless'	$35
Nr.	**Handle**	**Lgth.**	**Stamp**	**Mint**
G137	Green Delrin	3½		25
P137	Pakkawood	3½		25
5137	Stag	Carbon	3½	30

PROTO MODEL

6143	Jigged bone	5"	8 Dot 1972	$150
Nr.	**Handle**	**Lgth.**	**Stamp**	**Mint**
6143	Red Fiberloid, Rare		1940-45 Tested XX	225
5143	Stag handles	Case Founders		60
6143	Brown Bone	5	1920-40 Tested XX	200
6143	Green Bone	5	1920-40 Tested XX	200
6143	Green Bone	5	1940-55 XX	175

2138	**Black Comp.**	4⅝"	**USA**	**$25**
2138	Black Comp.	5⅝"	1970 10 Dot	22
2138SS	Black Comp.	5⅝"	1970 10 Dot	25
2138LSS	Black Comp.	5⅝"	1970 10 Dot	35
P138LSS	Alyeska Sod Buster	500 made		125

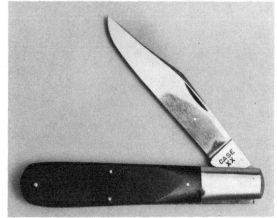

DADDY BARLOW

6143	**Slick Black bone**	5"	**XX**	**$100**
6143	Red Bone	5	1940-64 XX	85
6143	Bone	5	1940-64 XX	45
6143	Bone	5	1965-69 USA	30
6143	Bone	5	1970 10 Dot	30

Note:
  This book is a guide. Prices may vary a bit and are not absolute. Prices on more expensive knives may vary $100 or more depending on dealer.

Note:
  Prices are for mint knives although mint knives are not always available for photos.

1139	**Walnut Banana Knife** 4½"	**Case XX**	**$150**
1139	Walnut	4¼ 1920-40 Tested XX	185

CASE

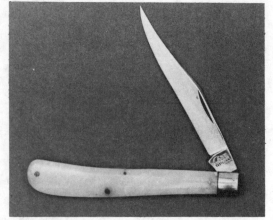

B1048	Imi. Onyx	4⅛"	Tested XX		$250

Nr.	Handle	Lgth.		Stamp	Mint
B1048	Christmas Tree	4⅛	1920-40	Tested XX	325
G.S.1048	Gold Stone	4⅛	1920-40	Tested XX	300
R1048	Candy Stripe	4⅛	1920-40	Tested XX	260
31048	Yellow Comp.	4⅛	1940-64	XX	30
31048SP	Yellow Comp.	4⅛	1940-64	XX	40

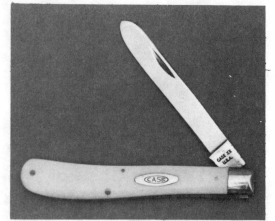

31048SP	Yellow	4⅛"	USA	$35

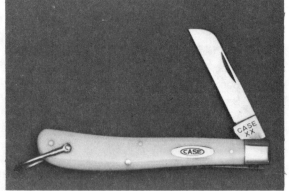

FLORIST KNIFE

31048	SHR Yellow	4⅛"		XX	$65
31048	Yellow Comp.	4⅛	1965-69	USA	22
31048	Yellow Comp.	4⅛	1970	10 Dot	22
31048SP	Yellow Comp.	4⅛	1970	10 Dot	35
61048	Green Bone	4⅛	1920-40	Tested XX	150
61048	Green Bone	4⅛"	1920-40	Tested XX	175
61048	Rogers Bone	4⅛	1920-40	Tested XX	235
61048	Green Bone	4⅛	1940-55	XX	110
61048SP	Green Bone	4⅛	1940-55	XX	135

Nr.	Handle	Lgth.		Stamp	Mint
61048	Red Bone	4⅛	1940-64	XX	50
61048SP	Bone	4⅛"	1940-64	XX	35
61048	Bone	4⅛"	1940-64	XX	30
61048	Rogers Bone	4⅛"	1940-64	XX	75
61048SP	Red Bone	4⅛	1940-64	XX	60
61048SP	Rogers Bone	4⅛	1940-64	XX	80
61048	Delrin	4⅛	1965-69	USA	22
61048	Bone	4⅛	1965-69	USA	28
61048SP	Delrin	4⅛	1965-69	USA	28
61048SP	Bone	4⅛	1965-69	USA	35
61048SSP	Bone	4⅛	1965-69	USA	
Stainless, Polished blade					40
61048SSP	Delrin	4⅛	1965-69	USA	
Stainless, Polished Edge					22
61048SSP	Bone Stag	4⅛	1965-69	USA	
blade etched "Tested XX Stainless" (1st mod.)					50
61048SSP	Bone Stag	4⅛	1965-69	USA	30
61048	Delrin	4⅛	1970	10 Dot	20
61048SP	Delrin	4⅛	1970	10 Dot	25
61048SSP	Delrin	4⅛	1970	10 Dot	
Stainless, Polished Edge					22

61049	Green Bone	4 1/16	1920-40	Tested XX	285
61049L	Rogers Bone	4 1/16	1920-40	Tested XX	400
R1049	Candy Stripe	4 1/16"	1920-40	Tested XX	350
R1049L	Candy Stripe	4 1/16"	1920-30	Tested XX	450

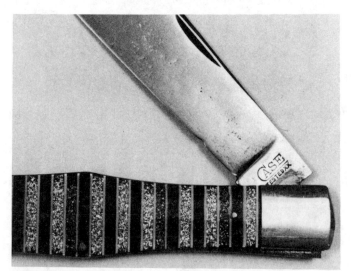

B10050	Glitter Stripe	5¼"	Tested XX	$900

Note- Stripes can run either crossways or lengthways

GS10050	Flat Blade, Goldstone	5¼	Tested XX	750

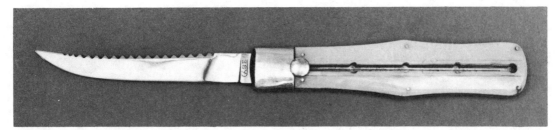

PUSH-OUT

PB1050F Onyx   5⅜"   Tested XX $600

Nr.	Handle	Lgth.		Stamp	Mint	Nr.	Handle	Lgth.		Stamp	Mint
CB105OR	Christmas Tree	5⅛	1920-40	Tested XX	900	C31050SAB	Yellow Comp.	5⅛	1920-40	Tested XX	600
CB1050SAB	Christmas Tree	5⅛	1920-40	Tested XX	900	C31050	Yellow Comp.	5⅛	1920-40	Tested XX	
HA1050	High Art	5⅛	1920-40	Tested XX	825		Flat Ground				600
PBB1050			1920-40	Tested XX	600	C51050SAB	Stag	5⅛	1920-40	Tested XX	700
PB31050 F			1920-40	Tested XX	525						

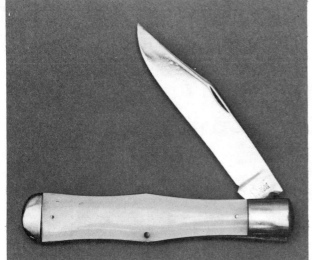

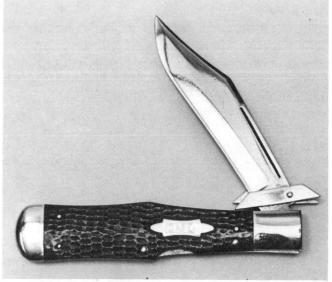

310050   Yellow   5⅛"   Tested XX $450   **C61050L SAB Green Bone LP 5¼"   Tested XX $2200**

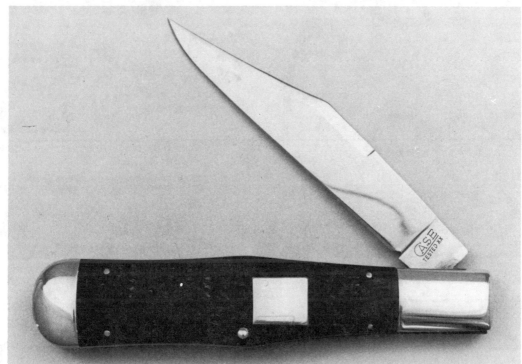

SWITCHBLADE - "Zipper" Release

C61050L Bone Flat Blade   5⅛" 1920-40 Tested XX $2500   C61050L Green Bone, Rare   5⅛" 1920-40 Tested XX $3000
No lower bolster

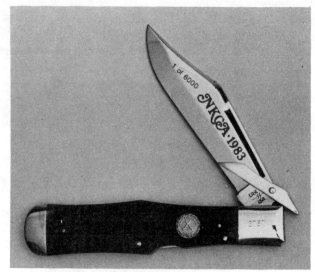

W.R. CASE & SONS, Made in U.S.A.

C61050   SAB Rogers Bone   2 Pulls   5¼" $1200

Nr.	Handle	Lgth.		Stamp	Mint
61050	Flat Blade, Green Bone	5⅛	1920-40	Tested XX	465
610050	Flat Blade, Green Bone	5⅛	1920-40	Tested XX	465
710050	Flat blade Tortoise	5⅛	1920-40	Tested XX	725
C91050SAB	Onyx	5⅛	1920-40	Tested XX	615
C61050SAB	Green Bone	5⅛	1940-55	XX	
	Coke Bottle				400
C61050SAB	Wood	5⅛	1940-64	XX	
	Coke Bottle				90
C61050SAB	Bone	5⅛	1940-64	XX	
	Coke Bottle				175
C91050	Flat Blade	5⅛	1940-64	Tested XX	
	Cracked Ice				600

1983 NKCA CLUB KNIFE

C61050L SAB SS Bone   5½" $90

Nr.	Handle	Lgth.		Stamp	Mint
C61050SAB	Wood	5⅛	1965-69	USA	
	Coke Bottle				80
C61050SAB	Bone	5⅛	1965-69	USA	200
C61050SAB	Wood	5⅛	1970	10 Dot	
	Coke Bottle				40

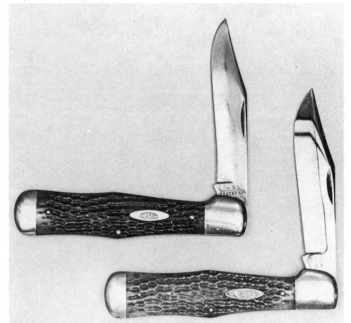

C61050	SAB Green Bone	5⅜"	Tested XX	$450
C61050	SAB Red Bone	5⅜"	XX	$250

651	Green Bone w/sheath	Tested XX	$900
551	Stag with sheath	Tested XX	750

**Older Case Knives
Begin Page 91**

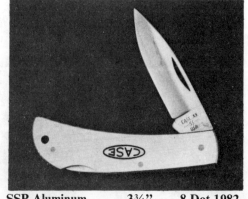

M1051L SSP Aluminum   3¾"   8 Dot 1982 $20

Nr.	Handle	Lgth.	Stamp	Mint

P10051L SSP Pakkawood, Brass Bolsters   3¾" $30

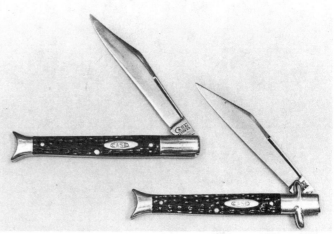

| 61051LP | Green bone | 3⅞" | Tested XX | $250 |
| 61051LP | Green bone w/guard | 3⅞" | Tested XX | $275 |

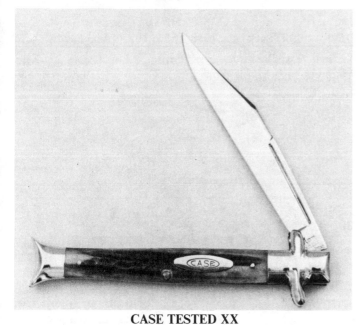

CASE TESTED XX

Nr.	Handle		Stamp	Mint
51051LP	**Bow Tie, Second cut Stag, Rare** 3⅞"			**$500**
B1051	Christmas Tree	1920-40	Tested XX	335
GS1051	Gold Stone	1920-40	Tested XX	310
R1051	Candystripe		Tested XX	325
81051	Pearl		Tested XX	400
31051L	Yellow Celluloid	1920-40	Tested XX	300
3R1051L	Candy Stripe	1920-40	Tested XX	400

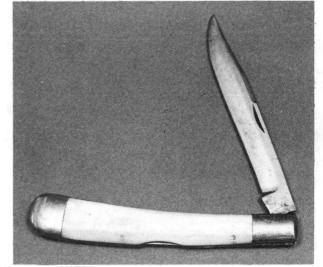

8151L	Pearl	5¼"	Tested XX	$1200
8151	Pearl	5¼"	Tested XX	1000
9151	Onyx		1920-40 Tested XX	550
B151L	Imi. Onyx		1920-40 Tested XX	600
3151SAB	Yellow		1920-40 Tested XX	550

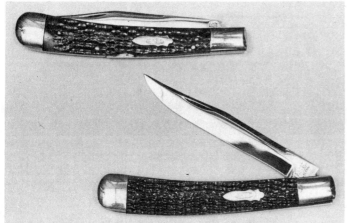

| 6151L | Green bone | 5¼" | Tested XX | $600 |
| 6151 | Green bone | 5¼" | Tested XX | $550 |

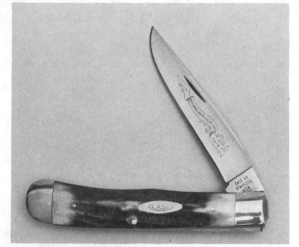

1979 NKCA TRAPPER

5154SSP Stag (year knife) 4⅛" $50

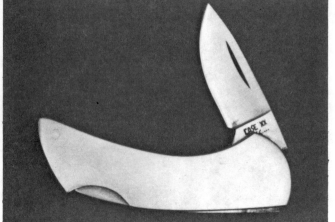

M1056L SSP Stainless   2½"   1980 $16

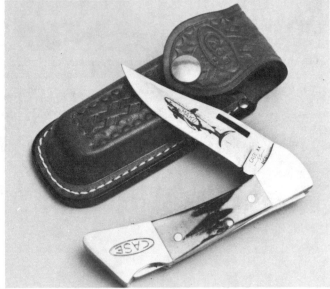

MAKO

5158L   SSP Stag 1980   4¼"   10 Dot Lighting S $45

Nr.	Handle	Lgth.	Stamp	Mint
P158LSSP	Pakkawood		Dots	25
7158LSSP	Curly Maple		Dots	45

HAMMERHEAD

5159L   SSP Black Stag 1980   5"   10 Dot Lighting S $60

Nr.	Handle	Lgth.	Stamp	Mint
P159LSSP	Pakkawood		Dots	30
2159LSSP	Black Comp.		Dots	25

6161L Green bone, 4⅜" Hinge type release   Tested XX $1000

5161LSAB	Genuine Stag	4⅜	1920-40 Tested XX	900
5161L	Geunine Stag	4⅜	1920-40 Tested XX	
Flat blade				1000

MOBY DICK

W165SAB SSP Scrimshaw w/case, blue box   5¼" $125

Nr.	Handle	Lgth.	Stamp	Mint
W165SABSSP	Scrimshaw w/case, Nantucket Sleigh Ride 5¼"			
Red Box				100
B165	Christmas Tree	5½	1920-40 Tested XX	1000
GS165	Gold Stone	5½	1920-40 Tested XX	1000
3165SAB	Yellow Comp.		1920-40 Tested XX	400
5165SAB	Genuine Stag		1920-40 Tested XX	335
5165	Genuine Stag		1920-40 Tested XX	
Flat blade				400
5165	2nd Cut Stag Flat blade		1920-40 Tested XX	600

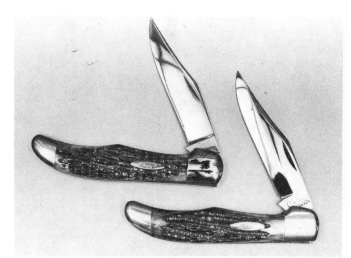
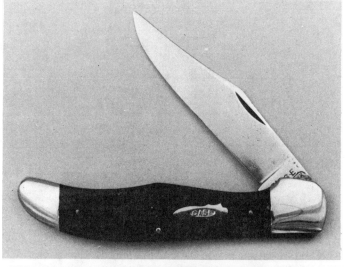

6165 2nd Cut Bone, flat blade 5¼" Tested XX $500
6165SAB 2nd Cut bone, 5¼" Tested XX $450

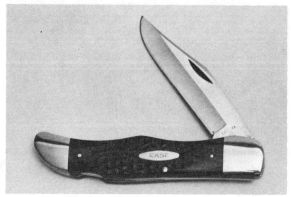

CASE TESTED XX
6165 Flat Blade, Green Bone, bottom photo shows thinness of knife bolsters compared to another 6165SAB Tested XX which is considered rare Thin bolster 5¼" $600

6165LSAB SSP Wood 5¾" 3 Dot $25

Nr.	Handle	Lgth.	Stamp	Mint
6165SAB	Green Bone	1920-40	Tested XX	350
6165	Green Bone	1920-40	Tested XX	
Flat blade				400
6165SAB	Rough Black	1940	Tested XX	300
9165SAB	Cracked Ice	1920-40	Tested XX	400
9165	Cracked Ice	1920-40	Tested XX	
Flat blade				450
5165SAB Dr. Stag		1964	XX	125
5165SAB	Stag	1940-64	XX	
Bolster not drilled				125
5165	Stag	1940-55	XX	
Flat blade				300
5165SAB	2nd Cut Stag	1940-64	XX	500
6165SAB	Rough Black	1940-50	XX	300
6165	Rough Black	1940-50	XX	
Flat blade				360
6165SAB	Green Bone	1940-55	XX	260
6165	Green Bone	1940-55	XX	
Flat blade				335
6165SAB	Red Bone	1940-64	XX	210
6165	Red Bone	1940-64	XX	
Flat blade				260
6165SAB	Rogers Bone	1940-64	XX	400
6165	Bone	1940-64	XX	
Flat blade				285
6165SAB	Wood	1940-64	XX	90

Nr.	Handle	Lgth.	Stamp	Mint
6165SAB	Bone Stag	1940-64	XX	125
5165SAB	Stag	1965-69	USA	
small pattern nr.				335
5165SAB	Stag	1965-69	USA	
Lrg. Pattern No.				335
6165SAB	Wood	1965-69	USA	
Bolster not drilled, XX frame				90
6165	Bone 5½	1965-69	USA	
large stamp with SAB deleted				200
6165SABDR	Wood	1965-69	USA	
XX frame				65
6165SABDR	Wood	1965-69	USA	40
6165SABDR	Wood	1965-69	USA	
letters SAB DR deleted				45
6165SABDR	Wood	1970	10 Dot	40

SWITCHBLADE
5171L Stag· bolster stamped   5⅜"   Tested XX $1250

Nr.	Handle	Lgth.	Stamp	Mint
5171L	Genuine Stag	5½	1920-40 Tested XX	
lower bolster not stamped				1200
6171L	Green Bone	5½	1920-40 Tested XX	
lower bolster not stamped				1200
6171L	Green Bone	5½	1920-40 Tested XX	
lower bolster stamped				1260

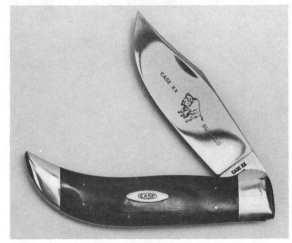

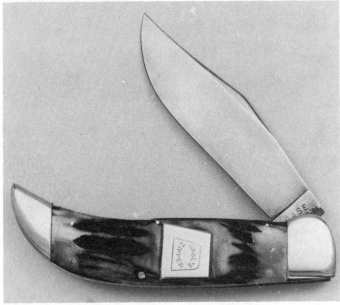

5172 Case's Zipper, Clasp Switch Blade   5½" $3500
(not shown)
6172 Case's Zipper, Clasp Switch Blade Green Bone, 5½" $4500

BUFFALO
P172   Pakkawood   5½"   USA $60

Nr.	Handle	Lgth.	Stamp	Mint
B172	Mottled Brown	5½	1920-40 Tested XX	1150
H172	Mottled Brown	5½	1920-40 Tested XX	1150
RM172	Christmas Tree	5½	1920-40 Tested XX	2000
2172	Slick Black	5½	1920-40 Tested XX	1000
3172	Yellow Comp.	5½	1920-40 Tested XX	1000
P172	Pakkawood	5½	1970 10 Dot	

Was not made
There were a few 1980 10 Dots. Dots were on top of tang backside$50

5172	Stag	5½"	1960-64 XX	$220
5172	Genuine Stag	5½	1920-40 Tested XX	1250

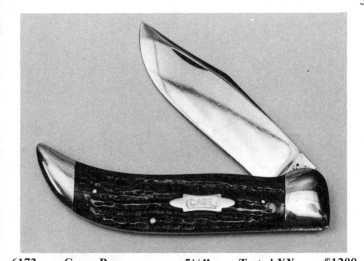

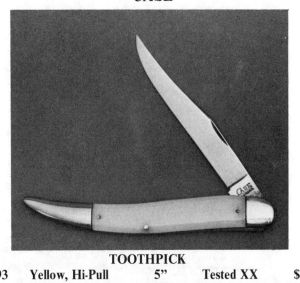

6172   Green Bone   5½"   Tested XX $1200

TOOTHPICK

31093   Yellow, Hi-Pull   5"   Tested XX $225

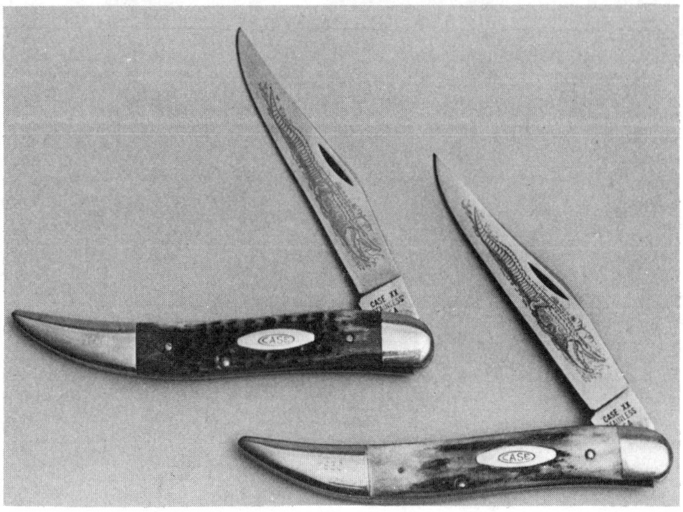

Nr.	Handle	Lgth.		Stamp	Mint
5172	Stag	5½	1965-69	USA	140
5172	Stag	5½	1965	USA	
Transition stamp & pattern Nr. on same side of blade					210

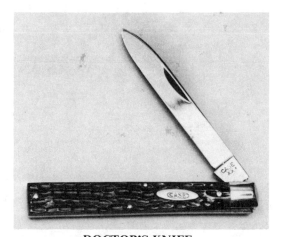

DOCTOR'S KNIFE

6185   Bone   3¾"   XX $65

Nr.	Handle	Lgth.		Stamp	Mint
B185	Christmas Tree	3⅝	1920-40	Tested XX	
Dr.'s Knife					400
3185	Yellow Comp.	3⅝	1920-40	Tested XX	225
3185	Yellow Comp.	3⅝	1940-64	XX	75
3185	Yellow Comp.	3⅝	1965-69	USA	60
3185	Yellow Comp.	3⅝	1970	10 Dot	90
6185	Green Bone	3⅝	1920-40	Tested XX	200
6185	Red Bone	3⅝	1940-64	XX	110
6185	Bone	3⅝	1965-69	USA	55
6185	Bone	3⅝	1970	10 Dot	55

GATOR SET (Toothpicks)

Top 61093S.S.P.   Bottom 51093S.S.P.   2750 Sets made Set-$100

Nr.	Handle	Lgth.		Stamp	Mint
B1093	Christmas Tree	5	1920-40	Tested XX	
Toothpick					400
GS1093	Gold Stone	5	1920-40	Tested XX	350
H1093	High Art	5	1920-40	Tested XX	400
P1093	Swirl Celluloid	5	1920-40	Tested XX	260
R1093	Candy Stripe	5	1920-40	Tested XX	310
RM1093	Mottled Red	5	1920-40	Tested XX	310
31093	Yellow Comp.	5	1940-64	XX	100
31093	Yellow Comp. Rare	5	1965-69	USA	300
61093	Green Bone	5	1920-40	Tested XX	225
61093	Green Bone	5	1940-55	XX	
Toothpick					225
61093	Red Bone	5	1940-64	XX	120
61093	Bone	5	1940-64	XX	70
61093	Bone	5	1965-69	USA	55
61093	Bone	5	1970	10 Dot	55

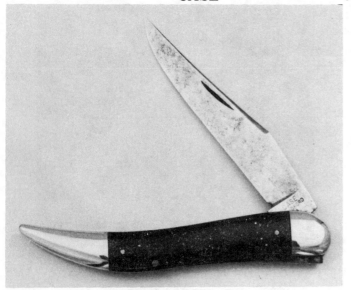

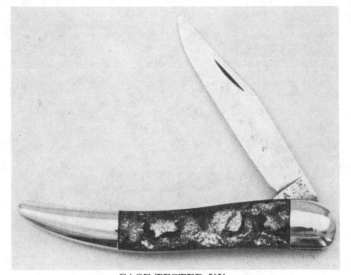

CASE BRADFORD, PA

Nr.	Handle	Lgth.		Stamp	Mint
GS1094	Goldstone	4¼"			$350
B1094	Onyx		1920-40	Tested XX	260
R1094	Candy Stripe		1920-40	Tested XX	310
61094	Rogers Bone		1920-40	Tested XX	300

CASE TESTED XX

Nr.	Handle	Lgth.		Stamp	Mint
B1096	Christmas Tree	3⅛"			$400
61096	Green Bone	3⅛"	1920-40	Tested XX	310
R1096	Candy Stripe	3⅛"	1920-40	Tested XX	325

LEG KNIFE

Nr.	Handle	Lgth.		Stamp	Mint
RM1097	Red Mottled	5"		Tested XX	$300
GS1097	Gold Stone		1920-40	Tested XX	360
31097	Yellow Comp Leg		1920-40	Tested XX	310
B1097	Christmas Tree		1920-40	Tested XX	400

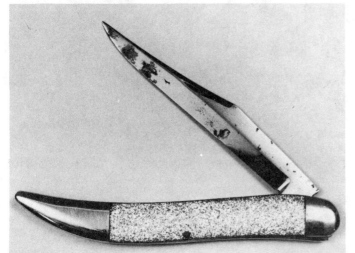

Nr.	Handle	Lgth.		Stamp	Mint
GS1095	SAB Goldstone	5"		Case, Bradford, Pa	$350
B1095	Christmas Tree	5	1920-40	Tested XX	400
B1095	Waterfall		1920-40	Tested XX	325
B1095	Imi. Onyx	1945		Case's Stainless	325
HA1095	High Art	5	1920-40	Tested XX	400
R1095	Candy Stripe	5	1920-40	Tested XX	310
31095	Yellow Comp.	5	1920-40	Tested XX	235
61095	Green Bone	5	1920-40	Tested XX	275

———— CITRUS KNIFE ————

4196X	White Comp.	1920-40	Tested XX
	Citrus, Case's Stainless		310

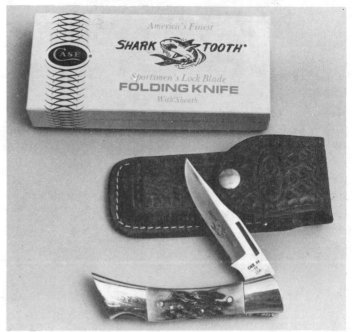

Nr.	Handle	Lgth.	Mint
5197L	SSP Stag	5"	$65
7197LSSP	Pakkawood		45
P197LSSP	Pakkawood		40
7197LSSP	Curly Maple		125

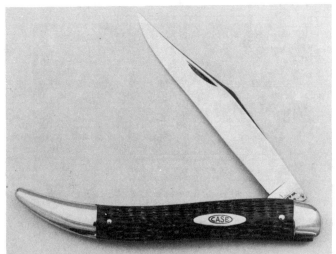

Nr.	Handle	Lgth.		Stamp	Mint
61098	**Green Bone**	**5½"**		**Tested XX**	**$300**
B1098	Christmas Tree	5½	1920-40	Tested XX	450
R1098	Candy Stripe	5½	1920-40	Tested XX	400
B1098	Waterfall	5½	1920-40	Tested XX	400
61098	Rogers Bone	5½	1920-40	Tested XX	350
3199EO	Yellow Comp.	4⅛	1920-40	Tested XX	260

— Navy Knife —

1199SHRSS	Walnut	4⅛	1940-64	XX	30
1199SHRSS	Walnut	4⅛	1965-69	USA	28
1199SHRSS	Walnut	4⅛	1970	10 Dot	25

HA199½ SSP Hi-Art with box   4⅛"   7500 made $32

CASE TWO BLADE

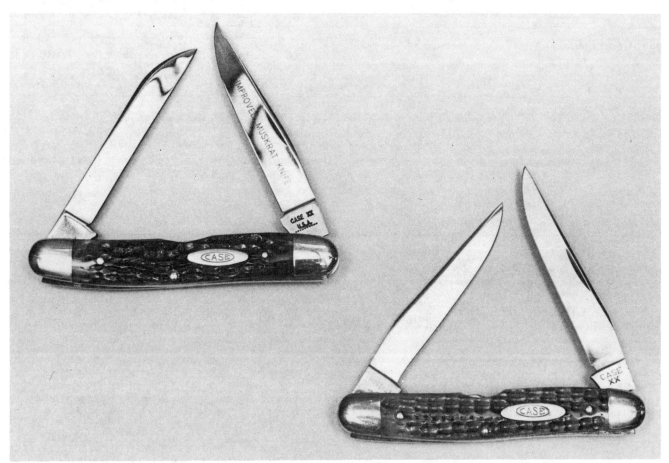

MUSKRAT Bone Hawbaker's Special 3⅞" 1970 10 Dot $300

MUSKRAT Green Bone 3⅞"   1940-55 XX $300

Nr.	Handle	Lgth.		Stamp	Mint
MUSKRAT Green Bone		3⅞	1920-40	Tested XX	650
MUSKRAT Rough Black		3⅞	1940-50	XX	260
MUSKRAT Red Bone		3⅞	1940-64	XX	135
MUSKRAT Rogers Bone		3⅞	1940-64	XX	275
MUSKRAT Bone		3⅞	1940-64	XX	60
MUSKRAT Bone		3⅞	1965-69	USA	35
MUSKRAT Bone		3⅞	1970	10 Dot	35
MUSKRAT Bone		3⅞	1940-64	XX	
Hawbaker's Special					350
MUSKRAT Bone		3⅞	1940-64	XX	
Hawbaker's Special XX to USA					200
MUSKRAT Bone		3⅞	1965-69	USA	
Hawbaker's Special					250
MUSKRAT Bone		3⅞	1965-69	USA	
Hawbaker's Special USA to 10 Dot					175
MUSKRAT Bone		3⅞	1970	10 Dot	
Hawbaker's Special 10 Dot to USA					175

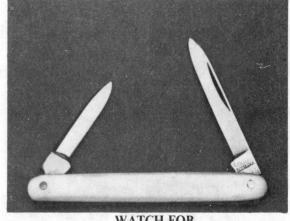

WATCH FOB

Unknown Pearl   2⅛"   **Tested XX**   **$150**

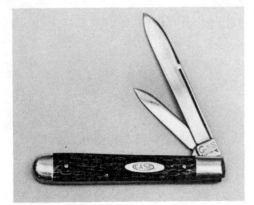

Unknown Green Bone, LP   **Tested XX**   **$175**

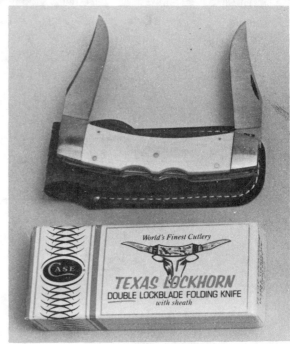

TEXAS LONGHORN

Double Lock back, Micarda   Imi. Ivory   (Discontinued)   4½"
$50

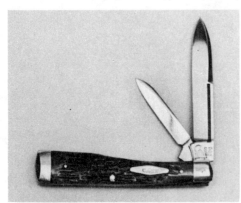

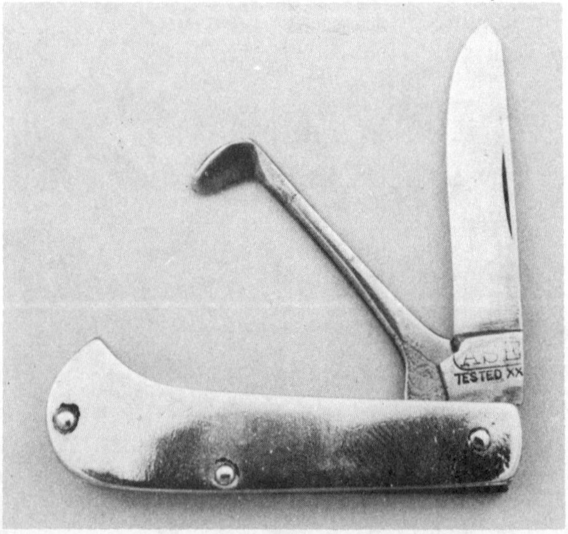

DOCTOR'S KNIFE/GUNSTOCK

Unknown Green Bone, LP   3"   Tested XX $400

Older Case Knives
Begin Page 91

METAL CASTRATING KNIFE
Unknown   Cord Cutter   2⅝"   Tested XX $175

Nr.	Handle	Lgth.		Stamp	Mint
4200SS	White Comp.	5½	1940-64	XX	
	Melon Tester				210
4200SS	White Comp.	5½	1965-69	USA	
	Melon Tester, Serrated Master Blade				150
4200SS	White Comp.	5½	1970	10 Dot	
	Melon Tester				60

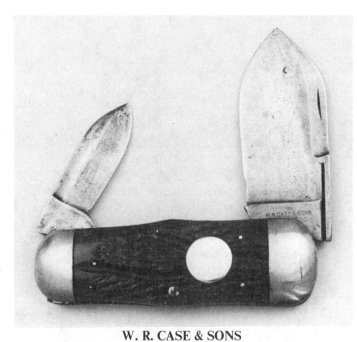

W. R. CASE & SONS

Rogers Bone, Toenail, (Platts)   4⅜"   **$900**

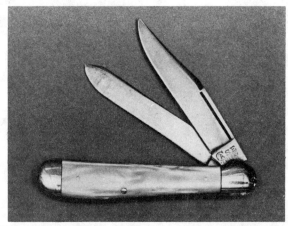

9200LP	Cracked Ice, Imi. Pearl		4"	Tested XX	**$600**
6200	Green Bone	3¹⁵⁄₁₆	1920-40	Tested XX	600
3200	Yellow Comp.	3¹⁵⁄₁₆	1920-40	Tested XX	550

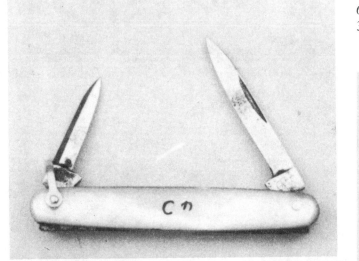

Watch Fob Pearl with Bail   1¾"   **Tested XX $175**

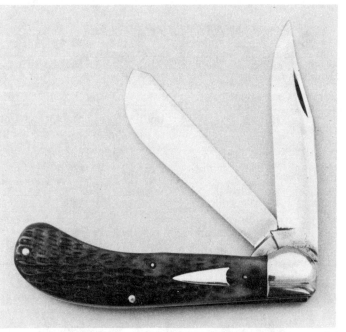

62100	Green Bone	4⅝"	1920-40	Tested XX	**$700**
92100	Imi. Pearl	4⅝	1920-40	Tested XX	700

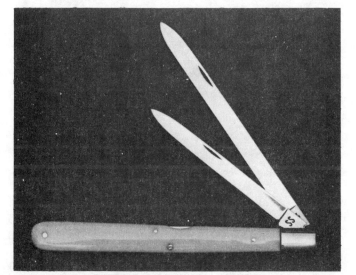

CITRUS OR MELON TESTOR

4200SS   White Comp.   5½"   USA $55
Has small & large stamp

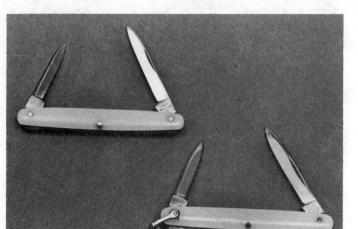

Nr.	Handle	Lgth.		Stamp	Mint
3201	Yellow Comp.	2⅝	1940-64	XX	30
6201	Bone	2⅝	1940-64	XX	38
8201	Bone	2⅝	1940-64	XX	65
9201	Imi. Pearl	2⅝	1940-64	XX	25
9201	Cracked Ice	2⅝	1940-64	XX	30
9201R	Imi. Pearl	2⅝	1940-64	XX	33
9201R	Cracked Ice	2⅝	1940-64	XX	35
3201	Yellow Comp	2⅝	1965-69	USA	28
6201	Bone	2⅝	1965-69	USA	30
9201	Imi. Pearl	2⅝	1970	10 Dot	28
3201	Yellow Comp.	2⅝	1970	10 Dot	28
3201	Flat Yellow Comp.	2⅝	1970	10 Dot	40
6201	Bone	2⅝	1970	10 Dot	25

3201	Yellow	2⅝"	Case Bradford	$110
3210R	Yellow with Bail	2⅝"	Tested XX	$100

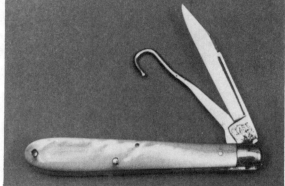

820028	Pearl (no lower bols)	2⅞"	Case Tested XX	$350

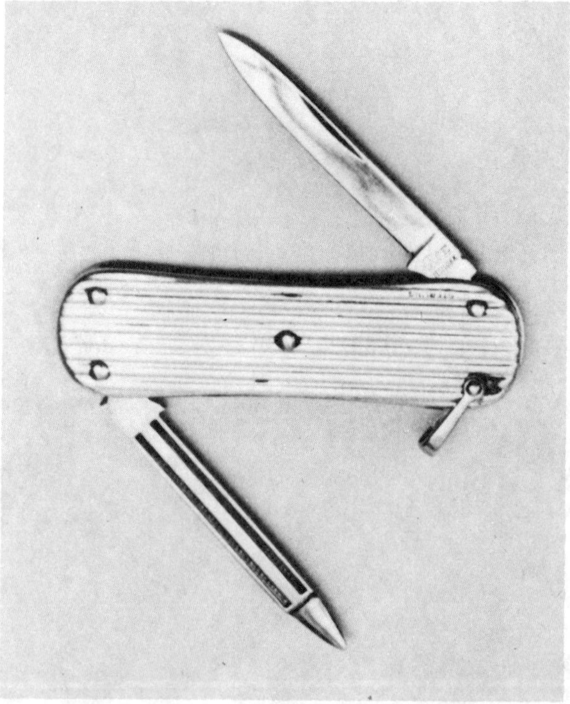

6201F	Green Bone	2⅝"	Tested XX	$130

Nr.	Handle	Lgth.	Stamp	Mint
B210	Christmas Tree	2⅝	1920-40 Tested XX	250
22001R	Slick Black	2⅝	1920-40 Tested XX	110
3201	Yellow Comp.	2⅝	1920-40 Tested XX	110
6201	Green Bone	2⅝	1920-40 Tested XX	115
62001	Green Bone	2⅝	1920-40 Tested XX	115
7201	Tortoise Shell	2⅝	1920-40 Tested XX	225
82001	Genuine Pearl	2⅝	1920-40 Tested XX	160
82101R	Genuine Pearl	2⅝	1920-40 Tested XX	150
9201	Imi. Pearl	2⅝	1920-40 Tested XX	100
9201R	Imi. Pearl	2⅝	1920-40 Tested XX	110
92101R	Imi. Pearl	2⅝	1920-40 Tested XX	100

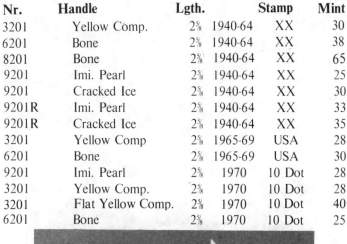

S2	Sterling Silver	2¼"	Tested XX	$150
S2 L.P.	Sterling Silver,	2¼	XX	125
S2	Sterling Silver	2¼	XX	115
S2 LP	Sterling Silver	2¼	U.S.A.	110

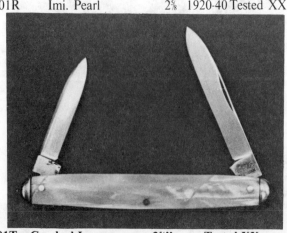
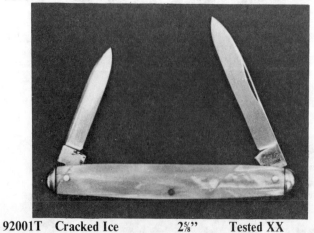

92001T	Cracked Ice	2⅝"	Tested XX	$110

CASE

Nr.	Handle	Lgth.		Stamp	Mint
5202RAZ	Stag	3⅜	1920-40	Tested XX	360
6202	Green Bone	3⅜	1920-40	Tested XX	125
2202½	Slick Black	3⅜	1920-40	Tested XX	135
6202½	Green Bone	3⅜	1920-40	Tested XX	135
6202½	Rough Black	3⅜	1920-40	Tested XX	135
6202½EO	Green Bone	3⅜	1920-40	Tested XX	150
6202SHREO	Bone	3⅜	1920-40	Tested XX	160
6202½	Rough Black	3⅜	1940-50	XX	45
6202½	Green Bone	3⅜	1940-55	XX	85
2202½	Slick Black	3⅜	1940-64	XX	120
6202½	Bone	3⅜	1940-64	XX	30
6202½	Bone	3⅜	1965-69	USA	22
6202½	Delrin	3⅜	1970	10 Dot	20
6202½	Bone Stag	3⅜	1970	10 Dot	28

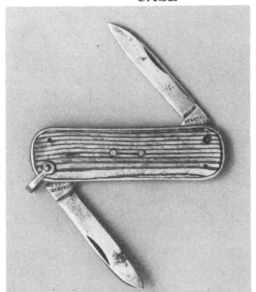

LOBSTER
Standard Knife Co., mfg. by Case - 1920-23
Green Stripe Celluloid   2¼"   **$55**

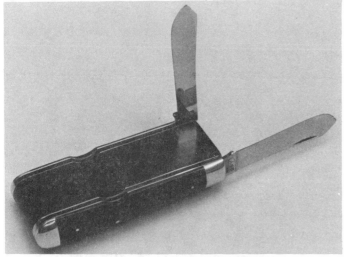

GRAFTING AND BUDDING KNIFE
1202   G&B Wood   3⅜"   Tested XX $400

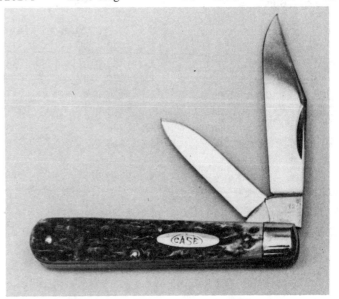

5202½	Stag		3⅜"		Tested XX	**$200**
62103	Green Bone	2⅞	1920-40	Tested XX	160
62103R	Green Bone	2⅞	1920-40	Tested XX	160
82103	Genuine Pearl	2⅞	1920-40	Tested XX	160
82103R	Genuine Pearl	2⅞	1920-40	Tested XX	160

6202SHR Rogers Bone LP   3⅛"   WR Case & Son $200
with Bail

ABBREVIATIONS

½	master blade is clip blade	½
B	Budding	B
EO	Easy Opener	EO
F	File	F
J	Long Spay Blade	J
K	Corkscrew	K
LR	Electrician's Knife	LR
M	Metal	M
PEN	Pen Blade	PEN
PU	Punch Blade	PU
R	Bail in handle	R
RAZ	Razor Blade	RAZ
SAB	Sabor Blade	SAB
SC/SCI	Scissors	SC/SCI
SH	Sheepfoot Blade	SH
SP	Spay Blade	SP
SSP	Stainless Steel, Polished Blade Edge	SSP
SS	Stainless Steel	SS
T	Tip Bolsters	T

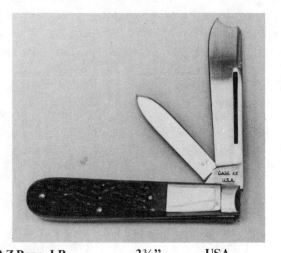

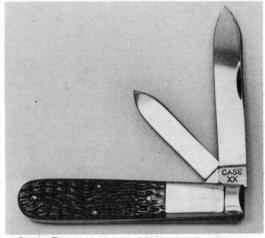

6205RAZ Bone, LP		3¾"	USA	$45

Nr.	Handle	Lgth.	Stamp	Mint
5205RAZ	Stag	3¾	1920-40 Tested XX	335
5205	Stag	3¾	1920-40 Tested XX	335
5205½	Stag	3¾	1920-40 Tested XX	350
6205	Green Bone	3¾	1920-40 Tested XX	310
6205RAZ	Green Bone	3¾	1920-40 Tested XX	335
6205RAZ	Rough Black	3¾	1940-50 XX	250
6205RAZ	Green Bone	3¾	1940-55 XX	185
6205Spear	Red Bone	3¾	1940-64 XX	130
6205RAZ	Red Bone	3¾	1940-64 XX	130
6205RAZ	Bone	3¾	1940-64 XX	60
6205RAZ	Bone	3¾	1965-69 USA	45
6205RAZ	Bone	3¾	1970 10 Dot	50

6205	Green Bone	3¾"	XX	$140

Nr.	Handle	Lgth.	Stamp	Mint
5206	Stag	2⅝"	1920-40 Tsted XX	200
6206	Green Bone	2⅝"	1920-40 Tested XX	175
8206	Pearl	2⅝"	1920-40 Tested XX	200

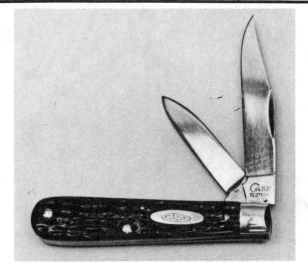

6206½	Green Bone	2⅝"	Tested XX	$160

6206½	Rough Black	2⅝	1920-40 Tested XX	160
5206½	Stag	2⅝	1920-40 Tested XX	210
62006½	Bone	2⅝	1920-40 Tested XX	185
8206½	Genuine Pearl	2⅝	1920-40 Tested XX	235
6206½	Rough Black	2⅝	1940-50 XX	120

6205½	Green Bone, LP	3¾"	Tested XX	$325

Note:
   This book is a guide. Prices may vary a bit and are not absolute. Prices on more expensive knives may vary $100 or more depending on dealer.

Note:
   Prices are for mint knives although mint knives are not always available for photos.

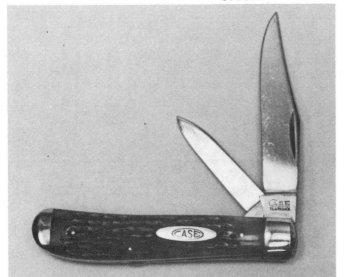

6207 Green Bone 3½" Tested XX $300

Nr.	Handle	Lgth.	Stamp	Mint
6207	Green Bone	3½"	Tested Frame XX	275
B207LP	Christmas Tree	3½	1920-40 Tested XX	415
2207	Slick Black	3½	1920-40 Tested XX	310
3207	Yellow Comp.	3½	1920-40 Tested XX	310
5207	Stag	3½	1920-40 Tested XX	335
6207LP	Rough Black	3½	1920-40 Tested XX	235
6207	Rough Black	3½	1940-50 XX	150
6207	Green Bone	3½	1940-55 XX	200
6207	Red Bone	3½	1940-64 XX	90
2207	Slick Black	3½	1940-64 XX	200
6207	Bone	3½	1940-64 XX	40
6207	Rogers Bone	3½	1940-64 XX	200
6207	Bone	3½	1965-69 USA	30
6207	Bone	3½	1970 10 Dot	30

6208 Bone 3¼" 10 Dot (1970) $20

5208	Stag	3¼	1920-40 Tested XX	175
6208	Green Bone	3¼	1920-40 Tested XX	135
6208	Rough Black	3¼	1940-50 XX	
	Half Whittler			50
6208	Green Bone	3¼	1940-55 XX	90
6208	Red Bone	3¼	1940-64 XX	50
6208	Bone	3¼	1940-64 XX	30
6208	Bone	3¼	1965-69 USA	25

2209 Bud Folding Budding Blade, Rare XX $250

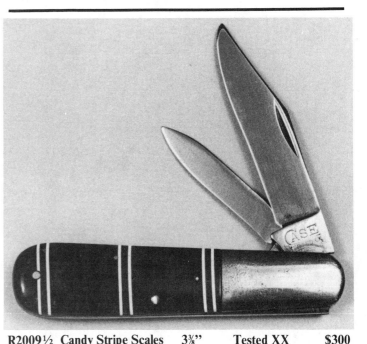

R2009½ Candy Stripe Scales 3⅜" Tested XX $300

Nr.	Handle	Lgth.	Stamp	Mint
62009½	Green Bone	3⁵⁄₁₆	1920-40 Tested XX	
	Bolster Stamped "Case's Tested XX"			260
62009½	Green Bone	3⁵⁄₁₆	1920-40 Tested XX	180
92009½	Cracked Ice	3⁵⁄₁₆	1920-40 Tested XX	260
62009½	Rough Black	3⁵⁄₁₆	1940-50 XX	
	Saw Marks			100
62009½	Slick Black	3⁵⁄₁₆	1940-64 XX	100
62009½	Green Bone	3⁵⁄₁₆	1940-55 XX	120
62009½	Red Bone	3⁵⁄₁₆	1940-64 XX	45
62009½	Bone	3⁵⁄₁₆	1940-64 XX	30
62009½	Bone	3⁵⁄₁₆	1965-69 USA	
	Master Blade in Back			28
62009½	Bone	3⁵⁄₁₆	1965-69 USA	
	Master Blade in Front			28
62009½	Delrin	3⁵⁄₁₆	1970 10 Dot	30
62009½	Bone Stag	3⁵⁄₁₆	1970 10 Dot	30

62009½ Green Bone, Round Bolster 3⅜" XX $120

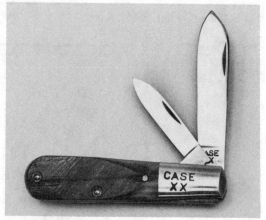

62009   **Bone**   3⅜"   XX $35

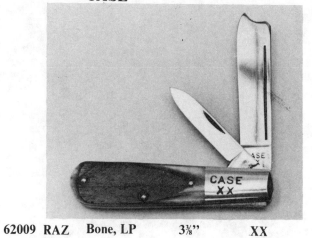

62009 RAZ   **Bone, LP**   3⅜"   XX $55

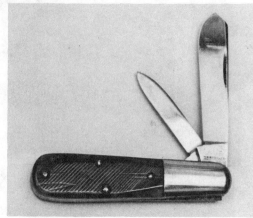

BARLOW SPEY BLADE

62009   **Green Bone**   3⅜"   **Tested XX** $210

Nr.	Handle	Lgth.		Stamp	Mint
Baby Barlow,	Green Bone	3	1920-40	Tested XX	260
62009	Green Bone	3⁵⁄₁₆	1920-40	Tested XX	175
62009RAZ	Green Bone	3⁵⁄₁₆	1920-40	Tested XX	235
62009SH	Green Bone	3⁵⁄₁₆	1920-40	Tested XX	235
62009	Red Bone	3⁵⁄₁₆	1940-64	XX	50
62009RAZ	Red Bone	3⁵⁄₁₆	1940-64	XX	60
62009RAZ	Green Bone	3⁵⁄₁₆	1940-55	XX	185
62009	Green Bone	3⁵⁄₁₆	1940-55	XX	135
62009	Bone	3⁵⁄₁₆	1940-64	XX	35
62009RAZ	Bone	3⁵⁄₁₆	1940-64	XX	50
62009RAZ	Bone Long Pull	3⁵⁄₁₆	1940-64	XX	55
62009	Slick Black	3⁵⁄₁₆	1940-64	XX	120
62009SH	Slick Black	3⁵⁄₁₆	1940-64	XX	150
62009	Bone Master Blade in Back	3⁵⁄₁₆	1965-69	USA	30
62009	Bone Master Blade in Front	3⁵⁄₁₆	1965-69	USA	30
62009RAZ	Bone Master Blade in Back	3⁵⁄₁₆	1965-69	USA	50
62009RAZ	Bone Master Blade in Front	3⁵⁄₁₆	1965-69	USA	50
62009	Delrin	3⁵⁄₁₆	1970	10 Dot	30
62009	Bone Stag	3⁵⁄₁₆	1970	10 Dot	30
62009RAZ	Delrin	3⁵⁄₁₆	1970	10 Dot	50
62009RAZ	Bone	3⁵⁄₁₆	1970	10 Dot	45

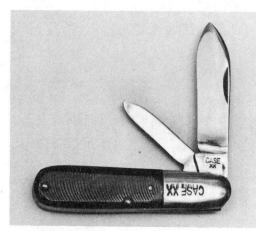

62009   **Black Comp**   3⅜" $90
Bolster Stamped upside down

62109 Spear, Little Copperhead, Green Bone   3⅛" **(Rare)** $350

Nr.	Handle	Lgth.	Stamp		Mint
62109X	Green Bone	3⅛	1920-40	Tested XX	200
62109X	Rough Black	3⅛	1920-40	Tested XX	200
62109X	Rough Black	3⅛	1940-50	XX	90
62109X	Green Bone	3⅛	1940-55	XX	125
62109X	Red Bone	3⅛	1940-64	XX	70
62109X	Bone	3⅛	1940-64	XX	32
62109X	Bone	3⅛	1965-69	USA	28
62109X	Bone	3⅛	10 Dot	(1970)	28

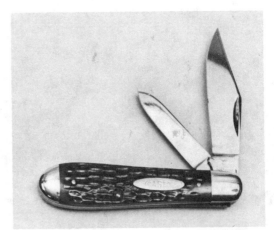

6210½	Green Bone	3⅛"	Tested XX	$175

DOUBLE SWITCHBLADE

T2210	Tortoise	3⅜"	Tested XX	$450
H2210	Mottled	3⅜	1920-40 Tested XX	450
62210	Bone	3⅜	1920-40 Tested XX	450
92210	Cracked Ice	3⅜	1920-40 Tested XX	450

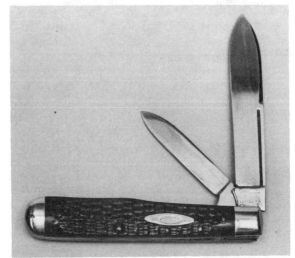

6211	Green Bone, LP	4½"	Tested XX	$450

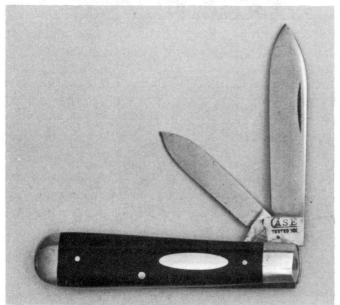

PLAIN SHIELD

2210	Slick Black	3⅛"	Tested XX	$125
3210½	Yellow Comp.	3⅛	1920-40 Tested XX	150
5210½	Stag	3⅛	1920-40 Tested XX	175

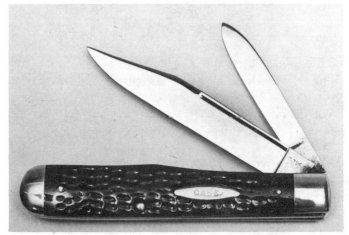

6211½	Green Bone, LP	4½"	Tested XX	$450

2212L	Slick Black	3⅝"	Tested XX	$150

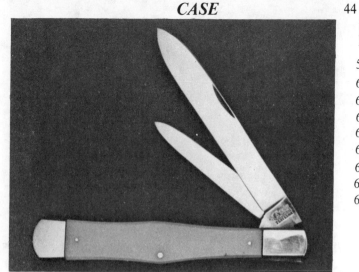

Nr.	Handle	Lgth.	Stamp		Mint
5214½	Stag	3⅜	1920-40	Tested XX	210
6214½	Rogers Bone	3⅜	1920-40	Tested XX	165
6214½	Rough Black	3⅜	1940-50	XX	45
6214½	Green Bone	3⅜	1940-55	XX	90
6214½	Red Bone	3⅜	1940-64	XX	45
6214½	Bone	3⅜	1940-64	XX	30
6214½	Bone	3⅜	1965-69	USA	30
6214½	Delrin	3⅜	1970	10 Dot	20
6214½	Bone Stag	3⅜	1970	10 Dot	30

32213Spear   Yellow, 5¼", Rare   Tested XX $800

Nr.	Handle	Lgth.	Stamp		Mint
6213	Rogers Bone	4	1920-40	Tested XX	600
6213	Green Bone	4	1920-40	Tested XX	350
62213	Spear Rogers Bone	5¼	Rare	Tested XX	1000
62213	Spear, Green Bone	4	1920-40	Tested XX	800

6216½   Bone   3⅜"   USA $27

Nr.	Handle	Lgth.	Stamp		Mint
6216	Green Bone	3⅜	1920-40	Tested XX	160
6216EO	Green Bone	3⅜	1920-40	Tested XX	210
6216½	Green Bone	3⅜	1920-40	Tested XX	170
6216	Bone	3⅜	1940-64	XX	75
6216½	Bone	3⅜	1940-64	XX	33

6214   Rough Black, LP   3⅜"   Tested XX $125

6214	Green Bone	3⅜	1920-40	Tested XX	145
6214	Rough Black	3⅜	1940-50	XX	
With Shield					65
6214	Rough Black	3⅜	1940-50	XX	
Without Shield					55
6214	Green Bone	3⅜	1940-55	XX	100
6214	Red Bone	3⅜	1940-64	XX	50
6214	Rogers Bone	3⅜	1940-64	XX	90
6214	Bone	3⅜	1940-64	XX	33
6214	Bone	3⅜	1965-69	USA	30
6214	Delrin	3⅜	1970	10 Dot	22
6214	Bone Stag	3⅜	1970	10 Dot	35

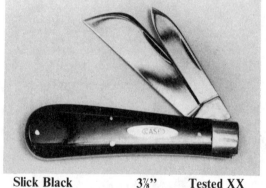

2217   Slick Black   3⅜"   Tested XX $250

6214½   Green Bone   3⅜"   Tested XX $150

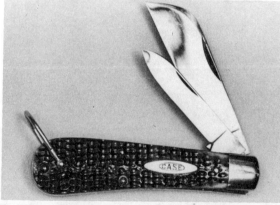

6217R   Green Bone   4"   Tested XX $225

Nr.	Handle	Lgth.		Stamp	Mint
6217	Green Bone	4	1920-40	Tested XX	210
6217	Green Bone	4	1940-55	XX	160
6217	Red Bone	4	1940-64	XX	85
2217	Slick Black	4	1940-64	XX	235
6217	Bone	4	1940-64	XX	50
6217	Wood	4	1965-69	USA	45
6217	Bone Stag	4	1965-69	USA	50
6217	Bone Stag	4	1970	10 Dot	50
6217	Laminated Wood	4	1970	10 Dot	50

─── JACK ───

Nr.	Handle	Lgth.		Stamp	Mint
6219	Green Bone	4⅛	1920-40	Tested XX	250
62019	Green Bone	4⅛	1920-40	Tested XX	275

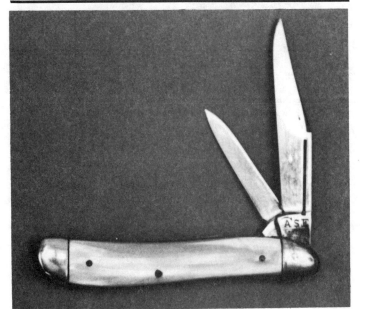

PEANUT

Nr.	Handle	Lgth.		Stamp	Mint
9220	**Cracked Ice LP**	2⅞"		**Tested XX**	**$250**
B220	Christmas Tree	2¾	1920-40	Tested XX	450
B220SAB	Christmas Tree	2¾	1920-40	Tested XX.	500
2220	Slick Black	2¾	1920-40	Tested XX	200
3220	Yellow Comp.	2¾	1920-40	Tested XX	200
5220	Stag	2¾	1920-40	Tested XX	275
6220	Rough Black	2¾	1920-40	Tested XX	225
6220	Green Bone	2¾	1920-40	Tested XX	275
6220SAB	Green Bone	2¾	1920-40	Tested XX	
Long Pull					350
8220	Genuine Pearl	2¾	1920-40	Tested XX	400
9220	Imi. Pearl	2¾	1920-40	Tested XX	190
2220	Slick Black	2¾	1940-64	XX	40
3220	Yellow Comp.	2¾	1940-64	XX	40
5220	Stag	2¾	1940-64	XX	45
6220	Rough Black	2¾	1940-50	XX	
Peanut					125
6220	Green Bone	2¾	1940-55	XX	200
6220	Red Bone	2¾	1940-64	XX	85
6220	Rogers Bone	2¾	1940-64		135
6220	Bone	2¾	1940-64	XX	40
9220	IMI Pearl	2¾	1940-64	XX	100
9220	Cracked Ice	2¾	1940-64	XX	120
2220	Slick Black	2¾	1965-69	USA	40

Nr.	Handle	Lgth.		Stamp	Mint
3220	Yellow Comp.	2¾	1965-69	USA	40
5220	Stag	2¾	1965-69	USA	45
6220	Bone	2¾	1965-69	USA	40
6220	Delrin	2¾	1965-69	USA	100
2220	Slick Black	2¾	1970	10 Dot	40
3220	Yellow Comp.	2¾	1970	10 Dot	40

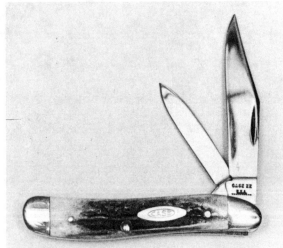

5220	**Stag**	**2⅞"**		**10 Dot**	**$40**
6220	Bone	2¾	1970	10 Dot	40
6220	Delrin	2¾	1970	10 Dot	75
6220	Bone	4	1971	9 Dot	90

06221½	**Green Bone, 3¼"**			**Tested XX**	**$200**
02221½	Slick Black	3¼	1920-40	Tested XX	180
07221	Tortoise	3¼	1920-40	Tested XX	
Spear					260
06221	Wharncliffe Green Bone	3¼	1920-40	Tested XX	260

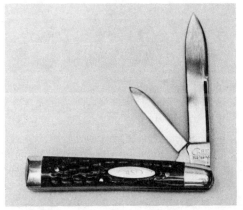

6222	**Green Bone, 3⅜", LP**	**(Phys.)**		**Tested**	**$400**

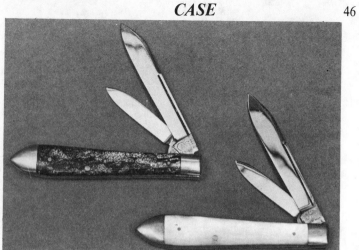

B2028	Christmas Tree, 2⅞", LP		**Tested XX**	**$400**	
82028	Pearl, 2⅞", LP	W.R. Case & Son Bradford, Pa		$350	
22028	Slick Black		Tested XX	300	
GS2028	Goldstone			350	

──── COKE BOTTLE (Coffin Bolster) ────

6223	Green Bone	3¼	1920-40	Tested XX	235
9223	Imi. Pearl	3¼	1920-40	Tested XX	235

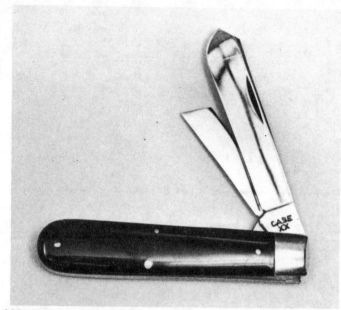

22024SP Slick Black, 3"   XX $175

Nr.	Handle	Lgth.		Stamp	Mint
52024	Stag	3	1920-40	Tested XX	185
62024	Green Bone	3	1920-40	Tested XX	135
62024SH	Green Bone	3	1920-40	Tested XX	185
62024RAZ	Green Bone	3	1920-40	Tested XX	200
220024SP	Slick Black	3	1940-64	XX	

"Little John Carver", (Extremely Rare, Price Quoted is for Knife in the Original Balsa Wood Block)   800

62024	Green Bone	3	1940-64	XX	85

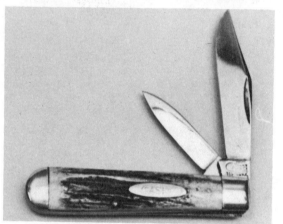

5224½   Stag, 3"   Tested XX $175

62024½   Bone, 3"   XX $28

52024½	Stag	3	1920-40	Tested XX	185
62024½	Green Bone	3	1920-40	Tested XX	135
32024½	Yellow Comp.	3	1940-64	XX	42
62024½	Green Bone	3	1940-55	XX	85
32024½	Yellow Comp.	3	1865-69	USA	35
62024½	Bone	3	1965-69	USA	30

6224½   Green Bone, 3"   Tested XX $125

3224½	Yellow Comp.	3	1920-40	Tested XX	135
2224SH	Slick Black	3	1920-40	Tested XX	200
2224RAZ	Slick Black	3	1920-40	Tested XX	225
3224	Yellow Comp.	3	1920-40	Tested XX	135
6224	Green Bone	3	1920-40	Tested XX	135
2224SP	Slick Black	3	1940-64	XX	145
2224SH	Slick Black	3	1940-64	XX	150
2224RAZ	Slick Black	3	1940-64	XX	160

**Older Case Knives
Begin Page 91**

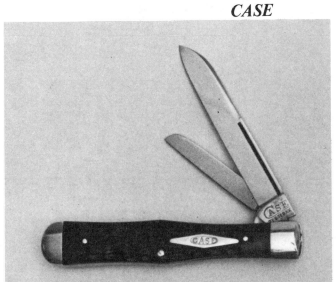

Nr.	Handle	Lgth.	Stamp		Mint
5225½	Stag	3	1920-40	Tested XX	235
6225½	Rough Black	3	1920-40	Tested XX	185
6225½	Rough Black	3	1940-50	XX	125
6225½	Green Bone	3	1940-55	XX	160
6225½	Red Bone	3	1940-64	XX	75
6225RAZ	Bone	3	1940-64	XX	225
6225½	Bone	3	1940-64	XX	38
6225½	Bone	3	1965-69	USA	30
6225½	Bone	3	1970	10 Dot	28

6225   Green Bone, 3", LP $240

Nr.	Handle	Lgth.	Stamp	Mint
32025	Yellow Spear Blade	3	Tested XX	225

32025½	Yellow Comp.	3"	1920-40 Tested XX	$200
62025½	Green Bone	3"	1920-40 Tested XX	$225
62025½	Rough Black	3"	1920-40 Tested XX	$200

——— DOGLEG JACK ———

B2026	Christmas Tree Long Pull	3	1920-40	Tested XX	360
82026	Genuine Pearl Long Pull	3	1920-40	Tested XX	310
6226½	Green Bone	3	1920-40	Tested XX	250

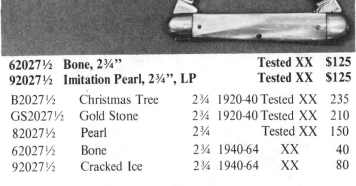

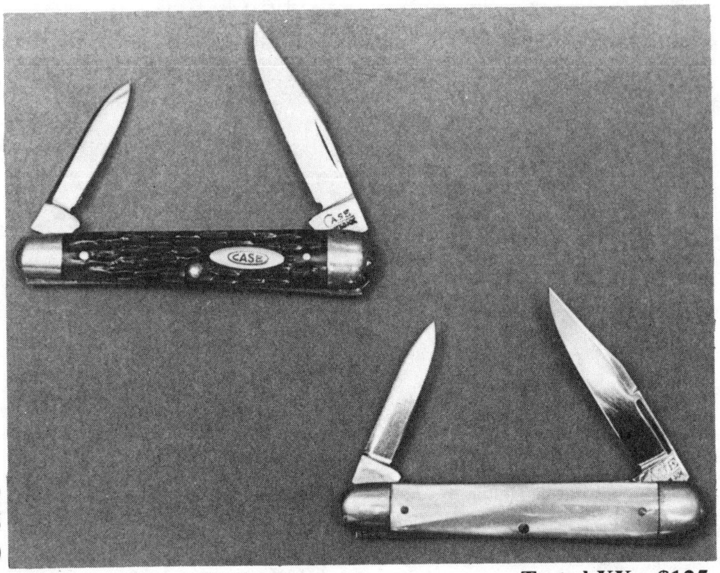

62027½	Bone, 2¾"		Tested XX	$125
92027½	Imitation Pearl, 2¾", LP		Tested XX	$125

B2027½	Christmas Tree	2¾	1920-40	Tested XX	235
GS2027½	Gold Stone	2¾	1920-40	Tested XX	210
82027½	Pearl	2¾		Tested XX	150
62027½	Bone	2¾	1940-64	XX	40
92027½	Cracked Ice	2¾	1940-64	XX	80

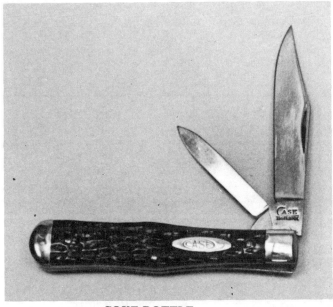

COKE BOTTLE
6225½   Green Bone, 3"   Tested XX $210

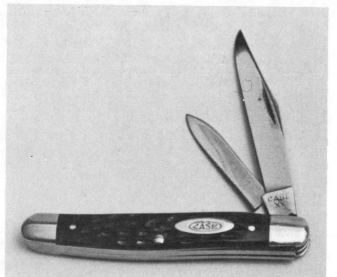

2229½	Black Comp, 2½"		Tested XX	$125
Nr.	**Handle**	**Lgth.**	**Stamp**	**Mint**
6229½	Green Bone	2½	1920-40 Tested XX	135
6229½	Rough Black	2½	Tested XX	125
7229½	Tortoise	2½	1920-40 Tested XX	235
8229½	Pearl			250
9229½	Cracked Ice	2½	1920-40 Tested XX	160
2229½	Slick Black	2½	1940-64 XX	45
6229½	Bone	2½	1940-64 XX	45
2229½	Slick Black	2½	1965-69 USA	
RARE				100
6229½	Bone	2½	1965-69 USA	45

EQUAL END

6230	Green Bone	3¼	1920-40 Tested XX	150
02230	Black Comp.	3¼	1920-40 Tested XX	135
05230	LP Stag	3¼	1920-40 Tested XX	200
06230	Green Bone	3¼	1920-40 Tested XX	
Long Pull				175
06230SH	Green Bone	3¼	1920-40 Tested XX	180
06230SP	Green Bone	3¼	1920-40 Tested XX	180
09230	Imi. Pearl	3¼	1920-40 Tested XX	185
02230½	Black Comp.	3¼	1920-40 Tested XX	135
05230½	Stag	3¼	1920-40 Tested XX	190
06230½	Green Bone	3¼	1920-40 Tested XX	160
09230½	Imi. Pearl	3¼	1920-40 Tested XX	185

6227	Bone,	2¾"	XX	$27
Nr.	**Handle**	**Lgth.**	**Stamp**	**Mint**
6227	Rogers Bone	2¾	1920-40 Tested XX	210
6227	Green Bone	2¾	1940-55 XX	85
6227	Red Bone	2¾	1940-64 XX	40
6227	Bone	2¾	1965-69 USA	28
6227	Delrin	2¾	1970 10 Dot	35
6227	Bone Stag	2¾	1970 10 Dot	30
H2027	Mottled	2¾	1920-40 Tested XX	185
B2027	Christmas Tree	2¾	1920-40 Tested XX	
Spear				235
RM2027	Red Mottled	2¾	1920-40 Tested XX	185
62027	Green Bone	2¾	1920-40 Tested XX	135
92027	Imi. Pearl	2¾	1920-40 Tested XX	120

22028½	Slick Black, 3½"		XX	$80
M2028½	Metal	3½	1920-40 Tested XX	110
22028½	Slick Black	3½	1920-40 Tested XX	120
62028½	Green Bone	3½	1920-40 Tested XX	160
62028½	Rough Black	3½	1940-50 XX	110
62028½	Bone	3½	1940-64 XX	100
2228	Slick Black	3½	1920-40 Tested XX	
Dog Leg				140
2228EO	Slick Black	3½	1920-40 Tested XX	160
2228PU	Slick Black	3½	1920-40 Tested XX	160
6228	Green Bone			200
62028	Green Bone	3½	1920-40 Tested XX	170
22028	Slick Black	3½	1940-64 XX	90

2231½	SAB Slick Black, 3¾"		Tested XX	$150
2231½	Slick Black	3¾	1920-40 Tested XX	
Flat Blade				185
6231½	Green Bone	3¾	1920-40 Tested XX	160
6231½	Rough Black	3¾	1920-40 Tested XX	150
2231½	Slick Black	3¾	1940-64 XX	
Long Pull is Standard				65

Nr.	Handle	Lgth.		Stamp	Mint
2231½SAB	Slick Black	3¾	1940-64	XX	
Long Pull is Standard					45
4231½	White Comp.	3¾	1940-64	XX	
Long Pull is Standard					210
6231½	Bone	3¾	1940-64	XX	
Long Pull is Standard					40
6231½	Red Bone	3¾	1940-64	XX	70
6231½	Green Bone	3¾	1940-55	XX	135
6231½	Rough Black	3¾	1940-50	XX	
Long Pull					80
2231½SAB	Slick Black	3¾	1965-69	USA	
Long Pull is Standard					28
6231½	Bone	3¾	1965-69	USA	
Long Pull is Standard					35
2231½SAB	Slick Black	3¾	1970	10 Dot	
Long Pull is Standard					28
6231½	Bone	3¾	1970	10 Dot	
Long Pull is Standard					35

Nr.	Handle	Lgth.		Stamp	Mint
6231	Bone	3¾	1940-64	XX	50
6231	Rough Black	3¾	1940-50	XX	80
6231	Red Bone Spear	3¾	1940-64	XX	70
6231	Bone	3¾	1965-69	USA	100

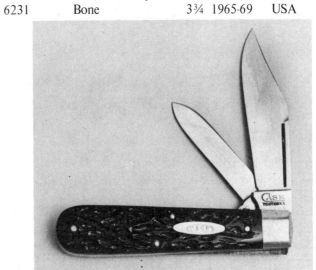

62031½	**Rough Black, 3¾"**			**Tested XX**	**$140**
22031½	Slick Black	3¾	1920-40	Tested XX	160
52031½	Stag	3¾	1920-40	Tested XX	235
52031½SAB	Stag	3¾	1920-40	Tested XX	310
62031½	Green Bone	3¾	1920-40	Tested XX	160
22031½	Slick Black	3¾	1940-64	XX	
Long Pull is Standard					75
62031½	Green Bone	3¾	1940-55	XX	135
62031½	Red Bone	3¾	1940-64	XX	75
62031½	Bone	3¾	1940-64	XX	
Long Pull is Standard					55
62031½	Rough Black	3¾	1940-50	XX	80
62031½	Rough Black	3¾	1940-50	XX	
Long Pull					80

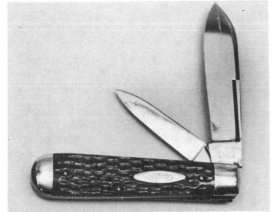

6231   Green Bone 3¾", LP with shield   Tested XX $150

6231   Green Bone, 3¾", LP no shield   Tested XX $150

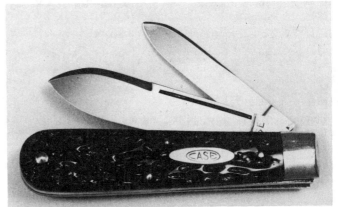

62031	**Rough Black, 3¾", LP**			**XX**	**$80**
22031	Slick Black	3¾	1920-40	Tested XX	160
52031	Stag	3¾	1920-40	Tested XX	235
62031	Green Bone	3¾	1920-40	Tested XX	160
62031	Rough Black	3¾	1920-40	Tested XX	160
62031	Bone	3¾	1940-64	XX	60
62031	Green Bone	3¾	1940-55	XX	135
62031	Green Bone	3¾	1940-55	XX	
Long Pull					150
62031	Red Bone	3¾	1940-64	XX	75

12031LR Walnut, 3¾", Electrician's Knife   XX   **$28**

Nr.	Handle	Lgth.		Stamp	Mint
12031L	Walnut	3¾	1920-40	Tested XX	100
12031LR	Walnut	3¾	1965-69	USA	
Electrician's Knife					22
12031LR	Walnut	3¾	1970	10 Dot	
Electrician's Knife					22

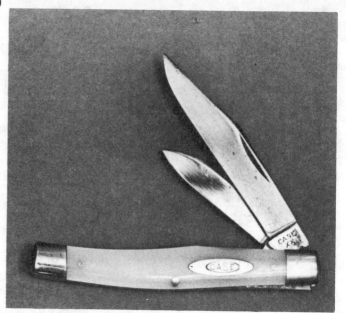

3232 Yellow Comp, 3⅝"   XX   **$90**

Nr.	Handle	Lgth.		Stamp	Mint
3232	Yellow Comp.	3⅝	1920-40	Tested XX	140
5232	Stag	3⅝	1920-40	Tested XX	160
6232	Green Bone	3⅝	1920-40	Tested XX	130
6232	Rough Black	3⅝	1940-50	XX	85
6232	Green Bone	3⅝	1940-55	XX	100
6232	Red Bone	3⅝	1940-64	XX	45
6232	Rogers Bone	3⅝	1940-64	XX	75
5232	Stag	3⅝	1940-64	XX	60
6232	Bone	3⅝	1940-64	XX	30
5232	Stag	3⅝	1965-69	USA	50
6232	Bone	3⅝	1965-69	USA	22
5232	Stag	3⅝	1970	10 Dot	50
6232	Bone	3⅝	1970	10 Dot	22

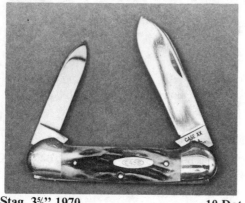

52131 Stag, 3⅝" 1970   **10 Dot**   **$65**

52131	Stag	3⅝	1920-40	Tested XX	350
52131	Stag, Long Pull	3⅝	1920-40	Tested XX	400
92131	Cracked Ice	3⅝	1920-40	Tested XX	450
52131	Stag	3⅝	1940-64	XX	125
52131	Stag Long Pull	3⅝	1940-55	XX	250
52131	Stag	3⅝	1965-69	USA	65
62131	Bone	3⅝	1965-69	USA	40
62131	Bone	3⅝	1970	10 Dot	40
62131	Bone	3⅝	1964	XX	200

Beware, few made in 1964 but was not sold in production, however a few could have gotten to the collector market.

Note:
  This book is a guide. Prices may vary a bit and are not absolute. Prices on more expensive knives may vary $100 or more depending on dealer.

Note:
  Prices are for mint knives although mint knives are not always available for photos.

6233 Green Bone, LP, 2⅝"   **Tested XX**   **$200**

3233	Yellow Comp.	2⅝	1920-40	Tested XX	140
3233	Yellow Comp.	2⅝	1920-40	Tested XX	
Long Pull					160
6233	Rough Black		1920-40	Tested XX	135
6233	Green Bone	2⅝	1920-40	Tested XX	
Long Pull					200

Nr.	Handle	Lgth.	Stamp		Mint
8233	Genuine Pearl	2⅝	1920-40	Tested XX	235
GS233	Gold Stone	2⅝	1920-40	Tested XX	290
B233	Christmas Tree	2⅝	1920-40	Tested XX	310
9233	Imi. Pearl	2⅝	1920-40	Tested XX	
Long Pull					130
6233	Rough Black	2⅝	1940-50	XX	90
6233	Rough Black	2⅝	1940-50	XX	
Long Pull					115
6233	Green Bone	2⅝	1940-55	XX	135
6233	Green Bone	2⅝	1940-55	XX	
Long Pull					160
6233	Red Bone	2⅝	1940-64	XX	45
6233	Rogers Bone	2⅝	1940-64	XX	60
3233	Yellow Comp.	2⅝	1940-64	XX	30
5233	Stag	2⅝	1940-64	XX	40
6233	Bone	2⅝	1940-64	XX	30
8233	Genuine Pearl	2⅝	1940-64	XX	40
9233	Imi. Pearl	2⅝	1940-64	XX	25
9233	Imi. Pearl	2⅝	1940-64	XX	
Long Pull					75
9233	Cracked Ice	2⅝	1940-64	XX	
Long Pull					90
3233	Yellow Comp.	2⅝	1965-69	USA	28
5233	Stag	2⅝	1965-69	USA	40
6233	Bone	2⅝	1965-69	USA	28
6233	Delrin	2⅝	1965-69	USA	
RARE					60
8233	Genuine Pearl	2⅝	1965-69	USA	40
9233	Imi. Pearl	2⅝	1965-69	USA	25
3233	Yellow Comp.	2⅝	1970	10 Dot	30
3233	Yellow Comp.	2⅝	1970	10 Dot	
Flat yellow					40

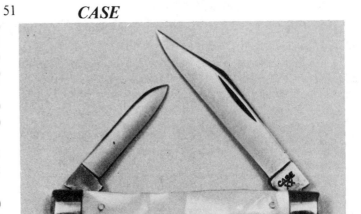

9233 Cracked Ice, 2⅝" XX $27

DOCTOR'S KNIFE

2234 Slick Black, LP, 3⅝" Tested XX $400

Nr.	Handle	Lgth.	Stamp		Mint
5234	Stag	3⅝	1920-40	Tested XX	
Doctor's Knife					450

9233 Shad Cracked Ice, 2⅝", Rare No Bolsters XX $250

5233	Stag	2⅝	1970	10 Dot	40
6233	Delrin	2⅝	1970	10 Dot	40
6233	Bone Stag	2⅝	1970	10 Dot	30
8233	Genuine Pearl	2⅝	1970	10 Dot	40
9233	Imi. Pearl	2⅝	1970	10 Dot	22

6235 Green Bone, 3¼" Tested XX $130

6235EO	Green Bone	3¼	1920-40	Tested XX	195
6235SH	Green Bone	3¼	1920-40	Tested XX	160
6235	Rough Black	3¼	1940-50	XX	45
6235	Green Bone	3¼	1940-55	XX	100
6235	Bone	3¼	1940-64	XX	32

Nr.	Handle	Lgth.	Stamp		Mint
6235EO	Bone	3¼	1940-64	XX	160
6235	Red Bone	3¼	1940-64	XX	40
6235EO	Rough Black	3¼	1940-50	XX	160
6235	Bone	3¼	1965-69	USA	60

Nr.	Handle	Lgth.	Stamp		Mint
620035	Black Plastic	3¼	1940-64	XX	
Long Pull					28
620035EO	Black Plastic	3¼	1940-64	XX	90

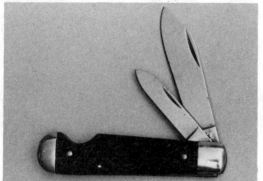

6235EO Black Imi. Jigged Bone, 3¼" XX $90

620035½ Black Imi. Bone, 3¼" XX $25

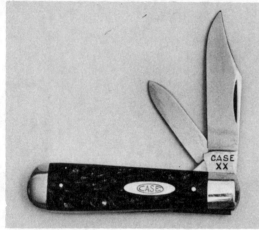

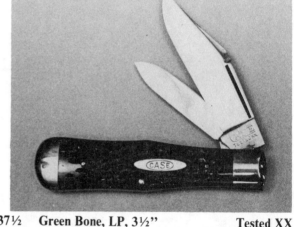

6235½ Rough Black, 3¼" XX $35

Nr.	Handle	Lgth.	Stamp		Mint
3235½	Yellow Comp.	3¼	1920-40	Tested XX	135
5235½	Stag	3¼	1920-40	Tested XX	150
6235½	Green Bone	3¼	1920-40	Tested XX	120
6235½PU	Green Bone	3¼	1920-40	Tested XX	185
6235½	Bone	3¼	1940-64	XX	30
6235½PU	Bone	3¼	1940-64	XX	160
6235½	Green Bone	3¼	1940-55	XX	100
6235½	Red Bone	3¼	1940-64	XX	35
6235½	Bone	3¼	1965-69	USA	
Master Clip Blade in Back					28
6235½	Bone	3¼	1965-69	USA	
Master Clip Blade in Front	Also with no shield				28
6235½	Bone	3¼	1970	10 Dot	22

6237½ Green Bone, LP, 3½" Tested XX $275

Nr.	Handle		Stamp		Mint
6237 LP	Green Bone		1920-40	Tested XX	300
6237½	Rogers Bone		1920-40	Tested XX	325

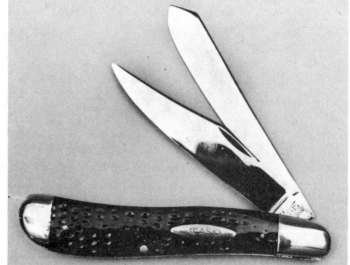

6240SP Green Bone, 4⁷⁄₁₆" Tested XX $550

Nr.	Handle	Lgth.	Stamp		Mint
3240SP	Yellow Comp.	4 7/16	1920-40	Tested XX	450
6240Pen	Green Bone	4 7/16	1920-40	Tested XX	450
9240SP	Imi. Pearl	4 7/16	1920-40	Tested XX	550

620035 Imitation Black Bone, 3¼" XX $25

62042	Imitation Black Bone, 2⅞"			XX	$35
Nr.	Handle	Lgth.		Stamp	Mint
52042	LP Stag	3	1920-40	Tested XX	
	Slant bolsters				175
52042	Stag, Reg. Pull	3	1920-40	Tested XX	135
62042	Green Bone	3	1920-40	Tested XX	120
82042	Genuine Pearl	3	1920-40	Tested XX	
	Slant Bolsters				235
92042	Imi. Pearl	3	1920-40	Tested XX	100
92042LP	Imi. Pearl	3	1920-40	Tested XX	115
62042	Rough Black	3	1940-50	XX	40
62042	Green Bone	3	1940-55	XX	70
62042	Red Bone	3	1940-64	XX	40
62042	Bone	3	1940-64	XX	30
62042R	Bone	3	1940-64	XX	30
92042	Imi. Pearl	3	1940-64	XX	25
92042	Cracked Ice	3	1940-64	XX	28
92042R	Imi. Pearl	3	1940-64	XX	30
92042R	Cracked Ice	3	1940-64	XX	35
62042	Bone	3	1965-69	USA	22
62042R	Bone	3	1965-69	USA	28
92042	Imi. Pearl	3	1965-69	USA	20
92042	Imi. Pearl	3	1965-69	USA	28
62042	Bone	3	1970	10 Dot	22
62042R	Bone	3	1970	10 Dot	26
92042	Imi. Pearl	3	1970	10 Dot	22
92042R	Imi. Pearl	3	1970	10 Dot	26

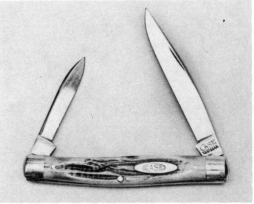

52044	2nd Cut Stag, 3¼", Rare			Tested XX	$200
Nr.	Handle	Lgth.		Stamp	Mint
62044F	Green Bone	3¼	1920-40	Tested XX	135
82044	Genuine Pearl	3¼	1920-40	Tested XX	185
82044F	Genuine Pearl	3¼	1920-40	Tested XX	210
2244	Slick Black	3¼	1920-40	Tested XX	120
3244	Yellow Comp.	3¼	1920-40	Tested XX	120
5244	Stag	3¼	1920-40	Tested XX	135
6244	Green Bone	3¼	1920-40	Tested XX	120
8244	Genuine Pearl	3¼	1920-40	Tested XX	210
9244	Imi. Pearl	3¼	1920-40	Tested XX	120
6244	Green Bone	3¼	1940-55	XX	70
6244	Red Bone	3¼	1940-64	XX	40
6244	Bone	3¼	1940-64	XX	30
6244	Bone	3¼	1965-69	USA	28
6244	Bone Stag	3¼	1970	10 Dot	30
6244	Delrin	3¼	1970	10 Dot	28

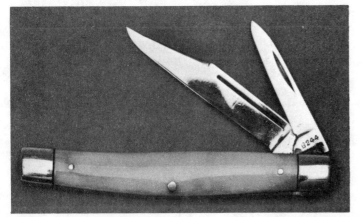

B244   Waterfall, LP, 3¼"   Tested XX $150

ABBREVIATIONS

½	master blade is clip blade
B	Budding
EO	Easy Opener
F	File
J	Long Spay Blade
K	Corkscrew
LR	Electrician's Knife
M	Metal
PEN	Pen Blade
PU	Punch Blade
R	Bail in handle
RAZ	Razor Blade
SAB	Sabor Blade
SC/SCI	Scissors
SH	Sheepfoot blade
SP	Spay Blade
SSP	Stainless Steel, Polished Blade Edge
SS	Stainless Steel
T	Tip Bolsters

2245SHSP	Slick Black, 3¾"		XX	$100

06244	Green Bone, 3¼"			XX	$75
Nr.	Handle,	Lgth.		Stamp	Mint
02244	Slick Black	3¼	1920-40	Tested XX	120
05244	Stag	3¼	1920-40	Tested XX	135
06244	Green Bone	3¼	1920-40	Tested XX	120
06244	Red Bone	3¼	1940-64	XX	40
06244	Bone	3¼	1940-64	XX	30
06244	Bone	3¼	1965-69	USA	25
06244	Delrin	3¼	1970	10 Dot	35
06244	Bone Stag	3¼	1970	10 Dot	30

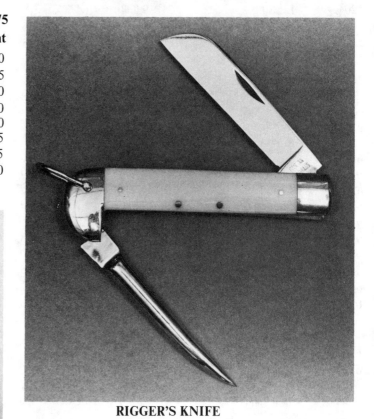

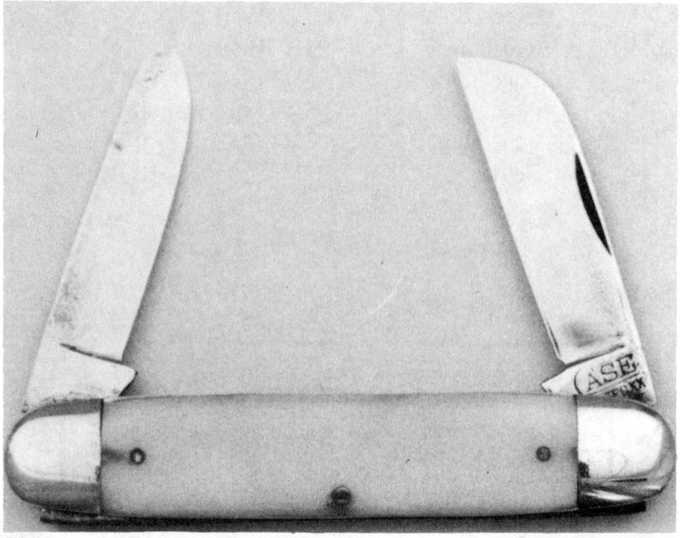

03245	Yellow Comp. 3¾"			Tested XX	$175
	Sheep Foot - Spey Blades				
02245	Slick Black	3¾	1920-40	Tested XX	160
04245B&G	White Comp	3¾	1920-40	Tested XX	200
06245	Green Bone	3¾	1920-40	Tested XX	
Spear					160
06245	Green Bone	3¾	1920-40	Tested XX	
Dog Grooming					350
06245	Green Bone	3¾	1940-55	XX	140
06245	Green Bone	3¾	1940-55	XX	
Dog Grooming					300
02245½	Slick Black	3¾	1920-40	Tested XX	160
05245½	Stag	3¾	1920-40	Tested XX	250
06245½	Green Bone	3¾	1920-40	Tested XX	130

RIGGER'S KNIFE

3246RSS	Yellow Comp., 4⅜"			XX	$65
3246RSS	Yellow Comp.		4⅜	USA	300
Nr.	Handle,		Lgth.	Stamp	Mint
3246R	Yellow Comp.		4⅜	1920-40 Tested XX	
Navy Knife					210
6246R	Green Bone		4⅜	1920-40 Tested XX	210
3246R	Yellow Comp.		4⅜	1940-64 XX	
Rigger's Knife (none stainless)					150
6246RSS	Red Bone		4⅜	1940-64 XX	
Stainless					100
6246RSS	Bone		4⅜	1940-64 XX	
Stainless					80
6246RSS	Bone		4⅜	1965-69 USA	
Stainless					45
6246RSS	Bone		4⅜	1970 10 Dot	
Stainless, Riggers Knife					45

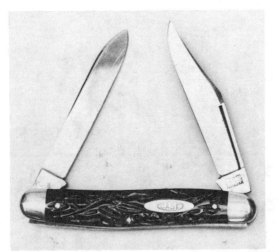

6247J   Rough Black, LP, 3⅞"   Tested XX $400

Nr.	Handle,	Lgth.		Stamp	Mint
5247J	Stag	3⅞	1920-40	Tested XX	500
6247J	Green Bone	3⅞	1920-40	Tested XX	450

04247SP   White Comp., 3⅞"   USA $100

05247SP	Stag	3⅞	1920-40	Tested XX	175
06247SP	Green Bone	3⅞	1920-40	Tested XX	125
06247PEN	Green Bone	3⅞	1920-40	Tested XX	125
06247PEN	Rough Black	3⅞	1940-50	.XX	85
06247PEN	Green Bone	3⅞	1940-55	XX	120
04247SP	White Comp.	3⅞	1940-64	XX	110
05247SP	Stag	3⅞	1940-64	XX	125
06247PEN	Red Bone	3⅞	1940-64	XX	50
06247PEN	Rogers Bone	3⅞	1940-64	XX	70
06247PEN	Bone	3⅞	1940-64	XX	35
05247SP	Stag	3⅞	1965-69	USA	140
06247PEN	Bone	3⅞	1965-69	USA	25

———GREENSKEEPER KNIFE———

4247FK	White Comp.	3⅞	1940-64	XX	
Greenskeeper's Knife					300
4247FK	Greenskeeper		1965-69	USA	300
4247FK	White Comp.	3⅞	1970	10 Dot	
Greenskeeper's Knife (very scarce)					300

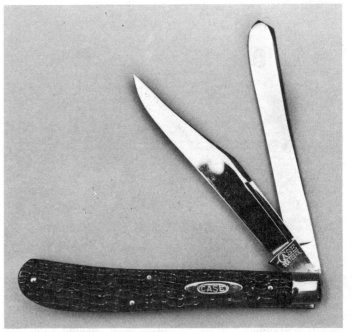

62048SP Green Bone, LP, 4"   Tested XX $225

Nr.	Handle,	Lgth.		Stamp	Mint
B2048	Christmas Tree	4	1920-40	Tested XX	325
B2048SP	Christmas Tree	4	1920-40	Tested XX	350
B2048	Onyx	4	1920-40	Tested XX	275
GS2048	Gold Stone	4	1920-40	Tested XX	300
R2048	Candy Stripe	4	1920-40	Tested XX	300
62048	Green Bone	4	1920-40	Tested XX	185
32048SP	Yellow Comp.	4	1940-64	XX	35
62048SP	Green Bone	4	1940-55	XX	135
62048SP	Red Bone	4	1940-64	XX	60
62048SP	Rogers Bone	4	1940-64	XX	75
62048SP	Bone	4	1940-64	XX	35
32048SP	Yellow Comp.	4	1965-69	USA	28
62048SP	Delrin	4	1965-69	USA	22
62048SP	Bone Stag	4	1965-69	USA	35
62048SPSSP	Delrin	4	1965-69	USA	22
62048SPSSP	Bone	4	1965-69	USA	
Stainless, Polished, Master Blade Etched "Tested XX Stainless" (First Model)					50
62048SPSSP	Bone	4	1965-69	USA	
Stainless Polished Edge					35
62048SPSSP	Bone	4	1965-69	USA	
Stainless Polished Blade					50
32048SP	Yellow Comp.	4	1970	10 Dot	28
62048SP	Delrin	4	1970	10 Dot	20
62048SPSSP	Delrin	4	1970	10 Dot	
Stainless, Polished Edge					28

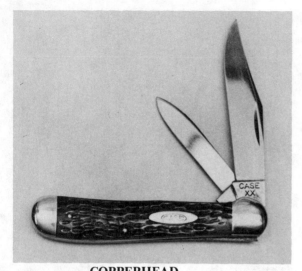

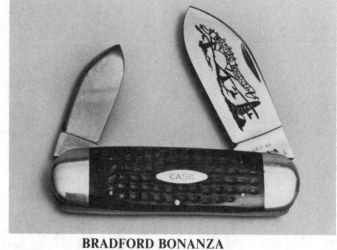

COPPERHEAD

Nr.	Handle,	Lgth.		Stamp	Mint
6249	Green Bone, 3¹⁵⁄₁₆"			XX	$300

Nr.	Handle,	Lgth.		Stamp	Mint
P249	Mottled Brown	3¹⁵⁄₁₆	1920-40	Tested XX	360
6249	Rough Black	3¹⁵⁄₁₆	1920-40	Tested XX	350
6249	Green Bone	3¹⁵⁄₁₆	1920-40	Tested XX	300
9249	Imi. Pearl	3¹⁵⁄₁₆	1920-40	Tested XX	400
6249	Red Bone	3¹⁵⁄₁₆	1940-64	XX	90
6249	Bone	3¹⁵⁄₁₆	1940-64	XX	50
6249	Bone	3¹⁵⁄₁₆	1965-69	USA	35
6249	Bone	3¹⁵⁄₁₆	1970	10 Dot	35

BRADFORD BONANZA

Nr.	Handle,	Lgth.		Stamp	Mint
6250	Laminated wood 4½"		10 Dot	(1980)	$45
6250	Green Bone	4⅜	1920-40	Tested XX	400
6250	Green Bone	4⅜	1940-55	XX	
Sunfish					350
6250	Red Bone	4⅜	1940-64	XX	200
6250	Bone Stag	4⅜	1940-64	XX	160
6250	Laminated Wood	4⅜	1940-64	XX	90
6250	Laminated Wood	4⅜	1965-69	USA	45
6250	Bone Stag	4⅜	1965-69	USA	225
6250	Laminated Wood	4⅜	1970	10 Dot	45

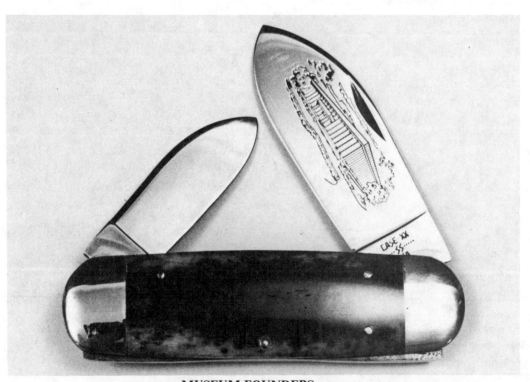

MUSEUM FOUNDERS
A6250   Appaloosa Bone, 4½"   1980 (Lightning S) $100

Nr.	Handle,	Lgth.	Stamp	Mint
6251	Green Bone	5¼	1920-40 Tested XX	
	Knife-Fork Combo			500
6251	Rogers Bone	5¼	1920-40 Tested XX	
	Knife-Fork Combo			600
9251	Imi. Onyx	5¼	1920-40 Tested XX	
	Knife-Fork Combo			550

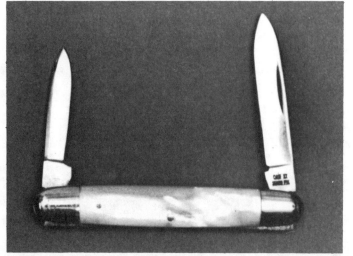

82053SS Pearl, 2¼", with Bolsters   XX $65

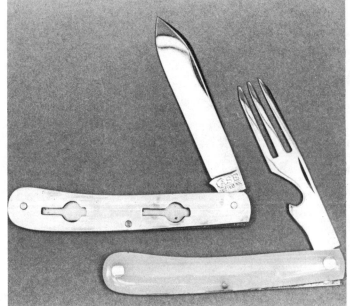

HOBO KNIFE

3252	Yellow, 3¾"		Tested XX	$350
6252	Green Bone	3¾	1920-40 Tested XX	
	Knife-Fork Combo			350

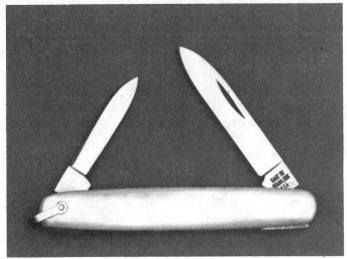

82053SRSS Pearl, 2¹³⁄₁₆"   USA $40

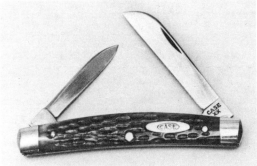

CONGRESS

62052	Bone, 3½"		XX	$35
52052	Stag	3½	1920-40 Tested XX	160
62052	Green Bone	3½	1920-40 Tested XX	135
62052	Rogers Bone	3½	1920-40 Tested XX	185
62052	Rough Black	3½	1940-50 XX	60
62052	Green Bone	3½	1940-55 XX	100
62052	Red Bone	3½	1940-64 XX	60
62052	Bone	3½	1965-69 USA	35
62052	Bone	3½	1970 10 Dot	35

Nr.	Handle,	Lgth.	Stamp	Mint
5253	Stag	3¼	1920-40 Tested XX	150
6253	Green Bone	3¼	1920-40 Tested XX	120
62053	Green Bone	2¾	1920-40 Tested XX	
Bolsters				150
82053SR	Pearl	2¹³⁄₁₆	1920-40 Tested XX	135
9253	Imi. Pearl	3¼	1920-40 Tested XX	110
62053SS	Bone	2¾	1940-64 XX	
Bolsters				40
82053SR	Genuine Pearl	2¹³⁄₁₆	1940-64 XX	60
82053SS	Genuine Pearl	2¹³⁄₁₆	1940-64 XX	
Stainless				45
62053SS	Bone	2¾	1965-69 USA	
RARE, Bolsters				135
82053SRSS	Genuine Pearl	2¹³⁄₁₆	1965-69 USA	
Stainless				40

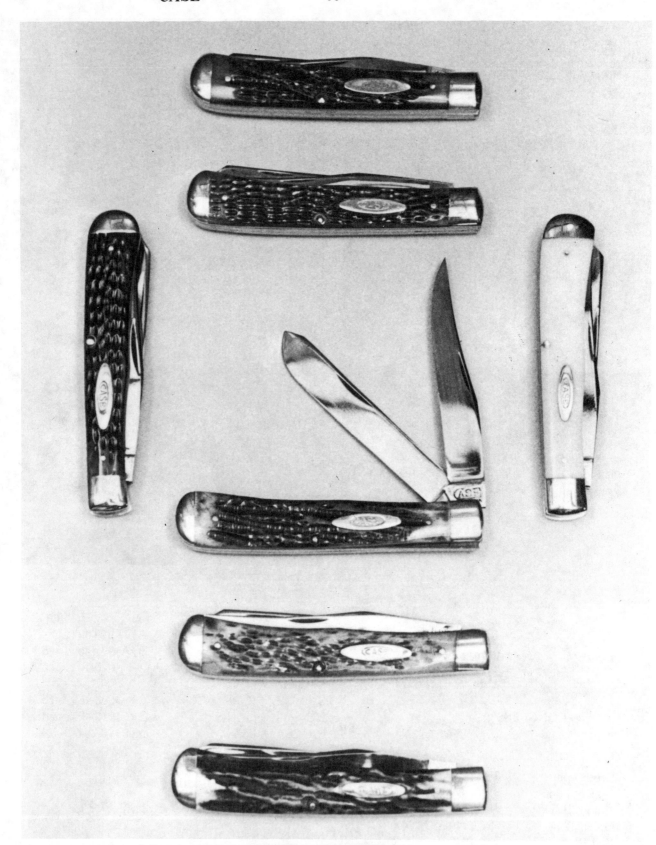

TRAPPER 54 PATTERN

Top to bottom: 5254, Red Stag, 4⅛", Tested XX, $1800; 6254, Green Bone, 4⅛", Tested XX, $1600;   5254, (blades open) 2nd Cut Stag, 4⅛", Tested XX, $1800   6254, Rogers Bone, 4⅛", XX with Tested Frame, $1800; 5254, Stag, 4⅛", Tested XX, $1600;
Left: 6254, Red Bone, 4⅛", Tested XX, $1500.
Right: 3254, Yellow Comp., 4⅛", Tested XX, $1500.

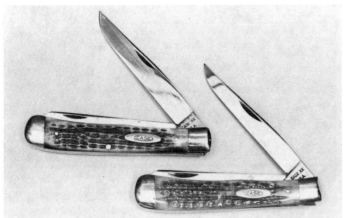

Top: 5254 2nd Cut Stag, Reg. blade, 4⅛"   USA $550
Bottom: 5254 2nd Cut Stag, Muskrat 4⅛"   USA $550

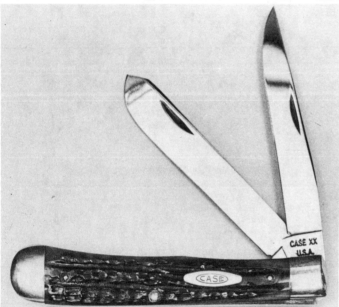

TRAPPER

6254 2nd Cut Bone, 4⅛"   USA $550

Nr.	Handle	Lgth.	Stamp	Mint
3254	Yellow Comp.	4⅛ 1920-40	Tested XX	
RARE				1500
5254	Red Stag	4⅛ 1920-40	Tested XX	
RARE				1800
5254	Stag	4⅛ 1920-40	Tested XX	1600
5254	2nd Cut Stag	4⅛ 1920-40	Tested XX	
RARE				1800
6254	Green Bone	4⅛ 1920-40	Tested XX	1600
6254	Red Bone	4⅛ 1920-40	Tested XX	
RARE				1500
6254	Rogers Bone	4⅛ 1920-40	Tested XX	
RARE				1800
9254	Imi. Pearl	4⅛ 1920-40	Tested XX	1650
3254	Yellow Comp.	4⅛ 1940-64	XX	135
3254	Yellow Comp.	4⅛ 1940-64	XX	
Tested Frame, First Model				260

First models read "Tested XX Stainless" etched lengthwise on Clip Blade.
Second models read "Tested XX Razor Edge" etched lengthwise on Clip Blade

Nr.	Handle,	Lgth.	Stamp	Mint
3254	Flat Yellow	4⅛ 1940-64	XX	
Tested Frame, First Model				285
3254	Yellow Comp.	4⅛ 1940-64	XX	
Muskrat Blade				175
6254	Green Bone	4⅛ 1940-55	XX	
Tested Frame, First Model, RARE				1800
6254	Red Bone	4⅛ 1940-64	XX	
Trapper				450
6254	Red Bone 1st model	Tested Frame	XX	800
5254	Stag	4⅛ 1940-64	XX	175
5254	Stag	4⅛ 1940-64	XX	
Tested Frame, First Model				300
5254	Red Stag	4⅛ 1940-64	XX	
RARE				950
5254	Stag	4⅛ 1940-64	XX	
Muskrat Blade				225
6254	Bone	4⅛ 1940-64	XX	200
6254	Bone	4⅛ 1940-64	XX	
Tested Frame, First Model				300
6254	Bone	4⅛ 1940-64	XX	
Muskrat Blade				185
6254	2nd Cut Stag	4⅛ 1940-64	XX	
RARE				650
6254	Rogers Bone	4⅛ 1940-42	XX	
RARE Tested Frame				1,800
3254	Yellow Comp.	4⅛ 1965-69	USA	55
3254	Flat Yellow	4⅛ 1965-69	USA	110
3254	Flat Yellow	4⅛ 1965-69	USA	
RARE, Muskrat Blade				175
3254	Yellow Comp.	4⅛ 1965-69	USA	
Muskrat Blade				100
5254	Stag	4⅛ 1965-69	USA	65
5254	Stag	4⅛ 1965-69	USA	
Muskrat Blade				135
6254	Bone	4⅛ 1965-69	USA	60
6254	Bone	4⅛ 1965-69	USA	
Muskrat Blade				110
6254	2nd Cut	4⅛ 1965-69	USA	600
6254	2nd Cut	4⅛ 1965-69	USA	
Muskrat Blade				575
6254SSP		4⅛ 1965-69	USA	
Both Blades Stamped "Case XX Stainless"				550
6254SSP	Bone	4⅛ 1965-69	USA	
Polished Blades				200
6254SSP	Bone	4⅛ 1965-69	USA	
Polished Edge				60
6254SSP	Bone	4⅛ 1965-69	USA	
Muskrat Blade, Polished Edge				200
6254SSP	Bone	4⅛ 1965-69	USA	
Muskrat Blade, Polished Blade				200
6254SSP	Bone	4⅛ 1965-69	USA	
First Model, ("Tested XX Stainless" Etched Lengthwise on Master Blade)				210
6254SSP	Bone	4⅛ 1965-69	USA	
First Model, Polished Blades				400
6254SSP	Bone	4⅛ 1965-69	USA	
First Model, Muskrat Blades				300
3254	Yellow Comp	4⅛ 1970	10 Dot	60

Nr.	Handle, Lgth.			Stamp	Mint
3254	Flat Yellow	4⅛	1970	10 Dot	100
5254	Stag	4⅛	1970	10 Dot	65
5254	2nd Cut Stag	4⅛	1970	10 Dot	
	Very RARE				750
6254	Bone	4⅛	1970	10 Dot	60
6254SSP	Bone	4⅛	1970	10 Dot	
	Polished Edge				60
6254SSP	Bone	4⅛	1970	10 Dot	
	Large Stamp				140
6254SSP		4⅛	1970	10 Dot	
	Gut Hook Proto (6 Made)				500

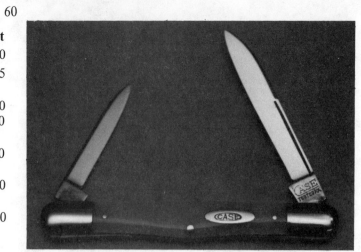

32056	Yellow/White Liner	3½"	Case Tested XX	$250

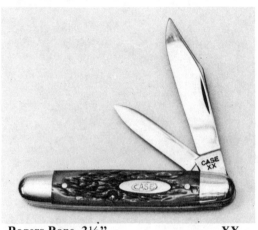

62055	Rogers Bone, 3½"			XX	$200
22055	Slick Black	3½	1920-40	Tested XX	160
32055	Yellow Comp.	3½	1920-40	Tested XX	175
32055	Yellow Comp.	3½	1920-40	Tested XX	
	Long Pull				210
62055	Green Bone	3½	1920-40	Tested XX	145
62055	Green Bone LP			Tested XX	200
62055	Rough Black	3½	1920-40	Tested XX	
	Long Pull				185
92055	Imi. Pearl	3½	1920-40	Tested XX	185
62055	Rough Black	3½	1940-50	XX	85
62055	Rough Black	3½	1940-50	XX	
	Long Pull				135
62055	Green Bone	3½	1940-55	XX	
	Long Pull				160
62055	Red Bone	3½	1940-64	XX	60
22055	Slick Black	3½	1940-64	XX	45
22055	Slick Black	3½	1940-64	XX	
	Long Pull				110
62055	Bone	3½	1940-64	XX	40
62055	Bone	3½	1940-64	XX	
	Long Pull				120
92055	Cracked Ice	3½	1940-64	XX	185
92055	Cracked Ice	3½	1940-64	XX	
	Long Pull				210
22055	Slick Black	3½	1965-69	USA	185
62055	Bone	3½	1965-69	USA	28
62055	Bone	3½	1970	10 Dot	28

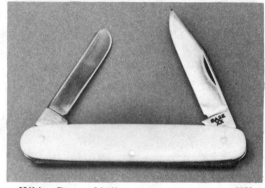

4257	White Comp, 3¾"			XX	$35

Nr.	Handle	Lgth.		Stamp	Mint
4257	White Comp.	3¾	1920-40	Tested XX	80
4257	White Comp.	3¾	1940-64	XX	
	"Office Knife" on Handle				95
42057	White Comp.	3⁵⁄₁₆	1920-40	Tested XX	80
92057	Imi. Pearl	3⁵⁄₁₆	1920-40	Tested XX	90
42057	White Comp.	3⁵⁄₁₆	1940-64	XX	
	"Office Knife" on Handle				95
42057	White Comp.	3⁵⁄₁₆	1940-64	XX	
	Office Knife, plain handle				35

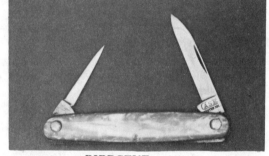

BIRDSEYE

92058	French Pearl, 3¼"			Tested XX	$125
32058	Yellow Comp.	3¼	1920-40	Tested XX	125
92058	Imi. Pearl	3¼	1920-40	Tested XX	125
92058	Cracked Ice	3¼	1940-50	XX	100

CASE

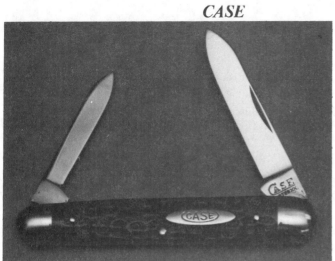

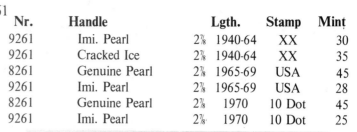

Nr.	Handle	Lgth.	Stamp	Mint
9261	Imi. Pearl	2⅞	1940-64	XX	30
9261	Cracked Ice	2⅞	1940-64	XX	35
8261	Genuine Pearl	2⅞	1965-69	USA	45
9261	Imi. Pearl	2⅞	1965-69	USA	28
8261	Genuine Pearl	2⅞	1970	10 Dot	45
9261	Imi. Pearl	2⅞	1970	10 Dot	25

SENATOR PEN

Nr.	Handle	Lgth.	Stamp	Mint
62059	Green Bone	3¼"	1920-40 Tested XX	$120
62059SP	Green Bone	3¼"	1920-40 Tested XX	$120
62059½	Green Bone	3¼"	1920-40 Tested XX	$120

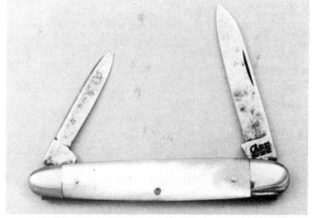

82063	Genuine Pearl	3⅛" 1920-40	Tested XX	$150

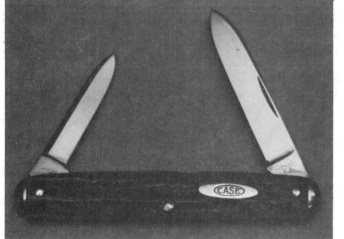

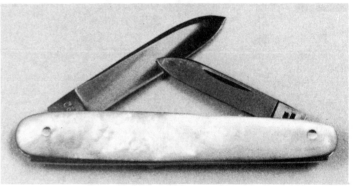

EQUAL END GENTLEMAN'S KNIFE

5260	Stag	3⁷⁄₁₆"	1920-40 Tested XX	$175
5260	Red Stag	3⁷⁄₁₆"	1920-40 Tested XX	$200
5620	Stag	3⁷⁄₁₆"	1940-64 XX	$150

SHADOW

82063	Pearl, 3¹⁄₁₆"		XX	$65
82063	Genuine Pearl	3¹⁄₁₆ 1920-40 Tested XX		
No Bolster				135
62063SS	Bone	3¹⁄₁₆ 1940-64	XX	40
62063	Green Bone	3¹⁄₁₆ 1940-55	XX	100
62063SS	Red Bone	3¹⁄₁₆ 1940-64	XX	50

8261	Pearl 2⅞" 1940	1964 XX	$45
6261	Green Bone	2⅞ 1920-40 Tested XX	120
6261F	Green Bone	2⅞ 1920-40 Tested XX	135
8261	Genuine Pearl	2⅞ 1920-40 Tested XX	145
8261F	Genuine Pearl	2⅞ 1920-40 Tested Xx	155
9261	Imi. Pearl	2⅞ 1920-40 Tested XX	100
9261F	Imi. Pearl	2⅞ 1920-40 Tested XX	120
8261	Genuine Pearl	2⅞ 1940-64 XX	45

06263	Green Bone, 3⅛"		XX	$110
05263	Stag	3⅛ 1920-40 Tested XX		
Non Stainless				150
06263	Green Bone	3⅛ 1920-40 Tested XX		120
08263	Genuine Pearl	3⅛ 1920-40 Tested XX		150
06263	Green Bone	3⅛ 1940-55	XX	
Non Stainless				110

Nr.	Handle	Lgth.	Stamp	Mint
06263	Green Bone	3⅛	1940-55	XX	
Stainless				85
06263SS	Red Bone	3⅛	1940-64 XX	45
05263	Stag	3⅛	1940-64 XX	120
05263SS	Stag	3⅛	1940-64 XX	50
06263	Bone	3⅛	1940-64 XX	85
06263SS	Bone	3⅛	1940-64 XX	35
05263SS	Stag	3⅛	1965-69 USA	45
06263FSS	Bone	3⅛	1965-69 USA	28
06263SSP	Bone	3⅛	1965-69 USA	
Polished Blade				28
06263SSP	Bone	3⅛	1965-69 USA	
Edge Polished				28
06263SSP	Bone	3⅛	1965-69 USA	
Master Blade Etched "Tested XX Stainless", First Model Brushed Finish				60
Also Polished Finish				
82063SHADSS	Genuine Pearl	3$\frac{1}{16}$	1965-69 USA	90
05263 S.S	Stag	3⅛	1970 10 Dot	45
06263SS	Bone	3⅛	1970 10 Dot	25
06263SSP	Bone	3⅛	1970 10 Dot	
Polished Blade				25
06263FSSP	Bone	3⅛	1970 10 Dot	
Polished Blade				25
06263FS	Bone	3⅛	1970 10 Dot	25

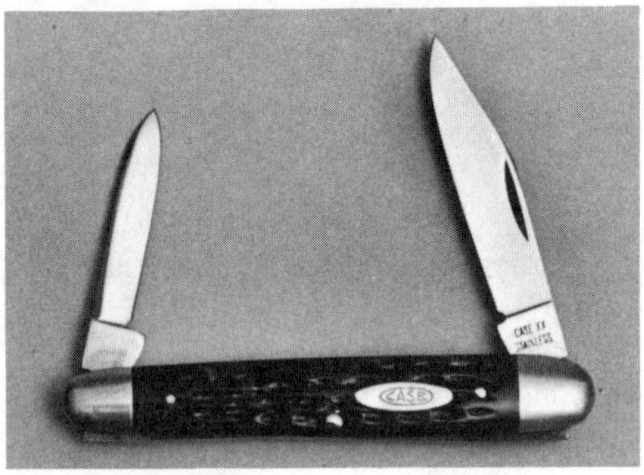

62063½ Bone, 3$\frac{1}{16}$" Stainless XX $40

62063½	Green Bone	3$\frac{1}{16}$	1920-40 Tested XX	120
82063½	Genuine Pearl	3$\frac{1}{16}$	1920-40 Tested XX	135
92063½	Imi. Pearl	3$\frac{1}{16}$	1920-40 Tested XX	110
62063½	Green Bone	3$\frac{1}{16}$	1940-55 XX	85
62063½SS	Red Bone	3$\frac{1}{16}$	1940-64 XX	50
92063½	Imi. Pearl	3$\frac{1}{16}$	1940-64 XX	85

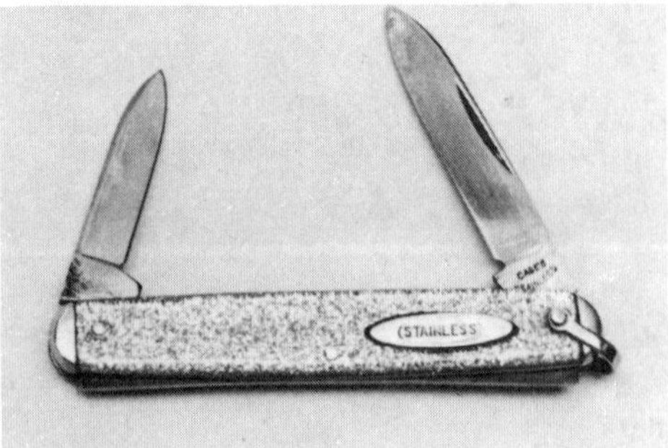

GS264R Gold Stone, 3⅛" Case's Stainless $250

Nr.	Handle	Lgth.	Stamp	Mint
6264T	Green Bone	3⅛	1920-40 Tested XX	
Tip Bolster				145
6264TF	Green Bone	3⅛	1920-40 Tested XX	145
8264T	Genuine Pearl	3⅛	1920-40 Tested XX	185
8264TF	Genuine Pearl	3⅛	1920-40 Tested XX	185
9264TF	Imi. Pearl	3⅛	1920-40 Tested XX	120

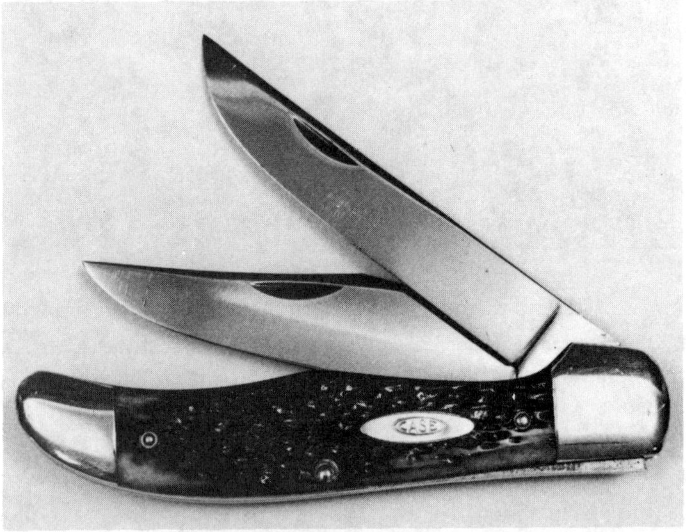

FOLDING HUNTER

6265SAB Rogers Bone, 5¼" XX $400

3265SAB	Yellow Comp.	5¼	1920-40 Tested XX	410
3265	Yellow Comp.	5¼	1920-40 Tested XX	
Flat Blade				460
5265SAB	Stag	5¼	1920-40 Tested XX	310
5265	Stag	5¼	1920-40 Tested XX	
Flat Blade				360
5265	2nd Cut Stag	5¼	1920-40 Tested XX	
Flat Blade				600
6265	2nd Cut Stag	5¼	1920-40 Tested XX	510
6265SAB	Green Bone	5¼	1920-40 Tested XX	285

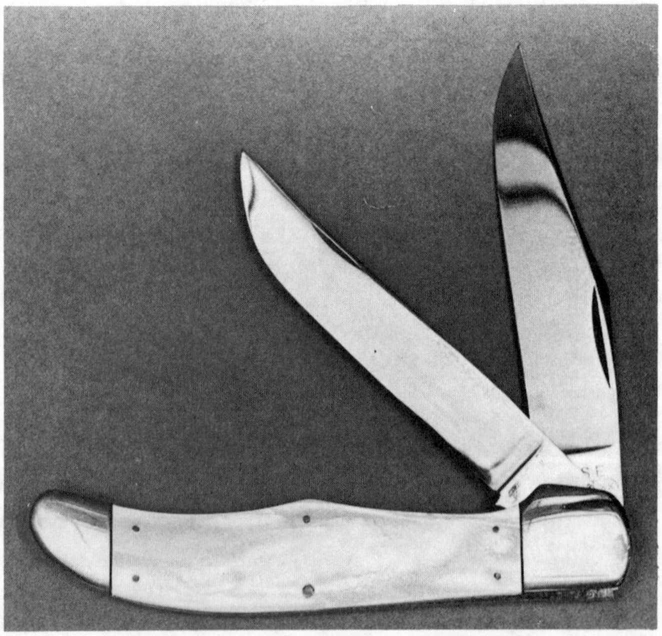

FOLDING HUNTER FLAT BLADE

9265 Cracked Ice, 5¼" Tested XX $600

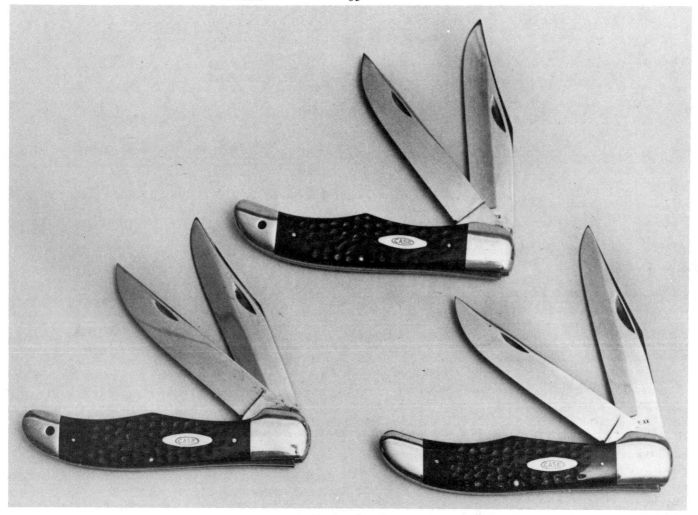

FOLDING HUNTERS
Top: 6265SAB Pakkawood, 5¼", USA Frame/drilled bolsters, $45;   Left: 6265SAB Pakkawood, 5¼", USA on XX Frame
Drilled Bolster, $75;   Right: 6265SAB Pakkawood, 5¼", USA on XX Frame/Bolster not drilled, $95.

Nr.	Handle,	Lgth.	Stamp	Mint	Nr.	Handle,	Lgth.	Stamp	Mint
5265	Stag	5¼ 1940-64	XX		6265SAB	Bone	5¼ 1940-64	XX	
Flat Master Blade				260	Small blade serrated, Bill Boatman Special				275
5265SAB	Stag	5¼ 1940-64	XX	145	6265SABDR	Bone	5¼ 1940-64	XX	
5265SABDR	Stag	5¼ 1940-64	XX	180	Small blade serrated, Bill Boatman Special				300
5265SAB	2nd Cut Stag	5¼ 1940-64	XX	510	6265SABDR	Laminated Wood	5¼ 1940-64	XX	
6265	Green Bone	5¼ 1940-55	XX		Serrated Small Blade, Bill Boatman				185
Flat Blade				310	6265SAB	Rogers Bone	5¼ 1940-64	XX	400
6265SAB	Red Bone	5¼ 1940-64	XX	160	5265SAB	Stag	5¼ 1965-69	USA	
6265	Red Bone	5¼ 1940-64	XX		XX Frame				160
Flat Blade				260	5265SABDR	Stag	5¼ 1965-69	USA	70
6265SAB	Red Bone	5¼ 1940-64	XX		5265SAB Stag Bols not drilled		XX Frame USA		150
Bill Boatman, Serrated				260	5265SABDR	Stag	5¼ 1965-69	USA	
6265	Bone	5¼ 1940-64	XX		XX Frame				120
Flatground Master				260	6265SAB	Bone	5¼ 1965-69	USA	
6265SAB	Laminated Wood	5¼ 1940-64	XX	90	XX Frame				210
6265SAB	Laminated Wood	5¼ 1940-64	XX		6265SABDR	Bone	5¼ 1965-69	USA	
Small blade serrated, Bill Boatman Special				185	Small Blade serrated				260
6265SAB	Bone	5¼ 1940-64	XX	135	6265SABDR	Wood	5¼ 1965-69	USA	
					XX Frame				75
					6265SABDR	Wood	5¼ 1965-69	USA	40

All Boatman Serrated Blade Folding Hunters are quite scarce.

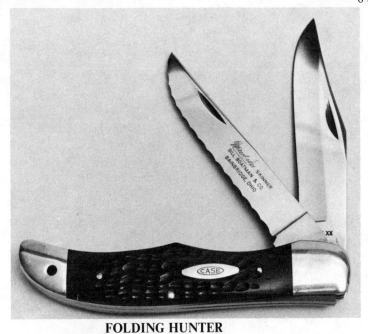

CONGRESS

| 6268 | Green Bone, 3¼", Pointed Shield | Tested XX | $350 |

FOLDING HUNTER

6265SAB /DR Pakkawood, 5¼",   **USA $150**
Serrated Edge, Bill Boatman

Nr.	Handle	Lgth.	Stamp	Mint
6265	Green Bone	5¼	1920-40 Tested XX	
Flat Blade				325
8265SAB	Genuine Pearl	5¼	1920-40 Tested XX	1800
8265	Genuine Pearl	5¼	1920-40 Tested XX	
Flat Blade				1800
9265SAB	Imi. Pearl	5¼	1920-40 Tested XX	410
9265	Imi. Pearl	5¼	1920-40 Tested XX	
Flat Blade				460
6265SAB	Rough Black	5¼	1940-50 XX	
Folding Hunter				285
6265	Rough Black	5¼	1940-50 XX	
Flat Blade				335
6265SAB	Green Bone	5¼	1940-55 XX	260
6265SABDR Bone		5¼	1965-69 USA	
XX Frame				210
6265SABDR Wood		5¼	1965-69 USA	
Serrated Small Blade, Bill Boatman				160
5265SABDR Stag		5¼	1970 10 Dot	85
6265SABDR Wood		5¼	1970 10 Dot	50
6265SABDR Wood		5¼	1970 10 Dot	
Bill Boatman				135

| 6269 | Rough Black, 3" | | XX | $60 |

Nr.	Handle	Lgth.	Stamp	Mint
6269	Green Bone	3	1920-40 Tested XX	125
8269	Genuine Pearl	3	1920-40 Tested XX	250
9269	Imi. Pearl	3	1920-40 Tested XX	150
6269	Rough Black	3	1940-50 XX	
Long Pull				85
6269	Green Bone	3	1940-55 XX	100
6269	Green Bone	3	1940-55 XX	
Long Pull				125
6269	Red Bone	3	1940-64 XX	50
6269	Bone	3	1940-64 XX	35
6269	Bone	3	1965-69 USA	28
6269	Bone		1970 10 Dot	25

| 6270F | Bone | 3 | 1920-40 Tested XX | 235 |

| 8271 | Pearl, LP, 3¼ | | XX | $200 |

06267	**Bone, 3¼"**		**USA**	**$65**
06267	Rogers Bone	3¼	1920-40 Tested XX	225
06267	Green Bone	3¼	1920-40 Tested XX	160
06267	Bone Long Pull	3¼	1940-64 XX	70

Nr.	Handle	Lgth.	Stamp	Mint
6271F	Bone	3¼	1920-40 Tested XX	
Flat Bolsters				210
8271	Genuine Pearl	3¼	1920-40 Tested XX	235
8271F	Genuine Pearl	3¼	1920-40 Tested XX	235
6271	Red Bone	3¼	1940-64 XX	65
6271SS	Bone	3¼	1940-64 XX	50
8271	Genuine Pearl	3¼	1940-64 XX	
Long Pull				200
8271SS	Genuine Pearl	3¼	1940-64 XX	160
8271SS	Genuine Pearl	3¼	1940-64 XX	
Long Pull				185
8271F	Genuine Pearl	3¼	1940-64 XX	160
8271F	Genuine Pearl	3¼	1940-64 XX	
Long Pull				185

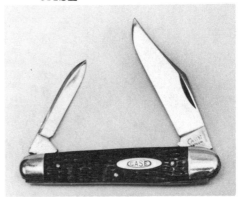

SLEEVEBOARD

6276½   Green Bone, 3⅝"   Tested XX $200

Nr.	Handle	Lgth.	Stamp	Mint
6276	Bone	3⅝	1920-40 Tested XX	210

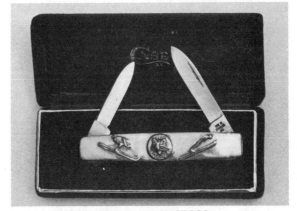

1980 WINTER OLYMPICS

OL278SS Sterling, 3 3/16" (1000 made)   1980
   Serial No. 1000-2000 $225

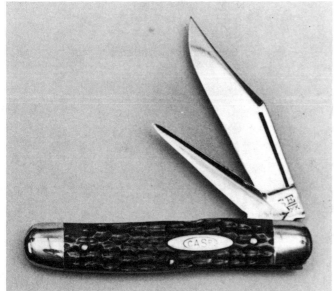

6207 4½PU Green Bone, LP, 3⅜"   Tested XX $225

2207 4½PU	Slick Black	3¼	1920-40 Tested XX	200

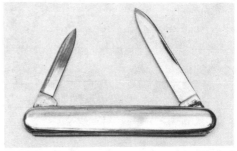

M279   All Metal, 3⅛"   Tested XX $80

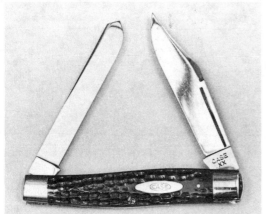

6275SP   Green Bone, LP, 4¼"   XX $225

6275SP	Rough Black	4¼	1940-50 XX	
Long Pull				225
6275SP	Green Bone	4¼	1940-55 XX	200
6275SP	Red Bone	4¼	1940-64 XX	110
6275SP	Red Bone	4¼	1940-64 XX	
Long Pull				200
6275SP	Bone	4¼	1940-64 XX	60
6275SP	Bone	4¼	1965-69 USA	35
6275SP	Bone	4¼	1970 10 Dot	35

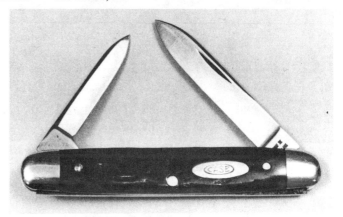

5279SS   Red Stag, 3⅛"   XX $85

6279F   Green Bone, 3⅛", Tip Bolsters   **Tested XX**   **$135**

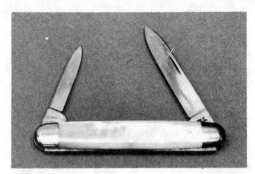

8279   Pearl, 3⅛"   **Tested XX**   **$130**

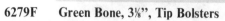

6279   Green Bone, 3⅛"   **Tested XX**   **$110**

8279F   Pearl, 3⅛"   **Tested XX**   **$150**

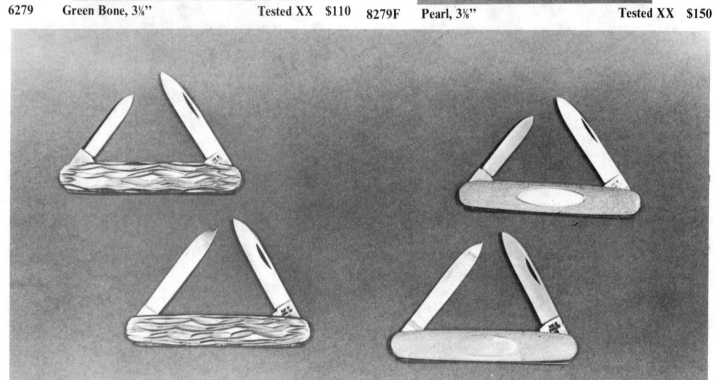

PROTO TYPE   250 of each produced

M279   Bark, 3¹⁄₁₆" Pen $25   File $25   **M279**   Jewel, 3¹⁄₁₆" Pen $25   File $25

Nr.	Handle,	Lgth.		Stamp	Mint	Nr.	Handle	Lgth.		Stamp	Mint
B279	Christmas Tree	3⅛	1920-40	Tested XX	200	M279SSF	Metal	3⅛	1940-64	XX	30
GM279	Green Mottled	3⅛	1920-40	Tested XX	175	2279SSSHAD	Slick Black	3⅛	1940-64	XX	75
M279R	Metal	3⅛	1920-40	Tested XX	90	5279	Stag	3⅛	1940-64	XX	90
2279	Slick Black	3⅛	1920-40	Tested XX	100	5279SS	Stag	3⅛	1940-64	XX	45
3279	Yellow Comp.	3⅛	1920-40	Tested XX	100	6279	Rough Black	3⅛	1940-50	XX	65
3279R	Yellow Comp.	3⅛	1920-40	Tested XX	100	6279SS	Rough Black	3⅛	1940-50	XX	40
6279	Green Bone	3⅛	1920-40	Tested XX	110	6279SSF	Rough Black	3⅛	1940-50	XX	45
8279SHAD	Genuine Pearl	3⅛	1920-40	Tested XX	185	6279	Green Bone	3⅛	1940-55	XX	90
82079	Genuine Pearl	3¼	1920-40	Tested XX	185	6279SS	Green Bone	3⅛	1940-55	XX	75
M279SS	Metal	3⅛	1940-64	XX	30	6279SSF	Green Bone	3⅛	1940-55	XX	85

Nr.	Handle	Lgth.		Stamp	Mint
6279SS	Red Bone	3⅛	1940-64	XX	45
6279	Bone	3⅛	1940-64	XX	60
6279SSF	Bone	3⅛	1940-64	XX	45
6279SS	Bone	3⅛	1940-64	XX	30
8279	Genuine Pearl	3⅛	1940-64	XX	80
8279SS	Genuine Pearl	3⅛	1940-64		65
9279	Imi. Pearl	3⅛	1940-64	XX	80
9279SSSHAD	Cracked Ice	3⅛	1940-64	XX	30
M279SC	Stainless	3⅛	1965-69	USA	35
M279SS	Stainless	3⅛	1965-69	USA	
Polished					28
M279SS	Stainless	3⅛	1965-69	USA	25
M279SSF	Stainless	3⅛	1965-69	USA	22
5279SS	Stag	3⅛	1965-69	USA	160
6279SS	Bone	3⅛	1965-69	USA	25
6279SS	Bone	3⅛	1965-69	USA	
Transition (XX to USA)					80
M279SCSS	Stainless	3⅛	1970	10 Dot	30
M279SSF	Stainless	3⅛	1970	10 Dot	22
6279SS	Bone	3⅛	1970	10 Dot	22
M279SS	Bone	3⅛	1970	10 Dot	22

2279½   Slick Black, 3¼"   Tested XX $110

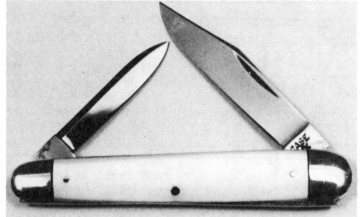

82079½	**Pearl, 3¼"**			**XX**	**$60**
62079½	Green Bone	3¼	1920-40 Tested XX		135
82079½	Genuine Pearl	3¼	1920-40 Tested XX		185
92079½	Cracked Ice	3¼	1920-40 Tested XX		120
62079½	Bone	3¼	1940-64	XX	85
62079½	Rough Black			XX	125
82079½SS	Genuine Pearl	3¼	1940-64	XX	40
92079½	Imi. Pearl	3¼	1940-64	XX	80
92079½	Cracked Ice			XX	90
82079½SS	Genuine Pearl	3¼	1965-69	USA	40
82079½SS	Genuine Pearl	3¼	1970	10 Dot	40

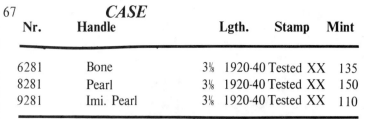

CASE

Nr.	Handle	Lgth.	Stamp	Mint
6281	Bone	3⅛	1920-40 Tested XX	135
8281	Pearl	3⅛	1920-40 Tested XX	150
9281	Imi. Pearl	3⅛	1920-40 Tested XX	110

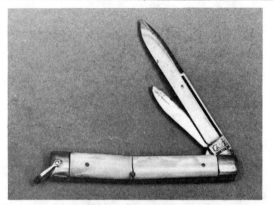

PHYSICIAN'S KNIFE

9282R   Cracked Ice, Imitation, LP, 2¾"   Tested XX
(Handle Cracked) $350

B282	Christmas Tree	2¾	1920-40 Tested XX	
Doctor's Knife				400
B282	Imi. Onyx	2¾	1920-40 Tested XX	310
5282	Stag	2¾	1920-40 Tested XX	300
6282	Green Bone	2¾	1920-40 Tested XX	285
6282	Rogers Bone	2¾	1920-40 Tested XX	360
8282	Genuine Pearl	2¾	1920-40 Tested XX	360

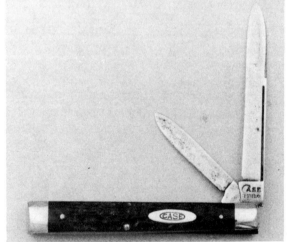

62082   Dr. Knife, Green Bone, LP 2⅞"   Tested XX
**   1920-40 $325**
GS2082 Dr. Knife, Goldstone 2⅞"   Tested XX   350

DOCTOR'S KNIFE

| 6285 | Green Bone, 3⅝" | | Tested XX | $350 |

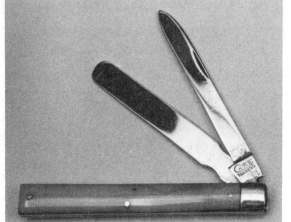

| B285 | Waterfall Dr.'s Knife 3⅝" | | Tested XX | $600 |

Nr.	Handle	Lgth.	Stamp	Mint
B285	Christmas Tree	3⅝	1920-40 Tested XX	500
B285	Waterfall	3⅝	1920-40 Tested XX	600
3285	Yellow Comp.	3⅝	1920-40 Tested XX	350
7285	Tortoise	3⅝	1920-40 Tested XX	500

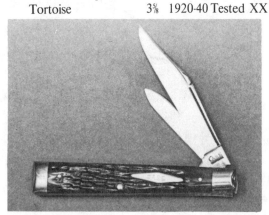

DOCTOR'S KNIFE

| 62086 | Green Bone, 3¼" | | Tested XX | $350 |

52086	Stag	3¼	1920-40 Tested XX	350
62086	Rogers Bone	3¼	1920-40 Tested XX	350
82086	Genuine Pearl	3¼	1920-40 Tested XX	375
92086R	Imi. Pearl	3¼	1920-40 Tested XX	375

GUNSTOCK

| 5287 | Stag, 3½" | | Tested XX | $550 |

Nr.	Handle	Lgth.	Stamp	Mint
8287	Pearl	3½	1920-40 Tested XX	600

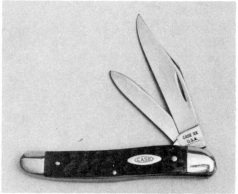

| 62087 | Bone, 3¼", odd shield | | 10 Dot | $26 |

Nr.	Handle	Lgth.	Stamp		Mint
22087	Slick Black	3¼	1920-40	Tested XX	100
42087	White Comp.	3¼	1920-40	Tested XX	135
62087	Green Bone	3¼	1920-40	Tested XX	120
22087	Slick Black	3¼	1940-64	XX	30
52087	Stag	3¼	1940-64	XX	60
62087	Bone	3¼	1940-64	XX	28
62087	Rough Black	3¼	1940-50	XX	65
62087	Green Bone	3¼	1940-55	XX	75
62087	Red Bone	3¼	1940-64	XX	40
22087	Slick Black	3¼	1965-69	USA	22
52087	Stag	3¼	1965-69	USA	45
62087	Bone	3¼	1965-69	USA	22
22087	Slick Black	3¼	1970	10 Dot	22
52087	Stag	3¼	1970	10 Dot	55
62087	Delrin	3¼	1970	10 Dot	22

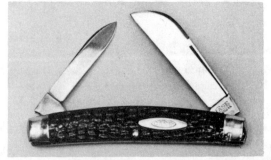

| 6288 | Green Bone, LP, 4⅛" | 1920-40 | Tested XX | $450 |

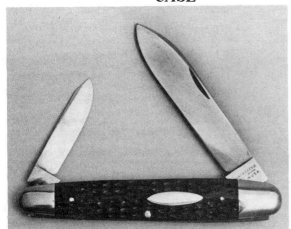

6291   Green Bone, 4½"
Contract made by Case for Winchester   **$950**

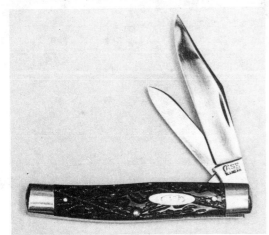

6292   Rough Black, 4" 1920-40   Tested XX $165

Nr.	Handle,	Lgth.		Stamp	Mint
3292	Yellow Comp.	4	1920-40	Tested XX	185
6292	Green Bone	4	1920-40	Tested XX	170
6292	Rough Black	4	1940-50	XX	120
6292	Green Bone	4	1940-55	XX	135
6292	Red Bone	4	1940-64	XX	70
6292	Bone	4	1940-64	XX	40
6292	Bone	4	1965-69	USA	28
6292	Bone	4	1970	10 Dot	28
32093F	Yellow Comp.	5	1920-40	Tested XX	175
62093F	Green Bone	5	1920-40	Tested XX	200

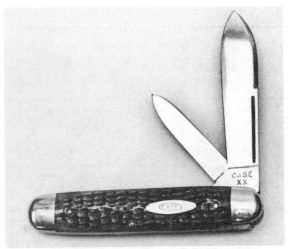

6294   Green Bone, LP 4¼"   1940-45   XX $300

Nr.	Handle	Lgth.		Stamp	Mint
6294	Green Bone	4¼	1920-40	Tested XX	350
6294	Green Bone	4¼	1920-40	Tested XX	
Long Pull					400
6294	Red Bone	4¼	1920-40	Tested XX	
Long Pull					350
6294JL.P.	Green Bone	4¼	1920-40	Tested XX	1000
6294	Rogers Bone	4¼	1920-40	Tested XX	
Long Pull, (Gunboat)					1000
6294	Green Bone	4¼	1940-55	XX	275
6294	Red Bone	4¼	1940-64	XX	200
6294L.P.	Red Bone	4¼	1940-64	XX	275
6294	Bone	4¼	1940-64	XX	125
6294	Bone	4¼	1940-64	XX	
Long Pull					175

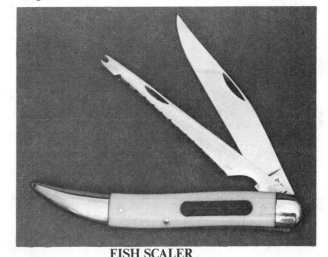

FISH SCALER

32095F   Yellow, 5"   XX $32

Nr.	Handle	Lgth.		Stamp	Mint
B2095F	Christmas Tree	5"	1920-40	Tested XX	
Fisherman's Knife					300
32095F	Yellow Comp.	5"	1920-40	Tested XX	175
32095FSS	Yellow Comp.	5"	1920-40	Tested XX	175
32095F	Yellow			Case's Stainless	225
32095FSS	Yellow Comp.	5"	1965-69	USA	30
32095FSS	Yellow Comp.	5"	1970	10 Dot	50

ABBREVIATIONS

½	master blade is clip blade	PU	Punch Blade
B	Budding	R	Bail in handle
EO	Easy Opener	RAZ	Razor Blade
F	File	SAB	Sabor Blade
J	Long Spay Blade	SC/SCI	Scissors
K	Corkscrew	SH	Sheepfoot blade
LR	Electrician's Knife	SP	Spay Blade
M	Metal	SS	Stainless Steel
PEN	Pen Blade	T	Tip Bolsters
	SSP Stainless Steel, Polished Blade Edge		

Nr.	Handle	Lgth.	Stamp	Mint
TOOTHPICK				
B2096	Christmas Tree	3⅛"	1920-40 Tested XX	460
R2096	Candy Strip	3⅛"	1920-40 Tested XX	460
62096	Rogers Bone	3⅛"	1920-40 TestedXX	400

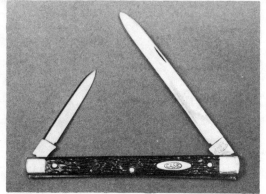

6296X	**Green Bone, 4¼" Case's Stainless**			**$500**

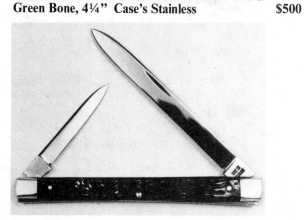

6296XSS	**Bone, 4¼"**		XX	**$100**
6296X	Clip Point		XX	150
6296XSS	Red Bone	4¼"	XX	125
6296X	Green Bone	4¼	1920-40 Tested XX	
	Half-Oval, Stainless			500
6296XSS	Green Bone	4¼	1940-55 XX	350
6296XSS	Bone	4¼	1965-69 USA	225

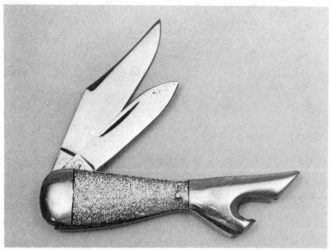

LEG

GS297	Gold Stone, 3¼"		Case Tested XX	$350

Nr.	Handle	Lgth.	Stamp	Mint
R297	Candy Stripe		1920-40 Tested XX	
	Small Leg			300
B297	Christmas Tree		1920-40 Tested XX	
	Small Leg			400
3297	Yellow Comp.		1920-40 Tested XX	
	Small Leg			300
8297	Genuine Pearl		1920-40 Tested XX	
	Small Leg			400

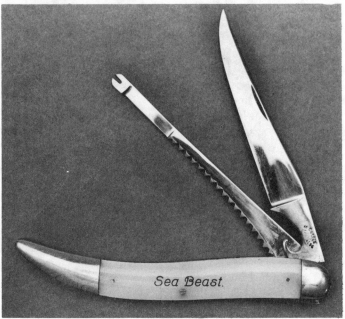

SEA BEAST

B2098F	**Imi Onyx**	**5½"**	**Case's Stainless**	**$250**
B2098F	Christmas Tree	5½	1920-40 Tested XX	400
B2098F	Imi. Onyx	5½	1920-40 Tested XX	250
32098F	Yellow Comp.	5½	1920-40 Tested XX	225
62098F	Green Bone	5½	1920-40 Tested XX	250

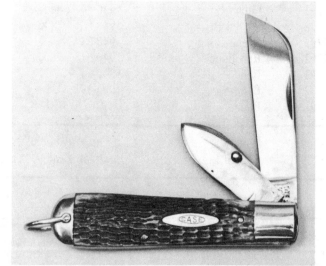

6299SHR Green Bone	**4⅛"**	**1920-40 Tested XX**	**$250**

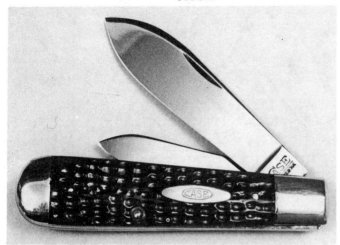

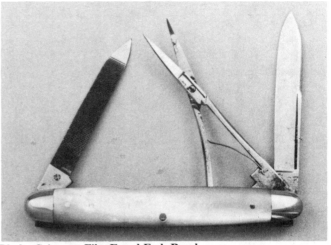

6299 **Green Bone, 4⅛"** **1920-1940** **Tested XX** **$210**

Nr.	Handle	Lgth.	Stamp	Mint
6299	Rough Black		Tested XX	175
5299SP	Stag	4⅛	1920-40	Tested XX	285
6299	Bone	4⅛	1940-64	XX	150
6299	Rough Black	4⅛	1940-50	XX	120

Blade, Scissors, File, Equal End, Pearl

Unknown 3¼" Tested XX $400

——— SENATOR/LOBSTER ———

GM2099R	Green Mottled	2⅞	1920-40	Tested XX	120
82099R	Genuine Pearl	2⅞	1920-40	Tested XX	150

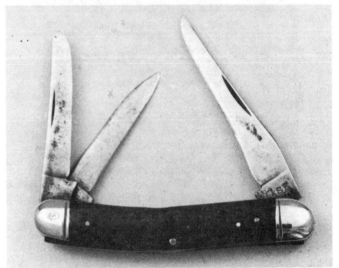

3 blade **3 Backspring, Whittler, Green Bone**

Pattern Unknown, 3⅜" Tested XX $350

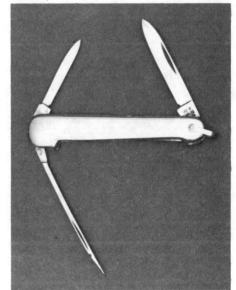

5299½ **Stag** **4⅛"** **1965-69 USA** **$70**

3299½	Yellow Comp.	4⅛	1920-40	Tested XX	185
5299½	Stag	4⅛	1920-40	Tested XX	260
6299½	Green Bone	4⅛	1920-40	Tested XX	225
6299½	Green Bone	4⅛	1940-64	XX	225
3299½	Yellow Comp.	4⅛	1940-64	XX	65
3299½	Yellow Comp.	4⅛	1940-64	XX	
"A" Blade					75
5299½	Stag	4⅛	1940-64	XX	110
5299½	Stag	4⅛	1940-64	XX	
"A" Blade					135
3299½	Yellow Comp.	4⅛	1965-69	USA	35
3299½	Yellow Comp.	4⅛	1970	10 Dot	40
3299½	Flat Yellow	4⅛	1970	10 Dot	65
5299½	Stag	4⅛	1970	10 Dot	70

M3102R **All Metal** **2¾"** **XX** **$30**

M3102R	Metal		1920-40	Tested XX	110
M3102RSS	Metal		1965-69	USA	35
M3102RSS	Metal		1970	10 Dot	28

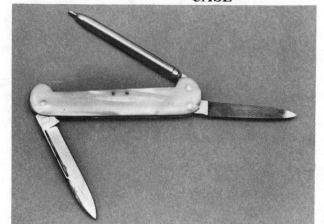

83102F   Pearl LP   Tested XX   **$175**
Ball Point Pen

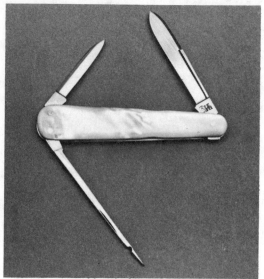

83102	Pearl	2¾"	1920-40 Tested XX	$150
Nr.	Handle	Lgth.	Stamp	Mint
63102	Green Bone		1920-40 Tested XX	
	Flat bolsters			160
83102SS	Genuine Pearl		1940-64 XX	135

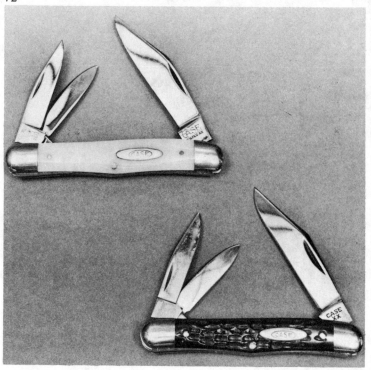

3308	Yellow Comp.	3¼"	1920-40 Tested XX	$300
6308	Green Bone	3¼"	1940-64 XX	$200
Nr.	Handle,	Lgth.	Stamp	Mint
2308	Slick Black	3¼	1920-40 Tested XX	275
5308	Stag	3¼	1920-40 Tested XX	335
6308	Green Bone	3¼	1920-40 Tested XX	280
8308	Genuine Pearl	3¼	1920-40 Tested XX	400
6308	Rough Black	3¼	1940-50 XX	185
6308	Red Bone	3¼	1940-64 XX	75
6308	Bone	3¼	1940-64 XX	40
6308	Bone	3¼	1965-69 USA	30
6308	Bone	3¼	1970 10 Dot	30

TOLEDO SCALE

T3105SS	File	3⅛"	Dots on Handles	$60
T3105SS	Metal		1940-64 XX	185

(Older knife has no dots on handle)

CITRUS PEELER & CAP LIFTER

63109	Green Bone LP	3⅝"	Tested XX	$400
63109	Green Bone		1920-40 Tested XX	350
93109	Cracked Ice		1920-40 Tested XX	375

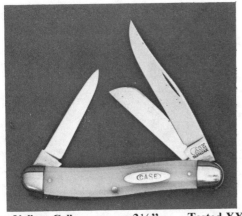

3318   Yellow Cell.   3½"   Tested XX

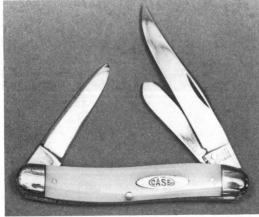

3318   Yellow Cell. Spay   3½"   Tested XX

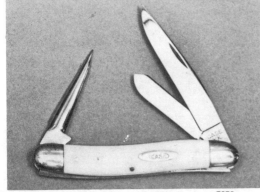

4318PU   White Comp   3½"   XX

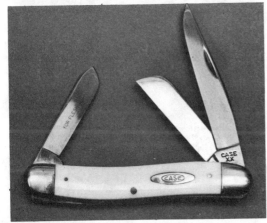

4318HP   White Comp   3½"   XX

Nr.	Handle,	Lgth.		Stamp	Mint
3318SHPEN	Yellow Comp.	3½	1920-40	Tested XX	150
3318SHSP	Yellow Comp.	3½	1920-40	Tested XX	150
3318SPPEN	Yellow Comp.	3½	1920-40	Tested XX	150
5318SHSP	Stag	3½	1920-40	Tested XX	185
6318SHPU	Green Bone	3½	1920-40	Tested XX	185
6318SPPU	Green Bone	3½	1920-40	Tested XX	185
6318SPPen	Green Bone	3½	1920-40	Tested XX	185
6318SHPEN	Green Bone	3½	1920-40	Tested XX	185
6318SHPEN	Green Bone	3½	1920-40	Tested XX	185
8318SHSP	Genuine Pearl	3½	1920-40	Tested XX	335
9318SHPEN	Cracked Ice	3½	1920-40	Tested XX	210
9318SHPU	Cracked Ice	3½	1920-40	Tested XX	210
3318SHPEN	Yellow Comp.	3½	1940-64	XX	35
4318SHSP	White Comp.	3½	1940-64	XX	50
4318SH	White Comp.	3½	1940-64	XX	
master blade California clip					50
6318SPPU	Rough Black	3½	1940-50	XX	110
6318SHSP	Rough Black	3½	1940-50	XX	100
6318SHPEN	Rough Black	3½	1940-50	XX	100
6318SPPU	Green Bone	3½	1940-55	XX	135
6318SHSP	Green Bone	3½	1940-55	XX	125
6318SHSP	Green Bone	3½	1940-55	XX	
Long Pull					160
6318SHPEN	Green Bone	3½	1940-55	XX	125
6318SPPU	Red Bone	3½	1940-64	XX	65
6318SHSP	Red Bone	3½	1940-64	XX	60
6318SHPen	Red Bone	3½	1940-64	XX	60
6318SPPU	Bone	3½	1940-64	XX	40
6318SHSP	Bone	3½	1940-64	XX	40
6318SHSPSSP	Bone Transition	3½	1964	XX	
XX to USA					140
6318SHPEN	Bone	3½	1940-64	XX	40
3318SHPEN	Yellow Comp.	3½	1965-69	USA	25
4318SHSP	WHite Comp.	3½	1965-69	USA	45
6318SPPU	Bone	3½	1965-69	USA	25
6318SHSP	Bone	3½	1965-69	USA	22
6318SHPEN	Bone	3½	1965-69	USA	22
6318HSSPSSP	Bone	3½	1965-69	USA	
blade edge polished					30
6318SHSPSSP	Bone	3½	1965-69	USA	
first model, edge etched "Tested XX Stainless"					55
3318SHPEN	Yellow Comp.	3½	1970	10 Dot	26
4318SHSP	White Comp.	3½	1970	10 Dot	50
6318SPPU	Bone	3½	1970	10 Dot	28
6318SHPEN	Bone	3½	1970	10 Dot	28
6318SHSP	Bone	3½	1970	10 Dot	28
6318HPSSP	Bone	3½	1970	10 Dot	
blade edge polished					30

$150

$150

$160

$50

Note:

   This book is a guide. Prices may vary a bit and are not absolute. Prices on more expensive knives may vary $100 or more depending on dealer.

Note:

   Prices are for mint knives although mint knives are not always available for photos.

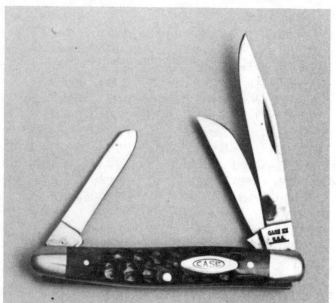

Nr.	Handle,	Lgth.		Stamp	Mint
13031LR	Walnut	3¾	1965-69	USA	
	Electrician's Knife				45
13031LR	Walnut	3¾	1970	10 Dot	
	Electrician's Knife				45

6327SHSP **Bone**		**2¾"**		**1970 10 Dot**	**$30**
6327SHSP	Bone	2¾	1940-64	XX	35
9327SHSP	Imi. Pearl	2¾	1940-64	XX	35
9327SHSP	Cracked Ice	2¾	1940-64	XX	50
6327SHSP	Bone	2¾	1965-69	USA	30
9327SHSP		2¾	1965-69	USA	30
6327SHSP	Delrin	2¾	1970	10 Dot	25
9327SHSP		2¾	1970	10 Dot	30

6332	**Bone**	**3⅝"**		**1970 10 Dot**	**$25**
5332	Stag	3⅝	1920-40	Tested XX	200
5332	Stag	3⅝	1940-64	XX	80
5332	Stag	3⅝	1940-64	XX	
Long pull					160
5332	Stag	3⅝	1965-69	USA	55
5332	Stag	3⅝	1970	10 Dot	55
6332	Green Bone	3⅝	1920-40	Tested XX	185
6332	Rough Black	3⅝	1940-50	XX	120
6332	Green Bone	3⅝	1940-55	XX	135
6332	Red Bone	3⅝	1940-64	XX	60
6332	Rogers Bone	3⅝	1940-64	XX	80
6332	Bone	3⅝	1940-64	XX	40
6332	Bone	3⅝	1965-69	USA	30

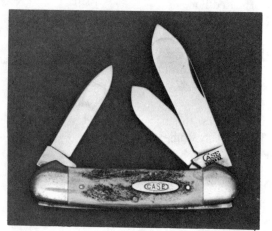

CANOE

53131	**Stag**	**3⅝"**	**1920-40 Tested XX**	**$1000**

ELECTRICIAN'S KNIFE

13031LR **Walnut**		**3¾"**		**XX**	**$45**

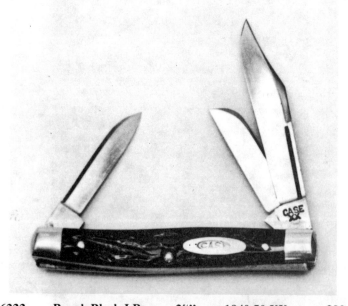

6333	**Rough Black LP**	**2⅝"**	**1940-50 XX**	**$90**
6333	Rough Black LP	2⅝	1920-40 Tested XX	125

Nr.	Handle,	Lgth.		Stamp	Mint
6333	Green Bone	2⅝	1920-40	Tested XX	135
6333	Rough Black	2⅝	1940-50	XX	65
6333	Green Bone	2⅝	1940-55	XX	120
6333	Bone	2⅝	1940-64	XX	35
6333	Rogers Bone	2⅝	1940-64	XX	60
9333	Imi. Pearl	2⅝	1940-64	XX	35
9333	Imi. Pearl	2⅝	1940-64	XX	
Long Pull					85
9333	Cracked Ice	2⅝	1920-40	Tested XX	120
9333	Cracked Ice	2⅝	1940-64	XX	
Long Pull					95
9333	Cracked Ice	2⅝	1940-64	XX	35
6333	Bone	2⅝	1965-69	USA	28
9333	Imi. Pearl	2⅝	1965-69	USA	25
6333	Delrin	2⅝	1970	10 Dot	22
6333	Bone Stag	2⅝	1970	10 Dot	26
9333	Imi. Pearl	2⅝	1970	10 Dot	22

6344	Green Bone	3¼" 1920-40 Tested XX	$125

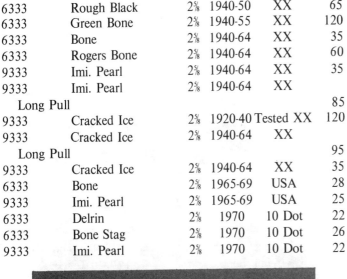

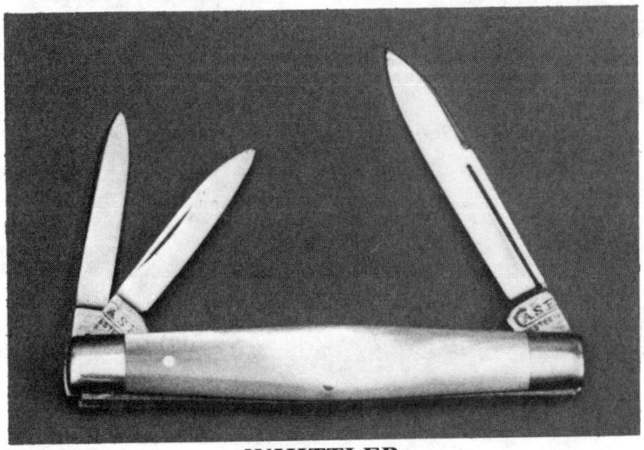

WHITTLER

83042	Pearl	1920-40 Tested XX	$350
93042	Imi. Pearl	1920-40 Tested XX	325

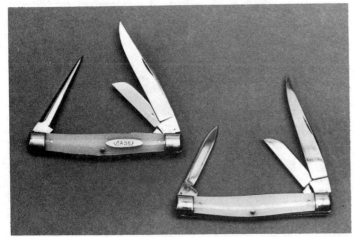

3344PU	Yellow Cell. w/Shield	3¼"	1920-40 Tested XX	$125
3344	Yellow Cell, no Shield	3¼"	1920-40 Tested XX	$125

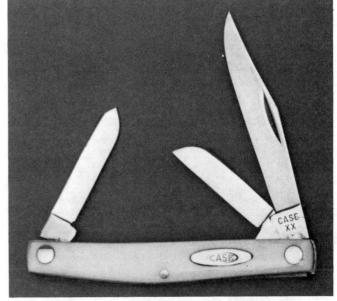

BIRDSEYE

33044HP	Yellow Comp.	3¼"	1964	XX	$65

Nr.	Handle,	Lgth.		Stamp	Mint
B344SHSP	Christmas Tree	3¼	1920-40	Tested XX	300
B3044F	Christmas Tree	3¼	1920-40	Tested XX	400
3344SPPU	Yellow Comp.	3¼	1920-40	Tested XX	145
5344SHSP	Stag	3¼	1920-40	Tested XX	175
5344SHPEN	Stag	3¼	1920-40	Tested XX	175
6344SHSP	Green Bone	3¼	1920-40	Tested XX	135
6344SHPEN	Green Bone	3¼	1920-40	Tested XX	135
6344SHPU	Green Bone	3¼	1920-40	Tested XX	145
6344SPPU	Green Bone	3¼	1920-40	Tested XX	145
6344SPPEN	Green Bone	3¼	1920-40	Tested XX	135
8344SHSP	Genuine Pearl	3¼	1920-40	Tested XX	235
9344SHPEN	Imi. Pearl	3¼	1920-40	Tested XX	145
6344SHSP	Green Bone	3¼	1940-55	XX	120
6344SHPEN	Green Bone	3¼	1940-55	XX	120
6344SHSP	Red Bone	3¼	1940-64	XX	45

Nr.	Handle	Lgth.		Stamp	Mint
6344SHPEN	Red Bone	3¼	1940-64	XX	45
6344SHSP	Bone	3¼	1940-64	XX	30
6344SHPEN	Bone	3¼	1940-64	XX	30
6344SHPEN	Bone	3¼	1965-69	USA	30
6344SHSP	Bone	3¼	1965-69	USA	30
33044SHSP	Yellow Comp. Birdseye	3¼	1965-69	USA	35
6344SHPEN	Bone	3¼	1970	10 Dot	30
6344SHSP	Bone	3¼	1970	10 Dot	30
6344SHSP	Delrin	3¼	1970	10 Dot	22
33044SHSP	Yellow Comp. Birdseye	3¼	1970	10 Dot	35
33044SH SP	Flat Yellow	3¼	1970	10 Dot	45

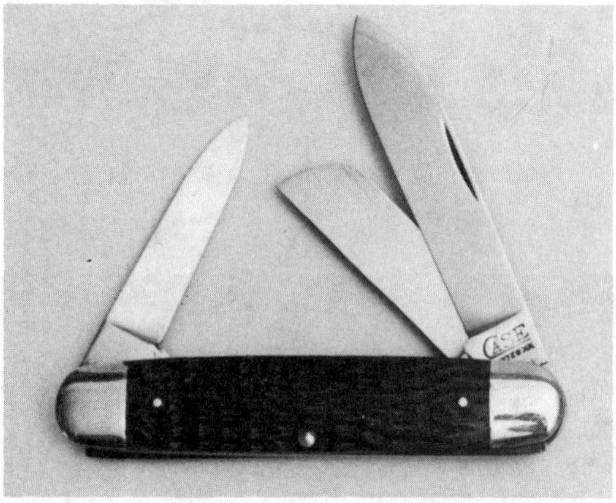

63045 Green Bone 3⅝" 1920-40 Tested XX $225

Nr.	Handle	Lgth.		Stamp	Mint
6345	Green Bone	3⅝	1920-40	Tested XX	250
6345PU	Green Bone	3⅝	1920-40	Tested XX	250

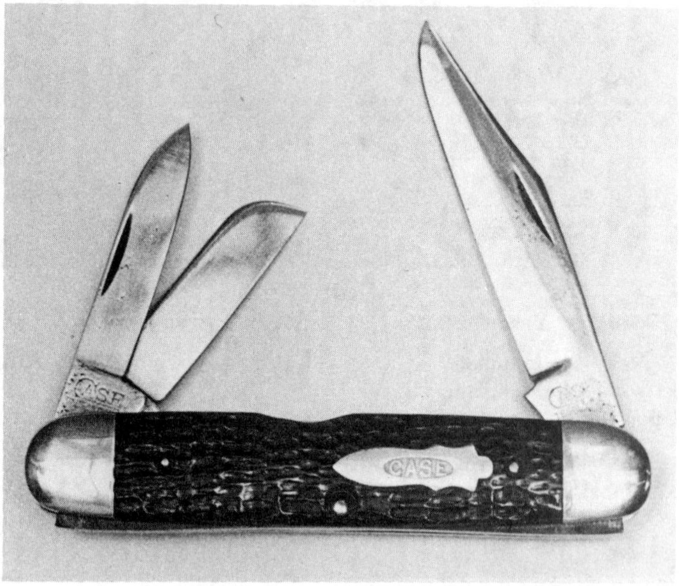

WHITTLER

6345½SAB Green Bone 3⅝" 1920-40 Tested XX $600

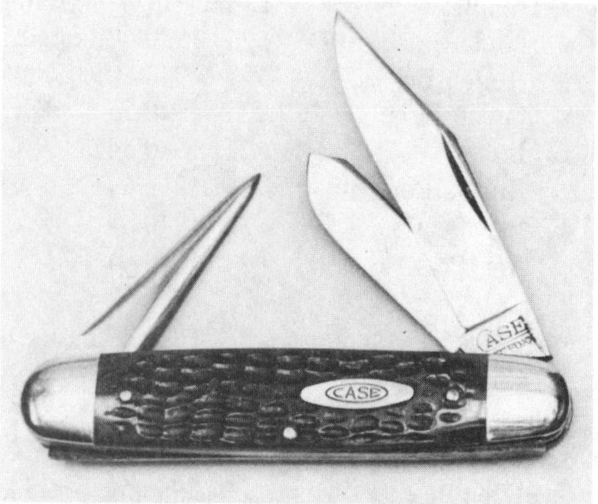

6345½PU Green Bone, 3¾" 1920-1940 Tested XX $250

Nr.	Handle	Lgth.		Stamp	Mint
2345½PU	Slick Black	3⅝	1920-40	Tested XX	210
6345½	Imi. Bone	3⅝	1920-40	Tested XX	90
6345½	Green Bone	3⅝	1920-40	Tested XX	225
6345½SH	Green Bone	3⅝	1920-40	Tested XX	250

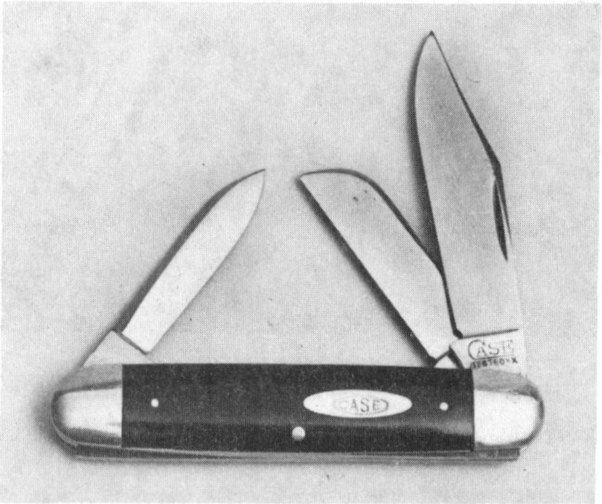

2345½ Slick Black 3⅝" 1920-40 Tested XX $190

Nr.	Handle	Lgth.		Stamp	Mint
2345½SH	Slick Black	3⅝	1940-64	XX	85
2345½P	Slick Black Long Pull	3⅝	1940-64	XX	135
6345½SH	Rough Black	3⅝	1940-50	XX	160
6345½SH	Green Bone	3⅝	1940-55	XX	235
6345½SH	Red Bone	3⅝	1940-64	XX	125
6345½SH	Bone	3⅝	1940-64	XX	90
2345½SH	Slick Black	3⅝	1965-69	USA	150
6345½SH	Bone	3⅝	1965-69	USA	210

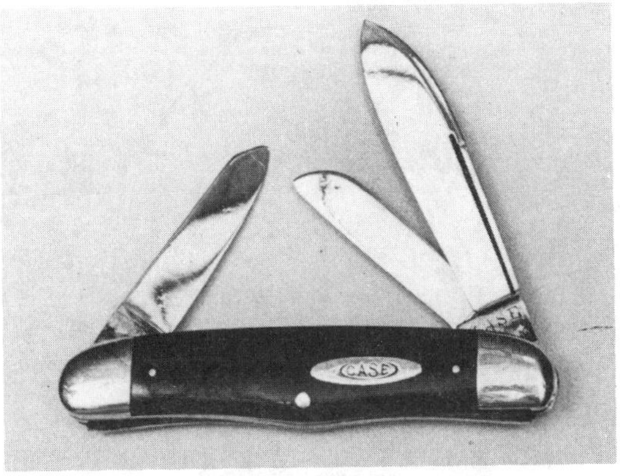

HUMPBACK

23046 Slick Black LP 3⅜" Tested XX $300

Nr.	Handle	Lgth.	Stamp	Mint
33046	Yellow Comp.	3⅝	1920-40 Tested XX	350
43046	White Comp.	3⅝	1920-40 Tested XX	350

NAVY KNIFE

M346 Aluminum Handles 3⅝" 1940-50 XX $150

M346	Metal	3⅝	1940-50 XX	
"Metal Stampings Ltd." English Navy Contract				135
M346	Metal	3⅝	1940-64 XX	
"Case XX Made For USA Navy"				110

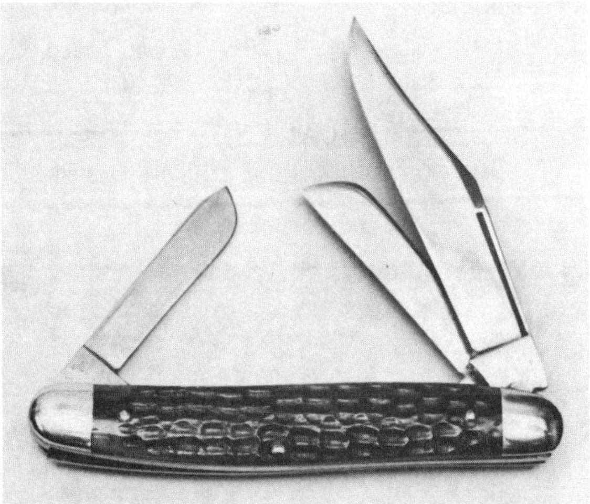

6347HP Green Bone LP 3⅞" 1920-40 Tested XX $200

M347SPPEN	Metal	3⅞	1920-40 Tested XX	160
M347SPPU	Metal	3⅞	1920-40 Tested XX	160
3347SHSP	Yellow Comp. Long Pull	3⅞	1920-40 Tested XX	200
3347SPPEN	Yellow Comp. Long Pull	3⅞	1920-40 Tested XX	200
3347SPPU	Yellow Comp.	3⅞	1920-40 Tested XX	200
5347SHSP	Stag	3⅞	1920-40 Tested XX	210
5347SHPEN	Stag	3⅞	1920-40 Tested XX	235
6347J	Bone	3⅞	1920-40 Tested XX	500
6347SHSP	Green Bone	3⅞	1920-40 Tested XX	190
6347SHSP	Green Bone Long Pull	3⅞	1920-40 Tested XX	200

Nr.	Handle	Lgth.	Stamp	Mint
6347SHPEN	Green Bone	3⅞	1920-40 Tested XX	190
6347SHPU	Green Bone Long Pull	3⅞	1920-40 Tested XX	200
6347SPPU	Green Bone Long Pull	3⅞	1920-40 Tested XX	200
6347PUPEN	Green Bone Long Pull	3⅞	1920-40 Tested XX	200
6347SPPen	Green Bone	3⅞	1920-40 Tested XX	200
6347H.P	Rogers Bone Long Pull	3⅞	1920-40 Tested XX	275
9347JPU	Cracked Ice Long Spay Blade	3⅞	1920-40 Tested XX	500
3347SHSP	Yellow Comp.	3⅞	1940-64 XX	45
3347SPPU	Yellow Comp. Long Pull	3⅞	1940-64 XX	135
3347SHSP	Yellow Comp. Long Pull	3⅞	1940-64 XX	110
5347SHSP	Stag	3⅞	1940-64 XX	80
5347SHSP	Stag Long Pull	3⅞	1940-64 XX	160
5347SHSP	Stag Stainless Steel all Blades Stamped	3⅞	1940-64 XX	150
6347SPPEN	Rough Black	3⅞	1940-50 XX	120
6347SHSP	Rough Black	3⅞	1940-50 XX	120
6347SHSP	Rough Black Long Pull	3⅞	1940-50 XX	135
6347SHPU	Rough Black	3⅞	1940-50 XX	135
6347SHPU	Rough Black Long Pull	3⅞	1940-50 XX	160
6347SHSP	Green Bone	3⅞	1940-55 XX	170
6347SHSP	Green Bone Long Pull	3⅞	1940-55 XX	210
6347SHPU	Green Bone	3⅞	1940-55 XX	185
6347SHPU	Green Bone Long Pull	3⅞	1940-55 XX	210
6347SPPU	Green Bone	3⅞	1940-55 XX	170
6347SPPU	Green Bone Long Pull	3⅞	1940-55 XX	210
6347SHSP	Red Bone	3⅞	1940-64 XX	70
6347SPPU	Red Bone	3⅞	1940-64 XX	70
6347SHSPSSP	Red Bone Stainless Steel	3⅞	1940-64 XX	100
6347SHSP	Bone	3⅞	1940-64 XX	40
6347SHSPSSP	Bone Stainless steel, polished all blades stamped	3⅞	1940-64 XX	150
6347HP	SSP Red Rogers Bone		All stamped XX	225
6347SPPEN	Bone	3⅞	1940-64 XX	40
6347SHPEN	Bone	3⅞	1940-64 XX	40
6347SHPU	Bone	3⅞	1940-64 XX	60
6347SPPU	Bone	3⅞	1940-64 XX	40
6347SP	PU 2nd Cut LP			500
6347SP	PU Green Bone LP		XX	200
3347SHSP	Yellow Comp.	3⅞	1965-69 USA	35
5347SHSP	Stag	3⅞	1965-69 USA	50
5347SHSP	Stag Stainless Steel Polished	3⅞	1965-69 USA	55

CASE

Nr.	Handle	Lgth.	Stamp	Mint
6347SHPU	Bone	3⅞	1965-69	USA	60
6347SHSP	Bone	3⅞	1965-69	USA	25
6347SHSPSSP	Bone	3⅞	1965-69	USA	30
6347SHPEN	Bone	3⅞	1965-69	USA	75
6347SPPU	Bone	3⅞	1965-69	USA	30
6347SPPEN	Bone	3⅞	1965-69	USA	35
6347SHSPSSP	Bone	3⅞	1965-69	USA	
Stainless, blade edge polished					35
6347SHSPSSP	Bone	3⅞	1965-69	USA	
Stainless, blades polished					50
6347SHSPSSP	Bone	3⅞	1965-69	USA	
Stainless, First model with blade polished					80
3347SHSP	Yellow Comp	3⅞	1970	10 Dot	28
5347SHSP	Stag	3⅞	1970	10 Dot	50
5347SHSPSS	Stag	3⅞	1970	10 Dot	
Stainless, polished blades					225
6347SHSP	Bone	3⅞	1970	10 Dot	26
6347SPPU	Bone	3⅞	1970	10 Dot	30
6347SPPEN	Bone	3⅞	1970	10 Dot	30
6347SHSPSSP	Bone	3⅞	1970	10 Dot	
Stainless, blade edge polished					35
630047	Green Bone	3⅞	1920-40	Tested XX	210
630047PUJ	Green Bone	3⅞	1920-40	Tested XX	210

CONGRESS Whittler

63052	Green Bone	3½"	1920-40	Tested XX	$600
3352	Yellow	3¾	1920-40	Tested XX	325

23055PU	Slick Black	3½"	1940-64	XX	$350
23055	Slick Black	3½	1920-40	Tested XX	350
23055PU	Slick Black	3½	1920-40	Tested XX	400

═══ EQUAL END ═══

8360SC	Genuine Pearl		1920-40	Tested XX	210

93047	Cracked Ice	3⅞"	1920-40	Tested XX	$250
43047	White Comp.	3⅞	1920-40	Tested XX	210
53047	Stag	3⅞	1920-40	Tested XX	235
63047	Green Bone	3⅞	1920-40	Tested XX	210
53047	Stag	3⅞	1940-64	XX	90
63047	Rough Black	3⅞	1940-50	XX	160
63047	Green Bone	3⅞	1940-55	XX	235
63047	Red Bone	3⅞	1940-64	XX	80
63047	Bone	3⅞	1940-64	XX	40
93047	Cracked Ice	3⅞	1940-64	XX	225
53047	Stag	3⅞	1965-69	USA	60
63047	Bone	3⅞	1965-69	USA	30
53047	Stag	3⅞	1970	10 Dot	60
63047	Bone	3⅞	1970	10 Dot	30

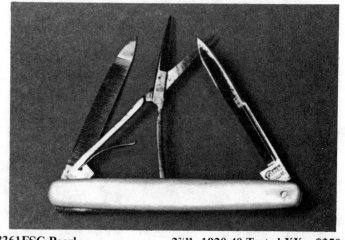

8361FSC	Pearl	2⅞"	1920-40	Tested XX	$350
2361F	Slick Black (Whittler)		1920-40	Tested XX	300
8361	Pearl 2⅞" Whittler	1920-1940	Tested XX	350

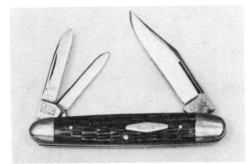

63063½   Green Bone LP   3¹⁄₁₆"   **Tested XX** $300

5364TF   Stag   3⅛" 1920-40 **Tested XX** **$225**

Nr.	Handle,	Lgth.	Stamp	Mint
8364T	Genuine Pearl	3⅛	1920-40 Tested XX	225
8364SC	Genuine Pearl	3⅛	1920-40 Tested XX	225
8364TSS	Genuine Pearl	3⅛	1940-64 XX	
Stainless, tip bolsters				100
8364SSSC	Genuine Pearl	3⅛	1965-69 USA	
Stainless				90
8364SSSC	Genuine Pearl	3⅛	1970 10 Dot	
Stainless				$95

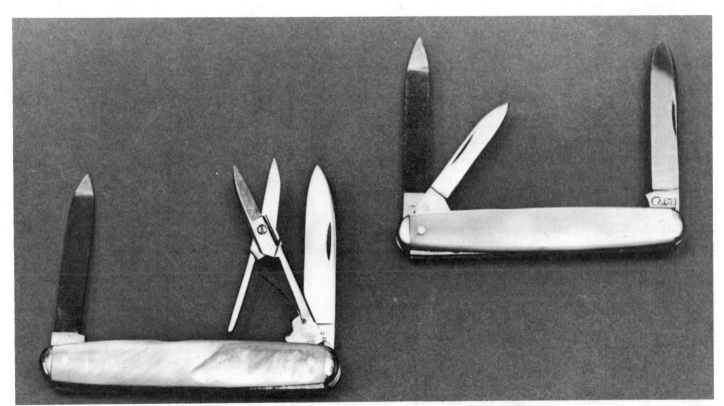

8364   TSCI SS Pearl   3⅛"   **1940-64 XX** $90   **8364TF   Pearl Whittler, Rare**   3⅛" 1920-40 **Tested XX** **$250**

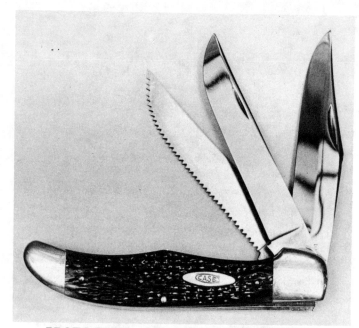

PROTO TYPE   3 BLADE FOLDING HUNTER
6365 SAB/SAW   Bone   5¼"   Very Rare,   XX
3 Back Springs (mid-'50s)   **$2,000**

Nr.	Handle,	Lgth.	Stamp	Mint
6366	Green Bone	3⅛	1920-40 Tested XX	210
6366PEN	Green Bone	3⅛	1920-40 Tested XX	200
8366PEN	Genuine Pearl	3⅛	1920-40 Tested XX	260

WHITTLER

Nr.	Handle,	Lgth.	Stamp	Mint
6367	Green Bone		1920-40 Tested XX	290
8367	Genuine Pearl		1920-40 Tested XX	310
9367	Imi. Pearl		1920-40 Tested XX	260

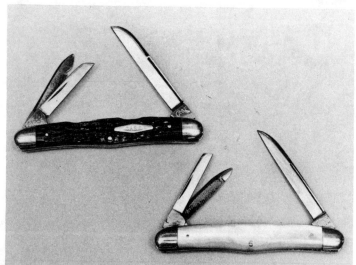

6370FLP	Green Bone	3⅛"	1920-40 Tested XX	$350
8370FLP	Pearl	3⅛"	1920-40 Tested XX	$400
6370LP	Green Bone		1920-40 Tested XX	350
8370LP	Genuine Pearl		1920-40 Tested XX	400

Nr.	Handle,	Lgth.	Stamp	Mint
6375LP	Rough Black	4¼" 1920-40 Tested XX		$300
5375	Stag	4¼" 1920-40 Tested XX		
Long Pull				310
5375LP	2nd Cut Stag	Tested XX		800
6375	Green Bone	4¼" 1920-40 Tested XX		
Long Pull				310
5375	Stag	4¼" 1940-64	XX	120
5375	Stag	4¼" 1940-64	XX	
Long Pull				235
5375	2nd Cut Stag	4¼" 1940-64	XX	650
5375	2nd Cut Stag	4¼" 1940-64	XX	
Long Pull				700
6375	Rough Black	4¼" 1940-50	XX	250
6375	Rough Black	4¼" 1940-50	XX	
Long Pull				300
6375	Green Bone	4¼" 1940-55	XX	235
6375	Green Bone	4¼" 1940-55	XX	
Long Pull				285
6375	Red Bone	4¼" 1940-64	XX	130
6375	Red Bone	4¼" 1940-64	XX	
Long Pull				200
6375	Bone	4¼" 1940-64	XX	65
6375	Bone	4¼" 1940-64	XX	
Long Pull				135
5375	Stag	4¼" 1965-69	USA	65
5375	2nd Cut Stag	4¼" 1965-69	USA	600
6375	Bone	4¼" 1965-69	USA	35
5375	Stag	4¼" 1970	10 Dot	60
6375	Bone	4¼" 1970	10 Dot	35

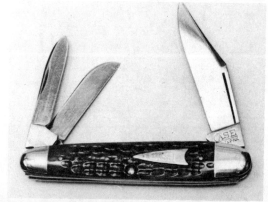

6376½LP Green Bone Whittler   3⅝"   **Tested XX**   **$350**

Nr.	Handle,	Lgth.	Stamp	Mint
2376½	Slick Black	4	1920-40 Tested XX	325
5376½	Stag	4	1920-40 Tested XX	375

6379½F	**Green Bone**	**3¼"**	**1920-40 Tested XX**	**$350**
63079½	Green Bone	3¼	1920-40 Tested XX	350

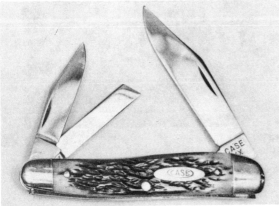

6380	**Rogers Bone Whittler**	**3⅞"**	**1940-55 XX**	**$550**
6380	Rogers Bone flat blade	3⅞	1920-40 Tested XX	800
6380	Green Bone flat blade, Whittler	3⅞	1920-40 Tested XX	700
6380	Green Bone Whittler	3⅞	1940-55 XX	400
6380	Red Bone	3⅞	1940-64 XX	140
6380	Bone	3⅞	1940-64 XX	75
6380	Bone	3⅞	1965-69 USA	40
6380	Bone	3⅞	1970 10 Dot	40

—— **LOBSTER** ——

83081	Genuine Pearl Lobster	3	1920-40 Tested XX	160

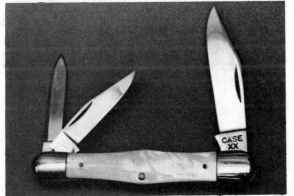

9383	**Cracked Iced**	**3½"**	**1940-55 XX**	**$250**

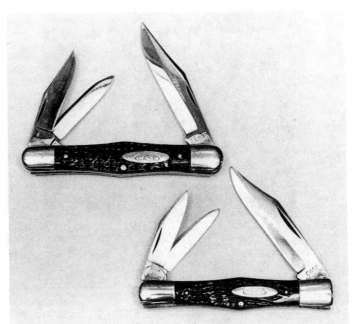

6383SAB	**Green Bone**	**3½"**	**1920-40 Tested XX**	**$350**
6383SAB	**Green Bone Square Bolsters**	**3½"**	**Case Bradford**	**$450**

Nr.	Handle,	Lgth.	Stamp		Mint
B383	Imi. Onyx	3½	1920-40	Tested XX	350
2383	Slick Black	3½	1920-40	Tested XX	275
5383	Stag	3½	1920-40	Tested XX	335
5383SAB	Stag	3½	1920-40	Tested XX	360
6383	Green Bone	3½	1920-40	Tested XX	325
8383	Genuine Pearl	3½	1920-40	Tested XX	460
9383	Imi. Pearl	3½	1920-40	Tested XX	300
2383	Slick Black	3½	1940-64	XX	90
2383SAB	Slick Black	3½	1940-64	XX	260
5383	Stag	3½	1940-64	XX	90
5383SAB	Stag	3½		XX	250
6383SAB	Green Bone	3½	1940-50	XX	350
6383	Rough Black	3½	1940-50	XX	250
6383	Green Bone	3½	1940-55	XX	300
6383	Red Bone	3½	1940-64	XX	90
6383	Bone	3½	1940-64	XX	65
9383	Imi. Pearl	3½	1940-64	XX	235
9383SAB	Imi. Pearl	3½	1940-64	XX	285
2383	Slick Black	3½	1965-69	USA	90
5383	Stag	3½	1965-69	USA	70
6383	Bone	3½	1965-69	USA	40
5383	Stag	3½	1970	10 Dot	70
6383	Bone	3½	1970	10 Dot	40

—— **LOBSTER** ——

63083	Green Bone	3³⁄₁₆	1920-40 Tested XX	210
83083	Genuine Pearl	3³⁄₁₆	1920-40 Tested XX	210

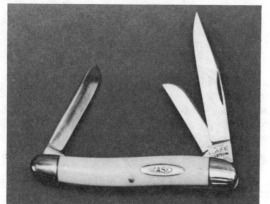

| 43087 | White Comp. | 3¼" 1920-40 Tested XX | $140 |

Nr.	Handle,	Lgth.		Stamp	Mint
23087ShPEN	Slick Black	3¼	1920-40	Tested XX	120
63087SPPEN	Green Bone	3¼	1920-40	Tested XX	135
63087SPPEN	Rough Black	3¼	1940-50	XX	90
63087SPPEN	Green Bone	3¼	1940-55	XX	120
63087SPPEN	Red Bone	3¼	1940-64	XX	40
23087SHPEN	Slick Black	3¼	1940-64	XX	28
53087SHPEN	Stag	3¼	1940-64	XX	60
63087SPPEN	Bone	3¼	1940-64	XX	35
23087HSPEN	Slick Black	3¼	1965-69	USA	25
53087SHPEN	Stag	3¼	1965-69	USA	50
63087SPPEN	Bone	3¼	1965-69	USA	25
23087SHPEN	Slick Black	3¼	1970	10 Dot	25
53087SHPEN	Stag	3¼	1970	10 Dot	50
63087SPPEN	Delrin	3¼	1970	10 Dot	22
63087SPPEN	Bone Stag	3¼	1970	10 Dot	30

GUNSTOCK WHITTLER

| 5387 | Stag | | 1920-40 Tested XX | 750 |

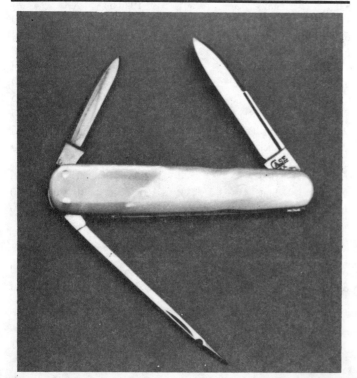

| 83088 | Pearl Lobster LP | 3⅛" | Tested XX | $150 |

Nr.	Handle,	Lgth.		Stamp	Mint
83088SS	Genuine Pearl	3⅛	1920-40	Tested XX	185
83088SS	Genuine Pearl	3⅛	1940-64	XX	135

THREE BLADE - LOBSTER SCISSORS

83089SCI	Genuine Pearl	3¹⁄₁₆	1920-40	Tested XX	185
83089SCISSF	Genuine Pearl	3¹⁄₁₆	1940-64	XX	135
83089SCSSF	Genuine Pearl	3¹⁄₁₆	1965-69	USA	200

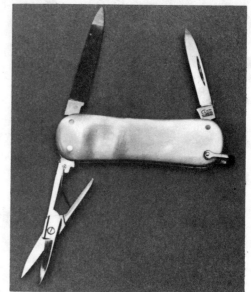

| 83090SCI Pearl Lobster | 2¼" 1920-40 Tested XX | $175 |

| 83090SCRSS | Genuine Pearl | 2¼ | 1940-64 | XX | 160 |

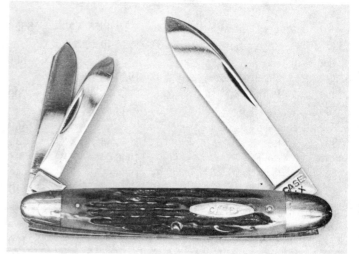

5391	Stag	4½"	1940-42 XX	$1300
3391	Yellow Comp.	4½	1920-40 Tested XX	1550
5391	Red Stag	4½	1920-40 Tested XX	1600
5391	Stag	4½	1920-40 Tested XX	1400
6391	Green Bone	4½	1940-42 XX	2000
5391	Red Stag	4½	1940-42 XX	1600

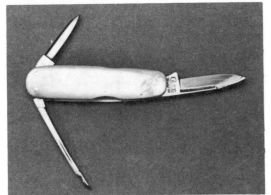

Nr.	Handle	Lgth.	Stamp	Mint
83091	Genuine Pearl	2¼"	1920-40 Tested XX	$185
GM3091	Gold Plate	2¼	1920-40 Tested XX	200

Nr.	Handle		Lgth.		Stamp	Mint
6392	Green Bone		4"		XX	$200
B392PU	Onyx				Tested XX	350
5392	Stag		4		1920-40 Tested XX	260
6392	Green Bone		4		1920-40 Tested XX	235
6392PU	Green Bone		4		1920-40 Tested XX	250
5392	Stag		4		1940-64 XX	90
6392	Rough Black		4		1940-50 XX	200
6392	Rough Black		4		1940-50 XX	
	Long Pull					235
6392	Green Bone		4		1940-55 XX	210
6392	Red Bone		4		1940-64 XX	110
6392	Bone		4		1940-64 XX	45
5392	Stag		4		1965-69 USA	60
6392	Bone		4		1965-69 USA	35
6292	Bone (transition)				USA	
	(Master Blade USA/Spey Blade 10 Dots					100
5392	Stag		4		1970 10 Dot	60
6392	Bone		4		1970 10 Dot	35
6392	Bone		4		1970 10 Dot to USA	135

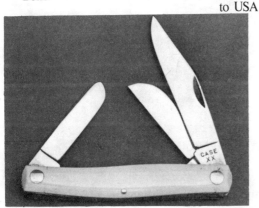

33092	Yellow w/o Shield	4"	1940-64	XX	$55
	with Shield				$65

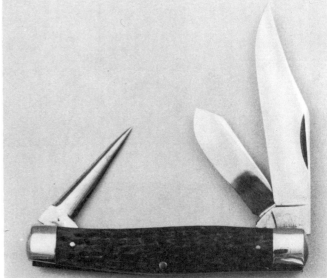

Nr.	Handle,	Lgth.	Stamp	Mint
63092	Green Bone Punch	4"	1920-40 Tested XX	$325
33092 Birdseye	Yellow Comp.	4	1920-40 Tested XX	
				185
630092	Green Bone	4	1920-40 Tested XX	250
33092 Birdseye	Yellow Comp.	4	1965-69 USA	
				40
33092 Birdseye	Yellow Comp.	4	1970 10 Dot	
				40

STOCKMAN/TRANSITION

5393	Stag	3¹⁵⁄₁₆	1920-40 Tested XX	310
6393	Green Bone	3¹⁵⁄₁₆	1920-40 Tested XX	260
6393R	Green Bone	3¹⁵⁄₁₆	1920-40 Tested XX	260
9393	Imi. Pearl	3¹⁵⁄₁₆	1920-40 Tested XX	310
93093	Imi. Pearl	3¹⁵⁄₁₆	1920-40 Tested XX	275

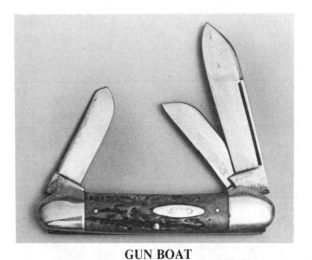

GUN BOAT

5394LP	Stag	4¼" 1920-40 Tested XX	$1250
6394	Green Bone	4¼ 1920-40 Tested XX	1500

CASE 84

| 6394½ | Green Bone LP | 4¼" | 1940-50 XX | **$800** |

Nr.	Handle,	Lgth.	Stamp	
5394½	Stag	4¼	1920-40 Tested XX	800
6394½	Green Bone	4¼	1920-40 Tested XX	800
6394½	Red Bone	4¼	1940-64 XX	650
6394½	Red Bone long pull	4¼	1940-64 XX	750
6394½	Red Bone Muskrat blade (Rare)	4¼	1940-64 XX	900
6394½	Bone	4¼	1940-64 XX	600
6394½	Bone long pull	4¼	1940-64 XX	700

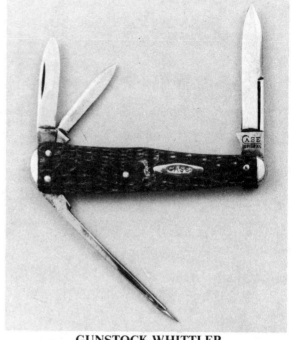

GUNSTOCK WHITTLER
Pattern unknown Green Bone, 3" Lobster Claw File Tested XX $400

FOUR BLADE

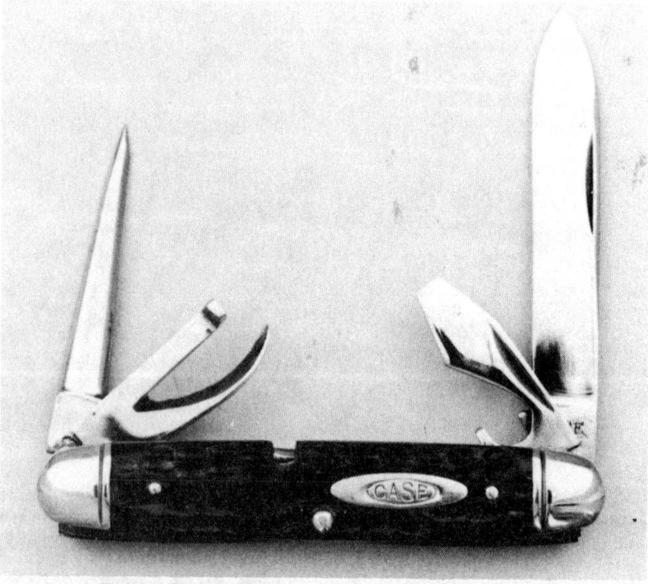

Scout Jr. 4 Blade Green Bone 3⅜" **1920-40 Tested XX $325**

Scout Jr., Gen. Pearl 3⅜ 1920-40 Tested XX 400

FLYFISHERMAN'S KNIFE

	Stainless Steel	3⅞"	1970	10 Dot	**$135**
Fly Fisherman SS		3⅞"	1920-40	Tested XX	190
Fly Fisherman Stainless		3⅞	1920-40	Tested XX	190
Fly Fisherman Stainless		3⅞	1940-64	XX	120
Fly Fisherman Stainless (XX To USA)		3⅞	1940-64	XX	120
Fly Fisherman Stainless (USA To 10 Dot)		3⅞	1965-69	USA	125
Fly Fisherman Stainless		3⅞	1965-69	USA	135
Fly Fisherman Stainless		3⅞	1970	10 Dot	135

Nr.	Handle	Lgth.	Stamp	Mint
Fly Fisherman				
Stainless	3⅞	1970	10 Dot	
Transition-(10 Dot to 9 Dot)				110
Fly Fisherman				
Stainless	3⅞	1970	10 Dot	
Transition 10 Dot to USA				125

Nr.	Handle,	Lgth.	Stamp	Mint
9445R	Imi. Pearl	3¾	1920-40 Tested XX	235
6445R	Red Bone	3¾	1940-64 XX	60
6445R	Bone	3¾	1940-64 XX	40
6445R	Bone	3¾	1965-69 USA	35
6445R	Bone	3¾	1970 10 Dot	35

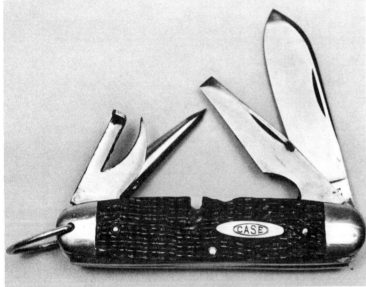

CAMP SCOUT or UTILITY

6445R	Green Bone	3¾" 1920-40 Tested XX	$200

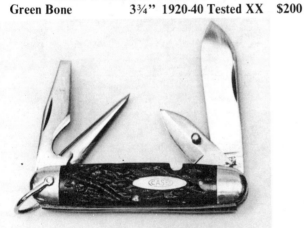

6445R	Rough Black	3¾" 1920-40 Tested XX	$200

9445R	Cracked Ice	3¾" 1920-40 Tested XX	$225

B445R	Imi. Onyx	3¾ 1920-40 Tested XX	260
6445R	Red Plastic	3¾ 1920-40 Tested XX	
	Navy Knife		260

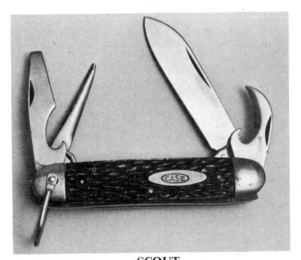

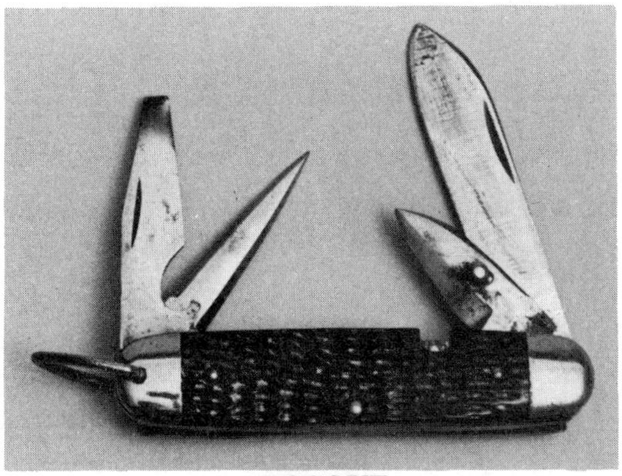

SCOUT

64045R	Green Bone, no shield	3⅝"	Tested XX	$175
64045	Rough Black	3¾ 1940-50	XX	50

SCOUT

640045R	Black Plastic	3⅝"	1940-50 XX	$25
640045R	Green Bone	3¾	1920-40 Tested XX	100
640045R	Brown Plastic	3¾	1940-64 XX	28
640045R	Black Plastic	3¾	1965-69 USA	25
640045R	Brown Plastic	3¾	1970 10 Dot	25

ABBREVIATIONS

½	master blade is clip blade	PU	Punch Blade
B	Budding	R	Bail in handle
EO	Easy Opener	RAZ	Razor Blade
F	File	SAB	Sabor Blade
J	Long Spay Blade	SC/SCI	Scissors
K	Corkscrew	SH	Sheepfoot blade
LR	Electrician's Knife	SP	Spay Blade
M	Metal	SS	Stainless Steel
PEN	Pen Blade	T	Tip Bolsters

SSP   Stainless Steel, Polished Blade Edge

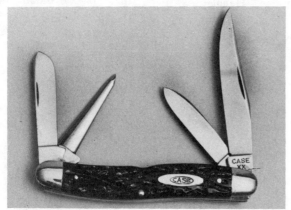

64047PU Rough Black   4"   1940-50 XX $225

Nr.	Handle,	Lgth.	Stamp		Mint
64047PU	Green Bone	4	1920-40	Tested XX	310
94047PU	Imi. Pearl	4	1920-40	Tested XX	335
64047PU	Green Bone	4	1940-50	XX	250
64047PU	Red Bone	4	1940-64	XX	125
64047PU	Bone	4	1940-64	XX	60
64047PU	Bone	4	1965-69	USA	35
64047PU	Bone	4	1970	10 Dot	35

ABBREVIATIONS

½	master blade is clip blade
B	Budding
EO	Easy Opener
F	File
J	Long Spay Blade
K	Corkscrew
LR	Electrician's Knife
M	Metal
PEN	Pen Blade
PU	Punch Blade
k	Bail in handle
RAZ	Razor Blade
SAB	Sabor Blade
SC/SCI	Scissors
SH	Sheepfoot blade
SP	Spay Blade
SSP	Stainless Steel, Polished Blade Edge
SS	Stainless Steel
T	Tip Bolsters

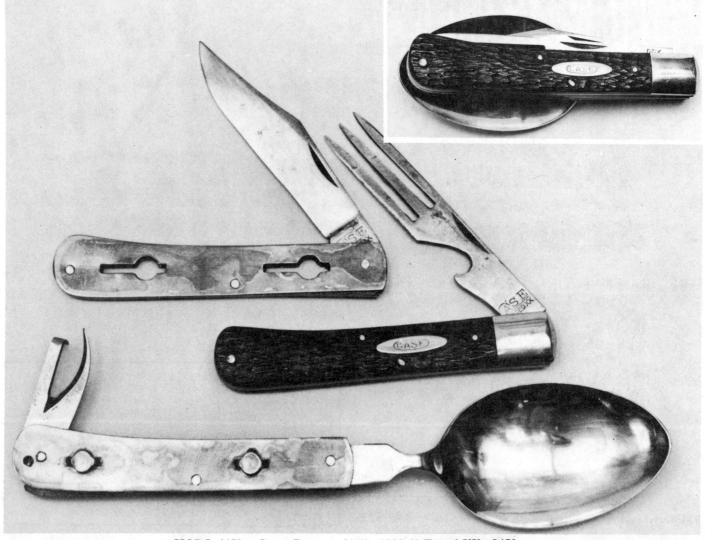

HOBO 6452   **Green Bone**   **3¾"**   **1920-40 Tested XX**   **$450**

M452	Metal	4	1920-40 Tested XX	385		3452	Yellow Comp.	4	1920-40 Tested XX	450

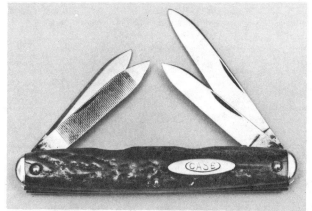

CONGRESS Transition

Nr.	Handle,	Lgth.		Stamp	Mint
64052	**Red Bone, Rare**	**3½"**		**XX to Tested XX**	**$500**
54052	Stag	3½	1920-40	Tested XX	600
64052	Green Bone	3½	1920-40	Tested XX	550
64052	Rogers Bone		Tested XX		650
54052	Stag	3½	1940-64	XX	100
54052	Stag	3½	1940-64	XX	
	(XX To USA)				100
64052	Green Bone	3½	1940-55	XX	225
64052	Red Bone	3½	1940-64	XX	90
64052	Red Bone	3½	1940-64	XX	
	Transition (Tested to XX)				500
64052	Bone	3½	1940-64	XX	60
64052	Bone	3½	1940-64	XX	
	(XX To USA)				90
54052	Stag	3½	1965-69	USA	70
54052	Stag	3½	1965-69	USA	
	(USA to 10 Dot				100
64052	Bone	3½	1965-69	USA	40
64052	Bone	3½	1965-69	USA	
	(USA To 10 Dot)				75
54052	Stag	3½	1970	10 Dot	70
54052	Stag	3½	1970	10 Dot	
	(10 Dot To USA)				100
64052	Bone	3½	1970	10 Dot	35
64052	Bone	3½	1970	10 Dot	
	(10 Dot To USA)				90

5460T	**Stag**	**3⅜"**	**1920-40 Tested XX**	**$275**
5460T	Red Stag	3⅜	1920-40 Tested XX	350

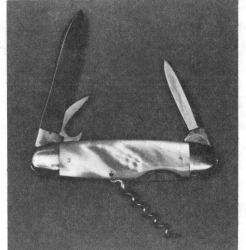

84062K	**Pearl**	**3¼"**	**1920-40 Tested XX**	**$400**
94062K	Imi. Onyx	3¼	1920-40 Tested XX	360

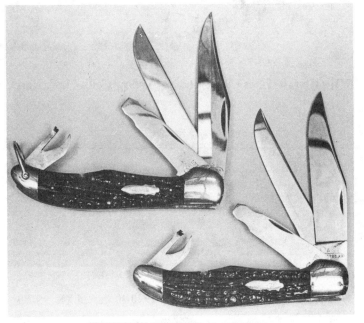

FOLDING HUNTER Saber Blade

6465R	**Green Bone**	**5¼"**		**Tested XX**	**$2,200**
6465	Green Bone	Flat Blade		Tested XX	2,200

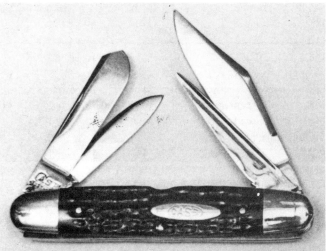

64055PU	**Green Bone**	**3½"**	**1920-40 Tested XX**	**$550**
64055PU	Green Bone	3½	1940-55 XX	500

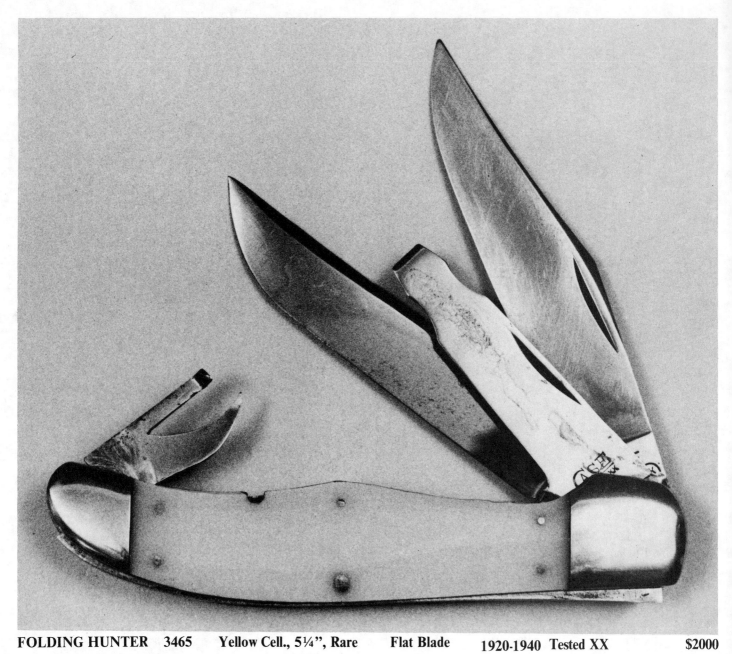

FOLDING HUNTER   3465   **Yellow Cell., 5¼", Rare**   **Flat Blade**   **1920-1940 Tested XX**   **$2000**

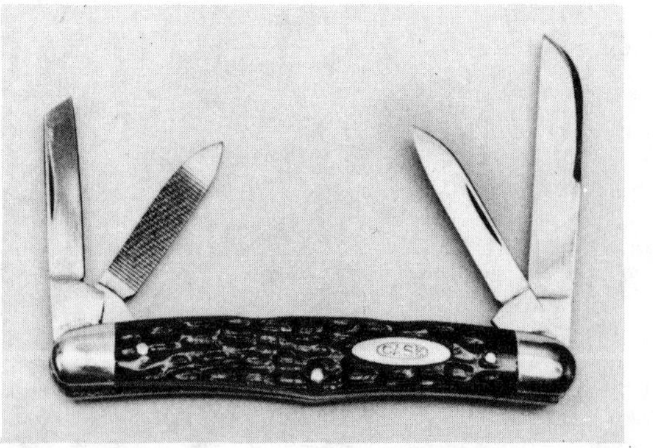

Nr.	Handle,	Lgth.	Stamp	Mint
5488	Stag	4⅛	1920-40 Tested XX	
Congress				600
5488	Stag	4⅛	1920-40 Tested XX	
Long Pull				650
5488	Winterbottom Bone	4⅛	1920-40 Tested XX	900
6488	Green Bone	4⅛	1920-40 Tested XX	600
6488	Green Bone	4⅛	1920-40 Tested XX	
Long Pull				700
6488	Rogers Bone	4⅛	1920-40 Tested XX	
Long Pull				800
6488	Rough Black Reg. Pull Rare	4⅛	1940-50 XX	600
6488	Rough Black	4⅛	1940-50 XX	
Long Pull				350
6488	Rough Black	4⅛	1940-50 XX	
Transition-blades arc Regular and Long Pull				450
6488	Green Bone	4⅛	1940-55 XX	550
6488	Green Bone	4⅛	1940-55 XX	
Long Pull				600

6470F   **Green Bone**   **3⅛"**   **1920-40 Tested XX**   **$400**

6470   Green Bone   3⅛   1920-40 Tested XX   400

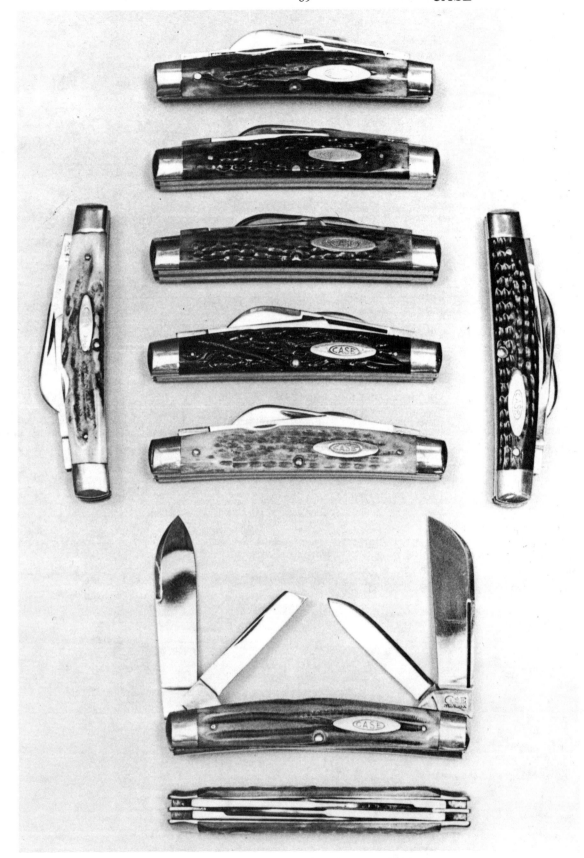

88 CONGRESS PATTERN (4⅛")

Top to bottom: **5488 Red Stag LP, XX, $450;   6488 Bone, 10 Dot, RP, $55;   6488 Green Bone, LP, XX $600; 6488 Rough Black, LP, XX $300;   5488 2nd Cut RP Stag, XX $450;   6488 Winterbottom Bone LP, Tested XX, $900; 6488 Green Bone with recessed Bolsters, Tested XX, $700**
Left: 5488 Stag, Tested XX, RP, $600   **Right: Red Bone RP, XX $300**

Nr.	Handle,	Lgth.		Stamp	
6488	Red Bone	4⅛	1940-64	XX	200
6488	Red Bone	4⅛	1940-64	XX	
	Long Pull				400
5488	Stag	4⅛	1940-64	XX	135
5488	Stag	4⅛	1940-64	XX	
	(XX To USA)				185
5488	Stag	4⅛	1940-64	XX	
	Long Pull				350
5488	2nd cut Stag	4⅛	1940-64	XX	450
5488	2nd cut Stag	4⅛	1940-64	XX	
	(XX To USA)				450
6488	Bone	4⅛	1940-64	XX	90
6488	Bone	4⅛	1940-64	XX	
	Long Pull				250
6488	Bone	4⅛	1940-64	XX	
	(XX To USA)				110
6488	2nd cut Stag	4⅛	1940-64	XX	400
5488	Stag	4⅛	$965-69	USA	90
5488	Stag	4⅛	1965-69	USA	

(USA To 10 Dot) (Caution: this one may never have been made by W.R. Case.)   200

5488	2nd cut Stag	4⅛	1965-69	USA	450
6488	Bone	4⅛	1965-69	USA	60
6488	Bone	4⅛	1965-69	USA	
	(USA To 10 Dot)				100
6488	2nd cut Stag	4⅛	1965-69	USA	400
5488	Stag	4⅛	1970	10 Dot	140
6488	Bone	4⅛	1970	10 Dot	60
6488	Bone	4⅛	1970	10 Dot	
	(10 Dot To USA)				125

No 9 Dot 1971 6488 Congress Made

──────── SCOUT ────────

64009OR	Green Bone		1920-40	Tested XX	160
9490R	Imi. Pearl		1920-40	Tested XX	210
34009OR	Yellow Comp.		1920-40	Tested XX	
	Scout				185

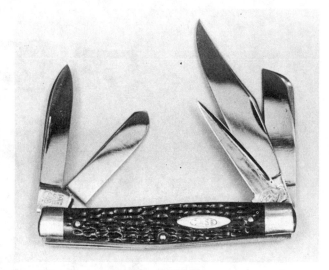

TRANSITIONAL

6592	Green Bone	3⅞"	Tested XX	$1600
B592	Imi. Onyx, Rare	3⅞	Tested XX	1600

CASE'S 7 BLADE SKATE WRENCH

97145PU SK.W   Cracked Ice, Very Rare   4" $4500
(only four have been seen)

FIVE BLADE

NKCA 10TH ANNIVERSARY

6592	Bone	4"	1983 - 1600 made	$80

ABBREVIATIONS

½	master blade is clip blade
B	Budding
EO	Easy Opener
F	File
J	Long Spay Blade
K	Corkscrew
LR	Electrician's Knife
M	Metal
PEN	Pen Blade
PU	Punch Blade
R	Bail in handle
RAZ	Razor Blade
SAB	Sabor Blade
SC/SCI	Scissors
SH	Sheepfoot blade
SP	Spay Blade
SSP	Stainless Steel, Polished Blade Edge
SS	Stainless Steel
T	Tip Bolsters

CASE OLDER KNIVES

Note: many of the Case knives will have the same pattern number but be totally different styles. Several of the older knives and numbers were retired only to have the retired number show up again on a newer but different style.

File   4½" Case Bradford, PA $750

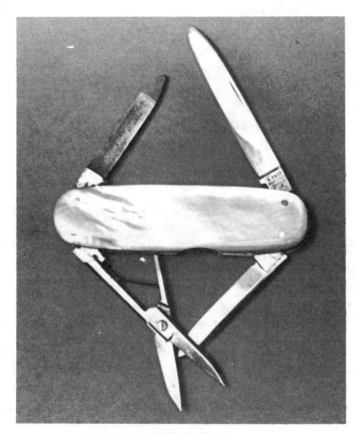

UNNUMBERED LOBSTER
Pearl, Rare   2⅞"   R. Case Bradford   Germany $250

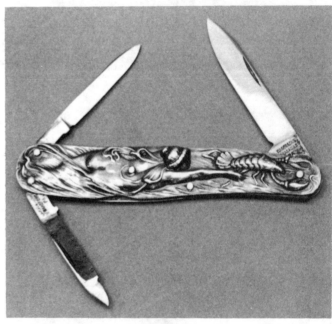

FIGURAL
Sterling Silver   3¾"   Case & Son $300

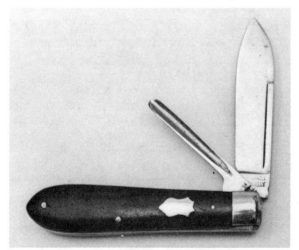

CASE BROS., LITTLE VALLEY, NY
Ebony with Punch $150

Maize, Walnut Handle, 1 blade   4" Case Tested XX $200

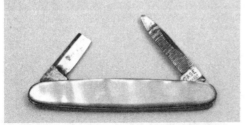

Unknown Abalone Pearl - Rare   1⅞"   Case, Germany $225
2 Blade Miniature

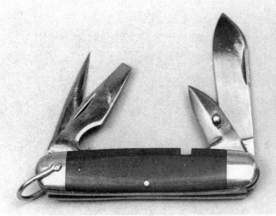

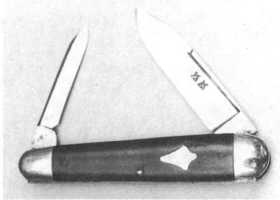

**6445R 4 Blade Scout Red Fibroid 3¼" Case Tested $275
WW II issue**

Unknown Plastic (odd shield) 3⅜" Case Bros.
Little Valley NY $225

**Knife & Razor Combination
Case Brothers, Little Valley, NY, 9¼" overall, solid piece steel**   **Rare**

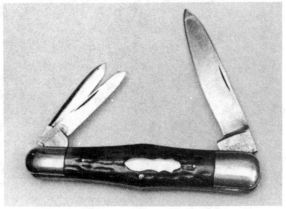

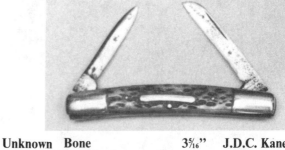

Unknown Bone 3⁵⁄₁₆" J.D.C. Kane Pa $200

**Unknown   Bone   3¾"   Case Bros & Co
LV, NY $550
(one small blade stamped 'Case Brothers', the other
small blade stamped 'Case Bros.')**

Unknown Plastic 3⁵⁄₁₆" XX Co. Kane, Pa. $150

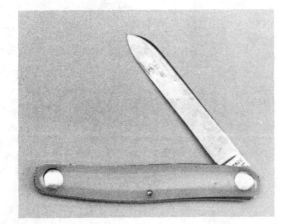

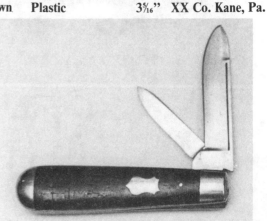

Unknown   Yellow Plastic Birdseye 3⅜"   J.D. Case $150

Unknown   Wood   3¾" R.Case & Son Little
Valley, NY $200

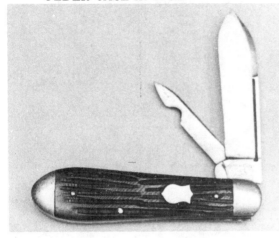

Unknown   Winterbottom Bone   3½"   W.R. Case & Son
                                    Bradford, Pa. $225

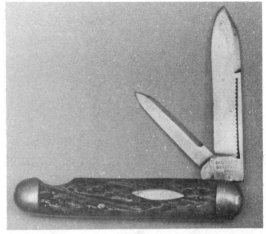

Unknown   Bone   3½"   Case & Sons
                                    Bradford Pa $200

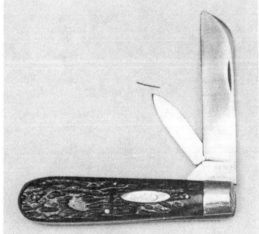

Unknown   Bone   3⅜"   W.R. Case & Son
                                  Bradford, Pa $150

Unknown   Metal (figural) Made for "Royal Order of Red Men"
W.R. Case & Sons   3¼" $175

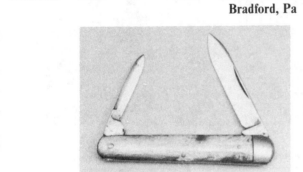

Unknown   Plastic   2¹³⁄₁₆"   Crandall Cut. Co.
                                    Bradford, Pa $150

Unknown   Cloisonne   2¹³⁄₁₆" W.R. Case & Sons
                                     Bradford Pa. $250
(back of blade reads "German Factory")

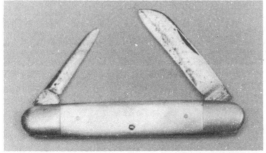

Unknown   Pearl   3⅜"   W.R. Case & Sons
                                  Cut'l. Bradford, Pa $225

Unknown   Pearl & Abalone   3"   R. Case Bradford,
Germany rare $200

Unknown   Pearl   1¹⁵⁄₁₆"   Case, Germany
(origin unknown) $125

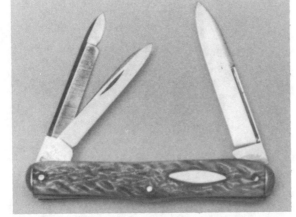

Unknown   Bone   3⅜"   W.R. Case & Sons
(whittler w/3 springs - rare stamp)   Bradford Pa $400

Unknown   Christmas Tree   3¹⁄₁₆"   Case (in script)
Rare stamp and handles $250

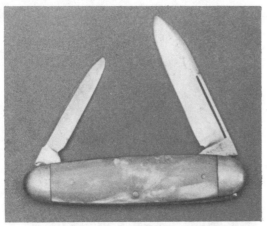

Unknown   Cracked Ice   3"   Case's Bradford, Pa $300

Unknown   Pyremite   3¹⁄₁₆"   Case & Sons
(covered backspring)   Bradford Pa. $350

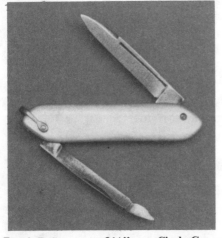

Unknown   Pearl, Bail   2½"   Circle Case $150

Unknown Hi Art   3⅜"   Case Bros. Little
(naughty lady)   Valley, NY $250

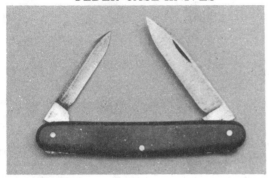

Unknown   Red Plastic   3"   Case Mfg. Co.
    rare stamp   Warren, Pa $200

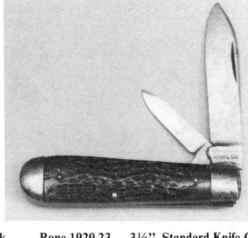

Jack   Bone 1920-23   3½"   Standard Knife Co. $150

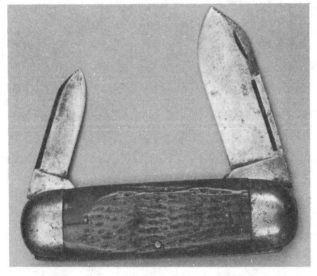

Sunfish   Bone   4¼" Crandall Cutlery Co $400
   (two pulls)

Unknown   Bone   3¹⁄₁₆"   W.R. Case & Son
                                Cutlery Co. $250

Unknown Goldstone   3"   Case Tested XX
  broken spear blade - rare stamp   (US Stamp) $200

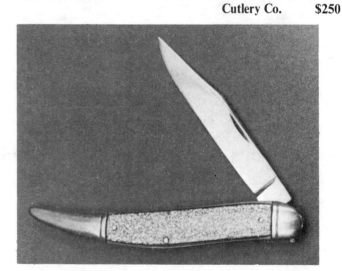

Unknown Goldstone   4⅜"   Case Mfg. Co.
                                 Warren, Pa $450

Unknown   Sterling (figural)   2¹⁄₁₆" Case Bro. Cut. Co. $200

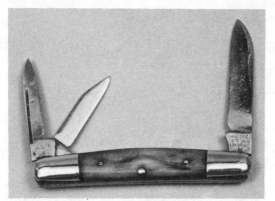

Unknown Stag Congress Whittler W.R. Case & Sons Bradford, Pa.   3" $350

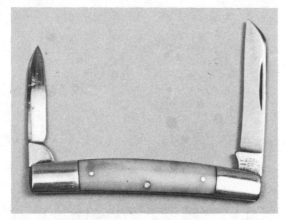

Waterfall   3¼" J.D. Case Co. Kane, Pa. $150

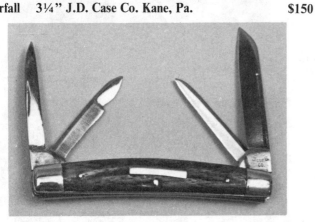

Unknown Stag 3¼" Case Bro. Cut. Co. $550

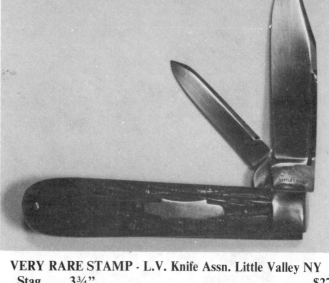

VERY RARE STAMP - L.V. Knife Assn. Little Valley NY
Stag   3¾" $275

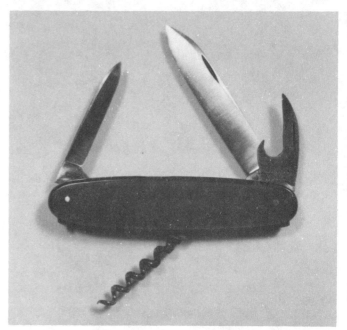

Y4062K   Amber Celluloid   3¼"   all blades stamped
                                W.R. Case & Sons $300

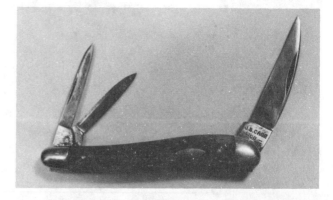

Dogleg Wharncliffe Whittler Rogers Bone 3" Main blade stamped
J.D. Case Co., Kane, PA, small blades stamped Case Kane, Pa.$700

Case Mfg. Co. Little Valley NY, Gold Swirl 3⅜"   all blades stamped, shield engraved "Chas Our"   **$550**

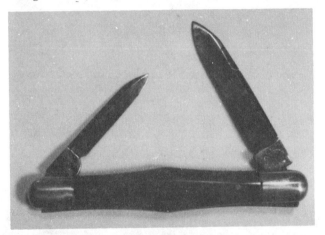

(similar to 2258) C. Platts & Sons, Eldred, PA. Black Celluloid 2⅞" Both blades stamped   **$100**

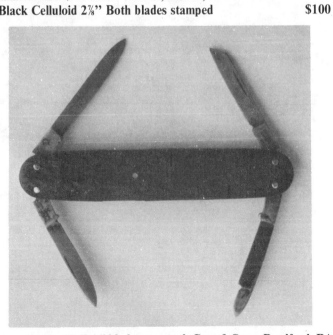

Rogers Bone 3⁵⁄₁₆" All blades stamped. Case & Sons, Bradford, PA
$200

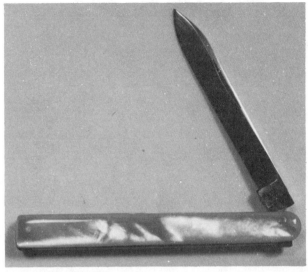

Kane Cutlery, Kane, PA. Pearl   3"   **$200**

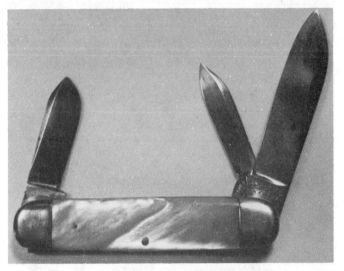

Kane Cutlery, Kane, PA. Pearl 3⅝" All blades stamped.   **$300**

Pearl   3"   Kane Cutlery Co.
both stamped $150

98

Unknown   Horn Scales   3¼"   Case Bros.,
Little Valley, NY $250

Unknown   Brown Bone   3½" W.R. Case & Son
(rare "Son" stamp)   Cutlery Co $250

Unknown French Pearl Scales 3⅜"   Case, Brad. Pa. $500

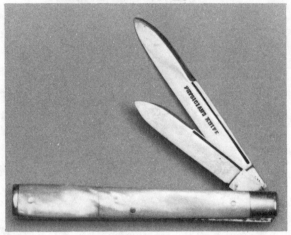

Unknown   Pearl Dr.'s Knife   3¾"   Tested XX $450

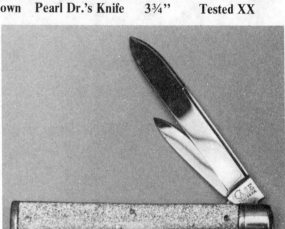

Unknown   Goldstone Dr.'s Knife 3¾"   Tested XX $400

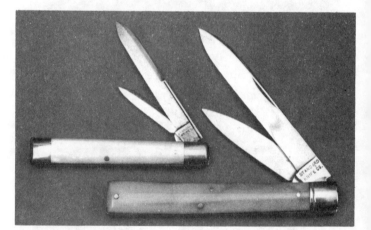

Unknown   Waterfall   3⅝" Standard Knife Co. $400
(made by Case 1920-23)
Unknown   Pearl Dr's Knife 2⅞" Standard Knife Co. $350
(made by Case 1920-23)

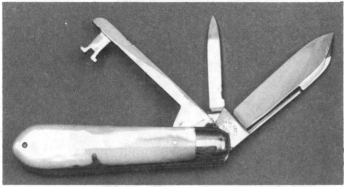

Unknown Pearl (3 backsprings) Skeleton Key 3⅛"
Case Bros. Little Valley NY $500

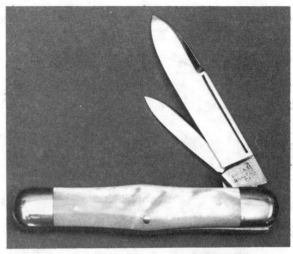

Unknown   3⅜"   Case & Sons
                                     Brad. Pa. $225

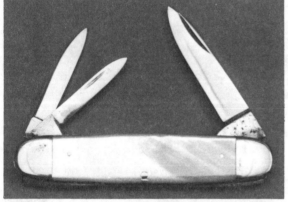

Unknown   Pearl   3¼" Case Bros. Cut. Co.
                           Little Valley NY $400

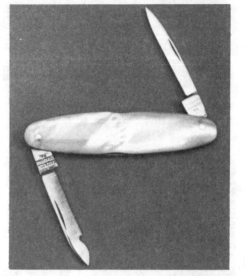

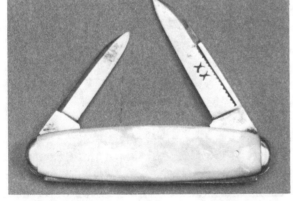

Unknown   Pearl   3"   Case Bros.
                                     Springville, NY $250

Unknown   Pearl   2⅜"   Case & Sons
                                     Brad. Pa $125

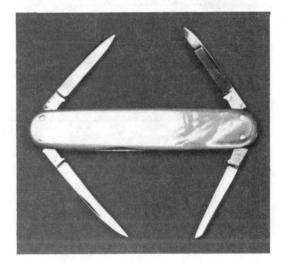

Unknown   Pearl   3¼"   W.R. Case & Son $200

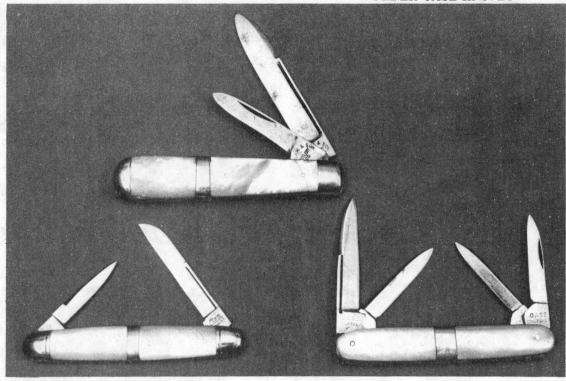

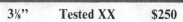

Unknown Pearl   3⅛"   Tested XX $250
Unknown   Pearl (nickel silver)   3¼"   W.R. Case & Sons   Unknown   Pearl (nickel silver)   3"   Case Brad. Pa $450
Cutley Co. $275

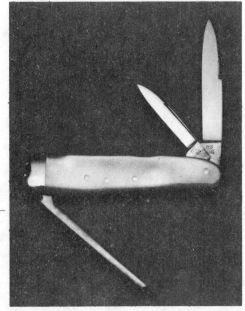

Unknown   Butter & Molasses   3¾"   W.R. Case & Sons,
Super Rare   Brad. Pa. $1000

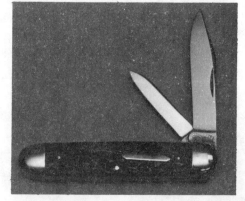

Unknown   Pearl   2⅞"   Case & Sons
Fingernail clipper in backspring - super rare $750

Cigar Pattern Brown Bone   4⅛"   Crandall, Brad. Pa. $450

W.R. Case & Son, Hobo Knife, 3 blades and sheath $2,500

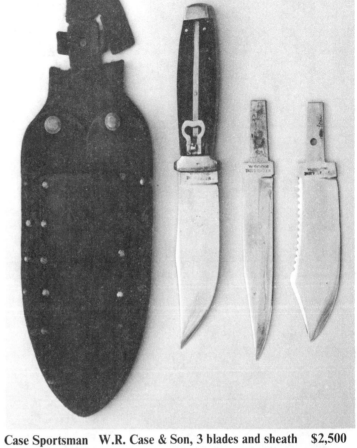

Case Sportsman W.R. Case & Son, 3 blades and sheath $2,500

Unknown Green Swirl Celluloid 3¹⁄₁₆" **Case & Sons Brad Pa.** $300
(enclosed backspring covered with same material as handle)

Unknown Red Fiberloid Scales 3¾" **Case XX** $150
WW II - Rare

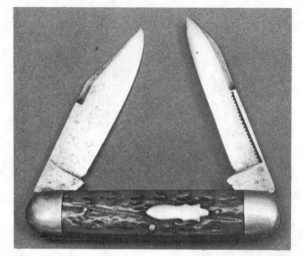

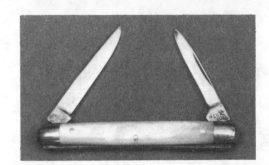

8201   Pearl   2¹¹⁄₁₆" Case Bros. Cut. Co. $150

J Pattern   Bone   3¹¹⁄₁₆" W.R. Case & Sons
Cut Co Bradford Pa $450

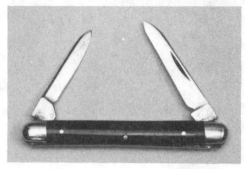

1201   Wood   2⅝"   W.R. Case & Son
1902-1905   Little Valley NY $200

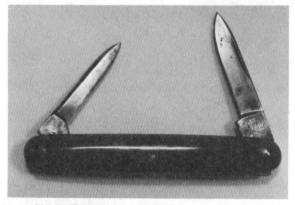

72001   Shad   Tortoise   2⅝"
both blades stamped W.R. Case & Son Little Valley NY $200

6100SAB Saddlehorn green bone   Case Tested XX $600

ABBREVIATIONS	
½	master blade is clip blade
B	Budding
EO	Easy Opener
F	File
J	Long Spay Blade
K	Corkscrew
LR	Electrician's Knife
M	Metal
PEN	Pen Blade
PU	Punch Blade
R	Bail in handle
RAZ	Razor Blade
SAB	Sabor Blade
SC/SCI	Scissors
SH	Sheepfoot blade
SP	Spay Blade
SSP	Stainless Steel, Polished Blade Edge
SS	Stainless Steel
T	Tip Bolsters

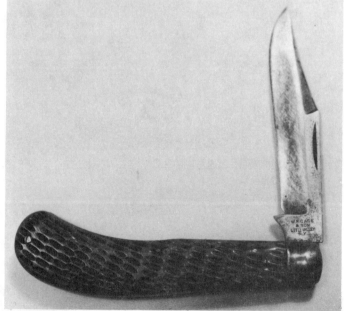

6100SAB Saddlehorn pick bone   W.R. Case & Son
1902-1903 (rare stamp)   Little Valley, NY $700

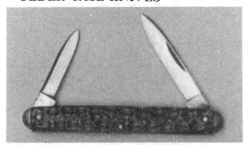

62001   Bone   2¹¹⁄₁₆"   Case Tested with no writing below line, Case is written in script)   **$125**

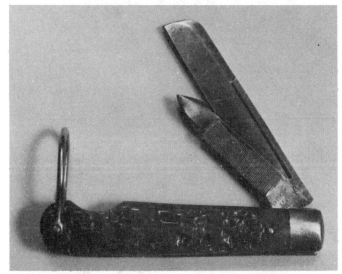

6202EO   SH FR Rogers Bone   3¼"
Both blades stamped W.R. Case & Sons, Bradford, Pa., main blade also stamped Made in USA (inside circle). This was a military stamp used in WWI   **$200**

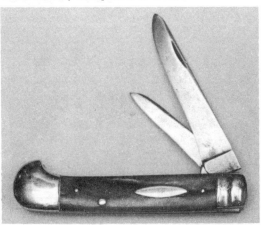

5203SP   Stag Budding Knife   3⅝"   W.R. Case & Sons $400

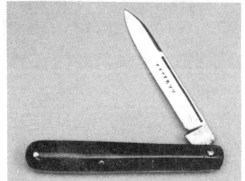

71006   Tortoise   2½"   Case Bros.
(shadow-no bols)   Little Valley NY $250

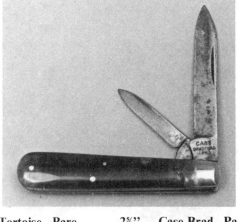

72006   Tortoise - Rare   2⅝"   Case Brad., Pa. $250

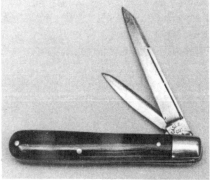

7206   Tortoise   2⅝"   Case Bro. Cut. Co $250
(also in Pearl 8206) $225

6106   Green Bone   2⁹⁄₁₆"   Case 25¢ Rare $250

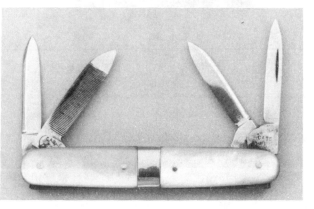

8407F   Pearl, 4 blade   3"   Case, Brad., PA $750

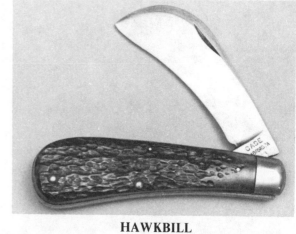

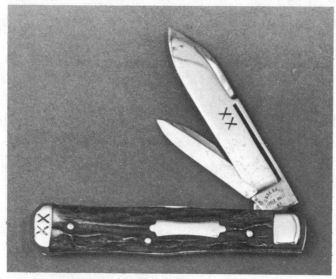

CASE BROTHERS, LITTLE VALLEY, NY
5208LP Gen. Stag (note "Coffin" bolster)　　　　$450

HAWKBILL
61011　　Rogers Bone　　　　4"　Case Bradford, PA　$175

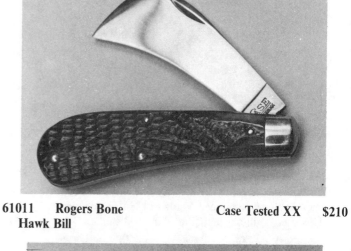

63109LP Green Bone　　　3½" Case Bradford, PA　$400

61011　　Rogers Bone　　　　Case Tested XX　$210
Hawk Bill

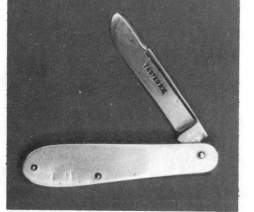

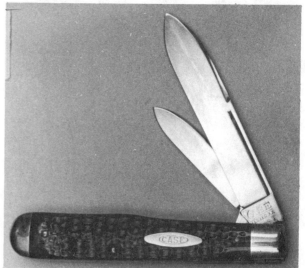

M110　　Spay Metal　　　3⅛"　Case Bros. Little
　　　　　　　　　　　　　　　　　Valley NY　　$175

6211　　Green Bone　　　4½"　Case Tested XX　$500

6213LP   **Rogers Bone**   3¹⁵⁄₁₆"   W.R. Case & Sons $700

6214   **Bone**   3⅜" Case Bros. L.V. NY $300
(Cline Hdwe Co. warranted) rare

8216F   **Pearl**   2½" Case Bros. Cut. Co.
                       Tested XX $250

6116   **Green Bone**   3½"   Case, Tested XX $160

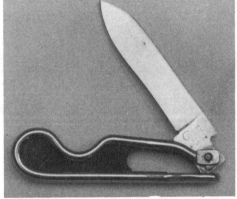

W1216   **Metal Wire**   3¼"   **Case Tested**
                              Pat. 9-21-26 $150

6216½   **Rogers Bone**   3½"
Main blade W.R. Case & Sons, Made in USA, also
Tested XX, secondary blade Case XX Tested (in circle) $200

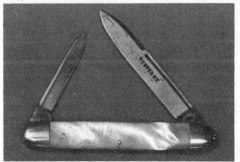

CASE BROTHERS LITTLE VALLEY, NY
8220LP   **Pearl**   3⅜" (Not a Peanut) $350

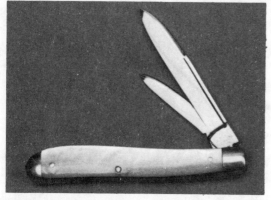

8220   Dogleg (not a Peanut) 2¾" W.R. Case & Sons
                                              Brad. Pa. $350

62020½   Rogers Bone   3¼"   Case XX Tested $150

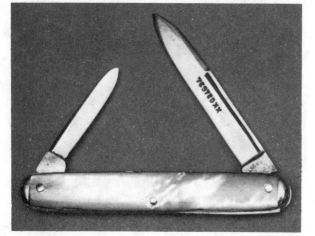

8220   Pearl (tip bols.)   3⅜"   Case Bros. LVNY $350

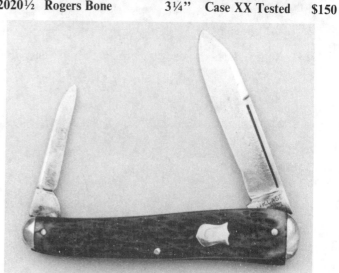

6221LP   Rogers Bone Tip Bols 3¼" W.R. Case & Sons $250

8222   Pearl   3¼"   Case Bros.
                                 Little Valley NY $275

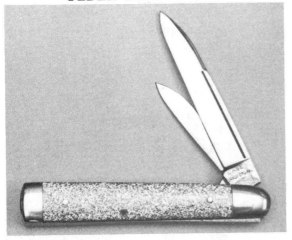

GS222   Goldstone LP   Case Brad. Pa   **$450**
(Doctor's Knife)

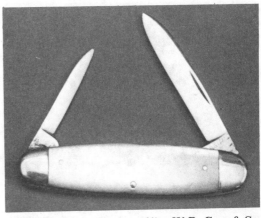

8224   Pearl   3"   W.R. Case & Sons
                              Brad. Pa.   **$250**

P3024   Green Cell., Rare   3¼" Case Bradford, PA $500

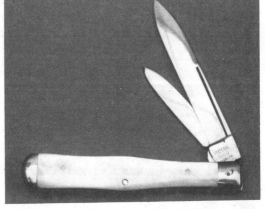

8225LP   Pearl   3"   W.R. Case & Sons
                              Bradford, Pa   **$300**

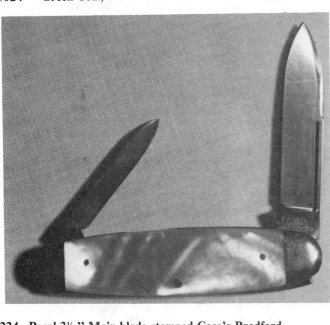

**8224   Pearl 3¹⁄₁₆" Main blade stamped Case's Bradford
Small blade stamped Case XX Tested**   **$300**

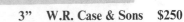

5225½   Gen. Stag   3"   W.R. Case & Sons   **$250**

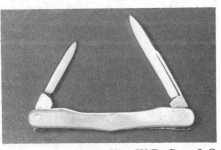

8227LP   Pearl   3"   W.R. Case & Sons   **$250**

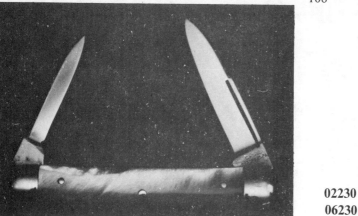

82027SP LP Pearl   2⅞"   Case, Brad. Pa $175

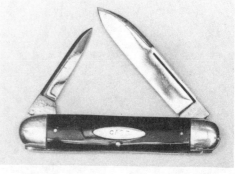

02230   Slick Black   3¼"   Case Bradford, Pa $150
06230   Bone 1902-1905   3¼"   W.R. Case & Son $250

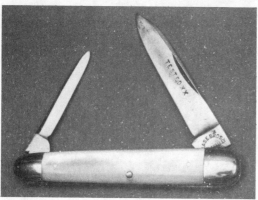

82027   Pearl   2⅞"   Case Bros.
                                    Little Valley, NY $200

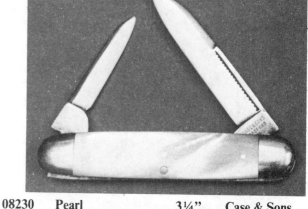

08230   Pearl   3¼"   Case & Sons
                                    Brad. Pa. $300

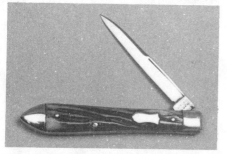

61028   Winterbottom, 1 Bl.   2⅞"   WR Case & Sons
Rare   Bradford, PA $275

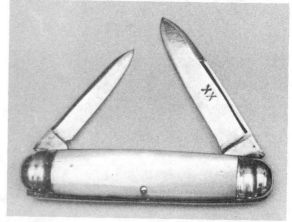

08230   Pearl   3¼"   Case Bros. Little
(also in bone) (recessed bolsters)   Valley, NY $300

6229½   Green Bone   2½" main blade Case XX $150

06230   Bone   3¼"   W.R. Case & Son
                                 Little Valley, NY $250

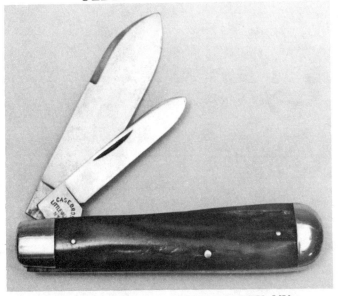

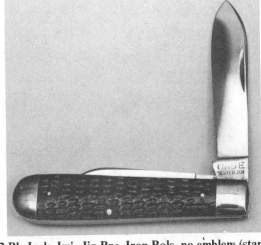

6231 2 Bl. Jack, Imi. Jig Bne, Iron Bols, no emblem (stamp not in any previous book). Case, Tested XX. The author believes this to be a W.W.I mil. contract knife. Rare. Approx. 1917 $200

CASE BROTHERS LITTLE VALLEY, NY

5231   Stag   3¾" $325

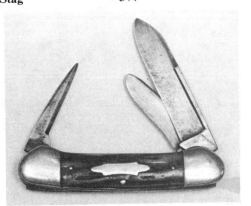

53131PU Stag LP   3⅝"   W.R. Case & Son $1200

62031½   Bone   3¾"   Case Bros. Little Valley, NY $200

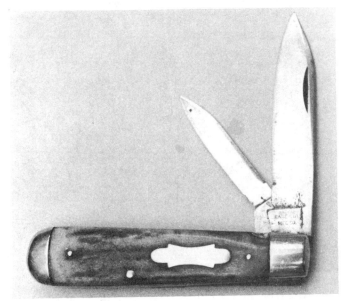

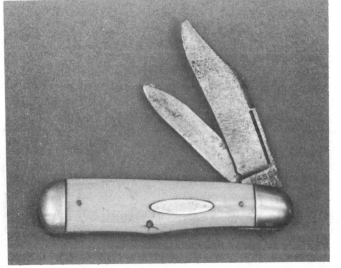

5231   Stag   3¾" Case Cut. Mfg. Co. $300

42035½   White Comp., LP   3¼" Case Bradford, PA $250

6237LP   Green Bone   3½" Case Bradford, PA $350

6539LP   Rogers Bone   3¾" Case Bradford PA $2500

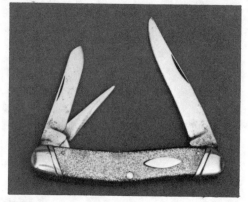

GS3038   Gold Stone   3½" W.R. Case & Son
Slant Bolsters $350

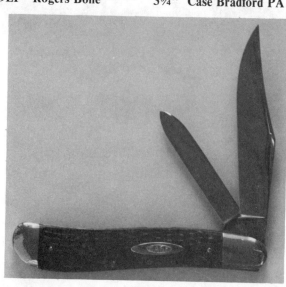

6240   Pen Green Bone   4½" Case Tested XX $500

6339LP   Rogers Bone   3¾" Case Bradford, PA $500

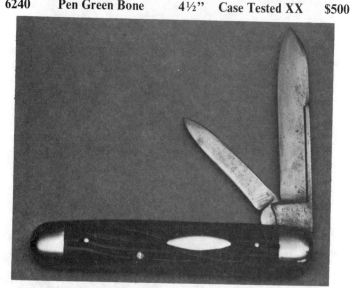

6241   Red Winterbottom Bone   3½" W.R. Case & Son
1902-1905 - rare $250

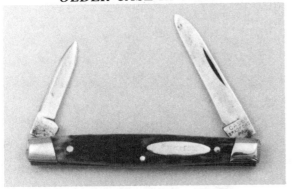

CASE BRAD., PA

62042 Slant Bols., stainless Emblem, small blade stamped
Case's STainless, Rogers Bone   3" $150

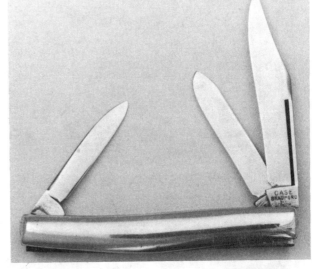

M344LP All Metal   3¼"   Case Brad., PA $140

63042   3"   Case Bradford, Pa $300

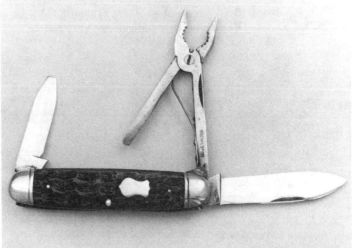

W.R. CASE & SONS BRADFORD, PA
6345 Rogers Bone Tool Knife $800

W.R. CASE & SON, BRAD., PA
5343   Whittler   3¾" $700

6445R   Green Bone, Case
Scout emblem   3¾"   Case Tested XX $300

6344   Rogers Bone - rare   3⅛" W.R. Case & Sons $250
(flat bolsters)

M445 Camp Pattern 3¾" Case Bradford, PA $450
Nickel Scales w/Boy Scout scene both sides - Very rare

W.R. CASE & SONS, BRADFORD, PA
6445RLP Rogers Bone 3¾" $250

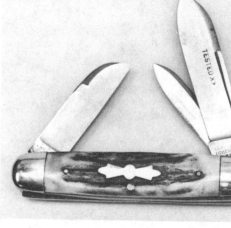

CASE BROTHERS LITTLE VALLEY, NY
5345LP Stag 2¾" $400

6345LP Bone 3⅝" Case Bros.
(rare stamp) Springville $400

G245 Pyremite 3⅝" W.R. Case & Sons
Brad. Pa. $225

W.R. CASE & SONS, BRAD., PA
6246 Bone 3⅝" $350

W.R. CASE & SONS, BRAD., PA

6346   Punch, 3 Backspring Whittler (Rare)   3⅝" $700

6347LP   Second Cut Bone   3⅞"   Case XX $400
    SP PU - Rare

W.R. CASE & SONS

6346   Rogers Bone 3 Backsprings   3⅝" $650

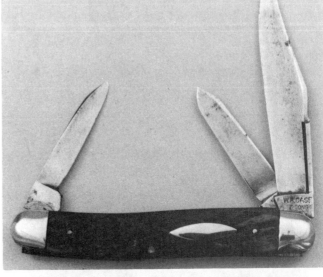

6347   Rogers Bone LP   W.R. Case & Sons $300

W.R.CASE & SONS, BRAD., PA

6346½   LP 3 Backsprings   3⅝" $600

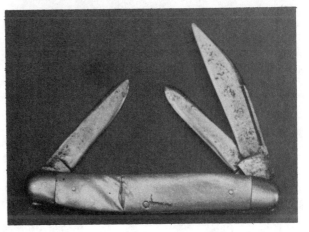

8347LP   Pearl   3¹⁵⁄₁₆"   Case & Sons
                                        Bradford, Pa. $400

114   *OLDER CASE KNIVES*

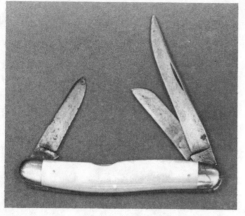

83047   Pearl   4"   W.R. Case & Sons $400

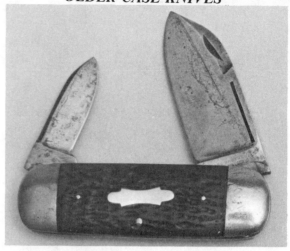

CASE BROTHERS LITTLE VALLEY, NY
6250LP   Sunfish (Toenail)   4" $700

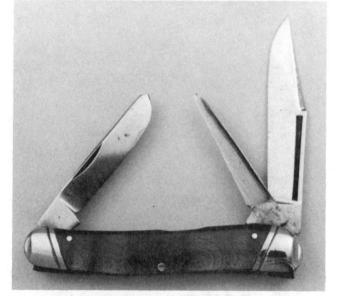

W.R. CASE & SONS
P348LP   Swirl, Made in U.S.A., Slant Pinch Bols.   3¼" $600

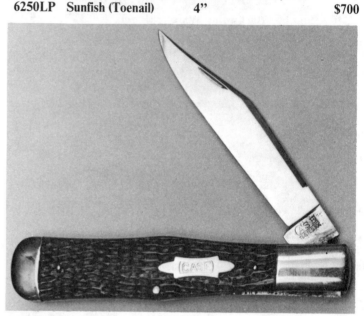

C61050   Green Bone   5⅜"   Case Tested XX $600
long flat bols., (small stamp), flat blade - rare

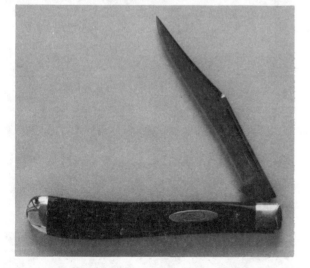

61049LP Green Bone   4⅛"   Case Tested XX $325

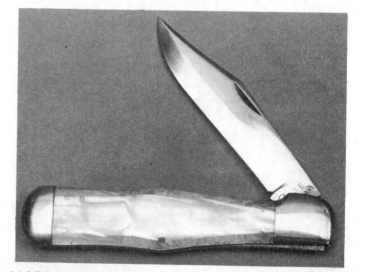

91050   SAB French Pearl   5⅜"   Case Tested XX $600
Rare Handles

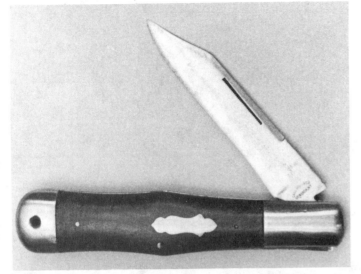

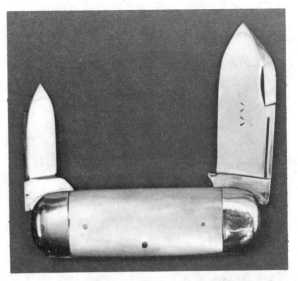

C21050   Ebony (rare stamp)   5⁵⁄₁₆"   Case Bros & Co
Gowanda NY $1200

CASE BROTHERS BRADFORD, PA
8250LP   Genuine Pearl   4"   Case Bros $900

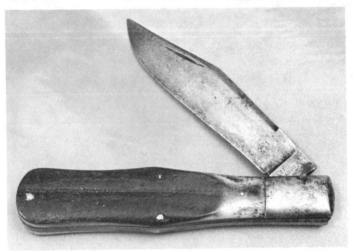

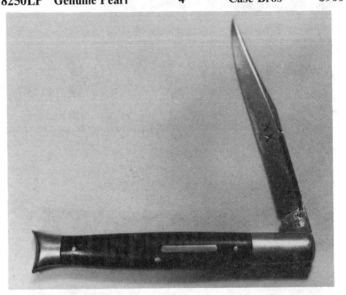

61050   Slab Stag, 1 Bl.   5⅜"   W.R. Case & Sons, $550
Brad. PA

B1051?   Fishtail Stripe Cell.   3⅞"   (arc) Case Bros.
(rare stamp)   Cut. Co. $350

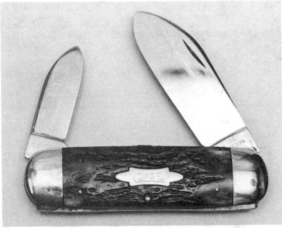

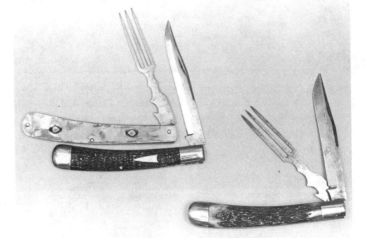

6250   Rogers Bone   4⅜"   Case Bradford, PA $650

CASE BRADFORD, PA   HOBO KNIFE
6251   Green Bone   5¼" $550

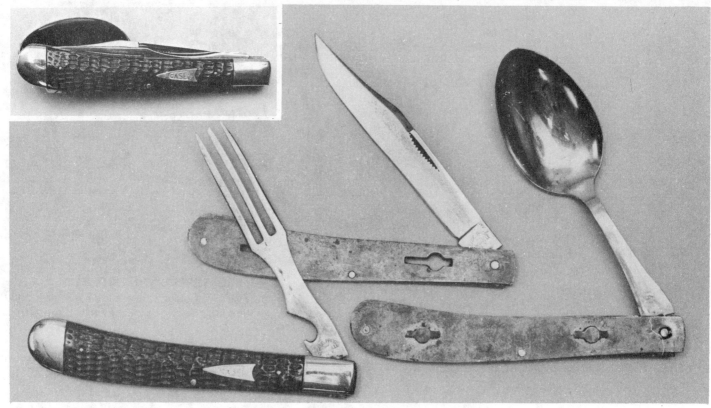

CASE BROS. SPRINGVILLE, NY   HOBO
6351SP   Green Bone, 5¼" Knife Fork & Spoon comes apart $1,000

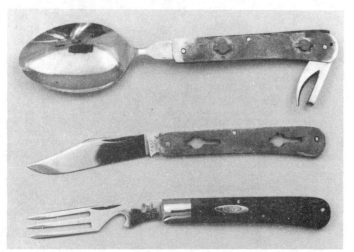

CASE BRADFORD, PA   HOBO
6452   Green Bone 4 blade, comes apart   3¾" $450

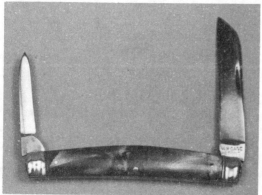

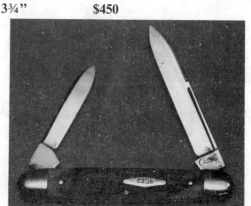

P2052   Pyramite   3⁹⁄₁₆" W.R. Case & Sons $225   5253LP   Gen. Stag   3¼"   Case Tested XX $175

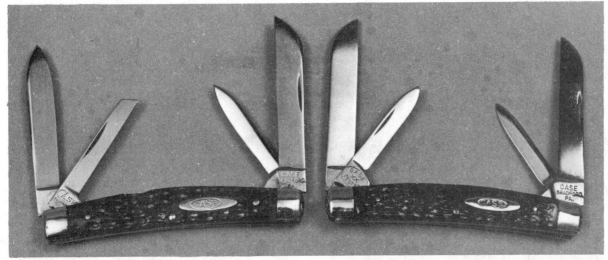

Left: 64052   Green Bone Transition   Master blade, Case Brad. Pa.
Other 3 - Tested XX   **$650**
64052   Green Bone   XX to Tested XX   550

Right: 64052   Green Bone   Tested oval stamp Case Brad. Pa., recessed
bolsters   3½"   **$700**
64052   Rogers Bone   Tested XX $650

CASE BROS. LITTLE VALLEY, NY
5355   Stag   3¾" w/Wharncliffe Blade $700

6154   Bone Proto Knife (Brass Liner Lock)   4¼"
Polished master blade, Case XX, USA Stainless $400

62056   Green Bone   3"   Case Bradford, PA $225

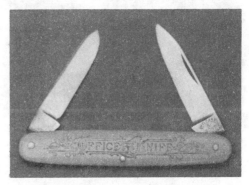

42057 3⁵⁄₁₆"   W.R. Case & Sons, Made in USA
(used around 1900)   Scarce $125

ABBREVIATIONS

½	master blade is clip blade
B	Budding
EO	Easy Opener
F	File
J	Long Spay Blade
K	Corkscrew
LR	Electrician's Knife
M	Metal
PEN	Pen Blade
PU	Punch Blade
R	Bail in handle
RAZ	Razor Blade
SAB	Sabor Blade
SC/SCI	Scissors
SH	Sheepfoot Blade
SP	Spay Blade
SSP	Stainless Steel, Polished Blade Edge
SS	Stainless Steel
T	Tip Bolsters

118   OLDER CASE KNIVES

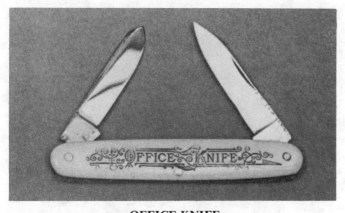

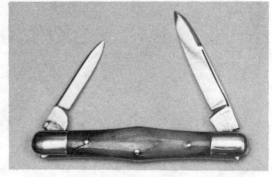

6258   Bone   2⅞"   W.R. Case & Sons
                              Little Valley NY $300
Rare stamp, most are Brad. Pa.)

OFFICE KNIFE
42057   Comp.   3⅜"   W.R. Case & Son $100

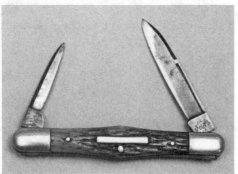
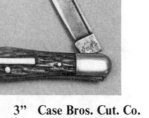

62058   Brown Bone   3"   Case Bros. Cut. Co. $250
                              Rare Stamp

R258F   Candy Strip   2⅞"   Case & Sons
(match striker pull) rare   Brad. Pa. $250

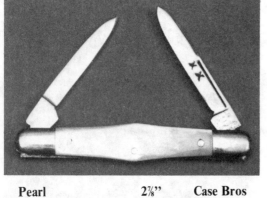

8258   Pearl   2⅞"   Case Bros
                              Springville, NY $250

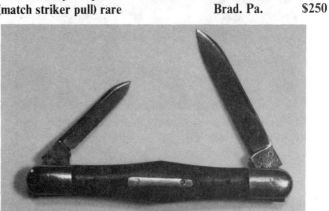

2258   Ebony   2⅞"
Both blades Case Bros. Cut. Co., main blade also XX $200

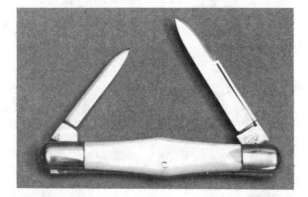

82058   Pearl   2⅞"   Case Bros. Cut Co $225

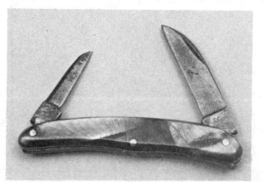

P259   Greenish Swirl - Rare 2¼" W.R. Case & Sons
                              Bradford, Pa $300

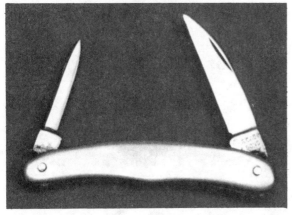

8259   Pearl, Wharncliffe   2¼"   W.R. Case & Sons $225

8361SC   Gold Pearl   2⅞"   W.R. Case & Sons
                                    Germany (rare) $400

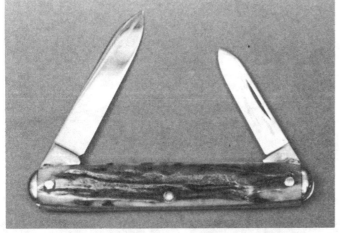

5260T   Stag   W.R. Case & Sons $225

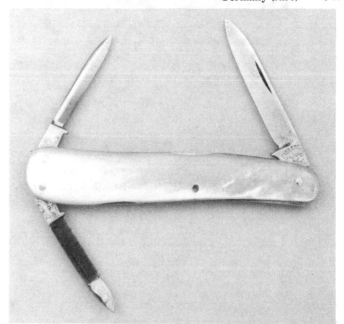

CASE BROTHERS, LITTLE VALLEY, NY
8363   Pearl   3¼" $350

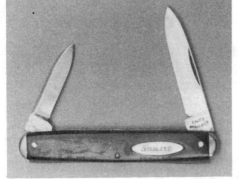

7260T   Red Plastic   3¹⁄₁₆"   Case's Stainless $225
(stainless shield)

83063   3¼"   Case & Sons
                                     Brad. Pa $225

8460   Pearl (1902-1905)   3⁷⁄₁₆"
All blades stamped W.R. Case & Son Bradford, Pa $450

120

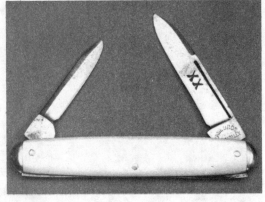

8264   Pearl   3⅛"   Case Bros.
Little Valley, NY $250

63067F   Rogers Bone   3⅞" Case Bradford, PA $300

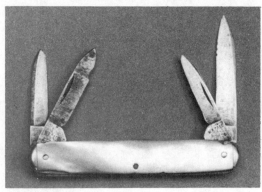

8464F   Pearl   3⅛"   Case & Sons
Bradford, Pa. $450

CONGRESS WHITTLER

6368F   Green Bone   3¼" Case Bradford, PA $600

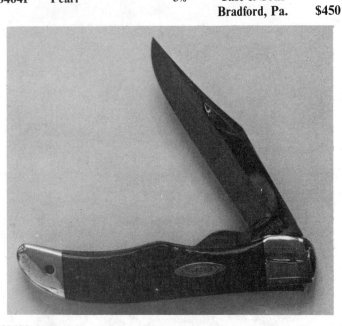

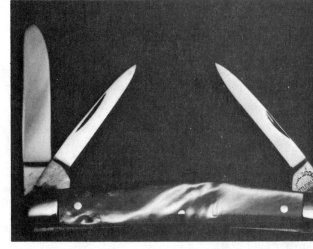

84068   Pearl   3¾" Case Bros., Little
Valley, NY $800

6165Sab. Dr. Proto Knife Wood Scales (Brass Liner Lock)
Case XX, USA $300

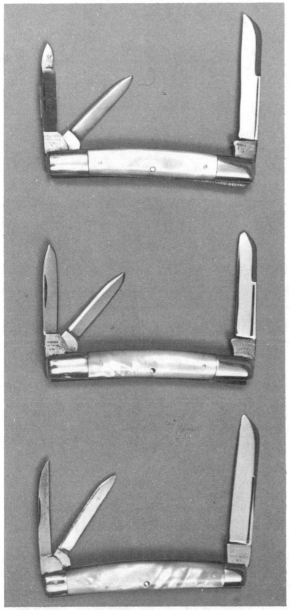

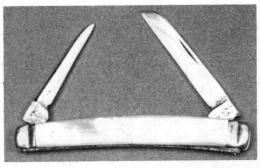

8269   Pearl   3"   W.R. Case & Sons
                                              Brad. Pa. $200

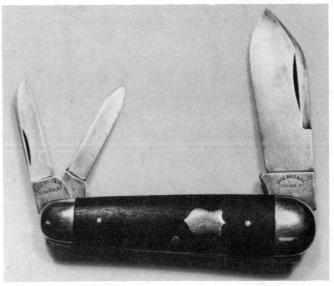

6370   Ebony c. 1896   Tested XX
       Case Bros. & Co., Gowanda, NY $1500

8368 Pearl 3¼"   Top: Case & Sons Bradford Pa $600
Center: Case & Sons Bradford Pa $600
Bottom: Case Bro. Little Valley NY $700

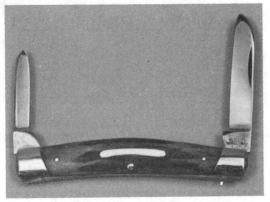

52068   Stag   3¹¹⁄₁₆"   W.R. Case & Son   Ca. 1902-05 $250

ABBREVIATIONS	
½	master blade is clip blade
B	Budding
EO	Easy Opener
F	File
J	Long Spay Blade
K	Corkscrew
LR	Electrician's Knife
M	Metal
PEN	Pen Blade
PU	Punch Blade
R	Bail in handle
RAZ	Razor Blade
SAB	Sabor Blade
SC/SCI	Scissors
SH	Sheepfoot Blade
SP	Spay Blade
SSP	Stainless Steel, Polished Blade Edge
SS	Stainless Steel
T	Tip Bolsters

122

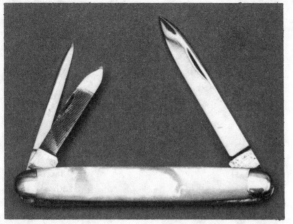

8371   Pearl   3¼" W.R. Case & Sons
                                    Brad. Pa. $500

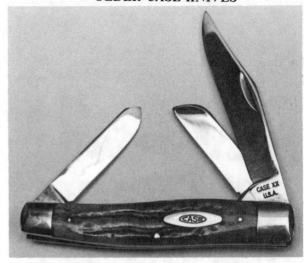

5375   Second Cut Stag   4¼"   Case XX, USA $600
Rare

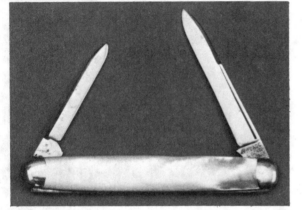

8271LP   Pearl   3¼" W.R. Case & Sons
                                    Brad. Pa. $300

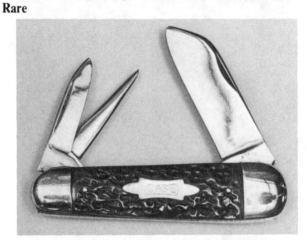

63076PU Green Bone, Rare   4"   W.R.Case & Sons,
                                    Bradford, PA $1800

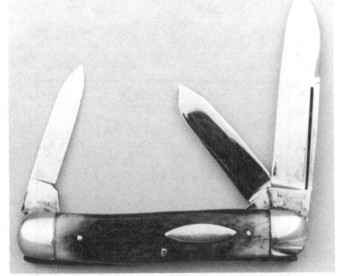

63074LP Rogers Bone   3½" W.R. Case & Sons
                                    Brad., PA $550

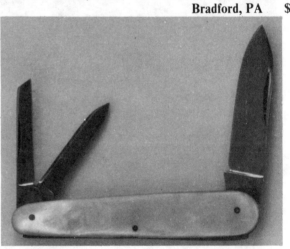

8377   Pearl Shadow   3⅜"   Case Bros.,
                                    Little Valley, NY $350

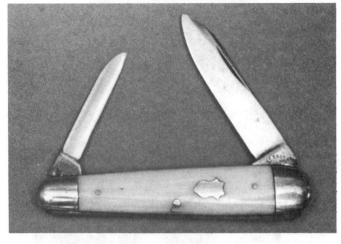

CASE BRO., LITTLE VALLEY, NY
SLEEVEBOARD

| 6278 | White Bone | 3½" | | $250 |

| RM3079 | Celluloid | 3⅛" | Case Mfg. Co. | |
| | | | Little Valley, NY | $225 |

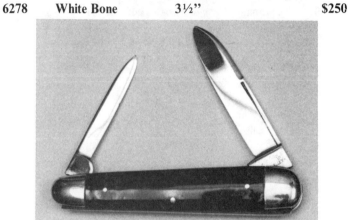

| 7278 | Tortoise | 3¼" | Case Bros. | |
| | | | Little Valley NY | $300 |

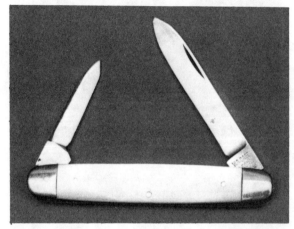

| 8279 | Pearl | 3⅛" | W.R. Case & Sons | |
| | | | Brad. Pa | $200 |

| M279 | Sterling | 3⅛" | Case's Stainless | $150 |

| 62079 | Green Bone SP | 3¼" | Case Tested XX | $150 |

ABBREVIATIONS	
½	master blade is clip blade
B	Budding
EO	Easy Opener
F	File
J	Long Spay Blade
K	Corkscrew
LR.	Electrician's Knife
M	Metal
PEN	Pen Blade
PU	Punch Blade
R	Bail in handle
RAZ	Razor Blade
SAB	Sabor Blade
SC/SCI	Scissors
SH	Sheepfoot Blade
SP	Spay Blade
SSP	Stainless Steel, Polished Blade Edge
SS	Stainless Steel
T	Tip Bolsters

| M279 | Metal (figural) | 3⅛" | Case Bradford, Pa | $250 |

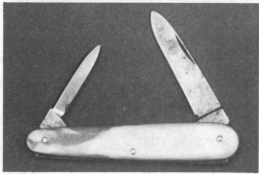

82079 & 62079 Pearl & Bone (salesman's sample) 3¼"
Case Bros. Little Valley, NY $250

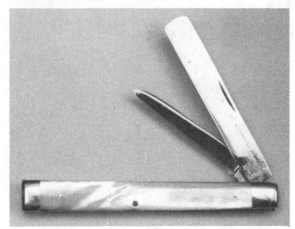

8280   Pearl Dr's Knife   3⅝"   W.R. Case & Son
Brad. Pa. $400

R2082   Candy Stripe Dr's Knife 2⅞"   Kane Cutlery Co.,
Kane, Pa. $250

RM383   Gold Swirl   3½"
All blades stamped Case & Sons Bradford, PA $300

Doctor's Knife
BC283   Green Swirl   2⅞"   W.R. Case & Sons
Brad. Pa. $400

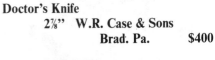

6284SH   Green Bone   3⅛"   Case Bradford, PA $400

OLDER CASE KNIVES

125

W.R. CASE & SONS, BRADFORD, PA

8385   Pearl   3⅝" $600

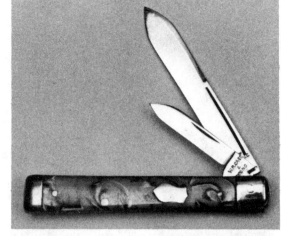

BM2086 Pyralin   3¼" W.R. Case & Sons $400

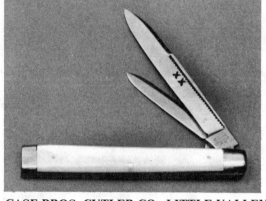

CASE BROS. CUTLER CO., LITTLE VALLEY
DOCTOR'S KNIFE

8285LP Pearl   3¾" $500

M2086   Linoleum Dr.'s Knife 3⅛" W.R. Case & Sons
                                           Brad. Pa. $400

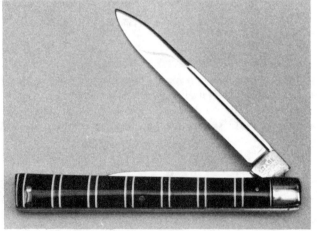

Doctor's Knife

R285   Candy Stripe   3⅝"   Case Brad. Pa. $450

CASE BRADFORD, PA

5387F   Stag Gunstock Whittler 3½" $800

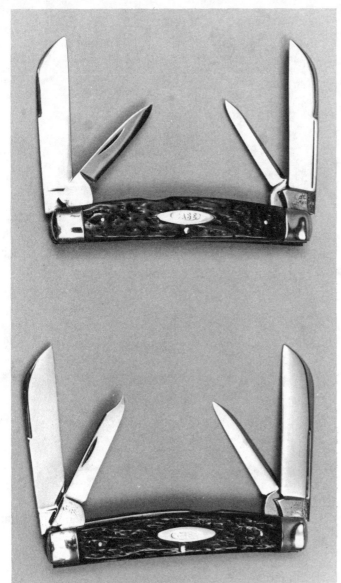

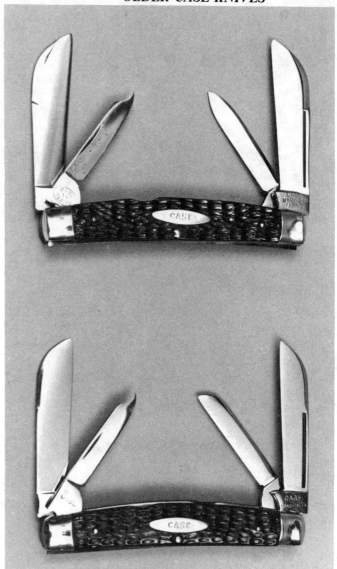

Top: 6488LP Rogers Bone, recessed bolster, center shield Case Bradford, PA   4⅛" $1,000
Bottom: 6488LP Rogers Bone, Recessed bolster, center shield W.R. Case & Sons, Brad. PA. (cuticle blade) $1,000

Top: 6488LP Green Bone, recessed bols. center shield, Case Bradford, PA (cuticle blade) oval stamp on cuticle blade $1,000
Bottom: 6488LP Green Bone, recessed bols., center shield   Case Bradford Pa. Patt. Nr. stamped on cuticle blade $1,000

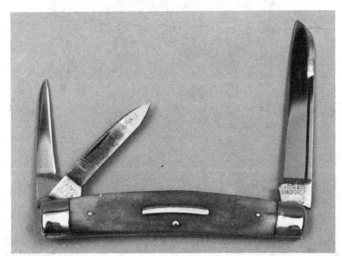

5388FLP Stag Bar Shield, Congress Whittler, recessed bols, W.R. Case & Sons Brad. Pa. 4⅛" $1,500

| 62089 | Green Bone | 3¾" | | $400 |
| 62089 | Green Bone | 3¾" | Tested XX | $400 |

W.R. CASE & SONS, BRAD., PA

6289   Semi-Wharncliffe Congress, Rare   3¾" $650

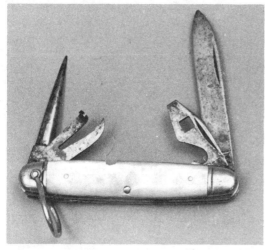

84090?   Gen. Pearl - Rare   3⅜"   Case Tested XX $500
4 Bl. Scout (Jr.), Skate Wrench

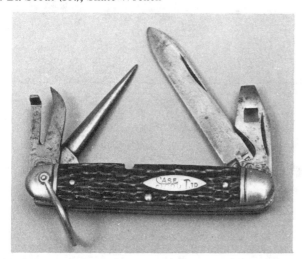

64090? ` Green Bone - Rare   3⅜"   Case Tested XX $400
4 Blade Scout Jr. w/Skate Wrench & Scout Jr. Emblem

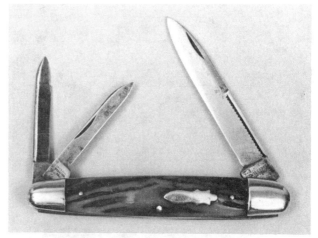

W.R. CASE & SONS, BRADFORD, PA
5391FLP Stag, Rare - 2 Pulls   4½" $1800

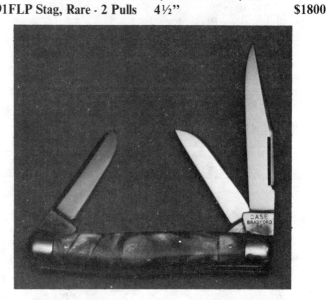

9393   **French Pearl**   3⅞"   **Case Bradford** $350

CASE BRADFORD, PA
6394LP   Rogers Bone Flat Bolsters   4½" $1500

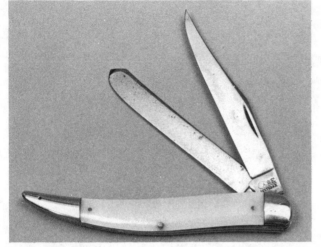

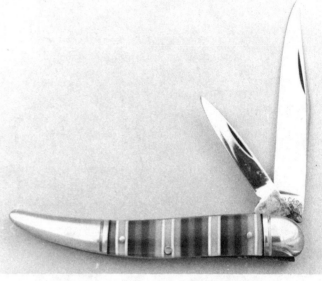

32094   Yellow Scale   4⅜"   Case Tested XX $400
Toothpick, Spey Blade, Rare

R2096   Candy Stripe   3¼"   W.R. Case & Sons $400

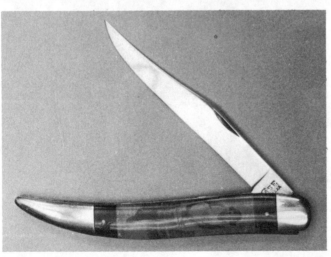

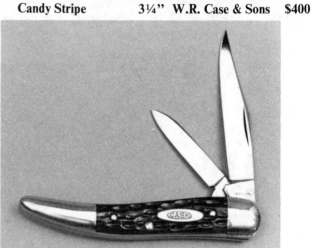

B1095   Christmas Tree rare   5"   Case Tested XX $400

62096   Green Bone T/P   3⅛"   Case Tested XX $400

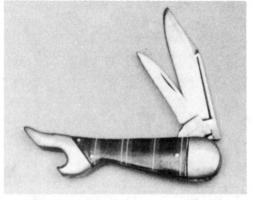

HA1095   High Art Toothpick   5"   Case Tested X $400

R2097   Red Plastic 1920-23   3¼"   Standard Knife Co. $300

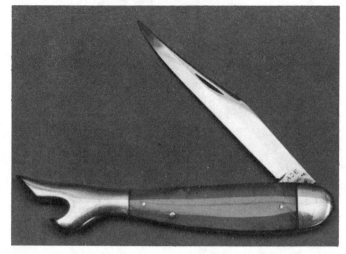

B1097   **SAB Waterfall**   **5"**   **Case, Bradford, Pa.**   **$450**
Leg Knife

62099   **Green Bone**   **4⅛"**   **Case Bradford, PA**   **$300**

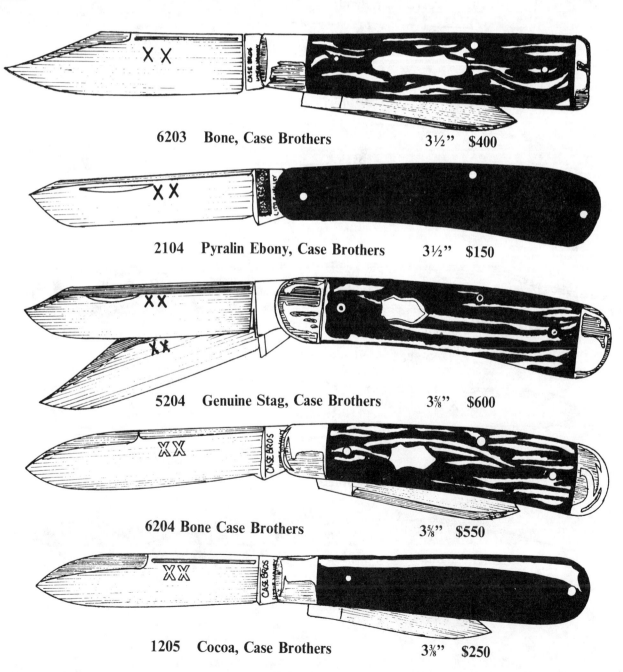

6203   **Bone, Case Brothers**   **3½"**   **$400**

2104   **Pyralin Ebony, Case Brothers**   **3½"**   **$150**

5204   **Genuine Stag, Case Brothers**   **3⅝"**   **$600**

6204 Bone Case Brothers   **3⅝"**   **$550**

1205   **Cocoa, Case Brothers**   **3⅜"**   **$250**

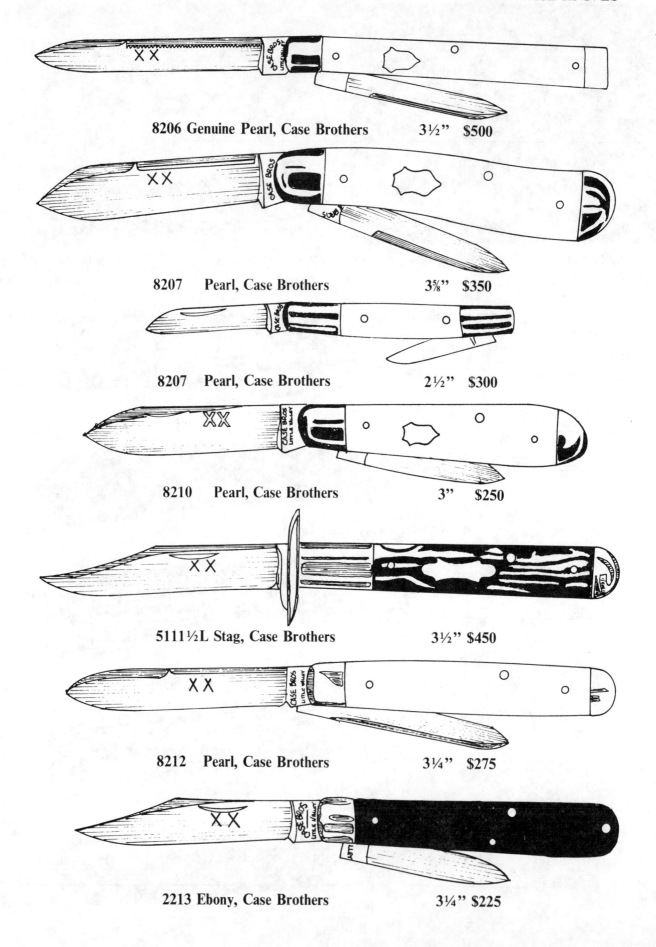

8206 Genuine Pearl, Case Brothers   3½" $500

8207   Pearl, Case Brothers   3⅝" $350

8207   Pearl, Case Brothers   2½" $300

8210   Pearl, Case Brothers   3" $250

5111½L Stag, Case Brothers   3½" $450

8212   Pearl, Case Brothers   3¼" $275

2213 Ebony, Case Brothers   3¼" $225

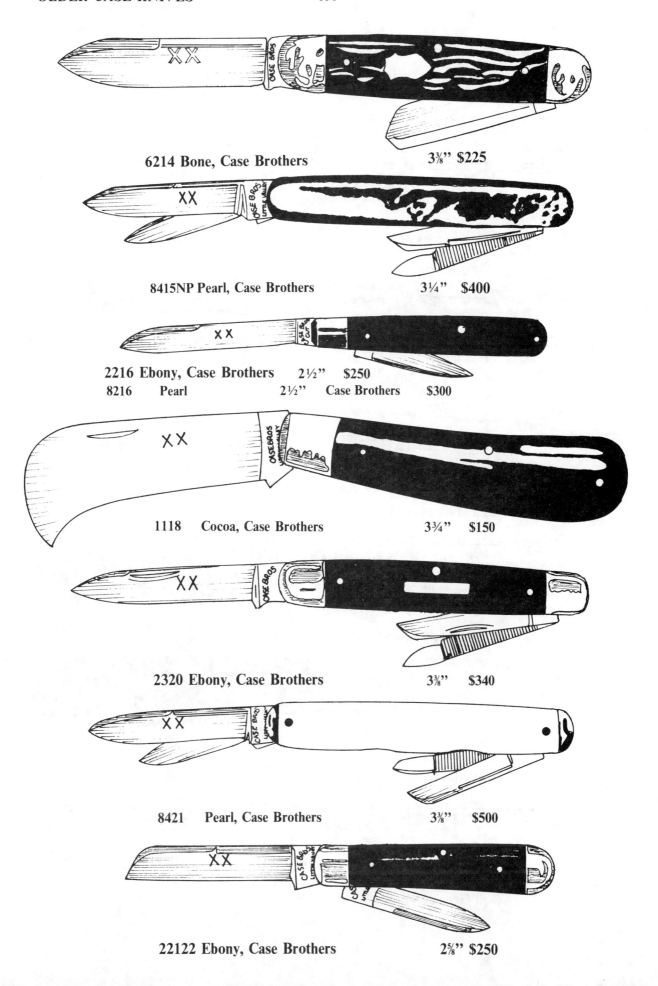

6214 Bone, Case Brothers   3⅜" $225

8415NP Pearl, Case Brothers   3¼" $400

2216 Ebony, Case Brothers   2½" $250
8216   Pearl   2½"   **Case Brothers** $300

1118   Cocoa, Case Brothers   3¾" $150

2320 Ebony, Case Brothers   3⅜" $340

8421   Pearl, Case Brothers   3⅜" $500

22122 Ebony, Case Brothers   2⅝" $250

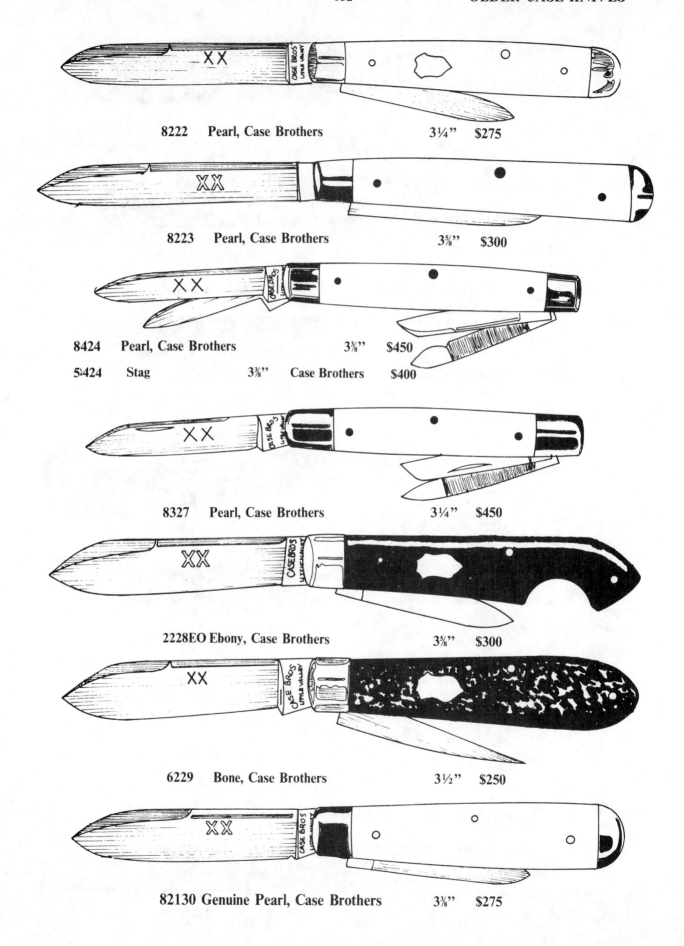

8222   Pearl, Case Brothers   3¼" $275

8223   Pearl, Case Brothers   3⅝" $300

8424   Pearl, Case Brothers   3⅜" $450

5424   Stag   3⅜"   Case Brothers $400

8327   Pearl, Case Brothers   3¼" $450

2228EO Ebony, Case Brothers   3⅝" $300

6229   Bone, Case Brothers   3½" $250

82130 Genuine Pearl, Case Brothers   3⅜" $275

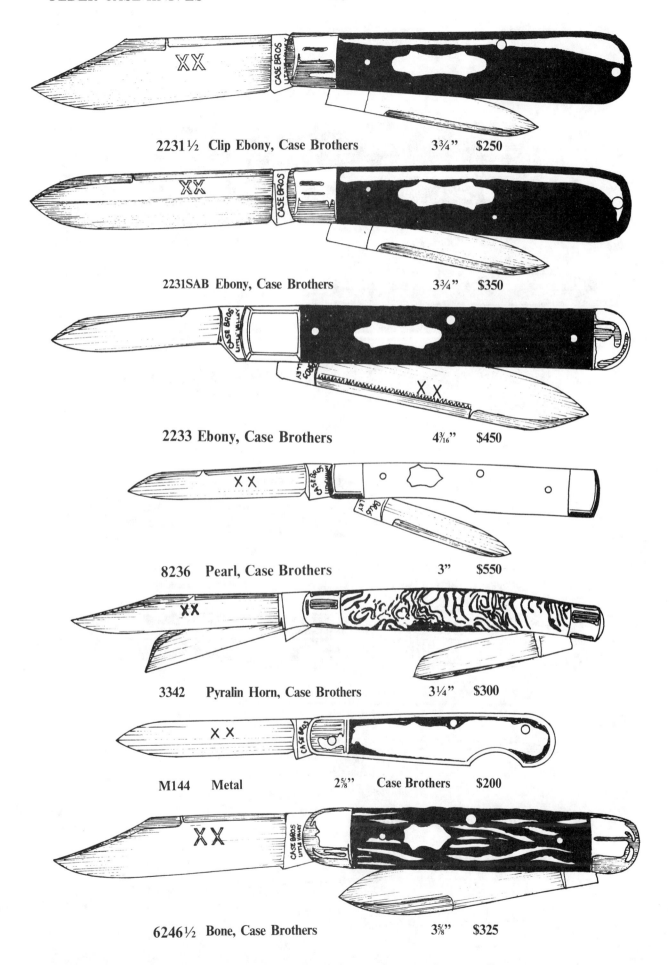

2231½ Clip Ebony, Case Brothers   3¾" $250

2231SAB Ebony, Case Brothers   3¾" $350

2233 Ebony, Case Brothers   4³⁄₁₆" $450

8236   Pearl, Case Brothers   3" $550

3342   Pyralin Horn, Case Brothers   3¼" $300

M144   Metal   2⅝"   **Case Brothers** $200

6246½ Bone, Case Brothers   3⅝" $325

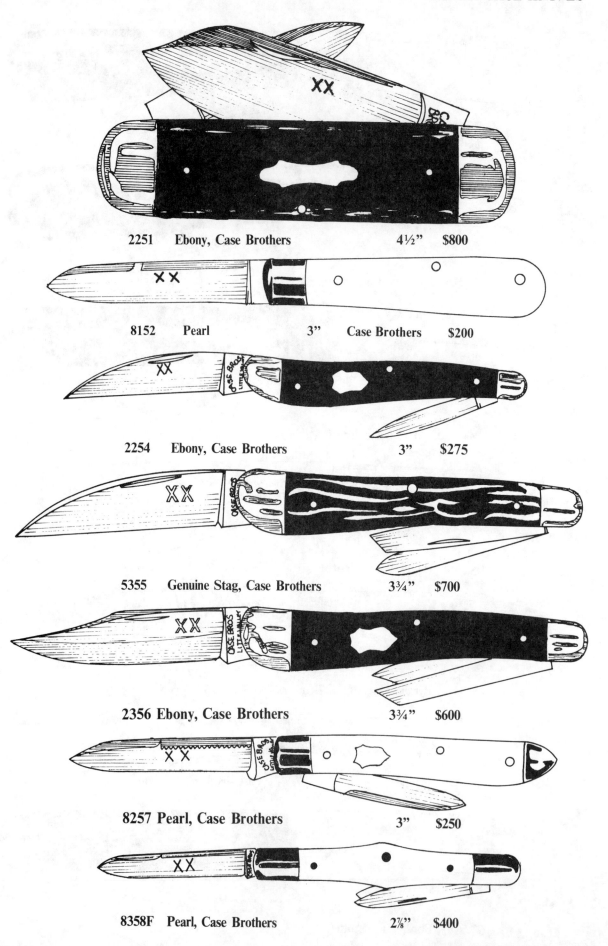

2251   Ebony, Case Brothers   4½" $800

8152   Pearl   3"   **Case Brothers** $200

2254   Ebony, Case Brothers   3" $275

5355   Genuine Stag, Case Brothers   3¾" $700

2356 Ebony, Case Brothers   3¾" $600

8257 Pearl, Case Brothers   3" $250

8358F   Pearl, Case Brothers   2⅞" $400

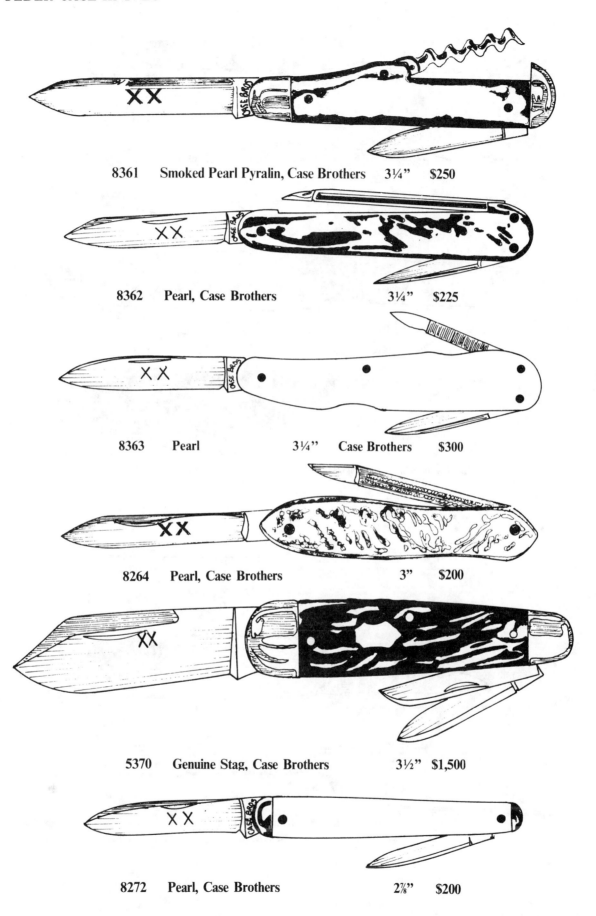

8361   Smoked Pearl Pyralin, Case Brothers   3¼" $250

8362   Pearl, Case Brothers   3¼" $225

8363   Pearl   3¼"   Case Brothers $300

8264   Pearl, Case Brothers   3" $200

5370   Genuine Stag, Case Brothers   3½" $1,500

8272   Pearl, Case Brothers   2⅞" $200

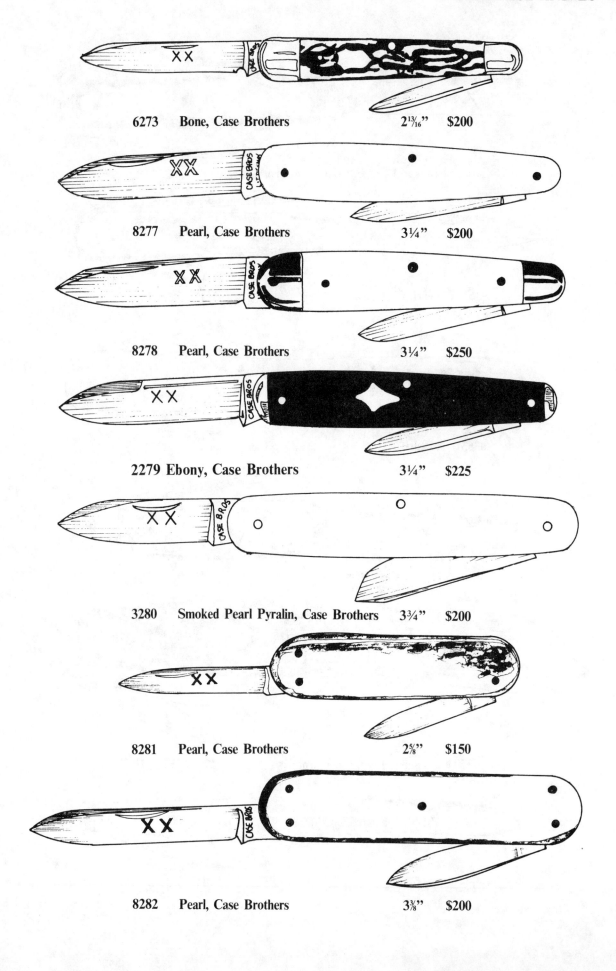

6273   **Bone, Case Brothers**   2¹³⁄₁₆" $200

8277   **Pearl, Case Brothers**   3¼" $200

8278   **Pearl, Case Brothers**   3¼" $250

2279 Ebony, Case Brothers   3¼" $225

3280   **Smoked Pearl Pyralin, Case Brothers** 3¾" $200

8281   **Pearl, Case Brothers**   2⅝" $150

8282   **Pearl, Case Brothers**   3⅜" $200

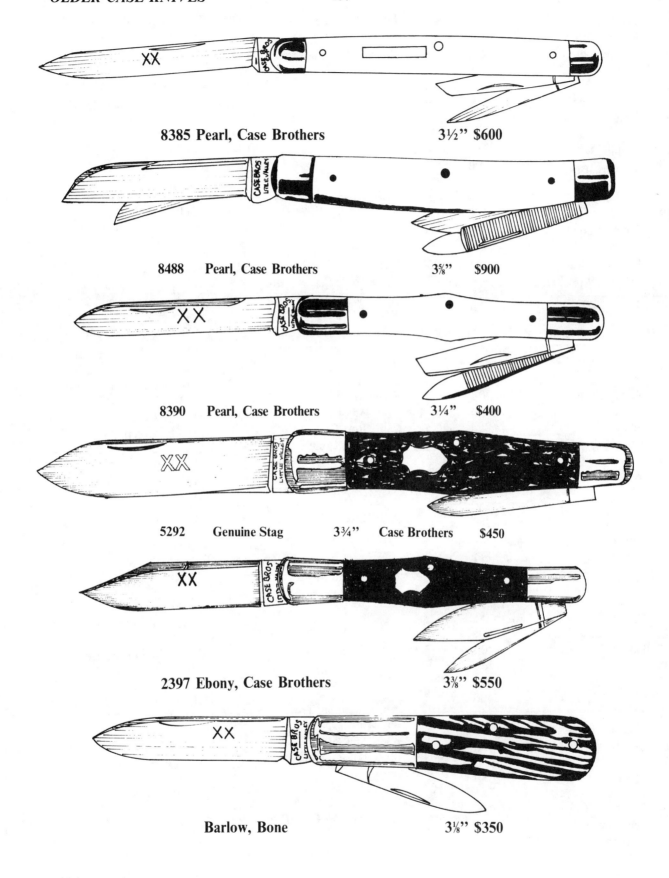

8385 Pearl, Case Brothers   3½" $600

8488   Pearl, Case Brothers   3⅝" $900

8390   Pearl, Case Brothers   3¼" $400

5292   Genuine Stag   3¾"   Case Brothers $450

2397 Ebony, Case Brothers   3⅜" $550

Barlow, Bone   3⅛" $350

Nr.	Handle	Price	Nr.	Handle	Price	Nr.	Handle	Price
6100	Honey Comb	600	B206	Christmas Tree	350	R211½	Candy Stripe	550
3100	Yellow Comb	475	5206	Physicians Case Bros.	400	B1011	Christmas Tree	250
P200	Celluloid	450	5206½		200	3111½		450
5200		500	6106		150	5111 L CP	Case Bros.	600
6200	Green Bone	500	6106	25¢	250	5111½LCP Gen. Stag 3½ Case Bro.		600
9200	Cracked Ice	500	6106	50¢	250	6111	Bone Case Bro.	500
1201	Ebony Wood	200	6206		175	6111½		500
M201	Metal	100	6206½		175	6111½L	W.R. Case & Sons	600
R201T	Candy Stripe	200	62006½		175	6211		500
2201		100	72006		300	6211½		450
3201		90	7206	Tortoise	250	61011	Rogers	225
3201R		100	7106	Tortoise	250	11011	Walnut	125
6001	Green Bone	600	8106	Pearl	275	61011	Green Bone	150
GS001	Goldstone	600	8206		250	1212	Cocoa 3¼ Case Bro.	150
6201	Green Bone	125	8206	Physicians Case Bros.	500	1212L		125
62001	Green Bone	110	1207	Cocoa 3⅜ Case Bro.	200	2212	Ebony 3¼ Case Bro.	225
8201		150	1207 LP	Case Bros.	250	6212	Bone 3¼ Case Bro.	250
72001	Tortoise Shell	200	3207	Yellow Celluloid	350	62012		150
82001		150	5207 LP	Case Bros.	350	7212	Pyralin 3¼ Case Bro.	275
9201		85	5207		350	8212	Spear Case Bros.	275
9201R		100	5307	Whittler	450	1213	Clip — Case Bros.	300
P202		150	6207	Green Bone	325	2213	Clip — Case Bros.	225
R202	Candy Stripe	200	6207	Rogers Bone	350	61013	Green Bone	225
1202	D&B	400	6207 LP	Case Bros.	300	61013	Rogers Bone	250
1502	Scout	250	6207	Case Bros. Congress	250	6213	Rogers Bone	700
B3102	Christmas Tree	200	8207	Case Bros. Congress	300	6213	Green Bone	400
5202		200	8407		750	6213	Clip — Case Bros.	400
5202	RAZ	375	2208	Ebony 3⅜ Case Bro.	300	5214		225
5202½		200	2308		275	5214½		225
6202	Green Bone	150	3308		275	6214		300
6202	SH R Rogers Bone WWI	200	5208	Case Bros.	450	6214½		225
6202½	Green Bone	150	5308		300	6214 LP	Spay Case Bros.	225
63102	Green Bone	175	6308		275	7214 LP	Spay Case Bros.	250
83102		200	6208	Bone 3⅜ Case Bro.	300	P215	Gunstock	550
1203 CP	Cocoa 3½ Case Bro.	350	6208		150	6215	Gunstock	550
1503	Jr. Scout	250	8308		400	8215	Gunstock	650
2203 CP	Ebony 3½ Case Bro.	400	6209		175	1215		550
5203 LP CP	Case Bros.	400	62009		200	8315 F	Pearl 3¼ Case Bro.	400
5203SP	Budding W.R. Case	400	62009 RAZ		250	8315 NP	Pearl 3¼ Case Bro.	400
6103 B&G		150	62009	Sheepfoot	250	8415	Shad Case Bros.	400
6203		400	62009	Spay	200	22016		140
6203 LP CP	Case Bros.	400	62009½		175	22016½		140
M204	Metal	140	B3109	Wh. Christmas Tree	550	6116		150
1204	Cocoa 3⅜ Case Bro.	150	63109	Wh. 3 Backsprings	400	6116½		200
5204 CP SP		600	83109	Wh. 3 Backsprings	500	61016½		110
6104B		250	92009	Onyx Bolster Stamped	250	6216		150
6204	Bone 3⅜ Case Bro.	550	92009½	Onyx	250	6216 EO		225
6204½		225	2210	Ebony 3⅜ Case Bro.	225	62016		125
1205	Spear Case Bros.	250	3210½		175	6216	Spear Case Bros.	225
2205	Spear Case Bros.	300	5210	Genuine Stag 3⅜ Case Bro.	300	62016½		125
3205	Pyralin 3⅜ Case Bro.	325	5210½		225	62016S		125
5205	Spear Case Bros.	350	6210		210	6216½		150
5205		325	6210S		225	7216	Spear Case Bros.	275
5205 RAZ		350	62010		200	8116	Pearl 2½ Case Bro.	200
6205		325	6210½		200	8116 F	Pearl 2½ Case Bro.	250
6205 RAZ		350	7210	Pyralin 3⅜ Case Bro.	350	8216	Spear Case Bros.	250
6205	Spear Case Bros.	325	8210	Pearl 3⅜ Case Bro.	250	2217		250
6205½		325	R111½	Candy Stripe	550	6217		200
7205	Pyralin 3⅜ Case Bro.	400	R211	Candy Stripe	550	B318 SH SP	Christmas Tree	400
						1118	Case Bros.	150

Nr.	Handle			Price
3318 SH SP				150
3318 SH PEN				150
5318 SH SP				300
6318 SH SP				160
6318 SP P				175
6318 SH PEN				160
8318 SH SP				350
9318 SH PEN	Onyx			250
9318 SH SP	Onyx			250
1119	Cotton Sampler Case Bros.			400
6219				300
62019				350
Y220				350
B220	Christmas Tree			400
2420	Case Mfg. Co.			200
3220				225
5220				300
5320	Whittler Case Bros.			325
6220				275
6220 SAB Long Pull				350
62020				225
62020S				225
62020½				225
2320				340
6320	Bone	3⅜ Case Bro.		400
7220	Shell	3⅜ Case Bro.		250
7320	Whittler Case Bros.			350
8220	Pearl	3⅜ Case Bro.		250
8220	(Not Peanut Pattern)			350
8220	Pearl Peanut			400
8320	Whittler Case Bros.			350
9220				250
B221	Waterfall			300
B221	Christmas Tree			325
5421	Case Bros.			450
6221	Rogers Bone			250
06221				200
06221½				200
6321				300
7421	Case Bros.			500
08221				275
8221	Pearl	3⅜ Case Bro.		250
8221 NP	Pearl	3⅜ Case Bro.		250
8321	Pearl	3⅜ Case Bro.		400
8321NP	Pearl	3⅜ Case Bro.		400
8421	Case Bros.			500
GS222	Gold Stone Phy.			450
2222	Ebony	3¼ Case Bro.		225
22122	Ebony	2⅝ Case Bro.		250
5222	Genuine Stag	3¼ Case Bro.		250
6222				175
6222	Bone	3¼ Case Bro.		250
62122 SH	Bone	2⅝ Case Bro.		300
62122	Bone	2⅝ Case Bro.		275
7222	Shell	3¼ Case Bro.		275
8222				275
P223				225
2223	Ebony	3⅜ Case Bro.		225

Nr.	Handle		Price
5223 LP	Spear Case Bros.		250
6223 LP	Spear Case Bros.		225
6223			200
8223 LP	Spear Case Bros.		350
9223			200
B224	Christmas Tree		250
P3024	Wh. Rare Gold Swirl		500
3124			125
3124½			125
3224			125
3224½			125
5224			200
52024			200
5224½			200
52024½			200
5424	Case Bros.		400
6124			125
6124½			125
6224			125
62024			125
62024 RAZ			250
62024	Sheepfoot		225
62024½			125
8224			300
8424	Case Bros.		450
32025½			225
5225½			250
6225			250
6225½			225
62025½			200
8225			300
B226	Christmas Tree		250
4226	Spear, Smooth White		200
6226			175
62026			125
6226½			175
82026			225
62027			125
62027½			125
7327	Whittler Case Bros.		450
8227			250
82027			200
B2027	Christmas Tree		250
8327	Whittler Case Bros.		450
92027			125
92027½			125
P228 EO			250
1228 EO	Walnut		200
2228			175
2228 EO			300
2228 PU			250
61028	W.R. Case		275
6228			190
6228 EO			250
6228 PU			200
62028			250
82028			300
820028			350
1229	Spear-Punch Case Bros.		225
5229½			200

Nr.	Handle			Price
6229	Spear-Punch Case Bros.			250
6229½				150
7229½	Tortoise			225
9229½				150
P0230				175
02230				200
02230½				200
05230½				225
06230				250
06230½				225
08230				300
09230				225
09230½				225
6230 SH				200
12130	Cocoa	3⅜ Case Bro.		225
22130	Ebony	3⅜ Case Bro.		225
62130				225
82130	Case Bros.			275
1131 SH				90
1231CP	Cocoa	3¾ Case Bro.		175
2231 SAB	Spear-Case Bros.			350
2231½	Case Bros.			250
2231				135
22031				140
2231½	Case Bros.			250
2231½SAB	Case Bros.			350
22031½				140
52031				250
52031½				300
52031½ SAB				350
52131LP				450
53131				1,000
53131	Punch			1,200
5231	Case Bros.			325
6231				165
62031				165
6231½				200
62031½				200
62031½ SAB				200
G232				225
3232				175
5332				250
6232				140
6332				200
B233 LP	Christmas Tree			300
GS233 LP	Gold Stone			300
2233				450
3233				150
6233	Case Bros.			450
6233				175
62033				165
6333				125
6333 LP				140
8233				225
9233 LP				150
9333				110
9333 LP				120
G234	Dr. Knife			450
5234	Dr. Knife			350
6234SH				400

Nr.	Handle	Price	Nr.	Handle	Price	Nr.	Handle	Price
G2035		225	3344 SH SP		135	3247J		400
3235½		150	5244		140	3347 SH SP LP		200
42035½ LP		250	05244		140	3347 SH PEN		175
5235½		175	5344 SH SP		250	04247 SP		200
6235		125	6244		125	43047		250
6235 EO		200	06244		125	5247J		700
62035		140	62044		110	05247 SP		225
6235½		135	62044F		135	5347 SH PEN		225
62035½	Green Bone	200	6344 SH SP		150	53047		225
62035½	Rogers Bone	250	6344 SH PEN		150	5447 SH SP		450
8236	Gunstock	550	8244		200	5447 SP PU		450
6236	Gunstock Case Bros.	500	82044		200	6247J		500
2237		200	82044F		200	06247 PEN		125
2237½		200	08244		200	06247 SP		135
6237	Long Pull	350	8344		250	6347 SH PEN		200
6237½		275	9144 E O	Case Bros.	150	6347 SH PU		200
5238		200	9244		125	6347 PU PEN		225
GS3038		350	9344 SH PEN		135	6347 LP W.H. Case Rogers Bone		300
5438		700	S445R	Sterling Silver Figural	500	6347 PU J		600
8438		700	02245		200	6347 SH SP		200
B239	Waterfall Sow Belly	350	02245½		200	63047		250
G2039	Gold Swirl	300	02245 Ebony	Case Bro.	225	630047		225
B339	Onyx Sow Belly	350	2345 Ebony	Case Bro.	300	630047 PU		225
62039 Rogers Bone Case Brad, Pa		250	2345½		250	64047 PU		325
G3039	Gold Swirl	350	04245 B&G		250	64047 PU Rogers Bone		425
1139		200	05245		225	8347 SH SP		400
6239		225	05245½		225	83047		400
6339		500	5345		400	9347 SH SP CI		250
63039		300	5345 PU		400	9347 SH SP Onyx		275
6539	5 Blade	2,500	5345½		350	9347 PJ		400
11040		150	06245		200	93047		250
3240 SP		450	08245 Case & Sons		250	94047 PU		325
6240		450	06245½		200	P348	Green Swirl	600
6240 SP		500	06245 Bone	Case Bro.	250	B1048	Christmas Tree	300
9240 SP		500	6345 SH	Case Bro.	325	G1048		275
6241	Winterbottom	250	6345		300	R1048		225
6241	Rogers Bone	250	6345 Pliers		800	B1048	Onyx	175
B242	Christmas Tree	225	6345 PU		325	B2048	Christmas Tree	325
B3042 F. Wh. Christmas Tree		350	6345½		300	B2048 SP Christmas Tree		350
3342	Case Bros.	300	6345½ PU		325	G2048		250
5342	Case Bros.	300	6445R		250	G2048S		250
52042		150	640045R		125	R2048		300
05242		200	6445R	Scout Shield	300	R2048 SP Candy Stripe		300
6242		125	G2046		200	61048		175
62042	Rogers Bone	150	B346PU Onyx		300	62048 SP		200
6342	Case Bros.	300	2246 Ebony	3⅝ Case Bro.	300	B249	Onyx	300
63042	Wh. Green Bone	300	G3046		450	BM249	Mottled	325
82042		200	3246		200	R1049L	Candy Stripe	450
63042	Case Brad., Pa	300	6246	Case Bros.	350	R2049	Candy Stripe	350
83042	Wh. Pearl	350	6246	W. R. Case & Sons, Brad, Pa	350	61049		250
93042	Wh. Onyx	325	6246½		325	61049L		325
92042		95	62046		200	6249		300
5343		700	6346	Whittler	650	62049		250
6143		200	6346	Punch Rogers Bone	700	B10050	Flat Blade Christmas Tree	900
M144		200	6346½	W. R. Case Whittler	600	CB1050 SAB Christmas Tree		900
B244	Christmas Tree	225	63046		300	C31050 SAB		650
B344 SH SP		300	P347 SH SP		250	C51050 SAB		900
M344 Sh SP Metal		150	B3047	Christmas Tree	400	610050	Flat	650
3244		110	P3047		250	61050	Flat	550

Nr.	Handle	Price
C61050	Flat Blade, Switch Blade, "Zipper" Release	2,500
C61050	Flat	650
C61050	SAB	550
C61050	SAB Lock Blade	2,000
C91050	SAB	650
M250	Nickel Silver	600
5250	Case Bros.	900
6250	Bone Case Bro.	700
6250		550
7250	Case Bros.	1,000
8250		900
R251	Candy Stripe	800
B1051	Christmas Tree	300
G1051		250
R1051	Candy Stripe	250
R1051	Lock Back Candy Stripe	375
2251	Sunfish-Ebony Case Bros.	800
31051	L	300
5251	Sunfish Case Bros.	1,000
6151		550
6151	Lock Back	650
61051		250
61051	Rogers Bone	300
61051	Lock Back	350
6251		550
6351	Springville	1,000
8151L		1,200
81051		325
8251	Knife-Fork Comb (Pearl)	1,200
9151	Onyx	650
8152		200
P2052		225
3252	Knife-Fork Comb	350
32052		200
3452		400
52052		225
6252	Knife-Fork Comb	350
62052		150
63052	Wh.	550
6452		450
64052		700
84052	Case Bros.	900
G253	Shad	150
HA253		225
5253		150
6253		125
62053		150
6353		200
6353 PU		200
8253		175
82053	Bolsters	200
82053SR		125
9253		110
2254		175
5254	Genuine Stag 3 Case Bro.	250
5354	Genuine Stag 3 Case Bro.	350
6254	Bone 3 Case Bro.	250
6254	Wharncliffe (Not Trapper)	225
6354	Bone 3 Case Bro.	350

Nr.	Handle	Price
8254	Pearl 3 Case Bro.	300
P254		300
82054	Lobster	225
P254	Lobster W.R. Case	150
8354	Pearl 3 Case Bro.	400
22055		200
23055		450
23055 PU		450
32055		200
5355	Whittler-Wharncliffe Case Bros.	700
6255	Bone 3¾ Case Bro.	400
62055		165
6355	Whittler-Wharncliffe Case Bros.	600
63055		450
64055 PU		550
82055		325
8355	Whittler-Wharncliffe Case Bros.	700
92055		200
62056	Swell Ctr.	200
62056	Swell Ctr. Rogers Bone	250
2356		600
6356	SAB Whittler Case Bros.	500
63056	Whittler	350
8256	Pearl 3¾ Case Bro.	400
82056		200
8356	SAB Whittler Case Bros.	500
83056		275
4257		100
42057		100
5257	LP Case Bros.	225
6257	LP Case Bros.	225
7257	Pyralin 3 Case Bro.	250
8257		250
92057		100
2258	Case Bros. Cut. Co.	200
32058		100
5358	Genuine Stag 2⅞ Case Bro.	400
6258	Case Mfg.	275
6358	Bone 2⅞ Case Bro.	350
7258	Shell 2⅞ Case Bro.	250
7358	Shell 2⅞ Case Bro.	400
8258		250
8358	Whittler Case Bros.	400
92058		110
P259		300
62059		125
62059	SP	110
8259		225
5260		225
5260	Red Stag	300
8460	W.R. Case & Son	450
3361	K Case Bros.	250
5161L	Springer	900
5161L	Flat Blade	950
5361K	Case Bros.	250
6161L	Springer	900
8261		150

Nr.	Handle	Price
8361K	Case Bros.	400
1162	LP Case Bros.	100
Y4062	K Shad	300
82062K		200
8362	Lobster Case Bros.	225
83062K		300
84062K		400
94062K		325
P263		165
B2063	Christmas Tree	250
B3063	Christmas Tree	250
05263	Non. Stainless	150
62063	Non. Stainless	125
06263	Non. Stainless	125
62063½	Non. Stainless	125
63063		350
08263		200
8363		300
82063½		200
83063		225
92063½		125
3264	Pyralin 3 Case Bro.	150
6264		125
6264F		150
62064		125
8264	Lobster Case Bros.	200
8264T		250
8264T	File	250
82064		200
9264T	File	200
8464F		450
B165	Flat Christmas Tree	1,000
G265		600
3165	SAB	500
3165	Flat	500
3265	SAB	450
5165	SAB	325
5165	Flat	400
5265	SAB	325
5265	Flat	425
6165	SAB	300
6165	Flat	350
6265	SAB	350
6265	Flat	400
8165	Flat	1,800
8265	Flat	1,800
9165	SAB	500
9165	Flat	500
9265	SAB	500
9265	Flat	500
6166	L Switchblade	4,000
6366		250
6366	PEN	250
8366	PEN Pearl	300
B3067	Christmas Tree	350
62067		140
06267		150
6367		200
63067F	wh	300
82067		200

Nr.	Handle	Price	Nr.	Handle	Price	Nr.	Handle	Price
08267		200	4277		150	63083	Lobster	200
8367		250	7277	Shell 3¼ Case Bro.	225	8383	Whittler	500
83067		250	8277		200	83083	Lobster	200
9367		200	8377	Pearl 3¼ Case Bro.	350	9383	Whittler	350
52068	Slant Bols. Congress	250	1278	Cocoa 3¼ Case Bro.	200	B285	Phy. Waterfall Spatula Bl.	500
6268	Slant Bols. Congress	200	2278	Case Bros.	250	B285	Christmas Tree	500
6368	Wh. Congress	600	2378	Ebony 3¼ Case Bro.	275	G285	(Phy's)	450
8268	Slant Bols. Congress	250	5278	Case Bros.	225	R285	Candy Stripe Phy.	450
8368	Whittler-Pearl	600	5378	Genuine Stag 3¼ Case Bro.	325	B385	Whittler	600
84068	Case Bros.	800	6278T		200	3185	(Phy's)	200
54068	W.R. Case	600	6278	Case Bros.	250	3285	(Phy's)	300
G2069		175	7278	Case Bros. T-Shell	300	3385	Pyralin 3½ Case Bro.	450
6269		125	7378	Shell 3¼ Case Bro.	325	5385	Whittler	500
6369		250	8278	Case Bros.	250	6185	(Phy's)	200
8269		200	8378	Pearl 3¼ Case Bro.	325	6285	(Phy's)	300
8369		400	2279		225	6385	Whittler	500
9269		125	GM279		125	8285	(Phy's)	500
2370	Ebony 3½ Case Bro.	1200	M279R		150	8385	Whittler	600
5370	Sleeveboard Whittler	1,500	B3079	Wh. Christmas Tree	550	B2086	Christmas Tree	400
6370	Rogers Bone	1,500	RM3079	Case Mfg. Co.	225	G2086	Gold Stone	400
6370F		350	3279		125	B2086	Christmas Tree Phy.	400
6470F		400	3279R		125	G2086	Gold Stone Phy.	400
8370F		450	5279		140	M2086	Phy's.	400
5171L	Springer	1,200	6279	Green Bone	140	52086	(Phy's)	400
8271		300	6279	Rogers Bone	200	62086	(Phy's)	325
8371	Wh.	500	62079		175	82086	(Phy's)	400
5172L	Zipper Switchblade	3,500	62079½		175	5287	Gunstock	500
6172L	"Zipper" Switchblade	4,500	63079	Wh.	350	5387	Gunstock Whittler	800
5172	Case Brad. Pa.	1,500	63079½	F Wh.	375	8387	Gunstock-Pearl	1,000
6172	Clasp	1,100	7279	Pyralin 3¼ Case Bro.	250	5488 F	Case Bros.	1,000
6272	Bone 2⅞ Case Bro.	200	8279	Pearl 3¼ Case Bro.	250	5488		1,000
8272	Case Bros.	200	8279		200	6288	Congress	300
6273	Case Bros.	200	8279S		200	6288	Bone 3⅝ Case Bro.	350
8273	Case Bros.	200	82079		200	6388	Bone 3⅝ Case Bro.	750
22074½	PU	225	82079½		175	6388	Whittler	1,500
B3074	Christmas Tree	400	83079	Wh.	400	5388		1,500
B3074½	Christmas Tree	400	92079½		130	6488	LP	1,000
B3074½	PU Christmas Tree	400	P280	Phy's. Knife	300	7488 F	Case Bros.	1,200
5374		350	2280	Case Bros. Phy.	275	83088	Lobster	200
62074½		250	3280	Case Bros. Phy.	300	8488 F	Case Bros.	1,000
63074	Rogers Bone	550	4280	Wh. Pyralin 3¾ Case Bro.	275	6289	Wharncliffe Congress	650
63074½		325	6280	Phy.	350	62089	W.R. Case & Sons Congress	400
63074½	PU	325	7280	Shell Pyralin 3¾ Case Bro.	850	83089		200
83074		400	8280	Phy.	400	8389	Covered Back Springs	350
G375		400	G281		175	84089	SCIS F (Bradford, Germany)	250
5275 SP	Stag	500	6281		140	B490R	Christmas Tree	350
5375		350	64081	Lobster	250	M2090R		125
6275 SP	Rogers	450	8281	Lobster Case Bros.	150	2290	Ebony 3¼ Case Bro.	225
06275½		300	83081	Lobster	200	6290	Bone 3¼ Case Bro.	250
6375		325	84081	Lobster	250	6390	Bone 3¼ Case Bro.	350
2376½		400	9281		130	63090	Whittler	500
5376½		450	6282	(Phy's) Green Bone	350	6490R		225
6276½		200	8282	Lobster Case Bros.	200	640090R		150
06276		225	8282	(Phy's) Pearl	400	8290	Genuine Stag 3¾ Case Bro.	300
06276½		225	BC283	Phy.	400	8390		400
6376		400	P383	Whittler	450	83090	Scis.	225
6376½		400	2383	Whittler	350	Y3091 F		225
63076	Whittler (Rare) lrg. Sleeveboard	1,800	5383	Whittler	425	GM3091		175
			6383	Whittler	400	GM3091R		175
			6383 SAB	Whittler	450	5391	Whittler	1,600
						5391	Whittler (2 pulls) File	1,800

Nr.	Handle		Price
82091 F			200
83091			200
2392	Ebony	3¾ Case Bro.	400
3292			225
33092			225
5292			225
5392	Genuine Stag 3¾ Case Bro.		450
6292			200
6592 (5 Blade)			1,600
5292 Case Bros. ½ Whittler			400
6292 Case Bros. ½ Whittler			400
2292 Case Bros. ½ Whittler			350
6392	Bone	3¾ Case Bro.	450
6392			225
6392 PU			250
630092			225
630092 PU			250
6392½ Whittler			800
B1093 Christmas Tree			325
B1093 Barn Door Hinge			400
G1093			300
R1093 Candy Stripe			300
HA1093 High Art			350
61093			250
32093F			175
5293 LP			225
6293			125
62093 F			200
B393 Christmas Tree			400
H393 Mottled			350
4393			300
5393			300
6393			300
6393R			300
6393 PEN			300
9393			350
93093			250
05294			325
GS1094 Goldstone			350
61094 T/P Rogers Bone			350
R1094 T/P Candy Stripe			350
6294 LP			350
6294 LP Roger Bone			500
6294 LP Flat Bols. Rogers B			1,500
6294J			900
5394 Gun Boat			1,200
6394 Gun Boat			1,200
6394 Rogers Bone			1,200
B1095 Christmas Tree			350
B1095 Water Fall			350
GS1095SAB			350
G1095			300
HA1095 High Art			400
R1095 Candy Stripe			400
31095			250
61095			250
61095 Rogers Bone			325
B2095F			225
32095F			175
5395			650
R2096 Candy Stripe			400
6296			400
B396			350
6396			350

Nr.	Handle	Price
B1097 Christmas Tree Leg Knife (Large Size)		550
G1097 Imitation Agate Leg Knife (Large Size)		450
GS1097 Gold Stone Leg Knife (Large Size)		450
R1097 Candy Stripe Leg Knife (Large Size)		450
P297 Celluloid Leg Knife (Small Size)		375
R297 Candy Stripe Leg Knife (Small Size)		375
3297 Yellow Leg Knife (Small Size)		325
8297 Pearl Leg Knife (Small Size)		400
2397 Whittler Case Bros.		550
8397 Whittler Case Bros.		700
5397 Whittler Case Bros.		700
6397 Whittler Case Bros.		650
61098		300
32098F		200
62098F		250
6199		175
GM2099R		150
3299		250
3299½		200
5299½		275
6299		275
6299½		300
62099		300
82099R		200
31100		500
61100		600
62100		600
82101R		175
92101R		125
83101	W.R.Case & Sons 2¼	200
M3102R		100
83102R		150
31113		325
61113		350
32113		375
62113		425
62122 Case Bros.		225
Muskrat		650
Fly Fisherman		250
1502 Scout		250
1503 Jr. Scout		250

CASE XX U.S.A. (9 DOT) 1971
ONE BLADE

4100 SS	"Melon Tester"	35
11011	"Hawk Bill"	20
61011	"Hawk Bill" Wood Handle	15
6111½L	"Lock Back"	45
1116SP	"Budding Knife"	30
11031SH		20
2137	"Sod Buster Jr."	20
2137SS	"Sod Buster Jr."	20
2138	"Sod Buster"	20
2138SS	"Sod Buster"	20
2138LSS	"Sod Buster" Blade Locks Open	25
6143	"Daddy Barlow" Delrin	25
6143	Bone	30
31048		15
31048SP		30
61048	Delrin	15
61048SP	Delrin	20
61048SSP	Delrin	15
61050SAB	"Big Coke Bottle" Wood Handle	40
6165SAB	DR "Folding Hunter" Wood Handle	40
P172	"Buffalo"	50
3185	"Doctors Knife"	45
6185	"Doctors Knife"	45
61093	Delrin	45
1199SHRS	Grafting Knife	20

TWO BLADE

	Muskrat	30
	Muskrat "Hawbaker's Special" (9 DOT to 8 DOT)	75
	Muskrat "Hawbaker's Special"	75
4200SS	"Melon Tester"	50
3201		25
6201		25
9201		20
6202½	Delrin	15
6205	"RAZ or One Arm Man"	40
6207		25
6208	"Half Whittler"	20
62009	"Barlow" Delrin	20
62009	"Barlow" "RAZ or One Arm Man" Delrin	30
62009½	"Barlow" Delrin	15
6214	Delrin	15
6214½	Delrin	15
6217	"Half Hawk Bill" Laminated Wood Handle	20
2220	"Peanut"	35
3220	"Peanut"	35
6220	"Peanut" Delrin Handle	35
6220	"Peanut" Bone Stag Handle	80
6225½	"Coke Bottle"	25
6227	Delrin	15
2231½SAB	Long Pull Standard	20

6231½	Long Pull Standard	25
12031LR	"Electricians Knife"	20
6232		20
5232		60
3233		30
6233	Delrin	15
8233		35
9233		20
6235½		16
62042		15
92042		15
06244	Delrin	15
6244	Delrin	15
6246RSS	"Riggers Knife"	35
06247PEN		20
32048SP		20
62048SP	Delrin	20
62048SPSSP	Delrin	20
6249	"Copperhead or Vietnam"	25
6250	"Sunfish" Laminated Wood Handle	40
62052		25
82053SRSS		35
3254	"Trapper"	90
6254	"Trapper"	40
6254SSP	"Trapper"	45
6254SSP	Large Stamp	100
62055		20
8261		40
9261		20
06263SSP		15
06263FSSP		25
6265SABDR	"Folding Hunter" Wood Handle	30
	Mariners Knife Set	40
6269		22
6275SP	"Moose"	25
6279SS	Delrin	15
82079½SS	"Sleeveboard"	35
M279SCSS	Stainless Steel Handle	20
M279FSS	Stainless Steel Handle	20
M279SS	Stainless Steel Handle	20
22087		15
62087	Delrin	15
6292	"Texas Jack"	20
32095FSS	"Fisherman's Knife"	25
3299½		25
62109X	"Baby Copperhead"	22
62131	"Canoe"	30

THREE BLADE

6308	"Whittler"	24
3318SHPEN		20
4318SHSP	See note	40
+4318SHSP	top next column	100
6318SHSP		20
6318SPP		20

6318SHPEN		20
6318SHSP	SSP Edge of Blade Polished	25

+ This knife (4318 SH SP) is the same as a regular 4318 SH SP 9 Dot, except the handle is inscribed—Dewey P. Ferguson, Author "ROMANCE OF COLLECTING CASE KNIVES". Quantity made 280.

6327SHSP	Delrin	20
9327SHSP		20
13031LR	"Electricians Knife" (Collectors Set)	30
5332		55
6332		20
6333	Delrin	15
9333		20
6344SHPEN	Delrin Handle	20
6344SHPEN	Bone Stag Handle	30
6344SHSP	Delrin	20
33044SHSP	"Birdseye"	25
3347SHSP		20
5347SHSP	SSP (Collectors Set)	40
6347SHSP		20
6347SPP		25
6347SPPEN		25
6347SHSP	SSP	25
63047		25
8364SCSS		75
6375		30
6380	"Whittler"	30
6383	"Whittler"	25
23087SHPEN		20
53087SHPEN	(Collector's Set)	55
63087SHPEN	Delrin	20
6392		26
33092	"Birdseye"	30
M3102RSS		20

FOUR BLADE

	Case's SS "Fly Fisherman"	100
6445R	"Scouts Knife"	30
640045R	"Scouts Knife"	20
64047P		30
64052		30

CASE XX U.S.A. (8 DOT) 1972
ONE BLADE

4100SS	"Melon Tester"	35
11011	"Hawk Bill"	25
61011	"Hawk Bill" Laminated Wood Handle	20
5111½L	SSP "Cheetah" Large Pattern Number	140
5111½LSS	"Cheetah" Small Pattern Number	140
6111½L	"Lock Back"	35
11031SH		15

CASE 8 DOT (cont'd.)

2137	"Sod Buster Jr."	15
2137SS	"Sod Buster Jr."	15
2138	"Sod Buster"	15
2138SS	"Sod Buster"	20
2138LSS	"Sod Buster" Blade Locks Open	20
6143 Bone		30
6143	"Daddy Barlow" Delrin	20
31048		15
61048	Delrin	15
C61050SAB	"Coke Bottle" Wood Handle	35
6165SABDR	"Folding Hunter" Wood Handle	30
P172	"Buffalo"	50
3185	"Doctor's Knife"	45
6185	"Doctor's Knife"	40
61093	"Texas Toothpick" Bone	40
61093	Delrin	30
7197LSSP	"Shark's Tooth" Pakkawood	45
7197LSSP	Curly Maple	140
P197LSSP	Pakkawood	35
1199SHRSS	"Grafting Knife"	20

TWO BLADE

Muskrat		24
Muskrat "Hawbaker's Special" (8 DOT to 7 DOT)		75
4200SS	"Melon Tester"	50
3201		20
6201		25
9201		20
6202½	Delrin	10
6205	"RAZ or One Arm Man"	35
6207		25
6208	"Half Whittler"	15
62009	"Barlow" Delrin	10
62009	"Barlow" "RAZ or One Arm Man" Delrin	25
62009½	"Barlow" Delrin	10
6214	Delrin	20
6214½	Delrin	15
6217	"Half Hawkbill" Wood Handle	18
2220	"Peanut"	35
3220	"Peanut"	35
6220	"Peanut" Delrin	30
6225½	"Coke Bottle"	26
6227	Delrin	10
2231½	SAB Long Pull Standard	15
6231½	Long Pull Standard	25
12031 L R	Electrician's Knife	20
62048SPSSP Delrin		20
6232		17
3233		26
6233	Delrin	15
8233		40

9233		18
6235½		15
62042		17
92042		14
06244	Delrin	14
6244	Delrin	14
6246RSS	"Rigger's Knife"	33
06247PEN		16
32048SP		20
62048SPDelrin		14
62048SPSSP		16
6249	"Copperhead or Vietnam"	28
6250	"Sunfish" Laminated Wood Handle	40
62052		22
82053SRSS		40
3254	"Trapper"	40
6254	"Trapper"	35
6254	SSP "Trapper"	35
6254	SSP Large Stamp	100
62055		22
8261		40
9261		25
06263F	SSP	22
06263	SSP	18
6265SABDR	"Folding Hunter" Wood Handle	30
6265SABDR SSP	"Folding Hunter" Wood Handle	32
	Mariner's Knife Set	35
	Mariner's Knife Set SSP	40
6269		18
6275SP	"Moose"	24
6279SS	Delrin	15
6279SS	Bone	15
82079½ SS	"Sleeve Board"	35
M279SC	SS Stainless Steel Handle	30
M279F	SS Stainless Steel Handle	24
M279SS	Stainless Steel Handle	25
22087		18
62087	Delrin	18
6292	"Texas Jack"	18
32095F	SS Fisherman's Knife	18
3299½		25
62109X	"Baby Copperhead"	20
62131	"Canoe" Bone	30

THREE BLADE

6308	"Whittler"	25
3318SH	SP PEN	20
4318SH	SP	36
6318SH	SP	16
6318SPP		18
6318SH	PEN	18
6318SH	SP SSP	20
6327	SH SP Delrin	20
9327	SH SP	25

13031 L R	"Electrician's Knife"	30
6332		20
6333	Delrin	18
9333		20
6344SH	PEN Delrin	18
6344SH	SP Delrin	18
33044SH	SP "Birdseye"	30
3347SH	SP	22
6347SH	SP	18
6347SP	P	20
6347SP	PEN	25
6347SH	SP SSP	25
63047		22
8364SC	SS	80
6375		25
6380	"Whittler"	30
6383	"Whittler"	24
23087	SH PEN	20
63087SP	PEN Delrin	18
6392		25
33092	"Birdseye"	35
M3102R	SS	18

FOUR BLADE

Case's SS "Fly Fisherman"		100
6445R	"Scout Knife"	30
640045R	"Scout Knife"	18
64047P		20
64052		30
6488		45

CASE XX U.S.A. (7 DOT) 1973
ONE BLADE

4100SS	"Melon Tester"	35
4100	"Melon Tester" Polished Blade	35
11011	"Hawkbill"	20
61011	"Hawkbill" Laminated Wood Handle	20
6111½L	"Lock Back" Bone Stag Handle	30
6111½L	"Lock Back" Delrin Handle	45
11031SH		12
2137	"Sod Buster Jr."	15
2137SS	"Sod Buster Jr."	15
2138	"Sod Buster"	15
2138SS	"Sod Buster"	18
2138LSS	"Sod Buster" Blade Locks Open	18
6143	"Daddy Barlow" Delrin	17
31048		15
61048	Delrin	15
61048	SSP Delrin	18
C61050	SAB "Big Coke Bottle" Wood Handle	30
6165SABDR	"Folding Hunter" Wood Handle	20

CASE 7 DOT (cont'd.)

P172	"Buffalo"	45
3185	"Doctor's Knife" With Shield	45
3185	"Doctor's Knife" No Shield	40
6185	"Doctor's Knife"	40
61093	"Texas Toothpick" (Rare) Delrin	110
7197L	SSP "Shark Tooth" Pakkawood	45
7197L	SSP Curly Maple	140
P197L	SSP Pakkawood	35
1199SH	R SS "Grafting Knife"	15

TWO BLADE

Muskrat		25
Muskrat "Hawbaker"—Bone		75
Muskrat "Hawbaker's Special" Delrin		65
4200SS	"Melon Tester"	50
3201		18
6201		18
9201		20
6202½	Delrin	10
6205	RAZ Delrin	30
6205	"RAZ or One Arm Man"	35
6207	Bone	22
6207	Delrin	25
6208	"Half Whittler"	18
62009	"Barlow" Delrin	15
62009	"Barlow RAZ or One Arm Man" Delrin	25
62009½	"Barlow" Delrin	10
6214	Delrin	15
6214½	Delrin	15
6217	"Half Hawkbill" Wood Handle	25
2220	"Peanut"	100
3220	"Peanut"	100
6220	"Peanut" Delrin	30
6225½	"Coke Bottle"	20
6227	Delrin	15
2231½	SAB Long Pull Standard	18
6231½	Long Pull Standard	22
12031	L R "Electrician's Knife"	15
6232		15
3233	Rare	60
6233	Delrin	25
8233		35
9233		20
6235½		15
62042		15
92042		15
06244	Delrin	15
6244	Delrin	15
6246R	SS "Rigger's Knife"	25
06247	PEN	18
4247FK	Greenskeeper (1300 made)	310
32048SP		15

62048SP	Delrin	14
62048SPSSP	Delrin	18
6249	"Copperhead or Vietnam"	22
6250	"Sunfish" Laminated Wood Handle	30
62052		22
82053SRSS		35
3254	"Trapper"	35
6254	"Trapper"	35
6254	"Trapper" Delrin	40
6254	SSP "Trapper" Bone	35
6254	SSP "Trapper" Delrin	40
62055		20
8261		35
9261		25
06263	SSP	18
06263F	SSP	20
06265SABDR	"Folding Hunter" Wood Handle	28
6265SABDR	SSP "Folding Hunter" Wood Handle	30
	Mariner's Knife Set	35
	Mariner's Knife Set SSP	45
6269		20
6275	SP "Moose"	22
6279	SS Delrin	12
M279SCSS	Stainless Steel Handle	18
M279F	SS Stainless Steel Handle	18
M279SS	Stainless Steel Handle	18
82079½	SS "Sleeveboard"	35
22087		14
62087	Delrin	14
6292	"Texas Jack"	16
32095 F	SS "Fisherman's Knife"	25
3299½		25
62109X	"Baby Copperhead"	16
62131	"Canoe" Bone	30
62131	"Canoe" Delrin Handle (Rare)	75

THREE BLADE

6308	"Whittler"	18
3318SH	PEN	18
4318SH	SP	40
6318SH	SP	18
6318SP	P	18
6318SH	PEN	20
6318SH	SP SSP	20
6327SH	SP Delrin	18
9327SH	SP	20
13031	L R "Electrician's Knife"	30
6332		18
6333	Delrin	20
9333		15
6344SH	PEN Delrin	15
6344SH	SP Delrin	12
33044SH	SP "Birdseye"	25
3347SH	SP	20

6347SH	SP	18
6347SP	P	20
6347SP	PEN	25
6347SH	SP SSP	22
63047		22
8364SC	SS	75
6375		30
6380	"Whittler"	30
6383	"Whittler"	24
23087	SH PEN	18
63087SP	PEN Delrin	15
6392		25
M3102R	SS	18

FOUR BLADE

Case's SS "Fly Fisherman"		100
6445R	"Scout's Knife"	20
640045R	"Scout's Knife"	20
64047P		22
64052		25
6488		35

CASE XX U.S.A. (6 DOT) 1974
ONE BLADE

4100SS	"Melon Tester" Brushed	30
11011	"Hawkbill"	22
11011	"Hawkbill" Pakkawood Handle (Rare)	35
61011	"Hawkbill" Laminated Wood Handle	20
6111½L	"Lock Back"	30
11031SH		15
2137	"Sod Buster Jr."	15
2137SS	"Sod Buster Jr."	15
2138	"Sod Buster"	14
2138SS	"Sod Buster"	16
2138L	SS "Sod Buster" Blade Locks Open	20
6143	"Daddy Barlow" Delrin	17
31048		12
61048	Delrin	15
61048	SSP Delrin	15
C61050	SAB "Big Coke Bottle Wood Handle	28
6165	SAB DR "Folding Hunter" Wood Handle	25
P172	"Buffalo" Scarce	50
3185	"Doctor's Knife" With Shield	40
3185	"Doctor's Knife" No Shield	40
6185	"Doctor's Knife" Delrin	25
61093	"Texas Toothpick" Delrin	30
P197L	SSP "Shark Tooth" "Lock Back"	80
7197L	SSP "Shark Tooth" "Lock Back"	65
1199SH	R SS "Grafting Knife"	14

CASE 6 DOT (cont'd.)

TWO BLADE

Muskrat		18
3201		20
6201		20
9201		20
6202½	Delrin	12
6205	"RAZ or One Arm Man" Delrin	30
6205	"RAZ or One Arm Man" Bone	35
6207	Bone	20
6207	Delrin	20
6208	"Half Whittler"	15
62009	"Barlow" Delrin	15
62009	"RAZ or One Arm Man" "Barlow" Delrin	18
62009½	"Barlow" Delrin	15
6214	Delrin	15
6214½	Delrin	15
6217	"Half "Hawkbill" Wood Handle	16
2220	"Peanut"	30
3220	"Peanut"	30
6220	"Peanut" Delrin	30
6225½	"Coke Bottle"	20
6227	Delrin	15
2231½	SAB	18
6231½		20
12031	L R "Electrician's Knife"	15
6232		14
3233		25
6233	Delrin	22
8233		35
9233		25
6235½		12
62042		12
92042		12
6244	Delrin	15
06244	Delrin	15
6246R	SS "Rigger's Knife"	22
06247	PEN	14
32048	SP	14
62048	SP Delrin	14
62048	SP SSP Delrin	18
6249	"Copperhead or Vietnam"	20
6250	"Sunfish" Laminated Wood Handle	35
6250	"Sunfish" Blade Etched	35
62052		25
82053	S R SS	35
3254	"Trapper"	30
6254	"Trapper"	30
6254	"Trapper" Delrin	40
6254	SSP "Trapper" Bone	30
6254	SSP "Trapper" Delrin	40
62055		15
8261		35
9261		20

06263	SSP	15
06263	F SSP	25
6265	SAB DR "Folding Hunter" Wood Handle	25
6265	SAB DR SSP "Folding Hunter" Wood Handle	28
6265	SAB "Bill Boatman" (506 made)	145
	Mariner's Knife Set	35
	Mariner's Knife Set SSP	40
6269		25
6275	SP "Moose"	25
M279	SS Stainless Steel Handle	20
M279SC	SS Stainless Steel Handle	20
M279F	SS Stainless Steel Handle	20
6279	SS Delrin	10
82079½	SS "Sleeveboard"	30
22087		12
62087	Delrin	15
6292	"Texas Jack"	15
32095	F SS "Fisherman's Knife"	25
3299½		25
62109X	"Small Copperhead"	16
62131	"Canoe" Blade Etched"	25

THREE BLADE

6308	"Whittler"	15
3318	SH PEN	18
6318	SH SP	15
6318	SH PEN	15
6318	SP P	20
6318	SH SP SSP	20
6327	SH SP Delrin	20
13031	L R "Electrician's Knife"	25
6332		16
6333	Delrin	18
6344	SH PEN Delrin	18
6344	SH SP Delrin	20
33044	SH SP "Small Birdseye"	30
3347	SH SP	16
6347	SH SP	16
6347	SH SP SSP	18
6347	SP PEN	25
63047		20
8364	SC SS	80
6375		20
6380	"Whittler"	30
6383	"Whittler" Bone Stag Handle	20
6383	"Whittler" Delrin Handle	30
23087	SH PEN	15
63087	SP PEN Delrin	15
33092	"Birdseye"	30
6392		25
M3102	R SS	15

FOUR BLADE

6455R	"Scout's Knife"	25
640045R	"Scout's Knife" Brown Plastic Handle	20
64047P		25
64052		20
6488		35
Case's SS "Fly Fisherman"		100

CASE RAZORS

The information contained in this section is the end result of over four years of meticulous research. I have endeavored to make this the most accurate and up to date information available. Although sometimes very frustrating, it was a labor of love.

With the exception of "Knifemakers Who Went West" (Platts) and Case related catalogs and literature, I have researched and evaluated all information from scratch. Available published dates and information was not relied upon.

Where precise dating was not possible, circa or approximate were used. In most instances exact day and month were not available and dates were given in whole years.

A great debt of gratitude is owed to those who let us photograph their collections: Jim Branch, Steve Cary, Steve Froehlich and Joe Kranz. With a special thanks to Larry Robertson for letting us photograph his extensive collection accumulated over a fourteen year period.

I also wish to thank the following people, without their information and advice I could not have completed this project: Robert Crandall, Jerry Hnot, Fred and Carol Marziotto, H. Platts, Cindy Rabb, Bob Richardson, Jim Sargent, W.R. Case and Sons Bradford, Pa., Dept. of Patents and Tradesmark, Washington, D.C., librarians, historians, Chamber of Commerces and the nice people of the following cities and towns: Bradford, Pa., Kane, Pa., Little Valley, NY, New York, NY, Philadelphia, Pa., Smethport, Pa., Springville, NY and Warren, Pa.
RICH KUPILLAS

COLLECTING CASE RAZORS

As the price of older Case knives rose to astronomical figures, so has the popularity of Case razors. Buying a Case Brothers, W.R. Case and Son, or an old Bradford knife is just out of the reach of most collector's budgets. Razors enable a collector of modest means to add rare marks and handle materials to their collection. While some Case razors are expensive, all are far below equal knives of the same rarity, and razors rapidly rising, they are an excellent financial investment. Razors with older marks, inlaid tangs, ornate handles and blade etchings seem to be the most sought after and consequently, have the highest rate of gain.

As a word of caution, please remember to use extreme care when handling, and in the storage of your razors! Razors, unlike knives do not have backsprings, therefore they can be opened by even the smallest hand.

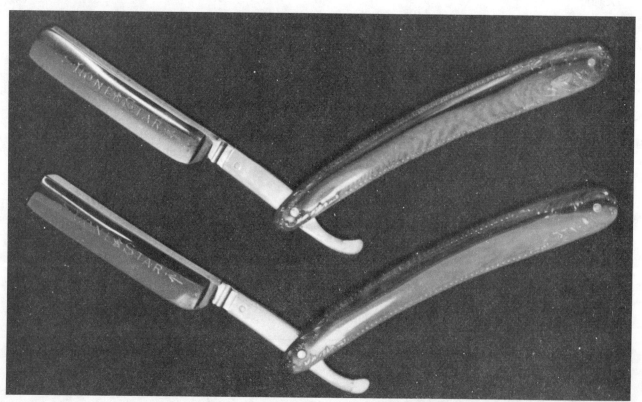

A rare pair of W.R. Case & Sons (1905-1920) "Lone Star" Razors

Larry Robertson was kind enough to pack up his whole collection of razors and travel to Nashville for an intensive photo session; the results are featured throughout this section. Larry is shown with an oversized display razor.

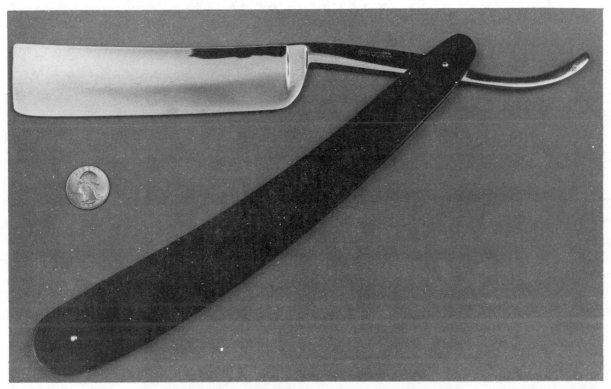

CASE BROTHERS CUTLERY CO., LITTLE VALLEY, N.Y.
Display razor, 14" closed, imitation tortoise shell handles. (This razor also came in slick black handles.) Value in mint condition
$1,000

CASE RAZOR

GRADING A "MINT" RAZOR

Due to the decline of straight razor use and their relative modern production, W.R. Case and Sons (1920-1955) razors in "mint" condition are still available. Razors manufactured by Case Cutlers between 1900-1920 graded as "true mint" are extremely rare. Razors for the most part were stropped, not ground like a knife edge. A man competent with a strop could keep a keen edge on his razor for years and the blade would show minimal wear. Razor blades were of higher temper than knife blades of the period and were stropped on leather, not stone.

Look at the blade carefully, especially along the top of the blade and the cutting edge where the strop rides. The point of the blade usually shows slight rounding, and the heel of the blade will show some wearing into the shoulderline due to the lapping of the strop. Case razors of this period did not have cut or ground edges. The edge was finely polished. When a blade is in true "mint" condition, there is simply no edge to see, just an even mirror-polished blade.

A Mint "Genco, Bradford, Pa., Easy Aces" (1930-55)

CLEANING

As with any collectible, you want to have as much of the original finish as you can. Buffing, polishing and reshaping only "destroys," not adds value to a razor.

The proper ways to clean razors is with soap, water, a soft toothbrush and a few Q-tips. Rust and most stuck-on substances can be removed by soaking the blade in oil overnight. Light stains on both blades and handles can be removed with semi-chrome polish. (DO NOT use on painted handles, it will remove the paint.) This is the only abrasive product I would recommend using on either knives or razors.

BLADE SHAPES

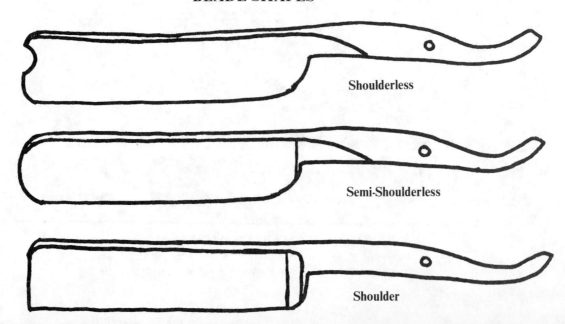

Shoulderless

Semi-Shoulderless

Shoulder

BLADE POINT   USE

SQUARE POINT   For decorative beards such as mutton chops and goatees. This point style was notorious for cutting ear lobes and noses.

HOLLOW POINT   For moustaches, to lift the ends up out of the way of the blade edge. Also just decorative in later years.

DISH POINT   For larger handle bar type moustaches.

ROUND POINT   General use, for the "clean shaving man," also called "safety point."

Larger, heavier blades were for men with heavy beards, smaller blades for men with light beards or those who shaved more frequently. Women who shaved used "ladies" or "travel" razors or (I'm sure without permission) their husband's razors.

COUNTERFEITS

Unfortunately, the rise in price and popularity of Case razors has also increased the likelihood of counterfeits. The simplest form of deceiving the buyer is to switch handles to a more ornate or rarer material. More complex methods are used as the value of the piece rises, ranging from false stampings, welded blades, to making complete razors. The best way to avoid most counterfeit razors is to gather as much information as you can and make use of it. Knowledge is the best defense against counterfeitors.

Prices that are just too good to be true are usually just that. You can still find a bargain, but you can get stung just as easily. With the wide availability of pricing guides, there are very few dealers who do not know the value of the "Case" mark.

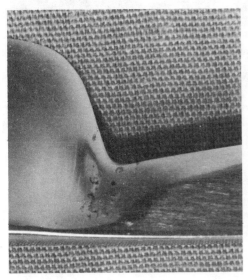
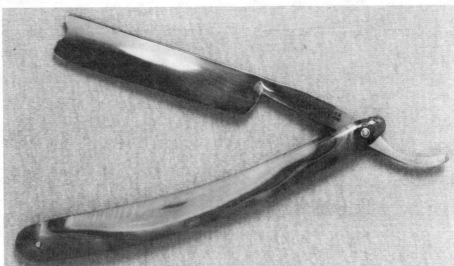

Counterfeit Case Brothers, Little Valley, N.Y.

The original blade for this razor must have been in such poor shape, it was cut off at the tang and replaced. You can clearly see the remaining weld marks where the new blade was attached. Although it does not show up well in photographs, the metal of the blade is of slightly different color than the tang. If it were a Case Brothers of the same period as the marking indicated, it should have a shoulder ground into the blade. The handles are genuine Case Brothers and belong with the tang.

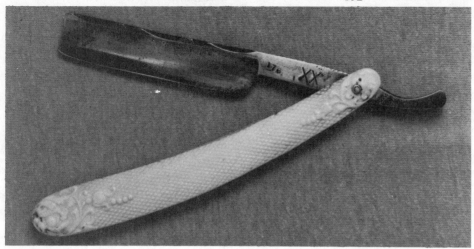

Counterfeit Case Brothers, Springville, NY

This is a good example of re-stamped tang. The razor is German circa 1940. Case Brothers razors (1900-1915) were all hand-forged and then ground to shape by hand. All surfaces of the Case Brothers blade have beautiful luster to them even the underside of the tang! If you compare them to most razors of the period, American, German, even W.R. Case and Sons Bradford (1905-20), you would see they are all made from stamped blanks with the tangs shaped in the stamping process, leaving the underside of the tang blackened. The number 176 is original, but the "XX" was added at the same time as the Case mark. If you look carefully, you can see that the scratches made by the handle opening are lower than the raised edges of the "XX". The Case Brothers Springville mark is incorrectly spelled as SRRINGVILLE, and you can see where someone tried to pick out the leg of the first "R". The style of stamps used were both for knives and not razors so I would think that this was just a test piece and I would check all your Case Brothers Springville knives "VERY CAREFULLY."

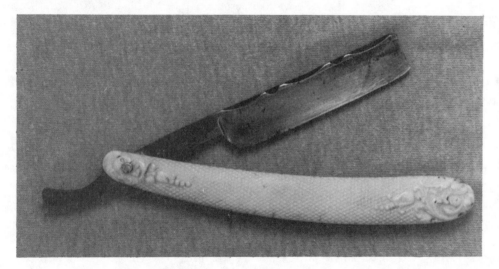

MODERN HANDLES USED BY CASE COMPANIES

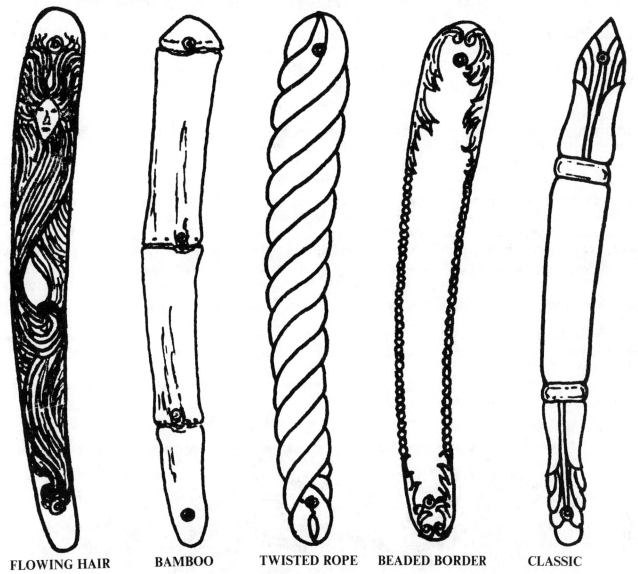

| FLOWING HAIR | BAMBOO | TWISTED ROPE | BEADED BORDER | CLASSIC |

Case Brothers, W.R. Case and Son, and W.R. Case and Sons used these handles only between 1900-1920. Not only are they rare, but add both beauty and value to razors of this period.

Because of this, many people switch handles of imported or lesser American razors. Fortunately there are some defenses against this practice.

HANDLE FACTS

Molded handles were used by Case Brothers, W.R. Case and Son and W.R. Case and Sons (until approx. 1915-1920) with the exception of the "Classic" pattern which was used only on W.R. Case and Son (Napanoch) and on W.R. Case and Sons German imports (1905-1914).

These handles were not used on Case razors after 1920 and were available in the following colors:

Flowing Hair	Imitation Ivory
	Black
Bamboo (both full-size and travel)	Imitation Tortoise
	Cream
Twisted Rope	Cream
	Cream & Rust (marble)
	Imitation Ivory
Beaded Border	Various Colored Celluloid
Classic	Various Colored Celluloid

Case Brothers and W.R. Case and Son used these handles indiscriminately. Therefore, blade style cannot be used as a judge.

W.R. Case and Sons (1905-20) the vast majority of molded handles were used on razors with inlaid tangs and/or blade etching. This doesn't mean you wouldn't find a plain blade with molded handles, but it should alert you to check the razor more carefully. Both Case Brothers and W.R. Case and Sons used the same handle supplier and are identical pattern for pattern. The "Classic" handles used by W.R. Case and Son (Naponoch) are larger than those used on W.R. Case and Sons German imports.

Rare cream bamboo handles are virtually identical to their less rare tortoise brothers and should be used for verification.

All handles were made both with and without handle pins and with and without handle pin collars.

OBSERVATION

First try to be objective, looking at a piece through "starry eyes" will not help you in anyway. Try to think of yourself as an appraiser, advising someone else whether to buy or not. Enjoy the razor after you buy it, not before.

TANG PINS

While it's true that tang pins were routinely replaced in barber shops up till the 1940's, this should in no way be used as an excuse for a replaced pin on a razor graded excellent to "mint." Razor pins were replaced normally on well used razors of the period. Even if the pin was replaced in the 1940's, it should have a gray pewter-like look.

Look closely at the finish on the pin. The hammering and grinding of the pin should match the other razors of the same mark.

BLADES

Look where the handle rides (rubs) against the tang. There should be rubmarks on the inside of the handles to match those on the tang.

The front of the blade sometimes will show a slight discoloration (graying) right where the blade hits the handle. If this mark is higher or lower the razor should be checked carefully. This could of course be from warping of the handle due to heat, but that should be obvious.

There is no way to be 100% sure all of the time. By using the information above, you should at least have a fighting chance against razor collecting's most common fraud – handle switching.

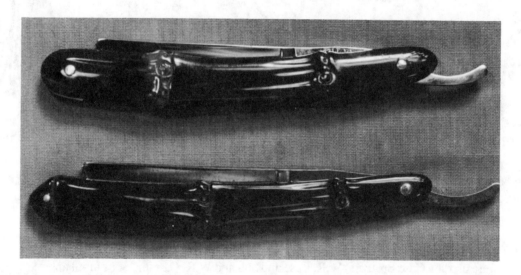

LITTLE VALLEY KNIFE ASS'N, LITTLE VALLEY, N.Y. (1900-1905) CASE BROTHERS, LITTLE VALLEY, N.Y. (1900-1905) Look at the handles carefully. The handle on the Case Brothers razor (lower) was manufactured just for use on travel razors, while the other one is a cut down handle for a full-size razor. This was correct for travel razors manufactured by Napanoch, but it should not be correct on a Case Brothers travel razor.

CASE RELATED BOXES AND PAPER

BOXES	RANGE
Case Brothers, Little Valley, N.Y. (red, green, tan, blue & black)	$5 to $25
	(depend on cond.)
W.R. Case and Son, Little Valley, N.Y.	$10 to $35
	(depend on cond.)
W.R. Case and Sons, Bradford, PA (1905-1920) (black, tan, gray & marble all with a "star" on the short end)	$5 to $25
	(depend on cond.)
W.R. Case and Sons, Bradford, PA (1920-1955) (black only, "CASE TESTED XX" on the short end)	$5 to $15
	(depend on cond.)
W.R. Case and Sons, Bradford, PA (1955-1962) (gray, red, etc.)	$1 to $10
	(depend on cond.)

CATALOGS:

Case Brothers, Little Valley, N.Y. complete in good condition	$100 to $200
W.R. Case and Sons, Bradford, PA (1905-1920) complete in good condition	$100 to $200
W.R. Case and Sons "Tested XX" (1920-1940) complete in good condition	$75 to $150
W.R. Case and Sons XX (1940-1960) complete in good condition	$25 to $75

NOTE: Salesmen's or full-line catalogs and those with complete line price list command highest price.

STROPS & HONES

Razor strops or hones enhance any collection and come in many various shapes and styles.

The above strops were all made by W.R. Case and Sons before 1920. As you can see there were many styles of strops available. Strops of this period in good condition are worth $45-65. "Mint" with the original box $100-$125.

Razor hones having the "W.R. Case & Sons" mark are very rare especially with their original box. One is marked "extra choice #232," the other "NON FILLING MALGMIT #32." They are valued at $125 each.

Rare "W.R. Case & Sons" common sense razor strop & hone with its own razor storage compartment. This one is complete with original box and papers and is worth $165.

Extremely rare folding (travel) razor strop, stamped Case Brothers Little Valley, NY. Brass button carries patent date July 11, 1901. $175

CONTRACT (JOBBER) RAZORS

All Case companies made "Contract Razors" for many different hardware stores, barber supply companies and jobbing house. They are identical to razors having a "Case" mark, except they bear a private linemark.

Contract razors usually sell for 40-50% less than equal razors having a "Case" mark.

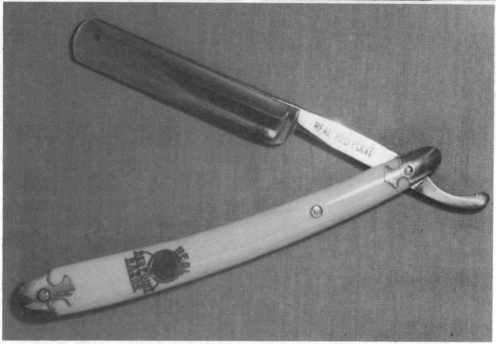

"REAL RED POINT" H. Geo. Henk, Columbia, Pa. While this razor is virtually identical to its W.R. Case and Sons brother, it does not bear the "Case" name and is worth $45.

CASE BROTHERS
And Related Companies

NOTE: Due to the rarity of razors in "true mint" condition, the prices in this section are based on razors in excellent condition.

JOHN D. CASE CO.
LITTLE VALLEY, N.Y.

While not as famous as Job or W.R. Case (who were real people but fictional cutlers), John D. Case was making razors around 1880 and in fact held a patent for his butterfly razor dated Feb. 8, 1881, a full 20 years before his future company Case Brothers was credited with being the first Case Cutlery Manufacturing Co. This John D. Case Co. mark is the oldest Case mark known, over 100 years old.

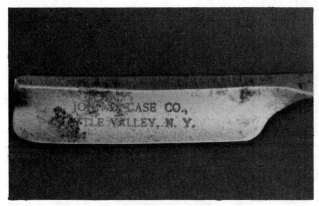

BLADE ETCHING

Values for Razors Pictured

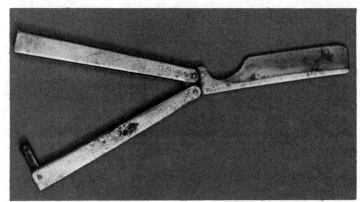

JOHN D. CASE CO., Little Valley, N.Y. (etched on blade)
butterfly razor metal handles
EXTREMELY RARE   **$525**

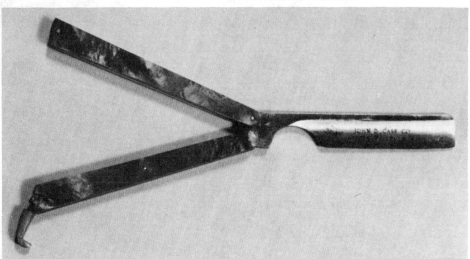

JOHN D. CASE CO., Little Valley, N.Y. (etched on blade) butterfly razor imi. green
pearl scales.
    EXTREMELY RARE   **$625**

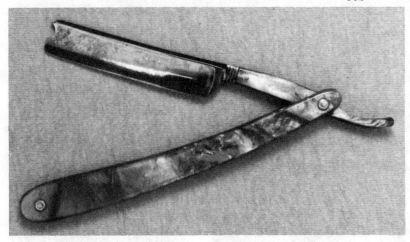

JOHN D. CASE CO., Little Valley, N.Y. (etched on blade) travel razor hollow point blade etched "CASHIER" green pearl handles with matching tang. **EXTREMELY RARE** **$425**

JOHN D. CASE KANE, PA (1909-1914)	JOHN D. CASE SONS CO. KANE, PA (1909-1914)	JOHN D. CASE LITTLE VALLEY, N.Y. (1909-1914)

After Case Brothers divested themselves of Case Brothers, Kane, Pa. (reorganized under the name Kane Cutlery Company in 1909) John D. Case retained some interest in the company, and they manufactured his own private line marked John D. Case Kane, Pa., John D. Case, Little Valley, N.Y. and J.D. Case Sons Co.

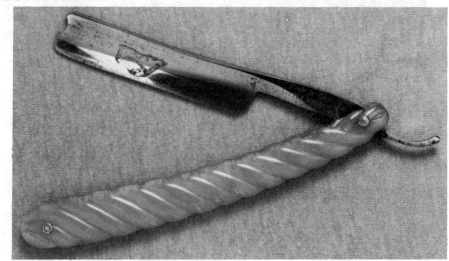

JOHN D. CASE, LITTLE VALLEY, N.Y.
Hollow point, Cream and Rust,
Twisted Rope Handles
RARE **$125**

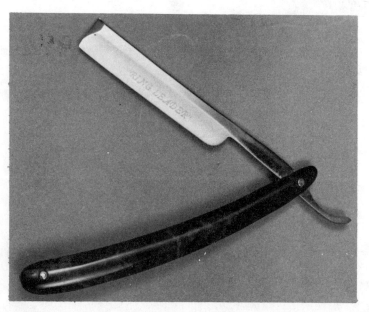

JOHN D. CASE SONS CO., KANE, P.A., Axe point, Blade etched "RINGLEADER", Brown and red mottled handles **RARE** **$150**

Values For Razors Pictured

KANE CUTLERY COMPANY

Sometime in 1909 Case Brothers Cutlery Company, Kane, Pa. was reorganized under the name Kane Cutlery Company. They manufactured razors under the name Kane Cut. Co., John D. Case, Kane, Pa., and John D. Case Sons Co., Kane, Pa.

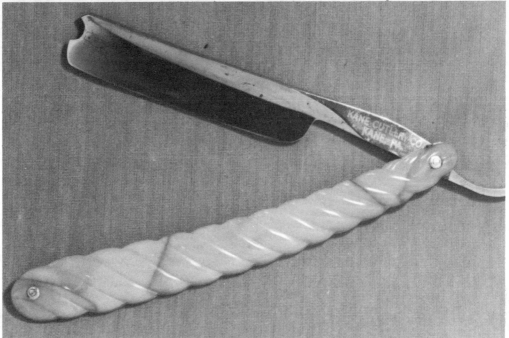

KANE CUTLERY CO., KANE, PA. hollow point, cream and rust twisted rope handles $40

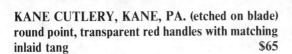

KANE CUTLERY, KANE, PA. (etched on blade) round point, transparent red handles with matching inlaid tang $65

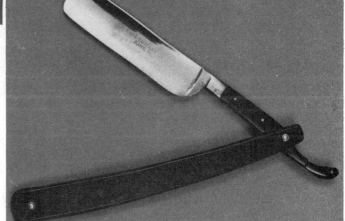

Values For Razors in Excellent Condition

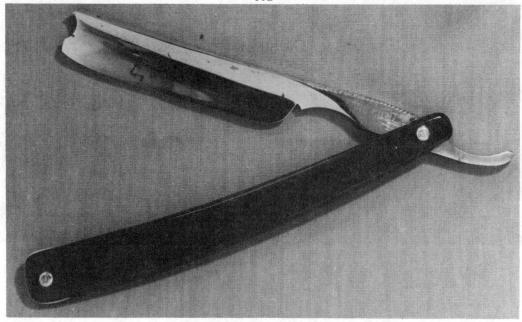

KANE CUTLERY hollow point
worked tang with transparent red
handles $35

J.B.F. CHAMPLIN & SON
LITTLE VALLEY, N.Y.
(1882-1886)

CATTARAUGUS CUT. CO.
LITTLE VALLEY, N.Y.
(1887-1963)

J.B.F. Champlin married Thersa Case in the late 1860's. They had a son named Tint, who with his father formed "J.B.F. Champlin and Son in 1882. In 1886 they were joined by John, Jean and Andrew Case and the company's name was changed to "Cattaraugus Cutlery Co.". Their association lasted for only a short period of time and the Case Brothers left sometime in 1887.

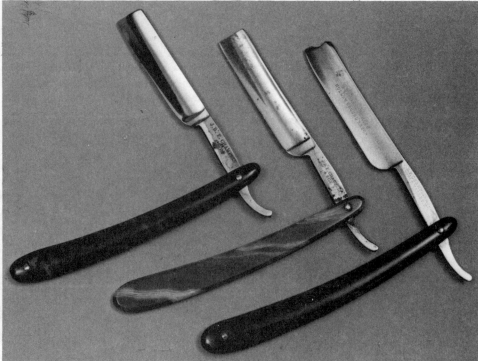

Left to right: J.B.F. Champlin & Son, square point, brown streaked celluloid handles
$85.; J.B.F. Champlin & Son, square point, red streaked celluloid handles $85.;
J.B.F. Champlin & Son, Little Valley, N.Y., hollow point, slick black handles, blade
etched "Warrented hollow ground" $105

Values For Razors Pictured

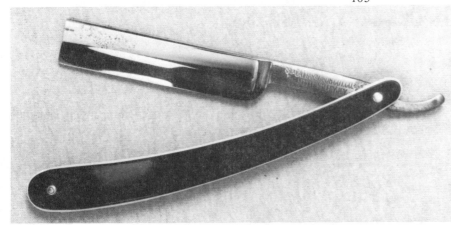

CATTARAUGUS CUT. CO. LITTLE VALLEY,
N.Y. square point, blue handles with white liners
$25

THE STANDARD KNIFE CO.
LITTLE VALLEY, N.Y.
(1901-1903)

In 1901 Dean and Elliot Case, sons of Jean Case, started a jobbing house in Little Valley, N.Y. under the name "THE STAN-DARD KNIFE CO." Their knives carried an unusual promise from the two brothers, "If you die with a Standard Knife in your pocket, we'll pay the funeral expenses."

Although the new company did well, Elliot Case's untimely death in 1903 forced the closing of the company.

Manufactured by:
NAPANOCH

Values For Razors Pictured

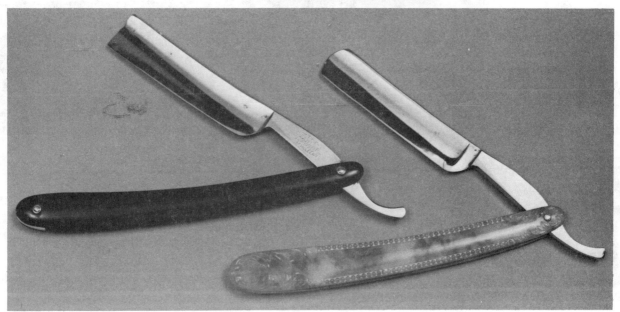

THE STANDARD KNIFE CO., LITTLE VALLEY, N.Y. (ARC MARK)
Square Point, Slick Black Handles   **$100**
Round Point, Yellow Mottled Beaded Boarded Handles   **$145**

NOTE: In the late 1920's W.R. Case & Sons marketed a line of razors under the name of "Standard Knife Co." The words "Little Valley, N.Y." do not appear in these tang stamps. Prices of Standard Knife razors are comparable to those of Kinfolks razors of the period.

UNION CUTLERY COMPANY
Olean, N.Y.
A.J. CASE
Shoo-fly
(circa 1912)

When Andrew Case left Case Brothers in 1909, he joined his nephew W.R. Brown at Union Cutlery Company in Tidioute, Pa., later moving to Olean, N.Y. in 1912. It is not known if he was involved with the workings of the company, or was a sales representative/jobber with his own private line.

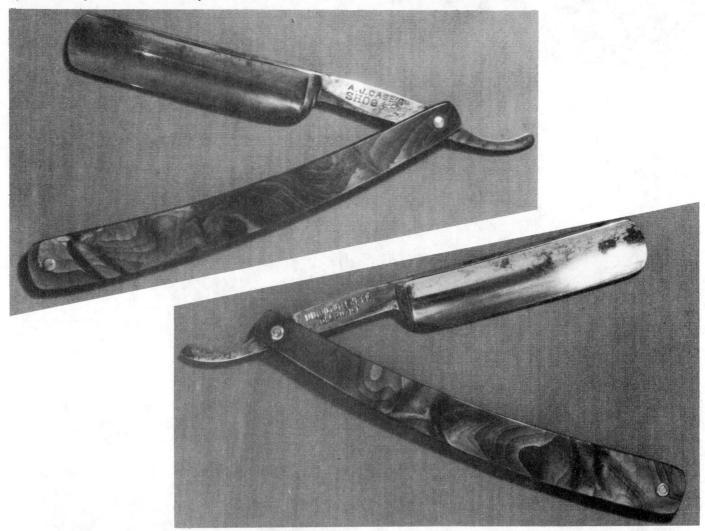

A.J. CASE'S SHOO-FLY UNION CUT. CO., OLEAN, N.Y.
Round point, tiger eye handle with shoo-fly pressed into it, rare.
$125

Values for Razors Pictured

CASE BROS.;
Wholesalers of Cutlery
Spring Green, Nebraska
(c. 1890-1900)

CASE BROTHERS CUTLERY CO.
Little Valley, N.Y.
(1896-1900)

Several years after the Case brothers left Cattaraugus Cutlery, they operated a cutlery wholesale house in Spring Green, Nebraska as a sideline to their livestock breeding business.

In 1896 John D. Case together with his brothers Jean and Andrew, formed Case Brothers Cutlery Co. in Little Valley, N.Y. jobbing for C. Platt's Sons Co. and other manufacturers of the period. Case Bros. & Co. is a shortened form of the company name (Platts). Some razors of this period have Case Bros. Cutlery Co., Little Valley, N.Y. etched in two lines on the back of the blade. These razors do not have the trademark "TESTED XX" and are identical to John D. Case Co. razors of this period.

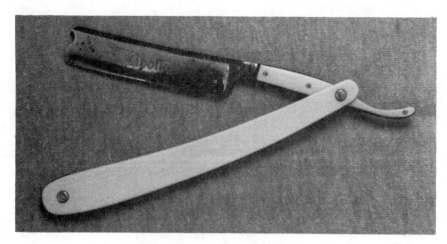

CASE BROS. CUTLERY CO.
LITTLE VALLEY, N.Y.
(JOBBER)
(c. 1896-1900) Travel Razor, Hollow Point Blade etched "APOLLO" on front, Case Bros. Cutlery Co., Little Valley, N.Y. on the back, Imitation Ivory Tang with Matching Handles,
EXTREMELY RARE $425

Values For Razors Pictured

RARE CASE BROTHERS RAZORS

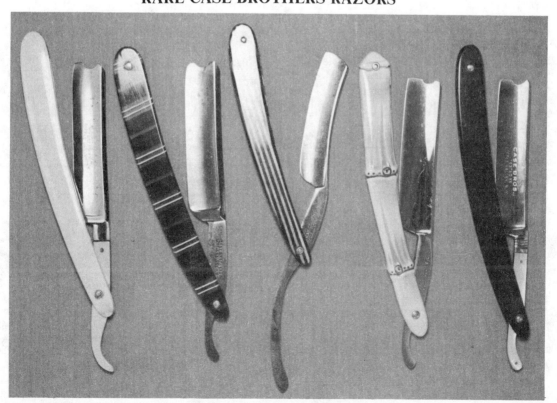

CASE BROTHERS CUTLERY COMPANY
Little Valley, N.Y.
(1900-1912)

Kane, Pa.
(1907-1909)

CASE MANUFACTURING COMPANY
Little Valley, N.Y.
(1910)

Warren, Pa.
(1911-1912?)

CASE BROTHERS CUTLERY COMPANY
Springville, N.Y.
(1912-1915)

In February 1900, Case Brothers Cutlery Company was incorporated in Little Valley, N.Y. Razor production played a large part in the early success of the company. It is interesting to note the reason for their famous "hand-forged cutlery" logo, was simply that they had to employ so many hand forgers for razor production it was financially prudent to hand forge all blades rather than use the new technology of the day – drop hammers.

Razors made by Case Brothers were extremely fine, well balanced razors with the largest variety of tang stampings. They are very sought after by collectors. The majority of razors manufactured by Case Brothers are of plain design with smooth handles but retain a refined beauty unique to the mark. Case Brothers, Little Valley manufactured some razors with inlaid tangs and etched blades but they are a very rare find and command high prices.

Another rare razor manufactured at Little Valley, N.Y. was the "Ladies" or travel razor. These are perfect half scale razors used for small hands or small spaces. Travel razors were produced from 1900 till 1912. Most have tortoise bamboo handles. Some early ones have slick black handles. Case Brothers was the only major Case related company to actually make this style of razor.

Case Brothers operated a second factory in Kane, Pa. from 1907 till 1909 when it was reorganized under the name Kane Cutlery Co. It was also about the same time that Andrew Case left Case Brothers to join Union Cutlery Co.

In January of 1910 Case Brothers purchased Smethport Cutlery Co. in Smethport, Pa. reportedly marking their razors Case Mfg. Co. Little Valley, N.Y. After only a short period of operation the factory burned down in June 1910. After receiving many incentives from the Board of Trade and Commerce, Case decided to rebuild in the town of Warren, Pa. under the name Case Manufacturing Company, Warren, Pa. This factory was most likely completed in early 1911 and remained in operation for only a short period of time. This mark may be the rarest of all Case Brothers marks.

On March 27, 1912 Case Brothers, Little Valley, N.Y. burned to the ground. They rebuilt in Springville, N.Y. in 1913 but were never able to recover from two devastating fires and went out of business late in 1914. On October 21, 1914 Case Brothers sold their rights to the "Tested XX" trademark to W.R. Case and Sons ending the 18 year history of the Case Brothers Cutlery Company.

KNOWN CASE BROTHERS RAZOR MARKS

ARC ETCHING WITH FULL SPELLING
(circa 1900-1907)

LINE ETCHING WITH "TESTED XX"
(circa 1900-1907)

ARC ETCHING WITH "TESTED X X"
(circa 1900-1907)

LITTLE VALLEY STAMPING
(circa 1907-1912)

KNOWN CASE BROTHERS RAZOR MARKS

LINE ETCHING circa 1900-1907

SPRINGVILLE STAMPING
(1912-1915)

KANE, PA., LITTLE VALLEY, N.Y.
1907-1909 EXTREMELY RARE

LITTLE VALLEY, N.Y. & KANE, PA.
EXTREMELY RARE

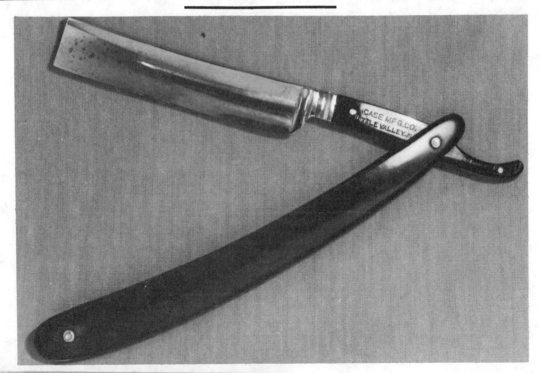

CASE MFG. CO., LITTLE VALLEY, N.Y. square
point, inlaid black tang with matching handles. Rare!
$260

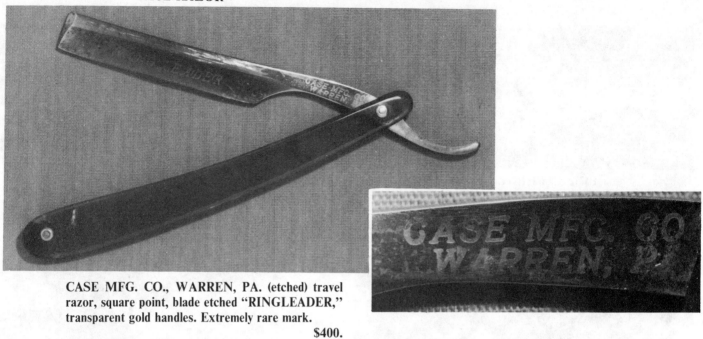

CASE MFG. CO., WARREN, PA. (etched) travel razor, square point, blade etched "RINGLEADER," transparent gold handles. Extremely rare mark.

$400.

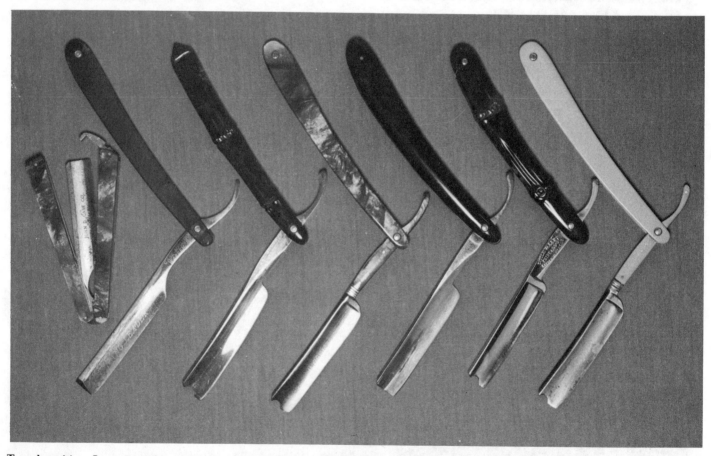

Travel rarities, L to R: John D. Case Co., Butterfly; Case Mfg. Co., Warren, Pa.; Case Brothers Cutlery Co., Little Valley, NY (rare arc etching); John D Case Co. Little Valley NY; Case Brothers, Cutlery Co., Little Valley, NY (arc etching rare slick black handles); Little Valley Knife Ass's, Little Valley, NY; Case Bros. Cutlery Co., Little Valley, NY (1896-1900)

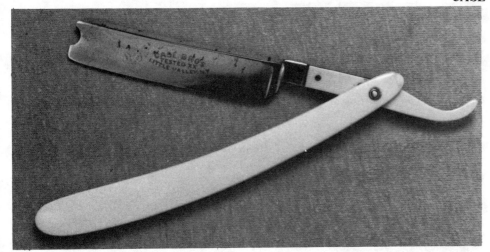

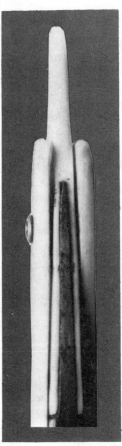

CASE BROS. "TESTED XX", LITTLE VALLEY, N.Y. (arc etching) hollow point, blade etched "MFG FOR JONES & CO" on rear of blade, with extremely rare style of inlaid tang, imitation ivory with matching handles (note the blade stops at the pivot pin, the entire finger loop is celluloid.) $375

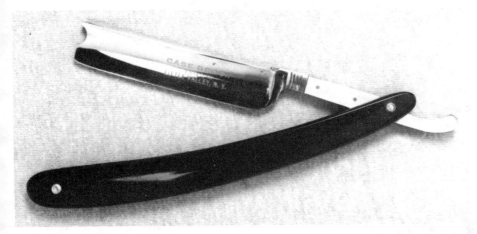

CASE BROS., TESTED XX, LITTLE VALLEY, N.Y. (line etching) Hollow Point Blade, Slick Black Handles W/RARE Mother Of Pearl Inlaid Tang $400

CASE BROTHERS CUTLERY CO., LITTLE VALLEY, N.Y. (arc etch) Hollow Point Blade, Butter & Molasses Handles $125
CASE BROTHERS, LITTLE VALLEY, N.Y. (arc etch) Square Point Blade w/Worked Tang, Cream Colored Beaded Border Handles $150

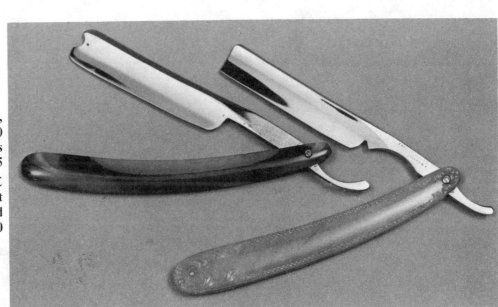

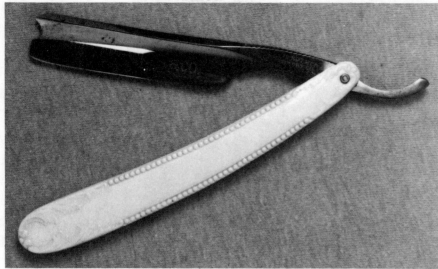

CASE BROTHERS CUTLERY CO., LITTLE VALLEY, N.Y. (arc etching) Hollow Point Blade Etched "MFG FOR JONES & CO" W/Worked Tang, Imitation Ivory Handles in the Beaded Border Pattern $165

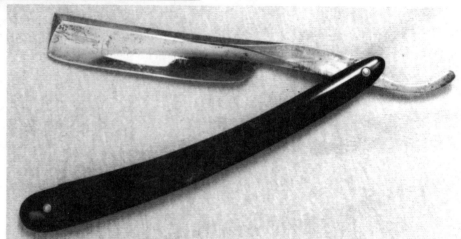

CASE BROTHERS CUTLERY CO. (arc etch) Ax Pont Blade Etched "SHARON HDW" Slick Black Handles $135

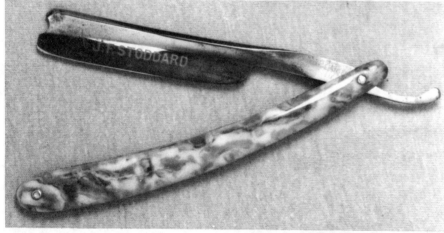

CASE BROTHERS CUTLERY CO. (arc etch) Hollow Point Blade Etched "J.F. Stoddard", Cream, Rust & Green Handles $150

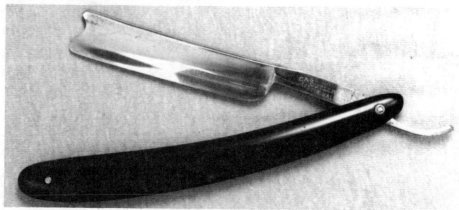

CASE BROTHERS CUTLERY CO., (arc etch) Hollow Point Blade, Slick Black Handles $100

CASE RAZOR

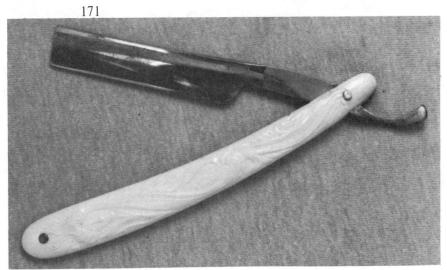

CASE BROTHERS CUTLERY CO., LITTLE VALLEY, N.Y. (arc etch) Square Point Imitation Ivory Flowing Hair Handles $100

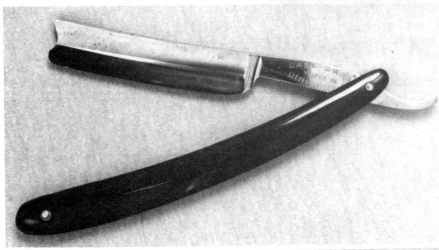

CASE BROTHERS, TESTED XX, LITTLE VALLEY, N.Y. (arc etch) Hollow Point, Slick Black Handles RARE MARK. $150

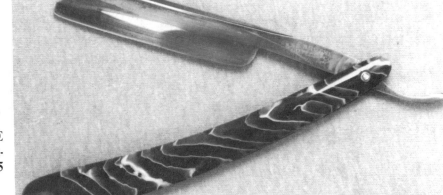

CASE BROTHERS, TESTED XX, LITTLE VALLEY, N.Y. (arc etch) Hollow Point, Imitation Horn Handles, RARE MARK $165

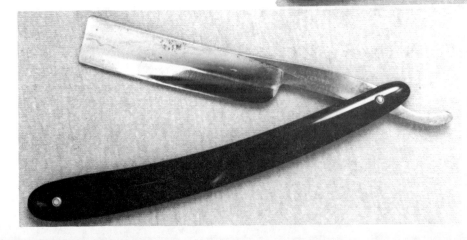

CASE BROTHERS, TESTED XX, LITTLE VALLEY, N.Y. (arc etch) Square Point, Slick Black Handles, RARE MARK $150

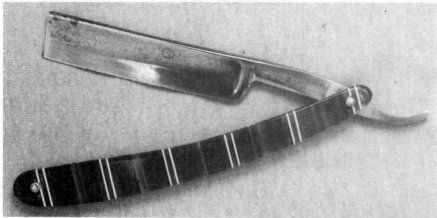

CASE BROS., TESTED XX, LITTLE VALLEY, N.Y. (arc etch) Square Point, Candy-stripe Handles, RARE MARK $225

CASE BROTHERS CUTLERY CO., LITTLE VALLEY, N.Y. (arc etch) Hollow Point, Imitation Ivory Handles, RARE MARK $150

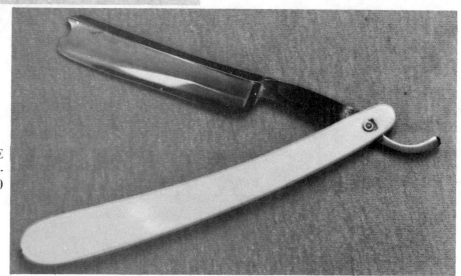

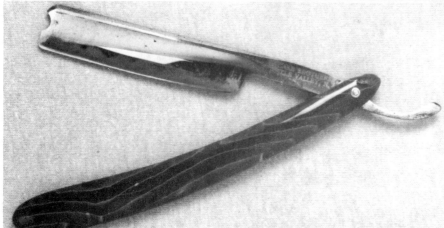

CASE BROTHERS, LITTLE VALLEY, N.Y. (line etch) Hollow Point, Imitation Horn Handles, RARE MARK $160

CASE BROTHERS, LITTLE VALLEY, N.Y. (line etch) Square Point, Blade has an extremely thick tang, Imitation Ivory Handles, RARE $185

Values For Razors in Excellent Condition

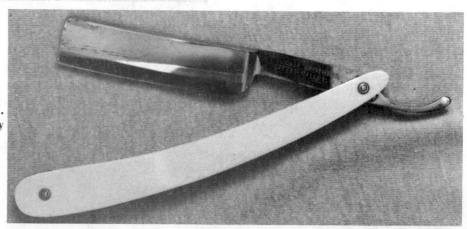

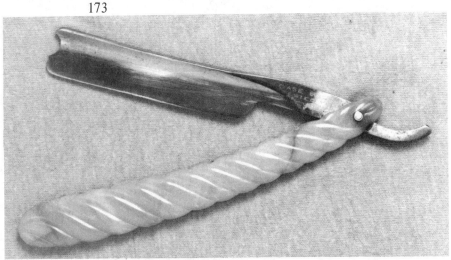

CASE BROS., "Tested XX" LITTLE VALLEY, N.Y. (line etch) Hollow Point, Cream and Rust Twisted Rope Handles, RARE MARK $160

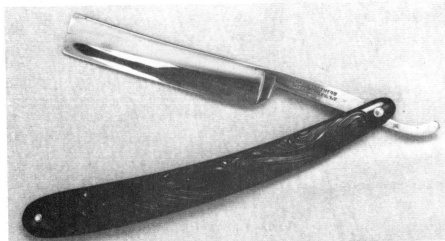

CASE BROTHERS, LITTLE VALLEY, N.Y. (stamp) Square Point, Black Flowing Hair Handles $135

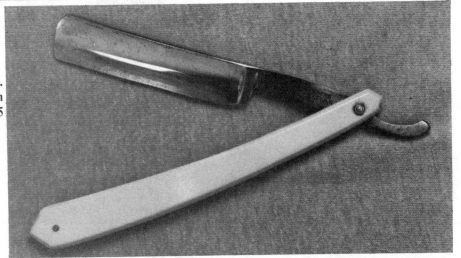

CASE BROTHERS, LITTLE VALLEY, N.Y. (stamp) Round Point, Imitation Ivory Coffin Handles $125

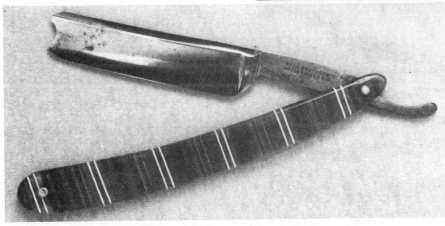

CASE BROTHERS, LITTLE VALLEY, N.Y. (stamp) Hollow Point, Candystripe Handles $200

Values For Razors in Excellent Condition

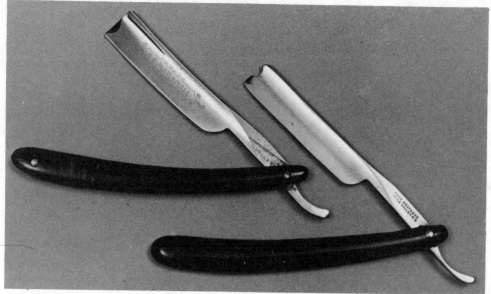

CASE BROS. TESTED XX, LITTLE VALLEY, N.Y. (arc etch) Square Point, Blade Etched "A.E. MARSHALL" Red & Brown Streaked Handles $160

CASE BROTHERS, LITTLE VALLEY, N.Y. (stamp) Hollow Point, Red & Brown Streaked Handles $125

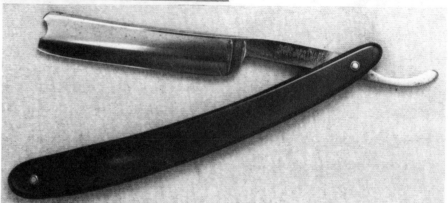

CASE BROTHERS, LITTLE VALLEY, N.Y. (stamp) Hollow Point, Slick Black Handles $100

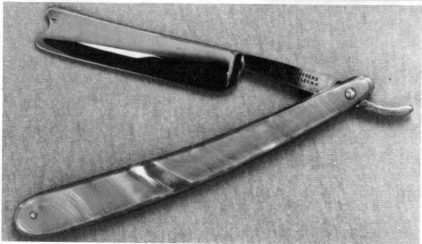

CASE BROTHERS, LITTLE VALLEY, N.Y. (stamp) Hollow Point, Green Pearl Handles $125

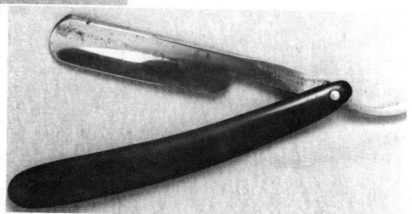

CASE BROTHERS, LITTLE VALLEY, N.Y. (stamp) Round Point, Slick Black Handles, very large blade $100

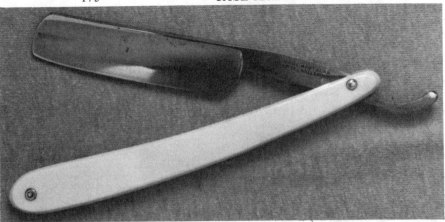

CASE BROTHERS, LITTLE VALLEY, N.Y.
(stamp) Round Point, Imitation Ivory Handles
$100

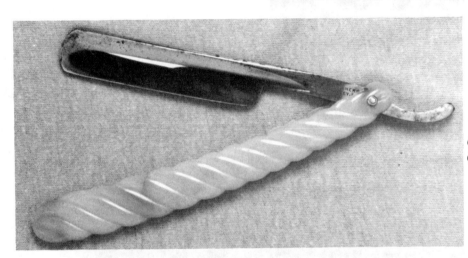

CASE BROTHERS, LITTLE VALLEY, N.Y.
(stamp) Cream & Rust Twisted Rope Handle
$125

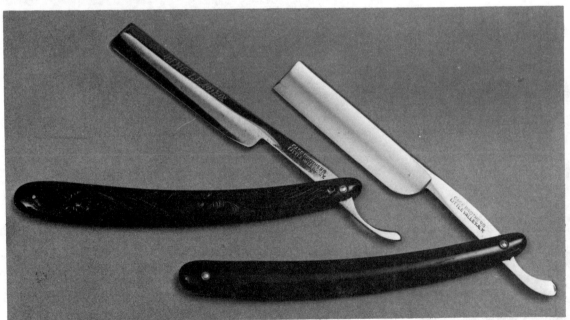

CASE BROTHERS, LITTLE VALLEY, N.Y. (stamp), Square Point Blade etched "RINGLEADER" Black
Flowing Hair Handles, RARE   **$175**
CASE BROTHERS, LITTLE VALLEY, N.Y. (stamp) Square Point, Slick Black   **$100**

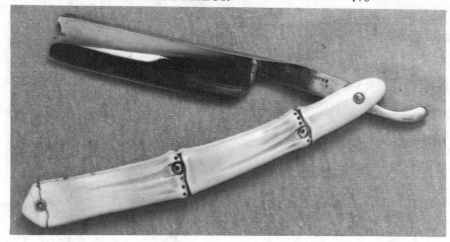

CASE BROTHERS, LITTLE VALLEY, N.Y. (stamp) Hollow Point, Rare Imitation Ivory Bamboo Handles $150

CASE BROTHERS TRAVEL RAZORS

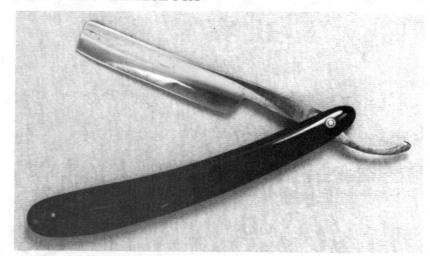

CASE BROTHERS CUTLERY CO., LITTLE VALLEY, N.Y. (arc etch) Travel Razor, Square Point, Rare Slick Black Handles, RARE MARK $175

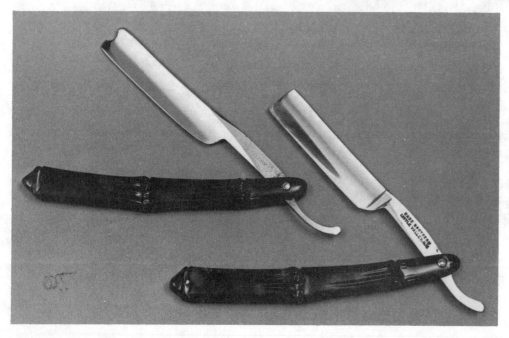

CASE BROTHERS CUTLERY CO., LITTLE VALLEY, N.Y. (arc etch), Hollow Point, Tortoise Bamboo Handles, RARE MARK $175

CASE BROTHERS, LITTLE VALLEY, N.Y. (stamp) Square Point Tortoise Bamboo Handles $150

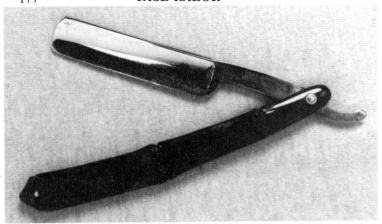

CASE BROTHERS, LITTLE VALLEY, N.Y.
(stamp) Round Point, Tortoise Bamboo Handles
$150

**CASE BROS. CUT CO.
KANE PA
LITTLE VALLEY, N.Y.**

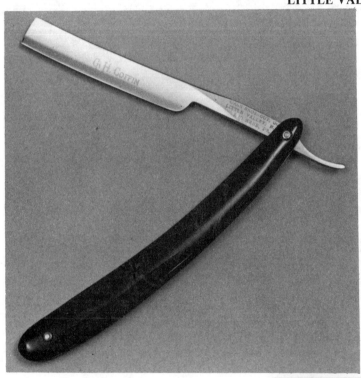

**CASE BROS. CUT CO., LITTLE VALLEY,
NY and KANE, PA (etch) Square Point Blade
Etched "G.H. COFFIN", Red & Brown Mottled
Handles, Extremely Rare Mark** $225

**CASE BROS. KANE, PA, LITTLE VALLEY,
N.Y. (etch), Square Point, Imitation Ivory Handles
In The Flowing Hair Pattern, Extremely Rare
Mark** $225

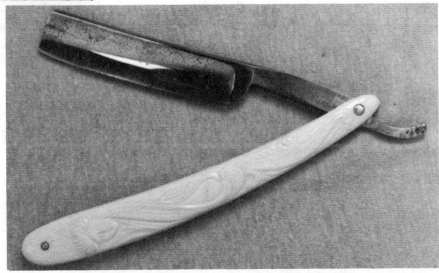

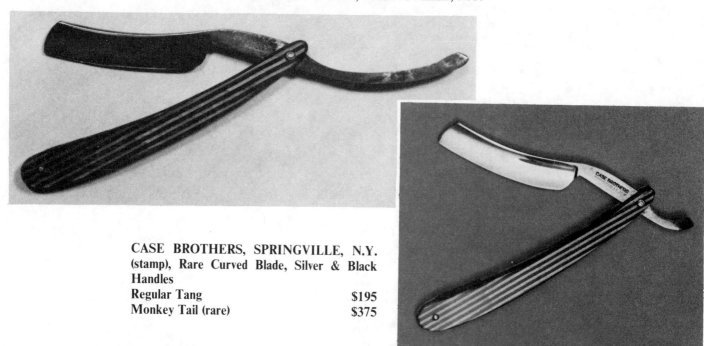

CASE BROTHERS, SPRINGVILLE, N.Y.
(stamp), Rare Curved Blade, Silver & Black
Handles
Regular Tang	$195
Monkey Tail (rare)	$375

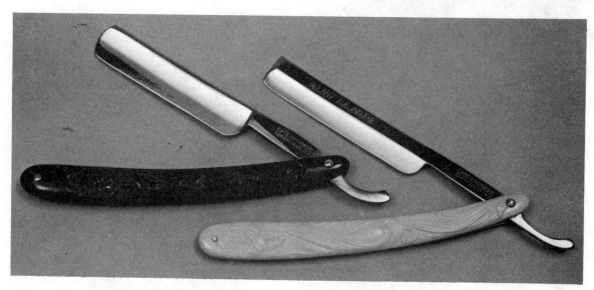

**CASE BROTHERS, SPRINGVILLE,
N.Y. (stamp)** Round Point, Black
Handles Molded in a Leaf Pattern
$150

**CASE BROTHERS, SPRINGVILLE,
N.Y. (stamp)** Square Point, Blade etched
"RINGLEADER", Imitation Ivory
Flowing Hair Handles $175

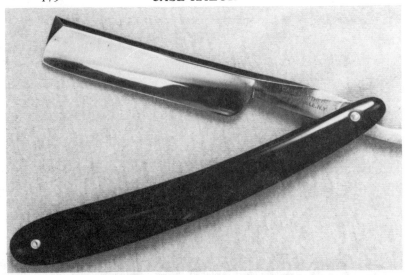

CASE BROTHERS, SPRINGVILLE, N.Y.
(stamp) Axe Point, Very Heavy Blade, Slick Black
Handles $140

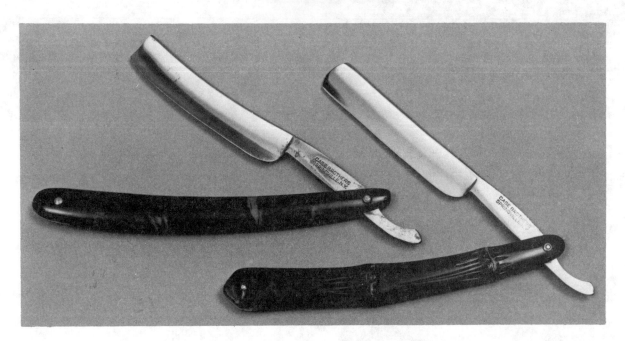

CASE BROTHERS, SPRINGVILLE,
N.Y. (stamp) Square Point, Red &
Brown Mottled Handles $125

CASE BROTHERS, SPRINGVILLE,
N.Y. (stamp) Round Point, Tortoise
Bamboo Handles $160

W.R. CASE & SONS
And Related Companies

NOTE: Due to the rarity of razors in "true mint" condition, the prices in this section are based on razors in excellent condition.

**LITTLE VALLEY KNIFE ASS'N
LITTLE VALLEY, N.Y.
(1900-1905)**

**CRANDALL CUTLERY
BRADFORD, PA
(1905-1912)**

Herbert E. Crandall (husband of Thersa Case) operated a jobbing house under the name Little Valley Knife Ass'n., later moving to Bradford, Pa., as a manufacturer under the name "Crandall Cutlery Company."

Crandall Cutlery Company was absorbed by W.R. Case and Sons in 1912. Herbert Crandall remained as an executive at Case.

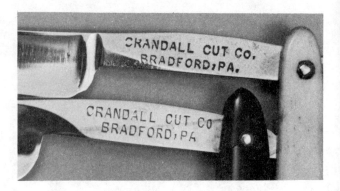

MANUFACTURED BY NAPANOCH

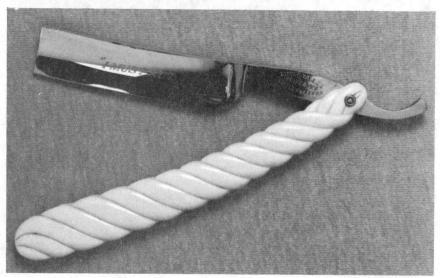

LITTLE VALLEY KNIFE ASS'N., LITTLE VALLEY, N.Y., Square point blade etched "I MUST KUT" Imitation Ivory, Twisted Rope Handle $125

LITTLE VALLEY KNIFE ASS'N., LITTLE VALLEY, N.Y. Travel Razor, Hollow Point Blade etched "I MUST KUT" $140

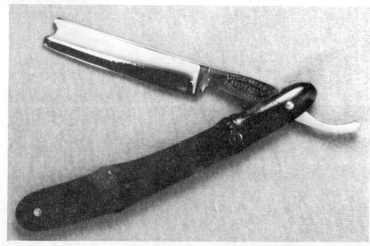

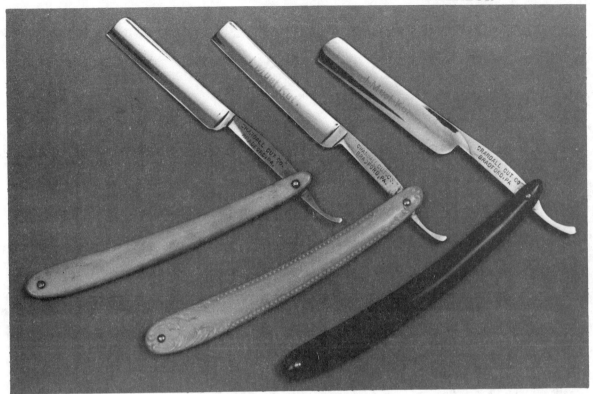

CRANDALL CUT. CO., BRADFORD, PA (stamp), Square Point, rear of tang stamped "GUILT EDGE," Smooth Bone Handles $65

Square Point, blade etched "I MUST KUT," Cream Colored Beaded Border Handles $65

Square Point, blade etched "I MUST KUT," Slick Black Handles $65

Values For Razors Pictured

KINFOLKS INCORPORATED
LITTLE VALLEY, N.Y.
(1926-1958)

Dean J., J. Russell, J. Elliott Case and Tint Champlin formed Kinfolks Incorporated in Little Valley, N.Y. in 1926, later to be joined by Jean Case in 1928.

While Kinfolks was a manufacturing company, most razors sold under the Kinfolks mark were made by W.R. Case and Sons. Kinfolks Incorporated went out of business sometime around 1958.

Robson Cutlery obtained the Kinfolks trademark and manufactured a line of pocket knives into the 1960's under the Kinfolks mark.

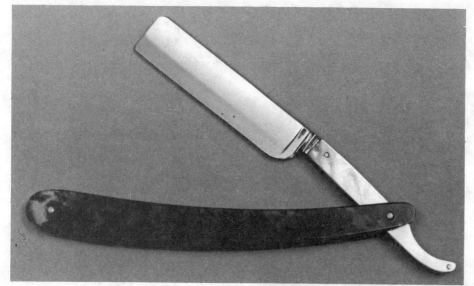

KINFOLKS INC. (etch) Square Point, Mother of Pearl inlaid tang with Tortoise Shell Handles $125

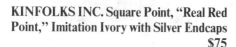

KINFOLKS INC. Square Point, "Real Red Point," Imitation Ivory with Silver Endcaps $75

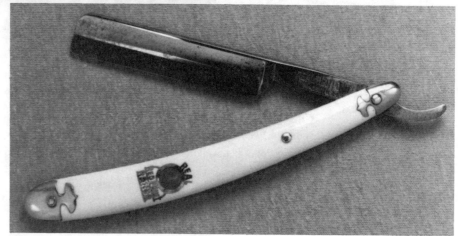

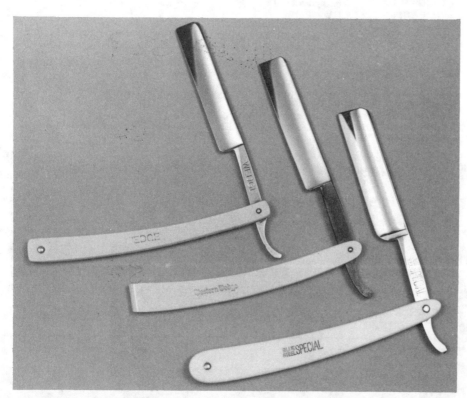

KINFOLKS INC. (stamp) Square Point, Imitation Ivory Handles with "WEDGE" stamped on them $40

Square Point, Imitation Ivory handles with "WESTERN WEDGE" stamped on them $50

Square Point, White Celluloid Handles with "BLUE STEEL SPECIAL" on them $35

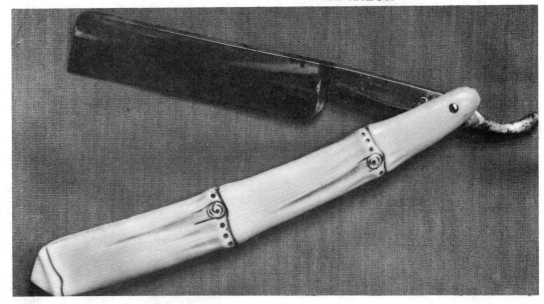

KINFOLKS INC. Square Point, Ivory Bamboo Handles   **$55**

GENCO COMPANY
BRADFORD, PA

In 1936, W.R. Case and Sons bought out the razor division of Geneva Cutlery Company in Geneva, N.Y. Only razors marked "GENCO" Bradford, Pa. were made at the Case factory and were marketed until about 1955.

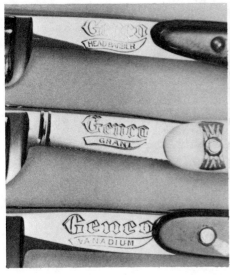

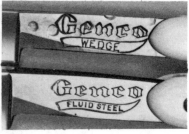

W.R. Case and Sons used various pattern names on the markside and the "GENCO" tang stamp was on the fileside of their Genco line, just as they did on their own line of razors during this period.

Mint "GENCO" Bradford, Pa. razors sell for between $35 to $65.

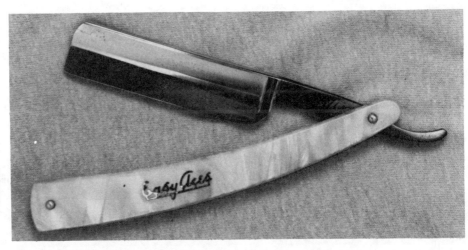

THE GENCO CO. BRADFORD, PA (1935-1955) Gun Blue tang marked "EASY ACES" (the GENCO version of the "CASE ACE," Square Point, Cracked Ice Handles with inlaid silver logo   **$65**

W.R. CASE AND SON
LITTLE VALLEY, N.Y.
(1902-1905)

   J. Russell Case broke away from his uncles at Case Brothers to form his jobbing company, incorporated in Little Valley, N.Y. in 1902 under the name of W.R. Case and Son Cutlery Company. Although Case and Son never manufactured cutlery, they were jobbing for Napanoch and other cutlery manufacturers of the day. This company went on to merge with N.H. Platts in late 1904, and later to form W.R. Case and Sons, Bradford, Pa. in 1905. This became the cornerstone of W.R. Case and Sons that we know today. Razors with these stampings are extremely rare and valuable, as well as historically interesting to the collector.

**MANUFACTURED BY
NAPANOCH**

**MANUFACTURED BY
GEORGE W. KORN**

**MANUFACTURED BY
C. PLATT'S SONS CO.**

THE RAZORS OF
W.R. CASE & SON

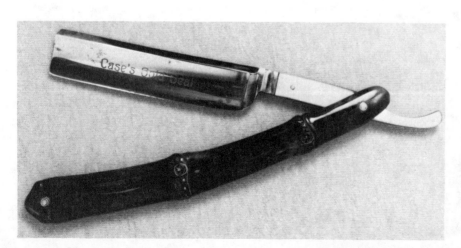

CASE'S GOLD SEAL, LITTLE VALLEY, N.Y., (mfg. by Platts) Square Point, blade etched "CASE'S GOLD SEAL," gold-wash, genuine Mother of Pearl tang with Tortoise Bamboo handles.
Extremely Rare $425

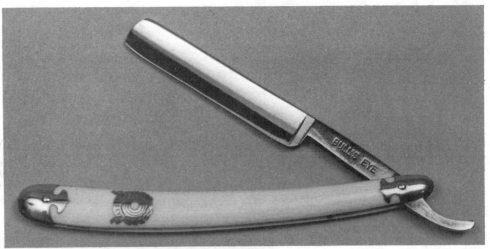

W.R. CASE & SON, LITTLE VALLEY, N.Y., (fileside) "BULLS EYE" on markside, Imitation Ivory handles with silver endcaps and inlaid logo. $280

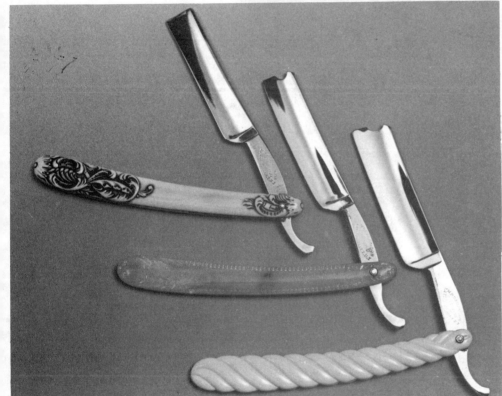

Values For Razors Pictured

W.R. CASE & SON CUTLERY CO., LITTLE VALLEY, N.Y. (arc mark), Square Point, Cream Handles with Wine colored Scroll $180

Hollow Point, Cream Beaded Border Handles $195

Hollow Point, Imitation Ivory Twisted Rope Handles $195

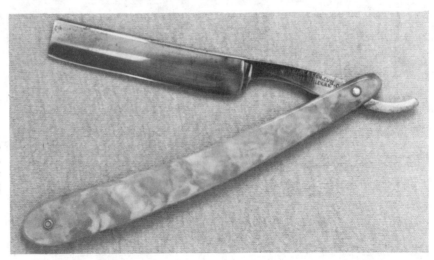

W.R. CASE & SON CUTLERY CO., LITTLE VALLEY, N.Y. (mfg. by G.W. Korn) Square Point, Mottled Yellow Celluloid Handles. RARE $175

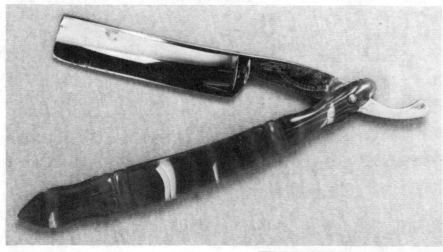

W.R. CASE & SON CUTLERY CO., LITTLE VALLEY, N.Y. (mfg. by Napanoch) Candy Stripe, Classic pattern, VERY RARE $275

W.R. CASE & SON, LITTLE VALLEY, N.Y. (mfg. by Platts) Square Point, Imitation Horn Handles $175

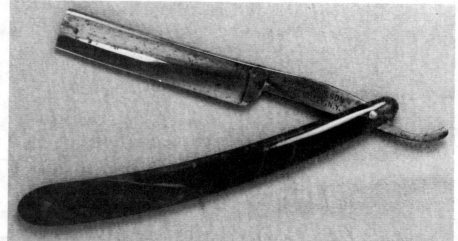

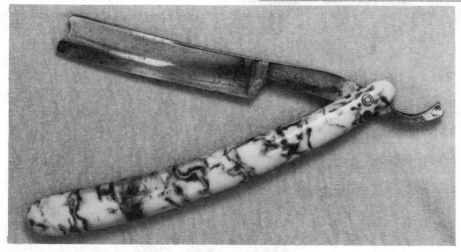

W.R. CASE & SON CUTLERY CO., LITTLE VALLEY, N.Y. (mfg. by Napanoch) Mottled Cream and Brown Celluloid Handles $160

May 12, 1914 Letterhead. Note artwork of factory with lettering on the roof which states: "W.R. Case & Sons manufacturers of Razors, razor strops, shears and butcher knives." No mention of pocket knives.

W.R. CASE AND SONS
BRADFORD, PA
(1905-1920)

These razors were the first razors actually manufactured by the merger of W.R. Case and Son and Platts Brothers, Eldrid, Pa., forming W.R. Case and Sons. All of these razors have the stamping on the mark side only. A few of these razors have pattern numbers on the finger loop. No information is available on the meaning of these markings, but they only appear on razors of this period.

Razors made during this period are the most beautiful of W.R. Case and Sons gender, having the widest selection of handles, some with very ornate molded designs, many having inlaid tangs of pearl, tortoise shell, imitation ivory, etc. Blades were more ornate too, with gimping or filework, and some with etching ranging from fancy "W.R. Case & Sons," to having a blade completely etched with a Damascus rosette pattern. While most razors made during this period were of plain design for the average man, many more ornate razors were made by W.R. Case and Sons in this timespan than any other period in their history. It was the only period W.R. Case and Sons etched their blades (with the few exceptions such as the "No Cussing" and the "Hand-Forged" (1920-1955) or used inlaid tangs. This was indeed a classic period for W.R. Case and Sons razor production.

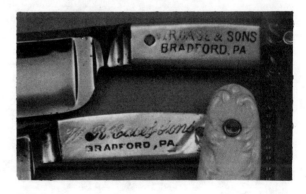

KNOWN W.R. CASE & SONS, BRADFORD, PA. MARKINGS   (markside 1905-1920)

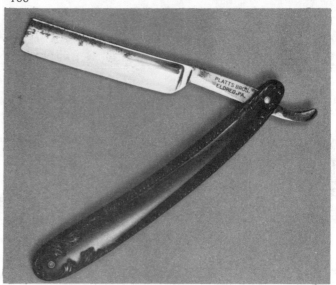

PLATTS BROS., ELDRED PA., Square Point, Brown Beaded Border Handles. $65

NOTE: W. R. Case (1905 to date) was a product of a merger with Platts Brothers Company. It was Platt's equipment, workers and expertise that made W.R. Case and Sons Cutlery. J. Russell Case was the office and sales end of the company. Therefore, W.R. Case Cutlery (1905-1920) and that of C. Platt's Sons (1895-1905) and Western States (1915-1925) look very much alike, and in fact were manufactured by the same man – N.H. Platts.

W.R. CASE & SONS, BRADFORD, PA razor box with hard to find original papers.

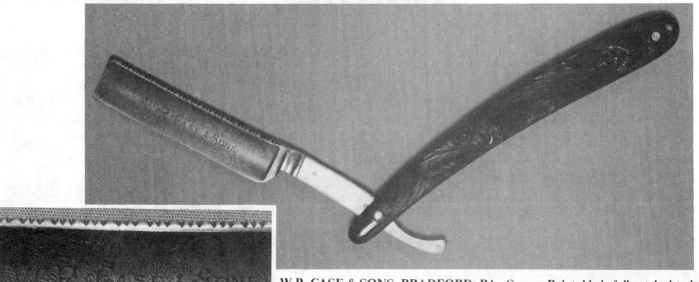

W.R. CASE & SONS, BRADFORD, PA., Square Point, blade fully etched to look like Damascus rosettes with "W.R. CASE & SONS" across it, top of blade fully gimped, genuine mother-of-pearl tang with black flowing hair handles. EXTREMELY RARE! $750

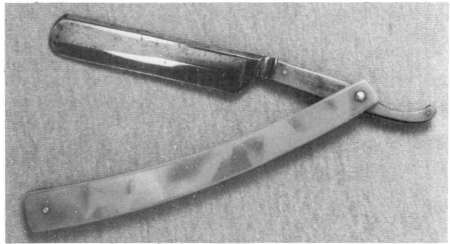

W.R. CASE & SONS, BRADFORD, PA.,
Round Point, Waterfall Tang with Waterfall
handles. EXTREMELY RARE $425

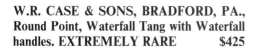

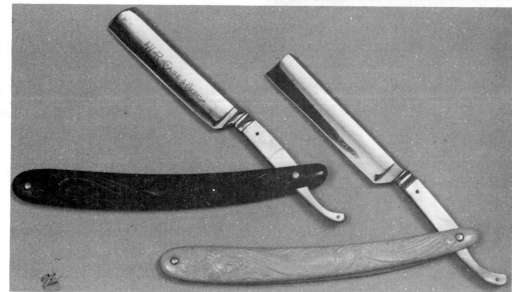

W.R. CASE BRADFORD, PA.
Round point blade etched "W.R.
CASE & SONS" Inlaid Mother of
Pearl tang, Black Flowing Hair
Handles $250
Square point, Inlaid Mother of Pearl
Tang with Imitation Ivory Flowing
Hair Handles $225

W.R. CASE & SONS, BRADFORD, PA.,
Round Point, Blade etched "W.R. CASE &
SONS" Black Tang with Black Flowing Hair
Handles $225

Values For Razors in Excellent Condition

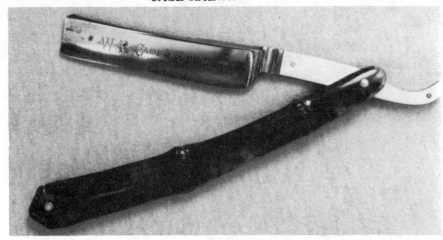

W.R. CASE & SONS, BRADFORD, PA., Square Point, Blade etched "W.R. Case & Sons," Genuine Mother of Pearl Tang, Tortoise Bamboo Handles $250

W.R. CASE & SONS, BRADFORD, PA. (script) Round Point, Inlaid Mother of Pearl Tang, Imitation Ivory Beaded Border Handles $275

Square Point Blade etched "W.R. Case & Sons" Inlaid Mother of Pearl Tang w/Butter & Molasses Beaded Border Handles $250

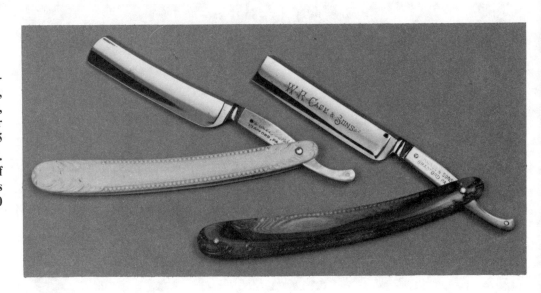

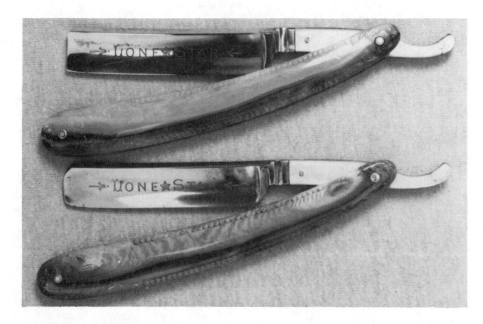

W.R. CASE & SONS, BRADFORD, PA., Round Point, blade etched "LONE STAR" with goldwash, genuine Mother of Pearl tang with Butter and Molasses Beaded Border $275

Square Point $275

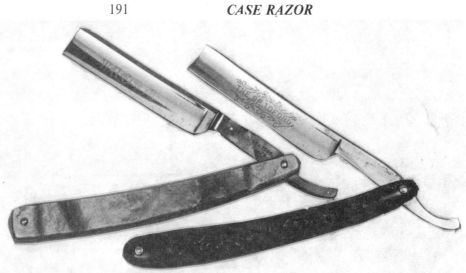

W.R. CASE & SONS, BRADFORD, PA. Square Point Blade etched "W.R. Case & Sons" Silver Swirl Inlaid tang w/matching handles $300

Square Point Blade with rare tang etching. Blade etched "The Bradford" Black Molded Leaf Handles $175

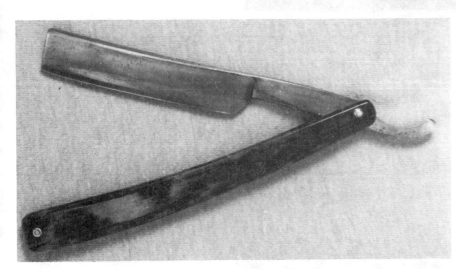

W.R. CASE & SONS, BRADFORD, PA. (Rare etching) Square Point, Imitation Bone Handles $155

W.R. CASE & SONS, BRADFORD, PA. Hollow Point, Butter & Molasses Beaded Border Handles $160

Hollow Point Blade etched "W.R. Case & Sons" Cream Streaked Beaded Border Handles $180

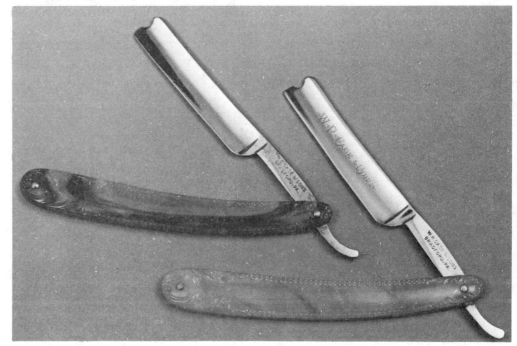

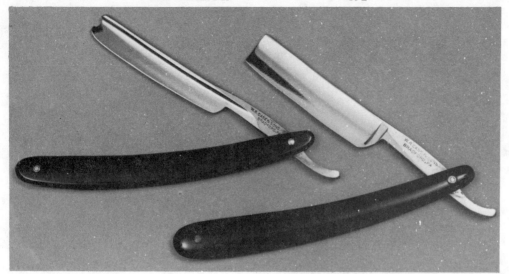

W.R. CASE & SONS, BRAD-FORD, PA. Hollow Point with unusual shape blade, Slick Black Handles $150

Square Point, Slick Black Handles $125

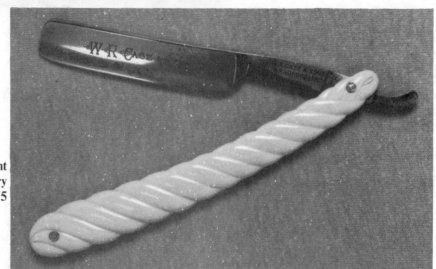

W.R. CASE & SONS, BRADFORD, PA. Round Point Blade etched "W.R. CASE & SONS" Imitation Ivory Twisted Rope Handles $175

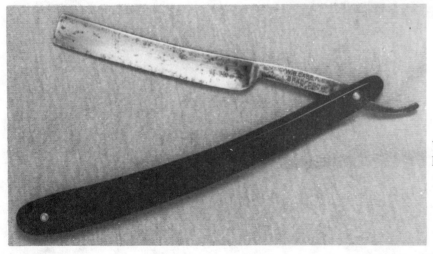

W.R. CASE & SONS, BRADFORD., Square Point Blade ground extremely thin, Slick Black Handles $140

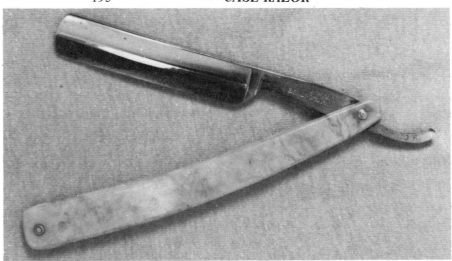

W.R. CASE & SONS, BRADFORD, PA.
Round Point, Mottled Yellow Celluloid
Handles $125

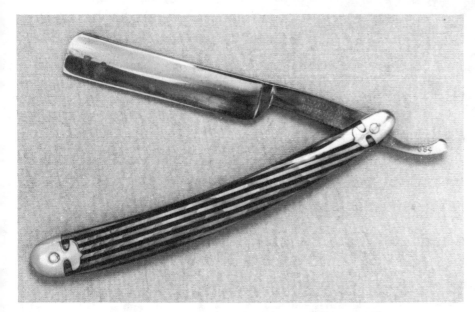

W.R. CASE & SONS, BRADFORD, PA. No.
354 Square Point, Silver & Black Handles
w/Silver End Caps $225

Values For Razors in Excellent Condition

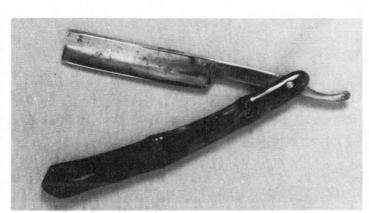

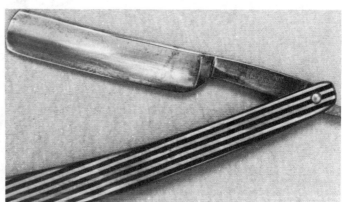

W.R. CASE & SONS, BRADFORD, PA., Square
Point, Tortoise Bamboo Handles $140

W.R. CASE & SONS, BRADFORD, PA., No. 334
Round Point Silver & Black Stripe Handles $135

W.R. CASE AND SONS
(made in Germany)
(1905-1915)

Razors having this German stamp were imported for a short period of time somewhere between 1905 and the start of World War I. All have the backs of the blades worked in a floral pattern with W.R. Case and Sons etched on them. Handles are of various colored celluloids, molded in the "Classic" pattern. As the war grew more and more imminent with Germany, many of these razors were imported without "Germany" stamped on the tang, and some have no marking at all except the blade etching.

ON FILESIDE

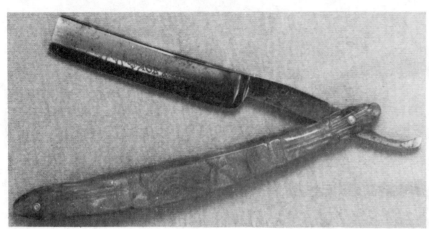

W.R. CASE & SONS, BRADFORD, PA. "Made in Germany" on fileside, worked back, blade etched "W.R. CASE & SONS", goldstone classic handles, RARE $225

(right) "W.R. CASE & SONS" etched on blade only, this tang escaped marking in Germany, worked back blade, black classic handles $150

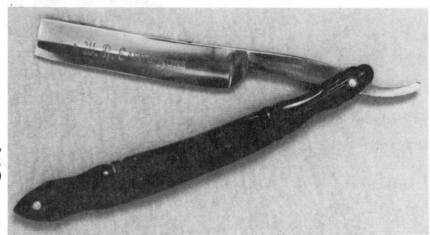

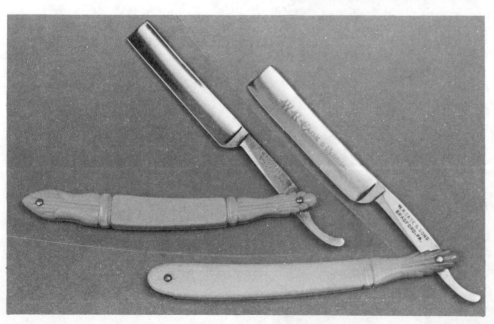

W.R. CASE & SONS, BRADFORD, PA., Square Point, Imitation Ivory Classic Handles $135

Square Point, blade etched "W.R. CASE & SONS" bone handles with the top carved in the classic pattern $200

Values For Razors in Excellent Condition

"W.R. CASE AND SONS"
"CORN RAZOR"
(1905-1920)

Although not actually manufactured by W.R. Case and Sons, they marketed a corn razor for a very short period of time between 1905 to 1920. They are very rare! $200

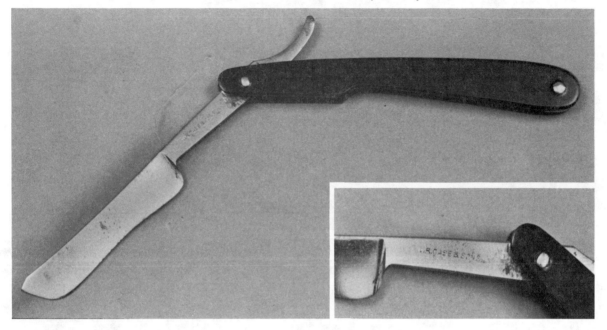

W.R. CASE AND SONS
BRADFORD, PA.
(1920-1955)

All razors of this period have a pattern name such as "Adoration," Gold Nuggett, etc.. . . on the mark side and the Case stamping appears on the fileside. Both style stamps seems to appear throughout the entire timespan, therefore, it cannot be used to date earlier razors. As a general rule, razors that are more ornate with silver inlays and endcaps on the handles, etc. are of the older gender.

Let's take for example the real "Red Point" razor. The "Red Point" circa 1920 had silver endcaps, imitation ivory handles, inlaid silver logo with red enamel center. The "Red Point" circa 1930 continued with the inlaid silver logo with the red enamel dot, however, the handle material was changed to cream-colored celluloid and no longer had the silver endcaps. "Red Point" razors of the 1940's had cream colored celluloid handles with a painted red dot logo. As you can see, as the years passed less and less extra work went into razor production.

With a very few exceptions, razor patterns of this period always had the same handle material. For example, "Gold Nuggett" razors always had gold-colored handles and the "Bull's Eye" razor used tortoise shell for their handles. There were no handles with molded designs such as beaded borders, or flowing hair. Except for rare decorations such as inlays, or endcaps, all razors were smooth handles.

Blades of this period, with a few exceptions, are identical in style, having either square or round point. A rare example of a hollow point razor of this period is the "Cornhusker." All razors had fully polished blades and were available in either 9/16" or 5/8" width, some with gun blue or goldwash tangs. The "Bulls Eye" and the "No Cussing" (circa 1920-1955) razors are some of the rare examples of etching during this period. Some are a combination of etching and goldwash, the "Bulls Eye" having a hand hammered tang.

Most of these razors were discontinued before 1940, but since there were large stocks of many of these razors, they were listed in catalogs and sold throughout the 1940's and into the early 1950's. Case still sold several of these patterns up until 1955.

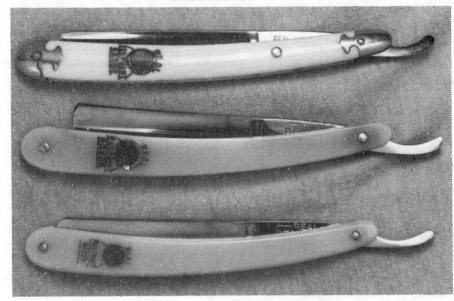

"REAL RED POINT" Silver Endcaps and in-laid logo   **$125**
Inlaid logo   **$90**
Painted logo   **$45**

"CASE'S ACE" Imitation White Pearl, stamped logo   **$75**

Cracked Ice, inlaid silver logo   **$95**

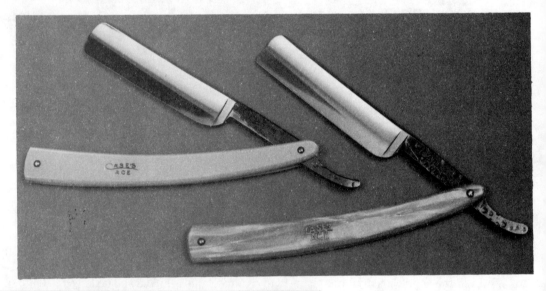

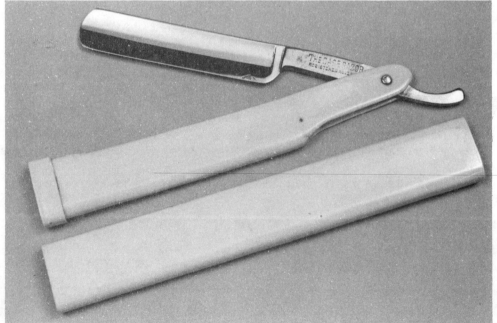

"THE CASE RAZOR" Reg. No. 1915, Imitation Ivory handles with matching case   **$125**

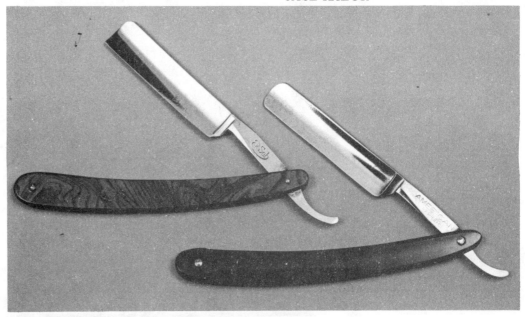

"EKSEL" Silver & Molasses
Celluloid handles $75
"AMERICAN   BARBER"
Slick Black handles $60

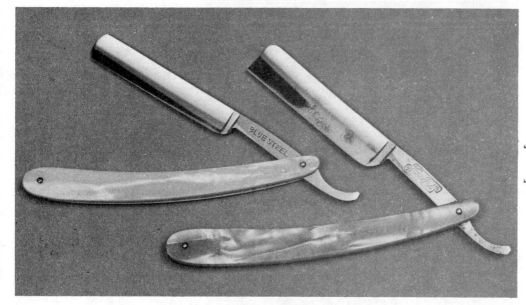

"BLUE STEEL" Cracked Ice handles
$65
"HONOR ROLL" Cracked Ice handles
$65

"BULL'S EYE" hammered tang, Imitation Tortoise handles, blade etched
"HAND FORGED"
Round point $100
Square point $100

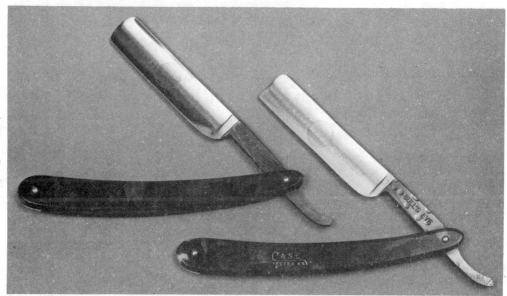

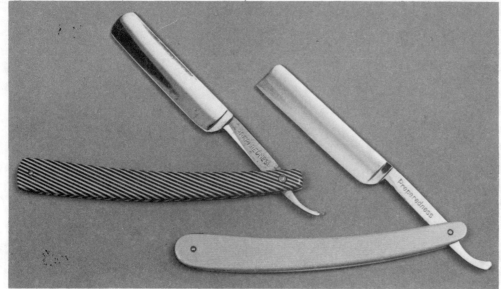

**"PREPAREDNESS" Black & White
Stripe $75
Imitation Ivory $60**

**"PREPAREDNESS" Slick Black $50
Clear Yellow $55**

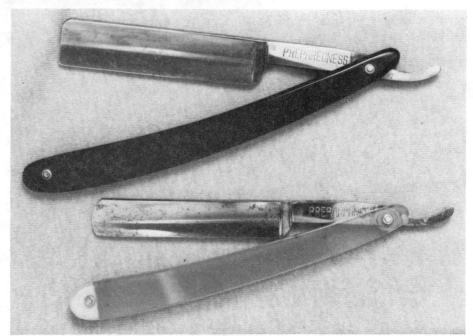

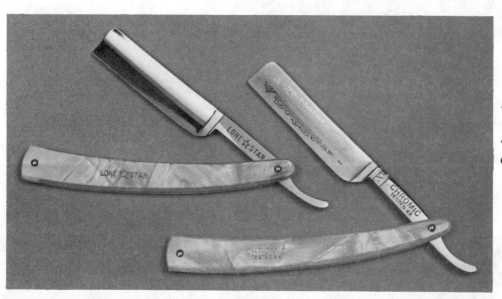

**"LONE STAR" Cracked Ice handles
                             $70
"CHROMATIC TESTED XX" blade
etched "OUR BEST RAZOR" $125**

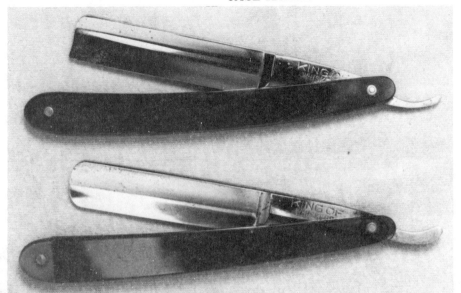

"KING OF WHISKERS" transparent
red celluloid handles
Square point $55
Round point $55

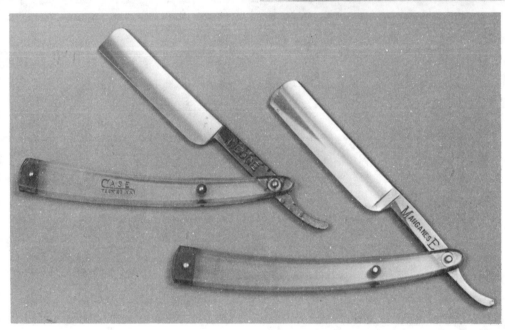

"WEDGE" Hammered tang, Clear
Smoke handles $65
"MANANESE" Clear Smoke handles
                                $65

"LIBERTY SPECIAL" Transparent
Blue Celluloid handles $65

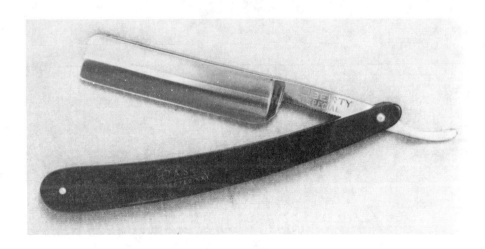

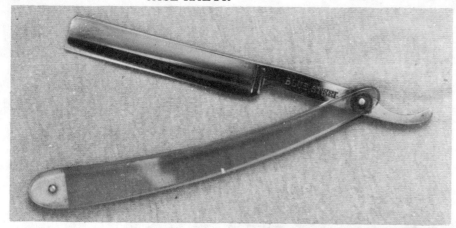

"BLUE STEEL" Transparent Yellow
handles $50

"REAL BLUE POINT" Inlaid Bowties
                                                     $75

Painted logo $45

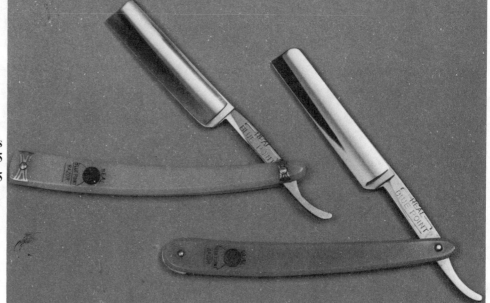

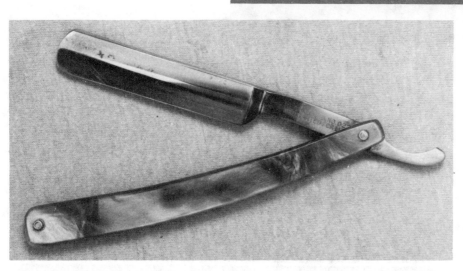

"Reg. No. 023"
"WARRENTED FOR LIFE" Green Pearl
handles $80

Values Are For Mint Razors

201　　　　　　　　　*CASE RAZOR*

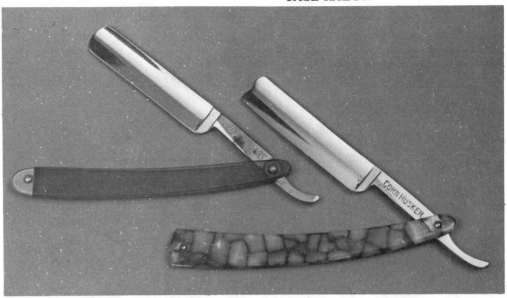

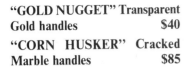

"GOLD NUGGET" Transparent Gold handles　　$40

"CORN HUSKER" Cracked Marble handles　　$85

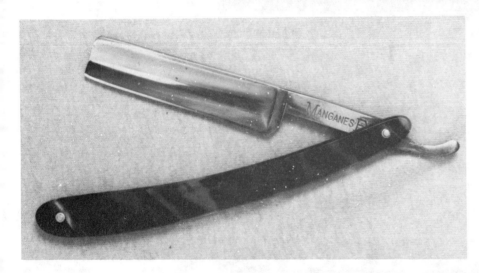

"MANGANESE" Imitation Tortoise handles　　　　$60

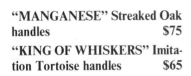

"MANGANESE" Streaked Oak handles　　$75

"KING OF WHISKERS" Imitation Tortoise handles　　$65

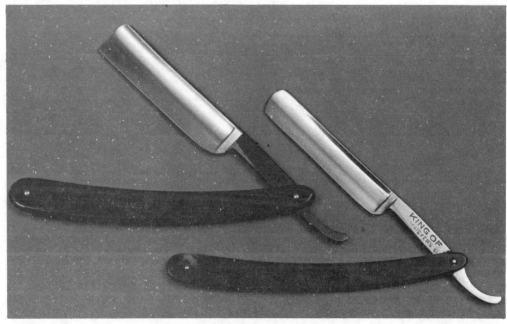

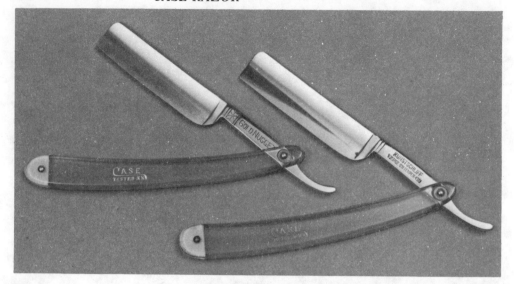

"GOLD NUGGETT" Gold Wash tang, Transparent gold handles $80

"KUNSTSCHIFF VOLTAGE TEMPER" Transparent Gold handles $65

"KUNSTSCHIFF VOLTAGE TEMPER" Goldwash tang, Gold Pearl handles $90

"BLUE STEEL" Green Pearl handles $75

WARNING! THE HANDLE MATERIAL USED ON THESE RAZORS ARE EXTREMELY CORROSIVE TO METAL SURFACES

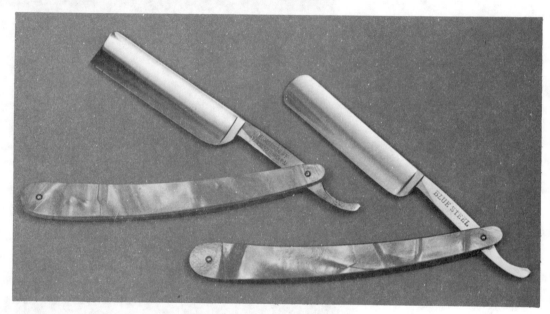

"Reg. No. 023 WARRENTED FOR LIFE" Imitation Tortoise handles $75

"KING OF WHISKERS" Transparent Red Celluloid handles $55

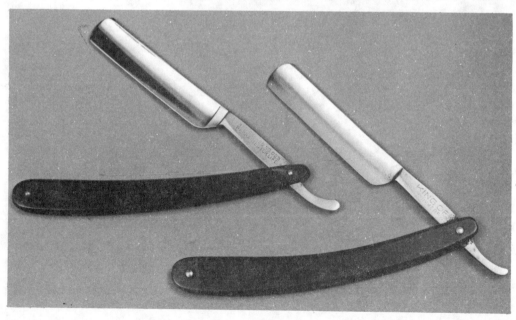

Values Are For Mint Razors

W. R. CASE & SONS CUTLERY CO.
BRADFORD, PENNSYLVANIA

RAZORS

No. 505

Hollow ground blade. fine glaze finish, tang highly polished, branded "EKseb". Made in 5/8 inch width blade, and in honed and round point.

Handle is beautifully mottled celluloid. "EK s e b" stamped on tang and handle.

No. B02

Hollow ground blade highly polished, tang blued, branded "BLUE STEEL." Made in 9/16 or 5/8 inch width blade, and in round or hone point.

Handle is dark blue celluloid, with our trade mark in gold.

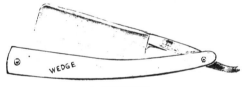

WEDGE

Wedge ground fine glaze finish blade. Tang gun-metal finish, stamped "WEDGE." Blade is made in 9/16 or 5/8 inch width with hone or round point.

Handle is imitation ivory branded "WEDGE," in red.

No. G03

Full concave ground blade highly polished. Oval tang, gold plated, branded "GOLD NUGGET." Made in 9/16, 5/8 or 6/8 inch width blade with hone or round point.

Handle is oval amber colored celluloid, with our trade mark stamped on handle in silver.

No. 182

Full concave ground blade, highly polished mirror finish tang branded "CORN HUSKER." Made in 5/8 inch width blade and hollow hone point.

Handle mottled cream and black celluloid, our trade mark stamped on handle in gold.

RAZORS

No. 183

Full concave ground blade. Etched "HAND FORGED" with gold center plated. Tang gun-metal finish, and hand hammered. Made in 9/16 or 5/8 inch blade in hone or round point.

Handle is imitation tortoise shell celluloid, our trade mark stamped in silver on the handle.

No. 023

Full concave ground blade. Gold etching highly finished, tang mirror finish branded "WARRANTED FOR LIFE." Made in 5/8 inch width blade and in hone or round point.

Handle cream colored celluloid with trade mark in red.

RED POINT

Full concave ground blade of the highest quality, fine glaze finish. Mirror finish tang branded "REAL RED POINT." Made in 9/16 or 5/8 inch width blade with hone or round point.

Cream color celluloid handle with metal inlay having a red center.

No. 844

Full concave ground blade the same as the finest barber's razor, beautiful finish. Gold plated tang branded "KUNTS CHIFF VOLTAGE TEMPER." Made in 9/16 and 5/8 inch width with round or hone point.

Handle is beautiful Pearl on amber celluloid. Trade mark on handle in gold.

No. 17114

Full concave ground highly finished blade. Gun-metal tang branded "MANGANESE." Blade made in 9/16 or 5/8 inch width blade in round or hone point.

Handle of oak colored celluloid. "MANGANESE" stamped on handle in silver.

"TESTED XX catalog dated 1939, notice "wedge tang stamp is 'GENCO' "

W. R. CASE & SONS CUTLERY CO.

BRADFORD, PENNSYLVANIA

No. G03

Full concave ground blade highly polished. Oval tang, gold plated, branded "GOLD NUGGETT." Made in $\frac{9}{16}$, $\frac{5}{8}$ or 6/8 inch width blade with hone or round point.

Handle is oval amber colored celluloid, with our trade mark stamped on handle in silver.

No. 023

Full concave ground blade. Gold etching highly finished, tang mirror finish branded "WARRANTED FOR LIFE". Made in $\frac{5}{8}$ inch width blade and in hone or round point.

Handle cream colored celluloid with trade mark in red.

No. 182

Full concave ground blade, highly polished mirror finish tang branded "CORN HUSKER". Made in $\frac{5}{8}$ inch width blade and hollow hone point.

Handle mottled cream and black celluloid, our trade mark stamped on handle in gold.

No. 183

Full concave ground blade. Etched "HAND FORGED" with gold center plated. Tang gun-metal finish, and hand hammered. Made in $\frac{5}{8}$ inch blade in hone or round point.

Handle is imitation tortoise shell celluloid, our trade mark stamped in silver on the handle.

No. 844

Full concave ground blade the same as the finest barber's razor, beautiful finish. Gold plated tang branded "KUNTS CHIFF VOLTAGE TEMPER". Made in $\frac{5}{8}$ inch width with round or hone point.

Handle is beautiful Pearl on amber celluloid. Trade mark on handle in gold.

No. 17114

Full concave ground highly finished blade. Gun-metal tang branded "MANGANESE". Blade made in $\frac{5}{8}$ inch width blade in round or hone point.

Handle of oak colored celluloid. "MANGANESE" stamped on handle in silver.

BLUE POINT

Full concave ground blade that is preferred by barbers. No finer razor for quality and workmanship has ever been made anywhere. Tang is mirror finished and branded "REAL BLUE POINT". Blade is made in either $\frac{5}{8}$ or $\frac{9}{16}$ inch width with either round, square or hone point.

Handle is cream colored celluloid with name stamped in blue.

CASE ACE

Full concave blade for barber or self shaver, finish and grind are of our finest quality. Tang is hand hammered and blue finish, branded "CASE ACE". Made in $\frac{9}{16}$ or $\frac{5}{8}$ inch width blade with round and hone point.

Handle of beautiful imitation pearl celluloid, metal tips on both ends. Name in metal inlay on handle.

COBALT

Full concave ground blade of the finest barber quality. Gun-metal finish tang branded "COBALT MAGNETIC". Blade made in $\frac{5}{8}$ inch width in either round or square point.

LONE STAR

This is one of our finest full concave blades perfectly ground and finished. Tang is mirror polished and branded "LONE STAR". Blade is made in $\frac{9}{16}$ or $\frac{5}{8}$ inches in width, and can be furnished in either round or hone point.

Handle is made of beautiful imitation pearl with metal tip and "LONE STAR" stamped in gold.

mark stamped on handle in gold.

(Specify width of blade and point wanted when ordering)

TESTED XX catalog dated 1942

W. R. CASE & SONS CUTLERY CO.
BRADFORD, PENNSYLVANIA

RAZORS

COBALT

Full concave ground blade of the finest barber quality. Gun-metal finish tang branded "COBALT MAGNETIC." Blade made in 5/8 inch width in either round or square point.

LONE STAR

This is one of our finest full concave blades perfectly ground and finished. Tang is mirror polished and branded "LONE STAR." Blade is made in 9/16 or 5/8 inches in width, and can be furnished in either round or hone point.

Handle is made of beautiful imitation pearl with metal tip and "LONE STAR" stamped in gold.

BLUE POINT

Full concave ground blade that is preferred by barbers. No finer razor for quality and workmanship has ever been made anywhere. Tang is mirror finished and branded "REAL BLUE POINT." Blade is made in either 5/8 or 9/16 inch width with either round, square or hone point.

Handle is cream colored celluloid with name stamped in blue.

RAZORS

RED BIRD

One of the most popular barber razors that is also used by self shavers. Blade is full concave perfectly ground and finished. Tang is mirror finished, branded "RED BIRD." Blade is made in 5/8 inch width in hone point only.

Handle is transparent celluloid with metal tips in both ends. Red Bird stamped in red on handle.

CASE ACE

Full concave blade for barber or self shaver, finish and grind are of our finest quality. Tang is hand hammered and blue finish, branded "CASE ACE." Made in 9/16 or 5/8 inch width blade with round and hone point.

Handle of beautiful imitation pearl celluloid, metal tips on both ends. Name in metal inlay on handle.

(Specify width of blade and point wanted when ordering)

TESTED XX catalog dated 1942

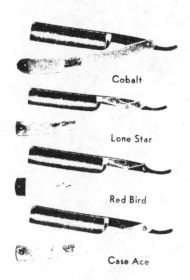

No. 1

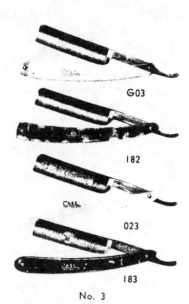

No. 2

No. 3

ILLUSTRATION NO. 1

COBALT Full concave ground blade of the finest barber quality. Gun-metal tang. Handle stamped "COBALT". Blade made in 5/8" width with hone point.

LONE STAR This is one of our finest full concave blades perfectly ground and finished. Tang is mirror polished and branded "LONE STAR". Blade is made in 9/16 or 5/8 inches in width, hone point. Handle is made of beautiful imitation pearl with "LONE STAR" stamped in gold.

RED BIRD One of the most popular barber razors that is also used by self shavers. Blade is full concave perfectly ground and finished. Tang is mirror finished, branded "RED BIRD". Blade is made in 5/8 inch width in hone point only. Handle is transparent celluloid. Red Bird stamped in red on handle.

CASE ACE Full concave blade for barber or self shaver, finish and grind are of our finest quality. Tang is hand hammered and blue finish, branded "CASE ACE". Made in 9/16 or 5/8 inch width blade with round and hone point. Handle of beautiful imitation pearl celluloid. Name in metal inlay on handle.

ILLUSTRATION NO. 2

RED POINT Full concave ground blade of the highest quality, fine glaze finish. Mirror finish tang branded "REAL RED POINT". Made in 9/16 or 5/8 inch width blade with hone or round point. Cream color celluloid handle with red stamping.

No. 844 Full concave ground blade the same as the finest barber's razor, beautiful finish. Gold plated tang branded "KUNSTSCHLIFF VOLTAGE TEMPER". Made in 5/8 inch width with hone point. Handle is amber celluloid.

No. 17114 Full concave ground highly finished blade. Gun-metal tang branded "MANGANESE". Blade made in 5/8 inch width blade in hone point. Handle of oak colored celluloid. "MANGANESE" stamped on handle in silver.

BLUE POINT Full concave ground blade that is preferred by barbers. No finer razor for quality and workmanship has ever been made anywhere. Tang is mirror finished and branded "REAL BLUE POINT". Blade is made in 5/8 inch width with hone point. Handle is cream colored celluloid with name stamped in blue.

ILLUSTRATION NO. 3

No. G03 Full concave ground blade highly polished. Tang, gold plated, branded "GOLD NUGGET." Made in 9/16, 5/8 or 6/8 inch width blade with hone or round point. Handle is amber colored celluloid, with our trade mark stamped in silver. loid, with our trade mark stamped on handle in silver.

No. 182 Full concave ground blade, highly polished mirror finish tang branded "CORN HUSKER". Made in 5/8 inch width blade and hollow hone point. Handle mottled cream and black celluloid, our trade mark stamped on handle in gold.

No. 023 Full concave ground blade. Highly finished gold etching on blade, tang mirror finished. Made in 5/8 inch width in hone point. Handle cream colored celluloid with trade marks in red.

No. 183 Full concave ground blade. Etched "HAND FORGED" with gold plated center. Tang gun-metal finish, and hand hammered. Made in 5/8 inch blade in hone point. Handle is imitation tortoise shell celluloid, our trade mark stamped in silver on the handle.

CASE XX catalog dated 1946

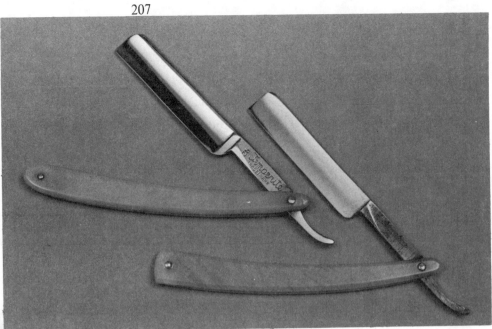

"ADORATION" Yellow Swirl
handles w/logo
Any type $45

"TEMPERITE" Yellow Swirl
handles
Any type $45

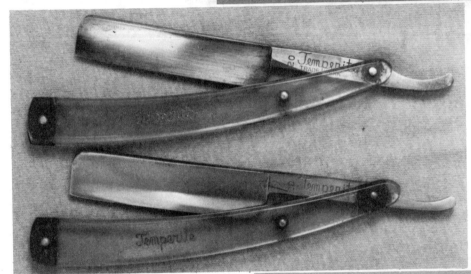

"TEMPERITE" Clear Yellow or
Smoke handles
Any type $45

"RED IMP" Red handles
Any type $25

Values Are For Mint Razors

W.R. CASE & SONS
Germany
(1920-1940)

These razors were made to look just like Case razors of the period. The tang reads "Made by Soligin Germany Experts" (on the markside). This is the second German invasion, it came sometime between 1920 and the start of World War II. Though they were not quite as rare as the early German razor, they are still very hard to find.

MADE IN USA
BY CASE
(1955-1962)

In the early 1950's W.R. Case started to exhaust their existing stock of straight razors. There was still a small demand for razors in the United States, but there was even a greater market in South America. In 1955 Case introduced a line of lesser quality razors mainly for the export market, marked "MADE IN USA BY CASE." Razors made during this period were of plain design and the blades were non-polished. In 1962 W.R. Case and Sons discontinued their production of straight razors, thus ending 57 years of razor production.

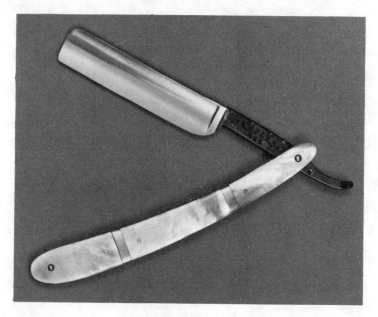

"CASE ACE"
Genuine Mother of Pearl handles, Gun Blue hammered tang   **$400**

Approximately 100 genuine mother-of-pearl "CASE ACE" razors were made in 1962 when W.R. Case and Sons ended razor production, 62 of the best were given to Case executives, salesmen and employees.

MISCELLANEOUS

These following pages contain photos of knives that arrived after this book was prepared for press. The author felt they warranted this special miscellaneous section.

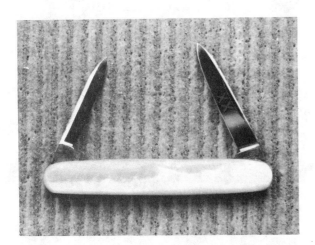

Case Bros. Cutlery Co. XX Stamped on blade   Pearl   3" $225

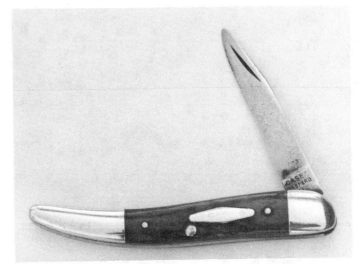

Pointed Shield   3⅛"   Case Brad.., Pa.
1 Blade mini Toothpick, Green Bone $350

Pearl (rare)   3⅝"   W.R. Case & Sons $700

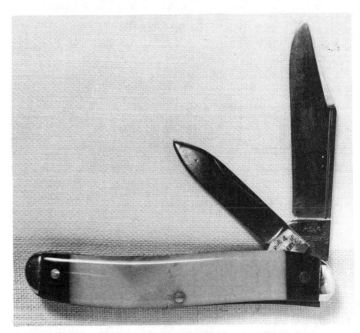

W.R. Case & Son Cutlery Co.   Waterfall   1902-1905
   (rare stamp) $350

Crandall "Cigar" Bone   4⅛" $500

210

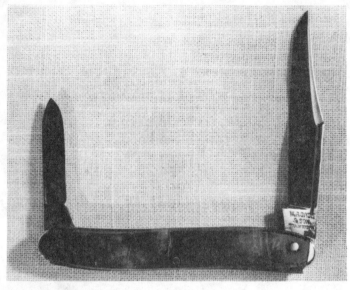

W.R. Case & Son, Brad. Pa. (rare stamp) 3⅛" 1902-1905 $250
Courtesy Ricky Cox

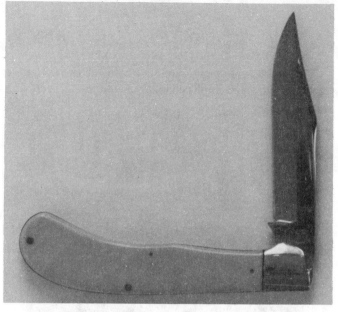

3100SAB Yellow Scales   4⅝"   Case Tested XX $500

Official Barnum & Bailey Circus Throwing Knife
Black Micarta, 1940 era. Case XX, 12" overall, 8" blade $150
Courtesy J. Merrigan

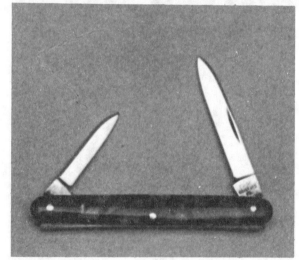

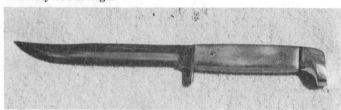

SHEATH KNIFE Case XX USA
Smooth Bone   5 Finn. James Giles Collection $75

M201 Blue, Red, Green, Grey Mottled 2⅝" Case Brad., Pa. $225

62100   Green Bone   4¾"   Case Tested XX $750

6206½   Rough Black   2⅝"   Case XX (rare) $175
Courtesy Ricky Cox

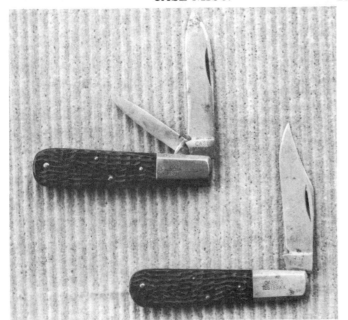

62005   Green Bone Barlow   3⅜"   Case Brad. Pa. $300
61005½   Green Bone Barlow   3⅜"   Case Brad Pa. $300

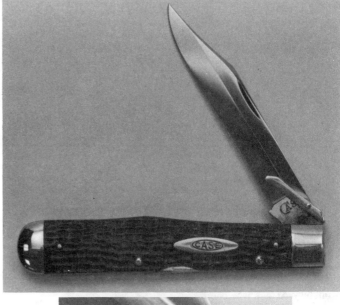

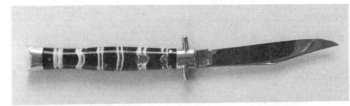

6111½L   Case Green Bone   4⅜"   Case (rare) $500
     1920-40

6110SP   Imi. Bone   3⅛"   Case Tested XX $225
Spey or Bud

R1212½   SB Candy Stripe   4"   Case Tested XX $550

ABBREVIATIONS	
½	master blade is clip blade
B	Budding
EO	Easy Opener
F	File
J	Long Spay Blade
K	Corkscrew
LR	Electrician's Knife
M	Metal
PEN	Pen Blade
PU	Punch Blade
R	Bail in handle
RAZ	Razor Blade
SAB	Sabor Blade
SC/SCI	Scissors
SH	Sheepfoot blade
SP	Spay Blade
SSP	Stainless Steel, Polished Blade Edge
SS	Stainless Steel
T	Tip Bolsters

SPEAR
62213   Rogers Green Bone   5¼"   Case Tested XX rare $1,000

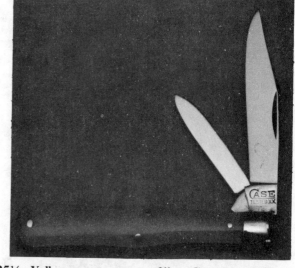

1215 Gunstock Walnut   W.R. Case & Sons, Bradford, PA $550
Courtesy Armand Micciuli

32025½ Yellow   3"   Case Tested XX $225

8215   Pearl   Tested XX $650

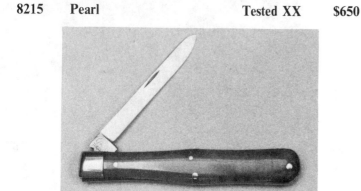

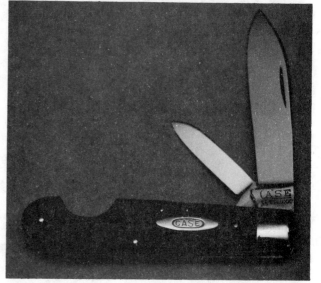

B1025   Waterfall   3"   Tested XX $225

6228EO Green Bone   3½"   Case Tested XX $200

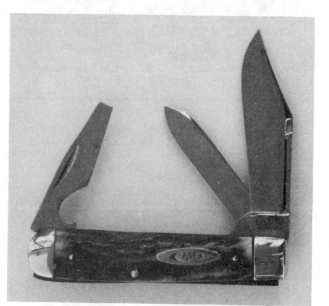

5225½   Stag LP   3" $250

5331½   LP Stag - rare   3¾"   Case Tested XX $350

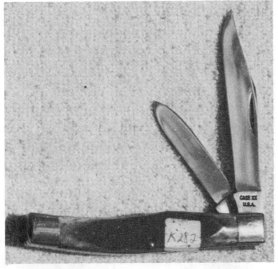

6232   **Smooth Bone**   **Case XX USA**   **$85**
James Giles Collection

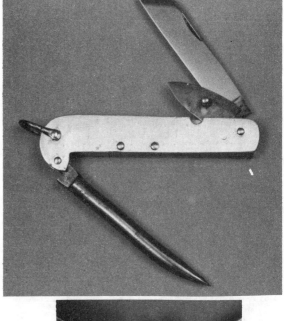

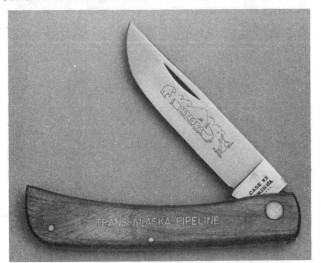

P138LSS Pakkawood 500 made 4¾"   **Case 5 Dot**
1975   Lockblade   Alyeska Pipeline   **$130**

M346R   Navy Knife - SH Blade, can opener, Marlin spike, aluminum
handles. 4⅞" Metal Stamping Ltd.   Case XX $150

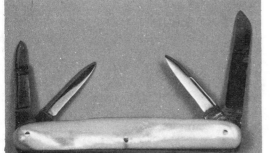

8438   **Pearl - 1902-1905**   **3⅝"   W.R. Case & Son**   **$700**

4247FK   Greenskeeper 1940-64 3⅞"   Case XX
Spl. Dandy Line Blade   **$300**

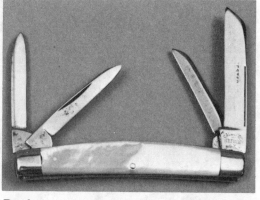

84052   Pearl   3¾"   Case Bros. Little
                                      Valley, NY $900

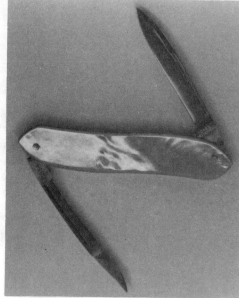

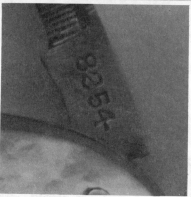

8254LP   Lobster Gen. Pearl   3"   Case Brad. Pa. $250

P254   Pyramite, very rare   3"   W.R. Case & Sons,
                                       Brad. Pa $300

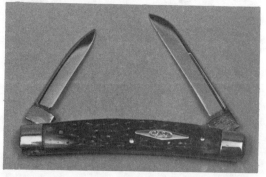

63056 Rogers Bone Whittler, 3"   small blades, Transitional
oval stamp - Case, Brad. Pa. $350

6268   Bone LP   3¼"   Case Bradford Pa. $200

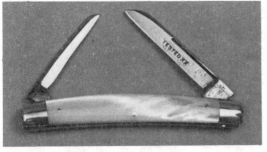

8268   **Pearl LP**   3¼"   Case Bros. Little
                                         Valley, NY $250

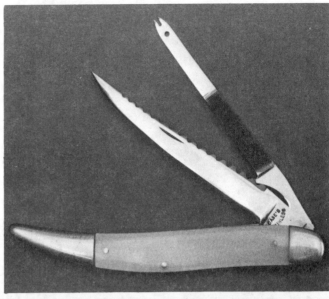

32095   Fish Scaler yellow Plastic   5"   Case's Stainless $225

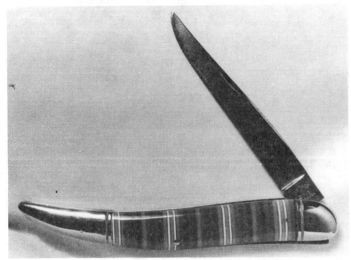

R1093   Celluloid   5"   W.R. Case & Sons
                                      Tested XX (rare) $350

Courtesy Ricky Cox

6154LSSP   Glazed Finish   2nd Model   Blade Etched   USA
Brass Liner Lock (proto model) John Osborne Collection $400

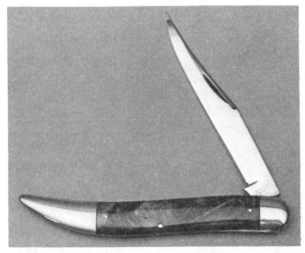

G1095   Green Swirl Saber   5"   W.R. Case & Sons
                                         Brad., Pa. $350

ABBREVIATIONS			
½	master blade is clip blade	PU	Punch Blade
B	Budding	R	Bail in handle
EO	Easy Opener	RAZ	Razor Blade
F	File	SAB	Sabor Blade
J	Long Spay Blade	SC/SCI	Scissors
K	Corkscrew	SH	Sheepfoot blade
LR	Electrician's Knife	SP	Spay Blade
M	Metal	SS	Stainless Steel
PEN	Pen Blade	T	Tip Bolsters
	SSP	Stainless Steel, Polished Blade Edge	

216   *CASE MISC.*

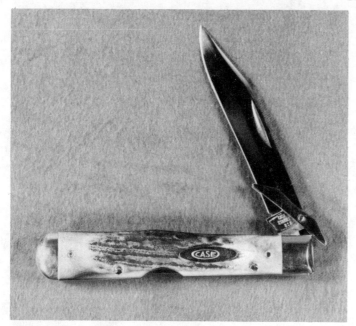

5111½LSS   Saber Ground   10 Dot 1970   Proto $500

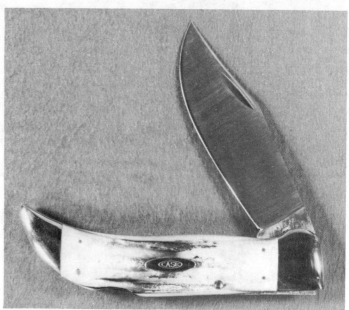

**5172LSSP   No etching, locking Stag pattern, Glazed finish
4 Dot (1976) $400
From John Osborne Collection**

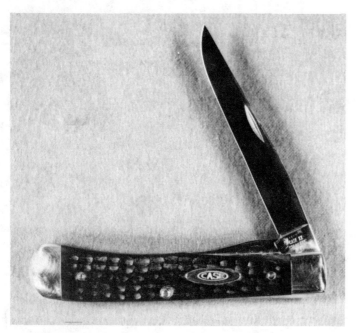

**6154LSS Muskrat   USA $500
(proto model)
John Osborne Collection**

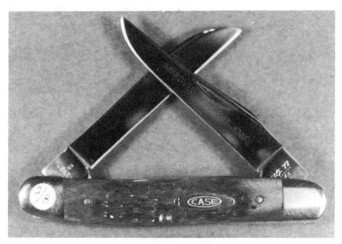

Hawbaker Special

Mr. S. Stanley Hawbaker

Facts on the "Hawbaker Special" Knife

Ralph H. Scruton, Jr.

I am writing this article to try and clear up the myths and mysteries about the fabled "Hawbaker Special" Knife. We would also like to commemorate the man who was its father, S. Stanley Hawbaker, and the man (a friend of Hawbaker's) who started this pen on its mission, Glenn N. Helmuth. Unfortunately, Hawbaker and Helmuth have both passed on to that place where all good Trappers, Hunters, Fishermen and Knife Collectors go.

S. Stanley Hawbaker started the S. Stanley Hawbaker & Sons, General Trapping and Supply Co., Fort Loudon, PA, in 1938 and put out his first catalogue in 1940. The first knives made for his trade were sheath knives, a 5 inch blade and a 7 inch blade, with maple handles and 3 copper rivets. These were made by a prisoner in State College, PA, the only markings on them were the prisoner's name and State College, PA. They also had a folding knife they sold, which was a Schrade "Improved Muskrat," pattern number 7817S, with a jigged bone handle. This knife was etched "Improved Muskrat Knife" on the front blade and no etching on the back blade. How many of these knives he sold from 1938 into the early 50s is anyone's guess.

Hawbaker wanted to put a personal touch into his business, so he contacted York Cutlery Co., 552 West Market Street, York, PA. Julius Guteman took an order for 50 dozen (600), 4416¼, "German Hawbaker Trappers Knives," thus the "Hawbaker Special" was conceived in 1955. These knives have a jigged bone handle, are stamped York Cutlery Company, Soligen Germany and the blades are etched, "Improved Muskrat Knife" on the front blade, with "Hawbaker Special" on the back blade. From 1955 thru August 1958, they purchased 1728 of these knives. But as we all know a trappers knife must take a lot of abuse and punishment, these proved weak at the knick and the blade would break off there. Unfortunately this made a lot of trappers unhappy, so Hawbaker started looking for another manufacturer.

He contacted W.R. Case & Sons, Bradford, PA, in February, 1960, and became a Case dealer on October 3, 1960. Case agreed to make the "Hawbaker Special," on October 12, 1960, if Hawbaker would purchase a blanking die to make the sheep-foot blade. They stated the knife would be in their Muskrat pattern, with the sheep-foot blade substituted for their current blade and the blanking die would be held there for the Hawbaker's exclusive use. This is still true today. Hawbaker had to order 50 dozen (600) knives at a time. This order could be broken in separate orders as long as the total was used within a one year period.

The first order for the "Hawbaker Special" was written on September 11, 1961 and they received the "Proto-Type" knife of September 18, 1961, which was approved at this time. The first shipment of knives, 180, was received in November 1961. To keep track of the rest of the knives received over the years, please refer to the graph I have made for this purpose (page 219). On the graph I have stated facts as per order dates, dates shipped and quantity shipped. As to the blade markings, I can only guess to what markings were in each shipment and thus it is only conjecture on the part of the author as to what is listed on the graph.

With Case's production schedule set on 600 knives there had to be over-runs, therefore we have many transition knives in the "Hawbaker Specials," sometimes even more than the regular stampings. Also keep in mind some of these knives were ordered and made one year, but some of them would be shipped the following year. Remember another thing, the "Hawbaker Special" is identical to the standard Case Muskrat, except the back handle and the back blade. The Hawbaker does not have a nail groove in the back handle and of course the sheepfoot back blade. Case never used regular Muskrat handles on the 4% handled in bone, in 1973. But some quick thinking counterfeitor has already changed some of these from Delrin to Bone, BEWARE. In May,

1971, Case informed them they had enough parts left over from previous (600) knife runs, to make approximately 180 knives. They shipped 182 knives, probably all transitions of some sort.

Contradictory to some thinking, I don't believe there were any USA-XX transitions, as neither order in this period was shipped in full (595-591), therefore, no over-runs on the XX blades. In 1982, 603 of the Green handled and 181 Red handled knives were sent back to the factory because of the colors. (So the reorder June 1982.)

Case made the "Hawbaker Specials" for the Hawbaker's from 1961 through 1982, but in 1974 Hawbaker placed his order too late for Case to put them in a production run and get them to him for that trapping season. Hawbaker contacted Queen Cutlery Company, Titusville, PA and placed an order with them for 600 knives. These knives had the same etching as the Case knife, but were stamped Queen Steel, on the tang, and had imitation Winterbottom plastic handles. They had sold this knife prior to this and after, but there were no etchings on the blades, therefore, not a true "Hawbaker Special."

As of this time I have or have seen 29 different "Hawbaker Specials," starting with the Schrade and continuing through the 1982 Case. At this time I have 23 different ones in my collection. There are other collections in this area with 22-23 different knives in them also, but none of us have the exact same variations, so therefore, there are 29 different variations. These knives were shipped all over the United States, including Alaska and Canada. They were bought and used by trappers. You must note the small quantities spread out over the years. With these things in mind, you can imagine the sheer exuberance of finding one of these fine knives at a show or for sale anywhere.

S. Stanley Hawbaker & Sons, 358 Hawbaker Drive South, Fort Loudon, PA, still operates today under his son, Edwin M. Hawbaker. Without whose help, along with that of Mrs. S. Stanley Hawbaker, this article of facts could not have been written, so many, many thanks from me and all the knife collectors and enthusiasts out there.

S. Stanley Hawbaker passed away October 27, 1983 following a timber cutting accident. His and my personal friend and confident, Glenn N. Helmuth, expired unexpectedly March 1, 1986.

Hawbaker Listings
Next Page

YEAR ORDERED	MAKE	HANDLE MATERIAL	QUANTITY ORDERED	QUANTITY SHIPPED	DATE SHIPPED	MASTER BLADE VARIATIONS	HAWBAKER BLADE VARIATIONS	MINT PRICE
1938-50's	Shrade	Jigged Bone	Unknown	Unknown	Unknown	"Improved Muskrat"	Not Etched	300
1955	York	Jigged Bone	600	600	Dec. 1955	"Improved Muskrat"	"Hawbaker Special"	350
Oct. 1956	York	Jigged Bone	600	600	Mar. 1957	"Improved Muskrat"	"Hawbaker Special"	350
1958	York	Jigged Bone	600	528	Aug. 1985	"Improved Muskrat"	"Hawbaker Special"	350
Sept. 1961	Case	Jigged Bone	600	180	Nov. 1961	Case XX	Case XX	375
				180	Dec. 1961	Case XX	Case XX	375
				235	Feb. 1962	Case XX	Case XX	375
Sept. 1963	Case	Jigged Bone	600	180	Oct. 1963	Case XX	Case XX	375
				411	Oct. 1964	Case XX	Case XX	375
Sept. 1966	Case	Jigged Bone	600	180	Oct. 1966	Case XX USA	Case XX USA	350
				420	Oct. 1967	Case XX USA	Case XX USA	350
July 1969	Case	Jigged Bone	600	180	Aug. 1969	Case XX USA	Case XX USA	350
				144	Oct. 1969	Case XX USA	Case XX USA	350
				282	July 1970	Case XX USA	10 Dots	375
						10 Dots	10 Dots	225
May 1971	Case	Jigged Bone	180	182	May 1971	10 Dots	Case XX USA Rare	400
						9 Dots	9 Dots	150
						9 Dots	Case XX USA Rare	400
						9 Dots	10 Dots	150
Nov. 1971	Case	Jigged Bone	600	300	Jan. 1972	9 Dots	9 Dots	125
				311	Oct. 1972	8 Dots	7 Dots	90
April 1973	Case	Delrin	600	180	June 1973	7 Dots	7 Dots	85
Nov. 1973	Case	Delrin	600	462	Sept. 1973	7 Dots	7 Dots	85
				600	Mar. 1974	7 Dots	7 Dots Rare	85
Sept. 1974	Queen	Plastic	600	600	Oct. 1974	"Improved Muskrat"	"Hawbaker Special"	400
March 1978	Case	Jigged Bone	1000	1000	Apr. 1978	3 Dots	9 Dots	200
						3 Dots	7 Dots	85
						3 Dots	2 Dost	85
						2 Dots	9 Dots	85
						2 Dots	7 Dots	85
						2 Dots	2 Dots	85
Oct. 1981	Case	Jigged Green	1000	1000	1982	S 9 Dots	8 Dots (1 Nail Gr.)	85
	Bone					S 9 Dots	8 Dots (2 Nail Gr.)	65
Nov. 1981	Case	Jigged Red	1000	1000	1982	S 9 Dots	8 Dots (1 Nail Gr.)	85
	Bone					S 9 Dots	8 Dots (2 Nail Gr.)	65
June 1982	Case	Jigged Green	1000	1114	1982	S 8 Dots	8 Dots (1 Nail Gr.)	85
	Bone					S 8 Dots	8 Dots (2 Nail Gr.)	65
June 1982	Case	Jigged Red	1000	681	1982	S 8 Dots	8 Dots (1 Nail Gr.)	65
	Bone					S 8 Dots	8 Dots (2 Nail Gr.)	65

All of these 29 Markings or Variations are confirmed.
Order dates, shipping dates and quantity shipped are confirmed, conjecture on the part of author, when variations shipped.

QUEEN
Titusville, PA

Back in 1918, nine men with a dream left their jobs, secured space in a garage in Titusville, Pa. and founded their own company.

All former employees of Schatt & Morgan Cutlery Co., they did what they knew best, produce knifes. For the first four years the company didn't have a name. It didn't need one because its entire production was under contract for other companies.

The company continues contract work to this day. Some of the production is private label work and some is very special. In the latter category is the National Knife Collectors Association 1981 club knife.

In 1922, just four years after starting up, the partners realized there was a place for a new name in the cutlery industry and named their organization Queen City Cutlery Co., Inc.

Genza Revitsky became the first president; Jess Baker, E. Clarence Erickson, and Frank Foresther were all Vice-presidents; Harry L. Matthews was secretary of treasury.

The name was derived from Titusville which was called Queen City because the petroleum industry was started when Col. Edwin L. Drake drilled the first oil well there in 1859.

Soon after adopting a name the company had to find larger quarters as it began to market its own knives under the Queen City stamp.

In 1930 Schatt & Morgan went broke and in 1932 Queen bought all property and equipment of the company which had originally employed Queen's founders.

The property included the building still occupied by Queen. It was built in 1895 by the City of Titusville to entice Schatt & Morgan to move from Gowanga, NY where it had been organized in 1890.

During the early 1940's two of Queen's founders (Erickson & Matthews) began to experiment with stainless steel for blades and springs, and by 1945, had switched from carbon steel to 440C Stainless for blades and other type stainless for springs.

Other cutlers were also switching to stainless steel but were using other grades that proved unsuitable for blades because they wouldn't hold an edge.

As a result, many knife makers returned to the use of carbon steel.

Queen's founders, having found the right grade of stainless and convinced of its high quality and serviceability, continued with the 440C.

To avoid the stigma attached by the public to stainless steel, Queen stopped using the word "stainless" on its knives. The company registered the name "Queen Steel" for use on the 440C blades and continues to use it.

Queen was purchased by Servotronics, Inc. of Buffalo, NY in 1969.

Courtesy THE OUTDOOR NEWS; Grove City, PA

JOHN M. LUSSIER
Central Falls, Rhode Island
(Queen contributor)

"I became interested in Queen pocket knives many years ago because of three reasons: 1.) their designs, 2.)Queen was the first to use all stainless steel and 3.) they were the only pocket knives to use Winterbottom Bone, a material not used by any other manufacturer. It is a real challenge to acquire all the patterns and tang stamps from 1946 to the present, especially the 'Q Stainless' and smoked pearls."

QUEEN CITY
ca. 1922-1932

QUEEN CITY
TITUSVILLE P.A.
ca. 1925-1932

ca. 1930-1932

ca. 1925-1945

QUEEN CUT. CO.
ca. 1932-1949

ca. 1932-1955

QUEENCUTLERYCO
TITUSVILLE, PA.
ca. 1932-1950

ca. 1935-1955

ca. 1946-1950

STAINLESS
ca. 1946-1948

ca. 1946-1950

ca. 1946-1948

STAINLESS
ca. 1946-1948

ca. 1946-1949

ca. 1949-1958

ca. 1958-1960

1972 Only

ca. 1973-1975

1976 Only

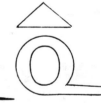
1976 Only

USA
1977 Only

USA
1978 Only

USA
1979 Only

USA
1980 Only

USA
1981 Only

USA
1982 Only

USA
1983 Only

USA
Starting in 1984

Key Figures Associated With Queen Throughout The Years:

Walter W. Bell became associated with Queen Cutlery in 1953. In 1958 he was elected to the Board of Directors and Vice President. In 1961 he was elected President upon the death of his father-in-law, E. Clarence Erickson. Although the company was sold to Servotronics, Inc. in October 1969, he remained as President until his retirement in 1972.

Louis P. Foresther joined Queen Cutlery Company at the time of his father's (Frank Foresther) death in October of 1939. At this time, he bought his father's interest in the company. He became 1st Vice President, Officer and Director and was also very active in the building and maintenance of machinery and tools until the time of his death on October 17, 1956.

Fred R. Sampson became associated with Queen Cutlery Company in August 1948. Working in all departments, he was appointed foreman of the Cover Room in 1952 and Assembly Room in 1955. He remained in these departments until 1976 when he was appointed Master Cutler and Designer.

Gerald J. Matthews, son of Adell Matthews and the late Harry Matthews became associated with Queen Cutlery Company in 1947. In 1958 he was elected to the board of directors and Secretary/Treasurer. He remained with the company until 1972.

John H. Erickson, son of the late E. Clarence and Rebecca Erickson became associated with Queen Cutlery Company in March 1946. He worked in the grinding room, later transferred to the hafting room and then to display work.

Carl C. Eldred joined Queen Cutlery in 1973 as Supervisor. In 1974 he was promoted to his present position, Plant Manager.

Robert E. Matthews, son of Adell Matthews and the late Harry Matthews became associated with Queen Cutlery in 1949. In 1958 he was elected Vice President and to the board of directors. He remained with the company until 1972.

Robert L. Stamp joined Queen Cutlery Company in July 1972 as Materials Manager. Bob was promoted to Plant Manager in 1973. In 1974 he was promoted to General Manager. He remained in this position until October 1983.

William J. Hunter was elected to the position of President in October 1983. He had previously held the position of Vice President of Sales and Marketing for Ontario Knife Company, sister company to Queen Cutlery. Along with the position of President of Queen Cutlery Company he was also promoted to Executive Vice President and General Manager of Ontario Knife Company.

Left to Right: Fred Sampson and Gerald Matthews

Note: A special thanks to Fred Sampson for all the following new information. Fred joined Queen Cutlery in 1948, retired in 1985 and, at present, is the most knowledgeable person on Queen Pocket Knives in the United States.

Type of Handle Material used by Queen 1922-1986

Rogers Bone, Winterbottom Bone, Celluloid, Metal, Ebony, Rosewood, Genuine Stag, Pearl, Imitation Pearl, Amber, Yellow Delrin, Red, Black, Black Micarta, Smoked Pearl, (Burnt Orange and Red Imitation Winterbottom Bone) and Imitation Brown and Black Winterbottom Bone.

Special Note: Burnt Orange - This Winterbottom Bone was used in 1959-1960 as a substitute for Winterbottom Bone. The handles were attached and the knives were then dipped in a vat of red dye. It was found that the colors were not uniform as they streaked and colors ranged from a Dark Red to Pink Red and even a Purple Red. It was decided to discontinue this material with all the problems Queen was having.

Genuine Stag - Queen used stag in their early Queen City Knives but reintroduced Stag in 1981 on a limited basis for a few patterns until 1986. At the present time, Stag is being used only on a limited basis for club knives, etc.

2nd Cut Stag - Used for one club knife - the Wolverine Knive Collectors 1986 Trapper.

Glazed Finish Stainless Steel Blades - used only on a very few patterns for market test. Six patterns known, possibly a few others. The six patterns are numbers 11 E.O., 24, 19, 49, 52 and 6280. They were made for a few months around 1960.

Winterbottom Knives Produced 1970-1986 - Very few patterns, produced with later tang marks. Some will be found with 1922-1972 tang stamps, others with Queen, Q76, etc. One Club Canoe produced in 1985. All are extremely scarce, very few made. Desirable in any condition.

Note: All patterns will not be found with all tang stamps. As some were introduced later and will be found in only one or two tang stamps.

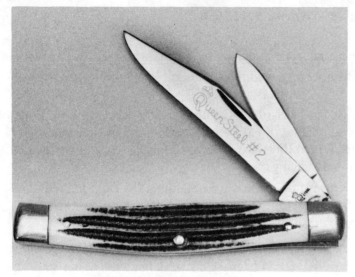

SERPENTINE JACK
2   Queen Steel, Imi. burnt orange   3¼" $30

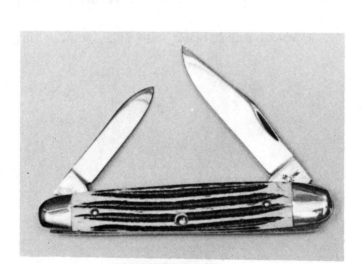

SLEEVEBOARD
3   Queen Steel, Winter bottom bone   3⁵⁄₁₆" $25

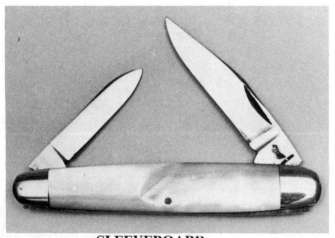

SLEEVEBOARD
#4   Queen, pearl, stainless stamp   3⅜" $35

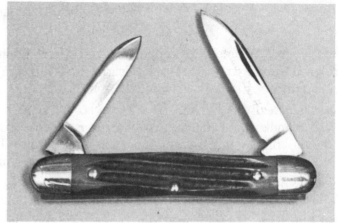

SENATOR
#5   Queen Steel, Winterbottom bone   2½" $20

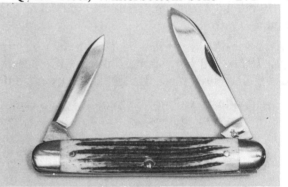

SENATOR
#6   Queen, Winterbottom bone, also pearl, smoked pearl   2½" $20

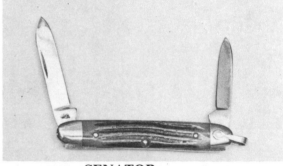

SENATOR
#7   Big Q, Winterbottom bone   2½" $35

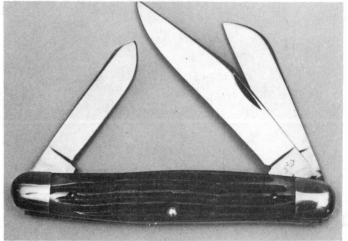

STOCKMAN
#9   Queen, Winterbottom bone   4" $35

225

QUEEN

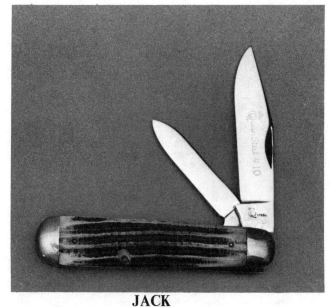

JACK

#10   Queen, Winterbottom bone   3½" $28

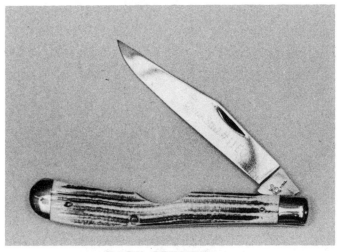

EASY OPENER
#11EO Queen Steel, Winterbottom bone   4" $25

GUNSTOCK
Queen USA 1979 (Master Cutler
Collection), Rogers bone   3½" $30

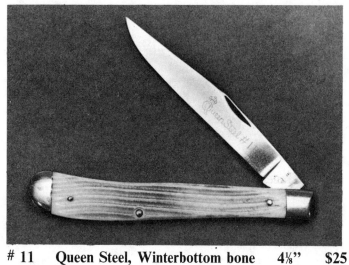

11   Queen Steel, Winterbottom bone   4⅛" $25

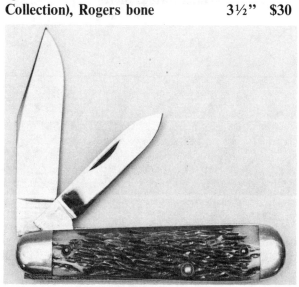

JACK

#10   Queen & Crown, Rogers bone   3⅝" $65

10   Big Q Crown, Rogers bone   75

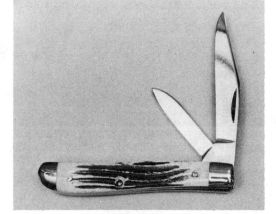

PEANUT
#14   Queen, Winterbottom bone   2¾" $25

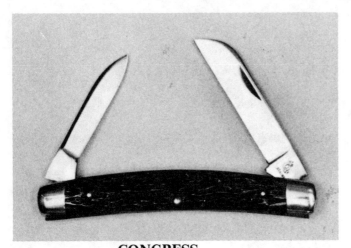

CONGRESS
#15   **Queen, Rogers bone**   3½" $40

CONGRESS
#15   **Queen, Winterbottom bone**   3½" $25

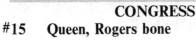

CONGRESS
15   Queen Stainless, Rogers bone   40

MEDIUM CONGRESS
15   Queen Steel,   25

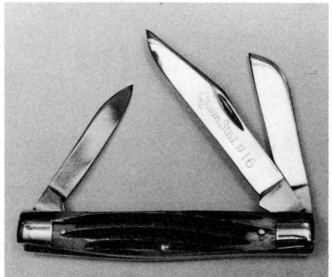

#16   **Queen Steel, Winterbottom bone**   3¼" $30

STOCKMAN
#16   **Queen, Rogersbone (Crown & Queen Stamp)**   3¼" $85

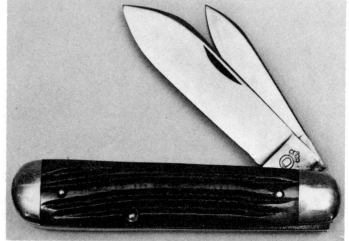

JACK
#18   **Big Q, Winterbottom bone**   3¹¹⁄₁₆" $50

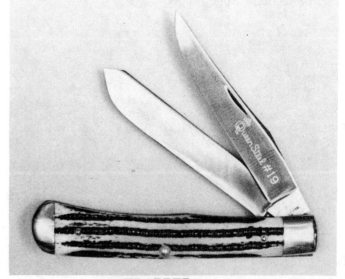

TRAPPER
#19   **Queen Steel, Winterbottom bone**   4⅛" $85
19   Queen Steel, glazed finish   75

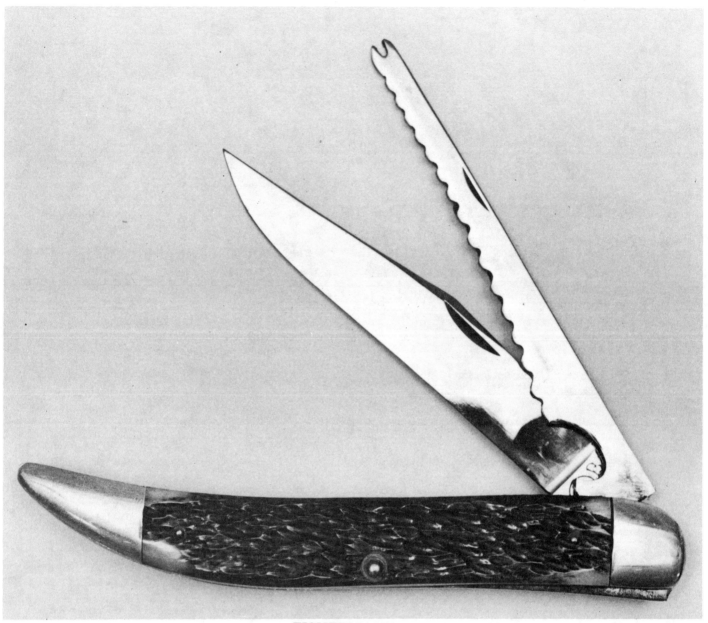

FISHERMAN'S

#19   Big Q, Rogers bone   5" $80

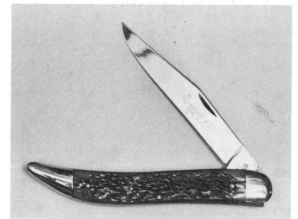

TEXAS TOOTHPICK

| #20 | Queen Steel, Rogers bone (1200 made) | 5" | $45 |

TEXAS TOOTHPICK

| 20 | Queen Stainless, Rogers bone | | 90 |

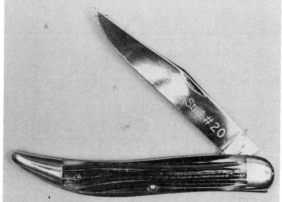

TEXAS TOOTHPICK

| #20 | Queen Steel, Winterbottom bone | 5" | $85 |

SLEEVEBOARD

| 21 | Queen Steel | | 25 |

BARLOW
#22   Queen, brown bone   3½" $45

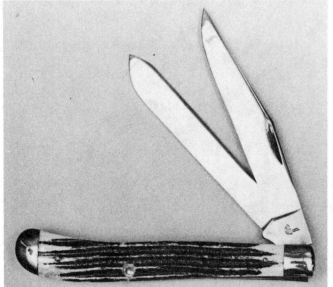

TRAPPER
#24   Queen Steel, Winterbottom bone   4" $35
MED. TRAPPER
24   Queen Steel   35

BARLOW
#25   Queen Steel, Brown bone   3½" $60

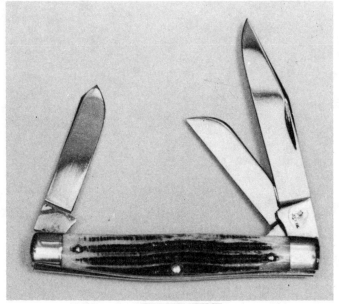

SERPENTINE
#26   Queen Steel, Winterbottom Bone   3¼" $35
        Also Burnt Orange Imi. Bone $35

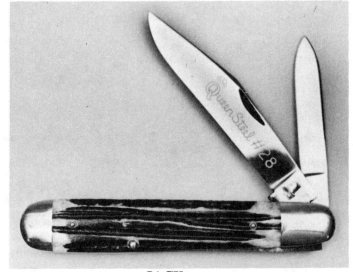

JACK
#28   Queen Steel, Winterbottom bone   4½" $40

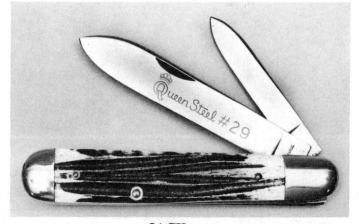

JACK
#29   Queen Steel, Winterbottom bone   4½" $40
JACK
29   Big Q   4½   75

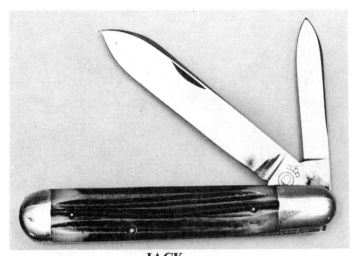

JACK

#29   Big Q, Winterbottom bone   4½" $75

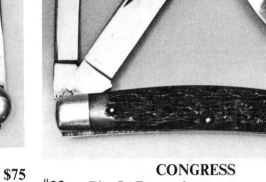

CONGRESS

#33   Big Q, Rogers bone   3½" $120

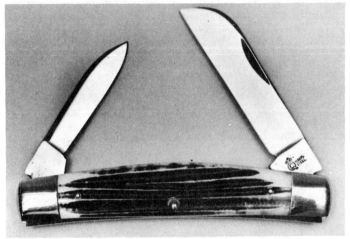

CONGRESS

#31   Queen Steel, Winterbottom bone   4" $40

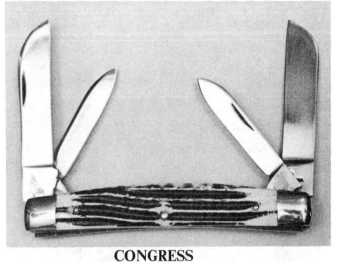

CONGRESS

#33   Queen, Winterbottom bone   3½" $40

33   Queen Steel   40

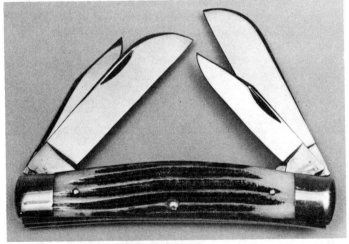

CONGRESS

#32   Queen, Winterbottom bone   4" $45

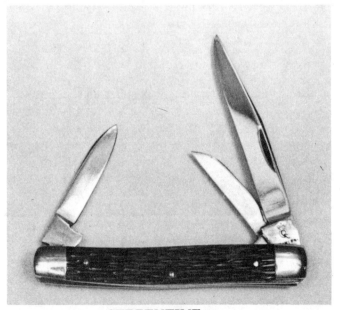

SERPENTINE

#35   Queen Stainless, rough black   2⅝" $50

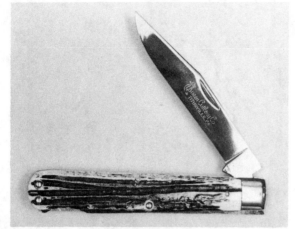

LOCKBACK

#36   Queen, Winterbottom bone   4½" $90

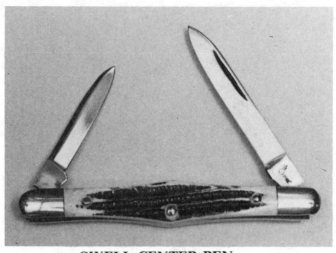

SWELL CENTER PEN

#38   Queen Steel, Winterbottom bone   3" $70

LOCKBACK

#36   Queen, Rogers bone   4½" $100

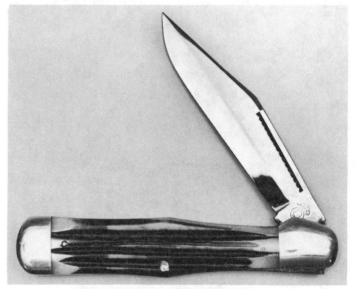

SWELL CENTER JUMBO

#38   Big Q, Winterbottom bone   5¼" $200

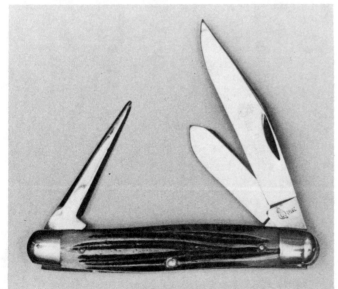

STOCKMAN

#37   Queen, Winterbottom bone   4" $60

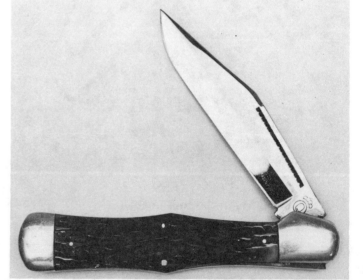

SWELL CENTER JUMBO

#38   Big Q, Jigged bone   5¼" $200

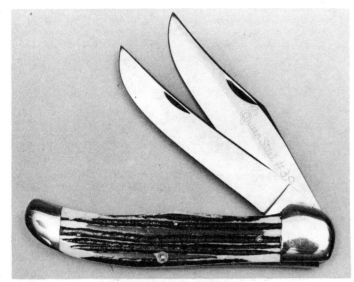

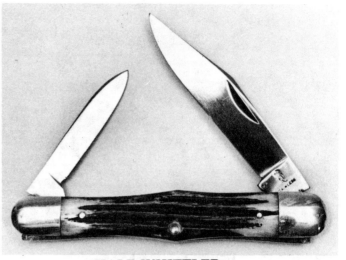

FOLDING HUNTER

| #39 | Queen Steel, Winterbottom bone | 5¼" | $65 |
| 39 | Queen, Winterbottom bone | | 60 |

HALF WHITTLER

#47 Queen Stainless, Winterbottom bone   3½" $35

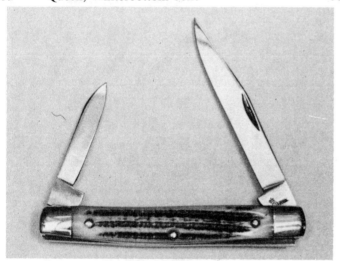

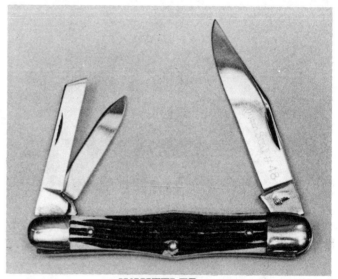

SERPENTINE

#43 Queen Steel, Winterbottom bone   2⅝" $20

WHITTLER

#48 Queen Steel, Winterbottom bone   3½" $45

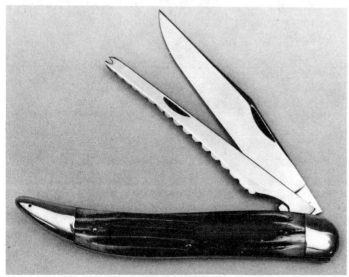

FISHERMAN'S

#46 Queen Steel, Winterbottom bone   5" $35

STOCKMAN

#49 Queen, Winterbottom bone   4¼" $40

DOG LEG JACK
#51   Queen Steel, Winterbottom bone   3½" $30

MOOSE
#52   Queen Steel, Winterbottom bone   4½" $40
52   Queen, Winterbottom bone   40

#54   Queen Steel, Pearl   2⅝" $30
54   Queen, Pearl   25

PEN
#55   Queen Steel, Green Rogers bone, (200 made)   3⁵⁄₁₆" $30

SWELL CENTER
#56   Queen Steel, burnt orange imi. bone   3½" $30

#57   Queen, Pearl   3⅜" $30

233

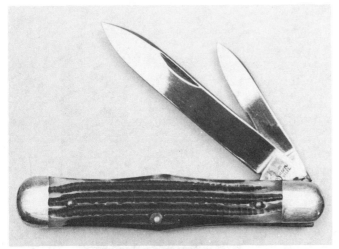

SWELL CENTER
#58   Queen Steel, Winterbottom bone $60

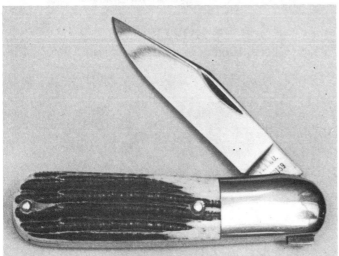

BARLOW
#60   Queen, Winterbottom bone   3½" $35
Aluminum lightweight enclosed backspring

BARLOW
#60   Queen Steel, Winterbottom bone   3½" $35
Aluminum lightweight enclosed backspring

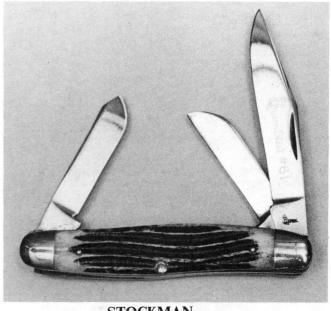

STOCKMAN
#61   Queen Steel, Winterbottom bone   3⅝" $50

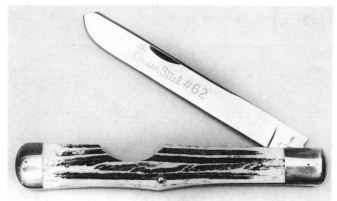

EASY OPENER
#62   Queen Steel, Winterbottom bone   5⅜" $50
62   Queen, Winterbottom bone   50

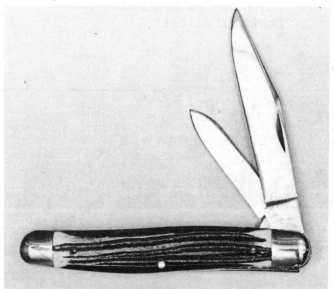

SERPENTINE
#63   Queen Steel, Winterbottom bone   4" $50
63   Queen, Winterbottom bone   4   50

73	Queen Steel	30
78	Queen Steel	75
82	Queen Steel	25
95	Queen Steel	30

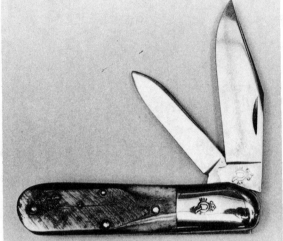

BARLOW

#139   Queen, brown bone   3½" $40

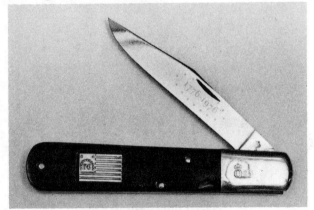

DADDY BARLOW

#1450 Bicentennial Edition, Queen, black
Delrin, flag emblem   5" $30

#1490 Queen, Rogers bone, 1st Edition
Trapper Set $60 set

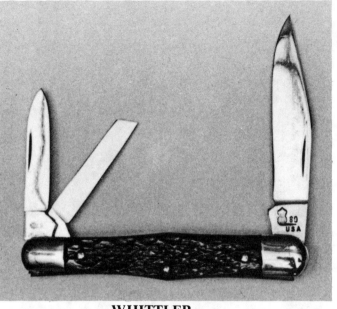

WHITTLER

#2175 Queen, Rogers bone (3rd Edition) 3½" $35

SWELL CENTER

#6105 Queen, Stag   3½" $35

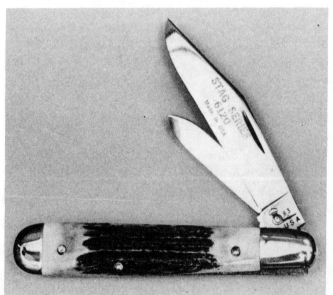

JACK

#6120 Queen, stag   4½" $35

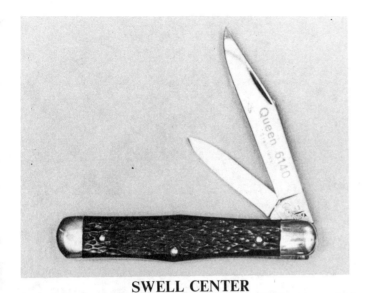

SWELL CENTER

#6140 Queen, bone   3½" $25

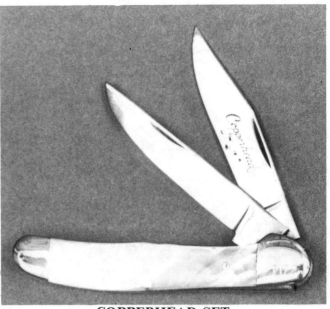

COPPERHEAD SET

#8145 Queen (set consists of pearl
and Stag   3½" $125 set

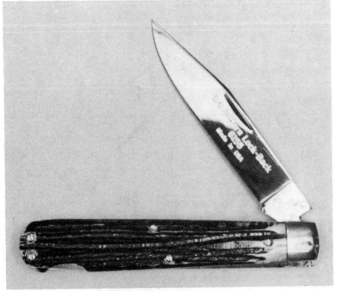

LOCKBACK

#6155 Queen, Winterbottom bone (1 of 700) $50

6207   Queen, Winterbottom bone   32

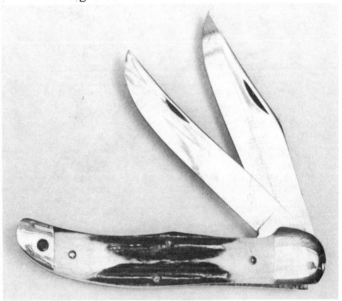

FOLDING HUNTER

#8150 Queen, genuine stag (800 made)   5¼" $50

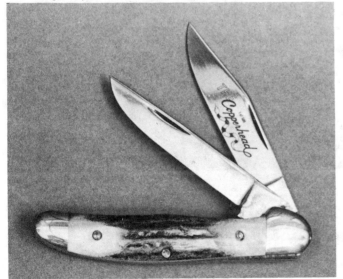

COPPERHEADS

8145 Queen, pearl and stag set $125 set

4TH EDITION PEANUT

8375 Queen, Rogers bone (3,000 made)   2¾" $30

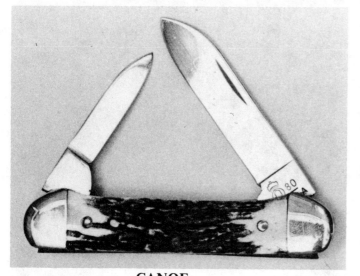

CANOE

\# 8415 Queen, stag (500 made) 3⅝" $35

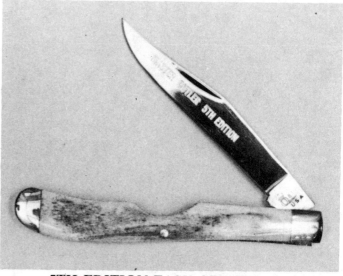

5TH EDITION EASY OPENER

\# 8470 Queen, smoothbone 4⅛" $30

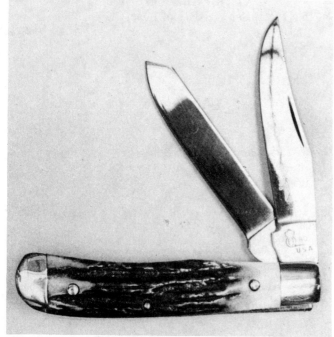

MINI-TRAPPER

\# 8420 Queen, genuine stag $35

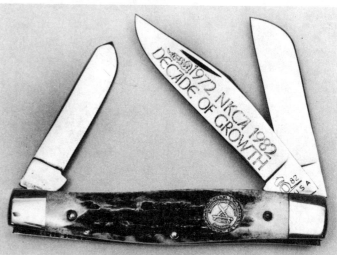

STOCKMAN

Queen USA, 1982 N.K.C.A. 10th
Anniversary, genuine stag, blade is
deep etched in gold (1200 made) 4¼" $75

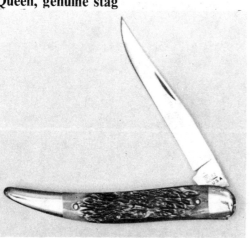

TOOTHPICK

\# 8460 Queen, Green Bone (1,000 made)
60th Anniversary $50

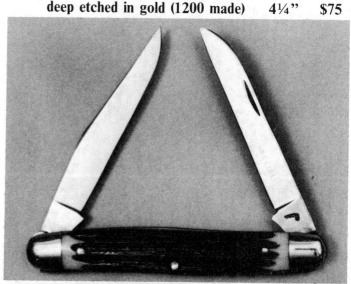

IMPROVED MUSKRAT

Queen Steel, imi. Winterbottom
bone Hawbaker's Special, RARE 4" $150

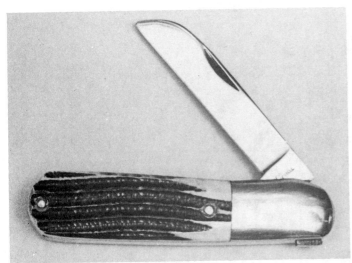

BARLOW
Queen Steel, Winterbottom bone   3½" $60
Aluminum lightweight enclosed backspring

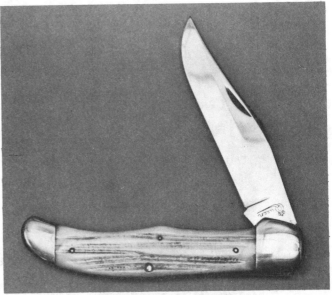

FOLDING HUNTER
Queen Stamp upside down, Winterbottom bone $90

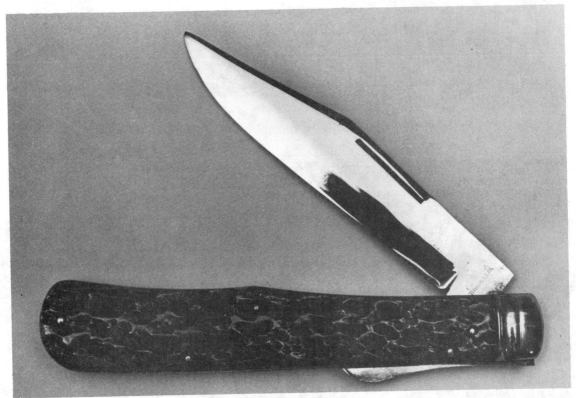

LOCKBACK
Schatt & Morgan (Queen forerunner) heavy bone scales   5½" $300

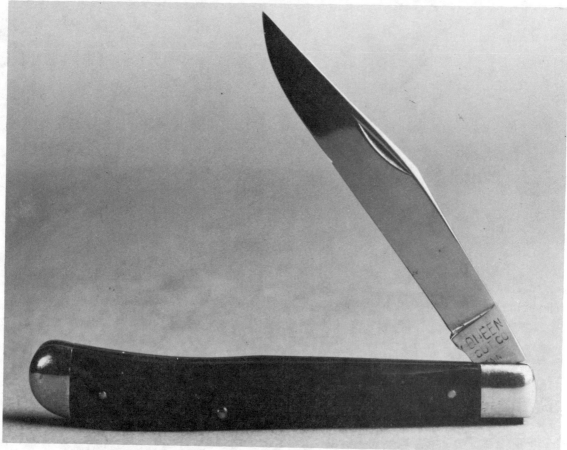

Early Stainless Queen (Rare Stamp) 5" $90

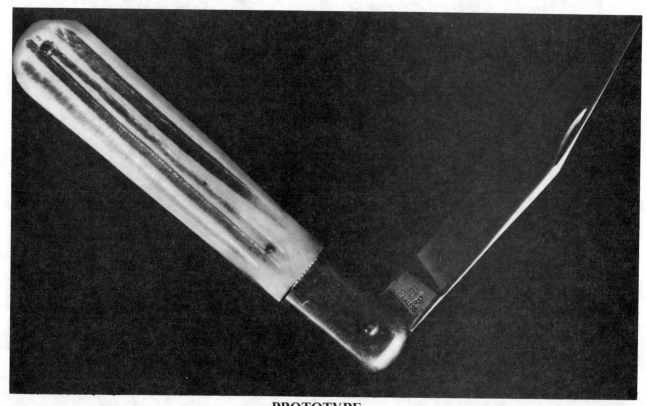

PROTOTYPE
Extremely Rare Queen Daddy Barlow (only a few made) 5" $200
Lightweight Aluminum Bols.

ADDITIONAL QUEENS

Rogers Bone   **2½"**   **Big Q**   **$35**

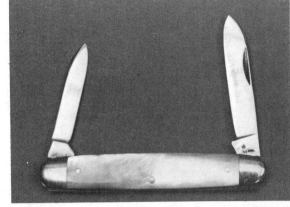

Gen. Pearl   **3¼"**   **$40**

Rogers Bone   **2½"**   **Crown & Dots**   **Rare**   **$38**

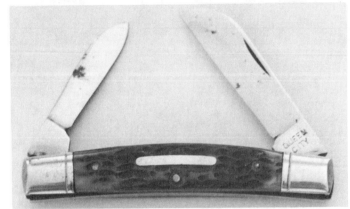

Queen City 3¾", 2 Bl. Congress, Rogers Bone   **$125**

Queen Big Q Carbon, 2½", Imi. Black Bone   **$28**

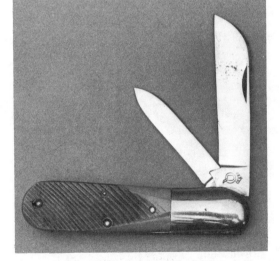

Barlow   **Brown Bone, Sheep Foot, Carbon Steel, 3½"**   **$55**

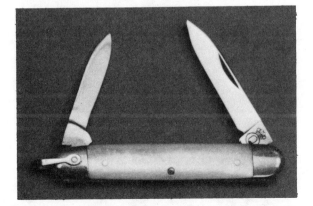

Queen Big Q Carbon, 2½", Gen. Pearl   **$35**

240

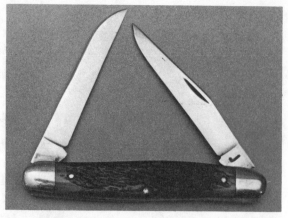

Queen Steel, Improved Muskrat, Rogers Bone, 4", 2 blade. Made as Prototype around 1975. Never sold on market. Rare $225

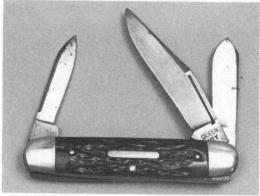

Green Bone   3¼"   Queen City $125
3 Bl. Small Cattle Pattern

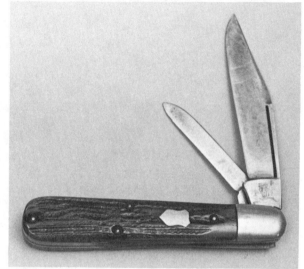

Rogers Stag   4½"   Queen City $90

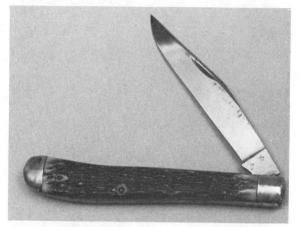

Rogers Bone 1 Bl   4⅛"   Queen Big Q $55

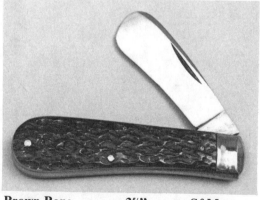

Brown Bone   3⅝"   S&M $200
1 Bl Cotton Sampler or Maize, Schatt & Morgan

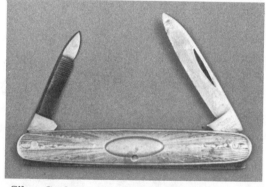

Silver Scales, 2 Bl   2⅝"   "Queen" Stainless $125
Very Rare Stamp

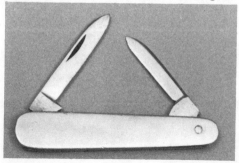
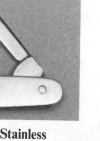

2 Bl Stainless Scales 2¼" "Queen" Stainless $100
Very Rare

Winterbottom 2 Bl   3⅞"   Queen City $90
2 Bl. Jack

QUEEN

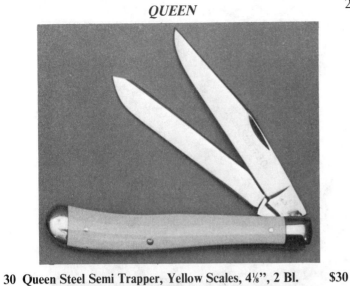

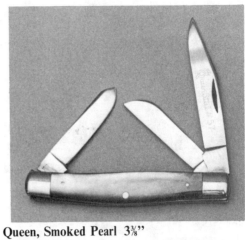

57   Queen, Smoked Pearl 3⅜" $125

30 Queen Steel Semi Trapper, Yellow Scales, 4⅛", 2 Bl. $30

42   Yellow Scales   2¾" $22

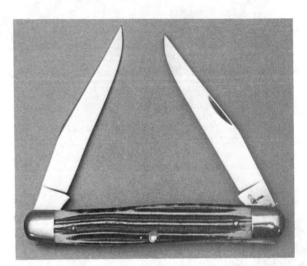

66 Queen Steel Muskrat, Winterbottom Bone, 2 Bl., Mint $125

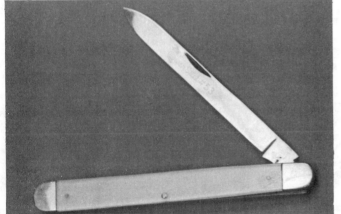

53   Imi. Onyx Celluloid   4¾" $30
Citrus Knife

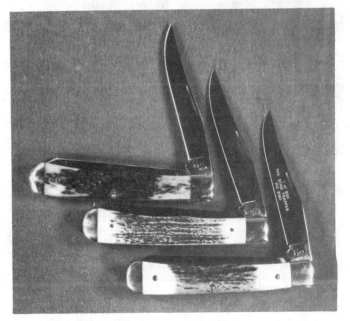

Q77   Overrun from Trapper   No blade etch, very few made
Q78 Stag Proto for 1981. Stag Trapper, no blade etch
Q81 Stag 8160 (1 of 800)   **$45 each**

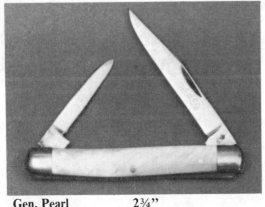

59	**Gen. Pearl** 2¾"	**$45**
59	**Smoked Pearl** 2¾"	**$100**

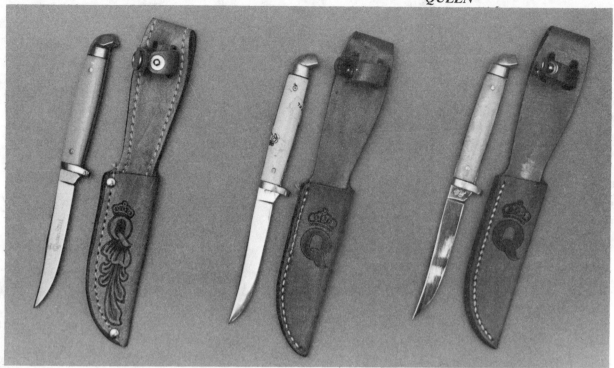

Queen Steel, Yellow scales, Bird Knife, 6⅛" overall, 3 " blade $30
Queen Steel, Imi. Ivory Bird Knife, 6⅛"-3" blade $30
Queen Steel, Imi. Onyx Scales Bird Knife 6⅛"-3" blade $30

Two blade Folding Hunter marked Q Stainless 5¼" closed   Winterbottom Bone   Excellent Mint $90

Queen Stainless, Winterbottom, 7¼"-3⅝" blade, intermediate size, scarce - Sabor blade $40
Same as above except flat blade $40

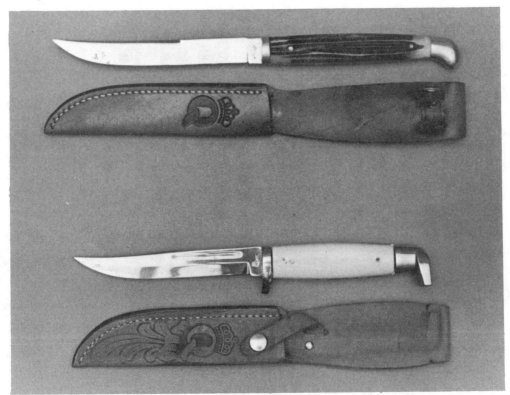

Queen Steel, Imi. Ivory, 8"-4¼" blade, Sab. Blood groove, very scarce
$50
Queen Steel, Winterbottom, 9¼"-4¾" blade, very scarce $35

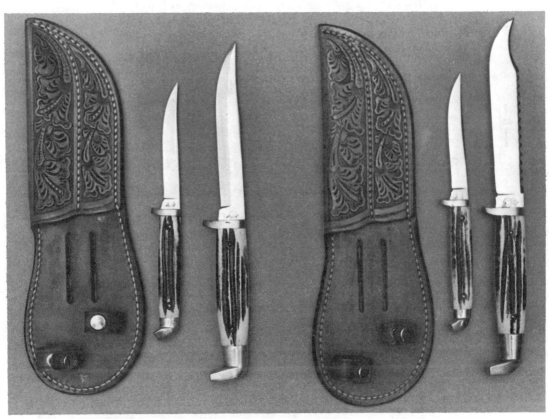

Queen Steel Twin Pak, winterbottom bone, stainless, Big Q's, 8"
4¼" blade and 6⅛"-3" blade $60
Right: Same as above except larger knife has Fish Scaler back $70

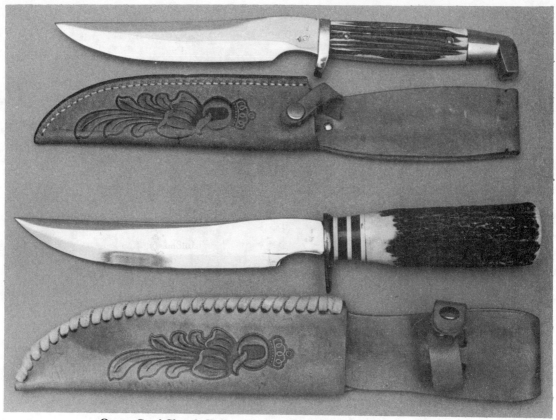

Queen Steel Sheath Knife, Winterbottom Bone, 10½"- 6" Blade, Double Edge, very scarce $60
Queen Steel Sheath Knife, Gen. Stag handles with Red & White spacers, 11½"-7" blade, 1" edge top of blade, very scarce $75

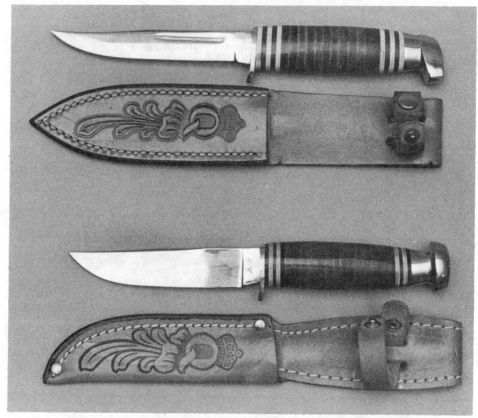

84, Queen Steel Sheath Knife, Leather Washer with white spacers, 9¼"-4¼" blade, rare $40
Queen Stainless, Leather Washer with Red, White, Black spacers, 8¾"-4" blade, Flat Ground $35

THE FRED HILL RASCOE JR.
WESTERN STATES CUTLERY COLLECTION

The Fred Hill Rascoe Jr. collection of Western States Cutlery Co. knives is unique. This magnificent collection represents the most complete assortment of this pioneer American cutlery company's folding knives in the world. A majority of the pieces in this collection came directly from the Western States Cutlery display collection which was dispersed by Harvey Platts prior to the sale of the Western States firm to the Coleman Company.

Fred had personal contact with Harvey Platts and others at the Western Cutlery firm during his years of active collecting and as a Western States dealer. Identification of several of the knives required clarification, which was provided by Mr. Platts if he had specific knowledge of the knife in question. Several of the knives, particularly the folding hunters and several multi-bladed knives, are in all likelihood the **only** mint specimens in existence. Knives in the collection span the period from the earliest years when the pocket knives were made by W.R. Case and Sons, Utica Cutlery and others for Western States, the post-war (WW II) years. Some of the handle materials are unique and may have been used on these display board knives only. Included in the collection are a Dog's Head Western States folding hunter lockback and other unusual four and five bladed knives.

In addition, there are mint examples of a line of commercial hair clippers, scissors and straight razors manufactured by Western States. There are two original Western States salesman sample canvas rolls included in the collection.

A select group of ten older fixed blade hunting knives and two knife/axe combinations, with original sheaths, are also a part of the collection.

KEY TO NUMBERING SYSTEM:

2 has imitation pearl handle
3 has brown or golden shell composition handle
4 has white or ivory handle
5 has genuine stag handle
6 has bone stag handle
7 has ivory or agate composition handle
8 has genuine pearl handle

> Note:
> Fred Rascoe passed away early 1987. This collection was sold at auction and prices in this book reflect prices realized in this auction.

The next figure following indicates the number of blades.
Example: No. 6342 is a bone stag handle knife with 3 blades.

The next two or three figures are the pattern numbers and these are arranged numerically in the price list from 00 to 99. Example: 6363 - 6264 - 6365 - 06266 are the patterns 63, 64, 65 and 66 and occur in that order in the price list.

KEY TO ABBREVIATIONS:

These abbreviations **follow** the pattern number figures and indicate:

½ - Clip blade
B - Bale or ring
BB - Black border
CH - Chain
KFS - Knife, fork and spoon
GS - Goldstone handle
T - Tip bolstered knife
TB - Tip bolstered with bale
C - Calif. Clip pocket blade

CSP — Calif. Clip pocket, sheep & pen blades
P - Punch blade
F - Nail file blade, florist, stamp
S - Long special spay blade
SP - Spay and Pen blades
PCS - Punch - Calif. Clip pocket and spec. long Spay
E - Emblem in handle

These abbreviations **precede** the figures and indicate:

A - Agate handle
B - Black composition handle
C - Cornelia red or candy-colored handle
G - Blade in each end of 2-bladed knife - otherwise jack

Y - Yellow composition handle
X - "Westaco" brand or cheaper brand of knives
AG - Knife was hand-made by experienced cutter nickel-silver lining

WESTERN STATES
BOULDER, COLO.

W TESTED S
TRADE **SHARP** MARK
© TEMPER ©

WESTERN STATES
SHARP CUTLERY

WESTERN
BOULDER, COLO.

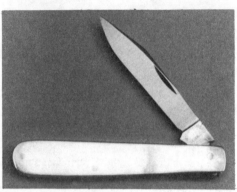

Metal Handle   1 Blade   3¼"   **$25**

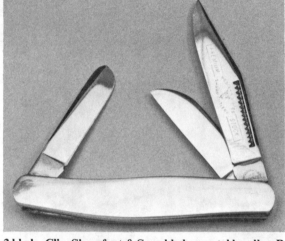

Heavy 3 blade, Clip, Sheepfoot & Spey blades, metal handles, Buffalo skull etching and premium stock on m. blade. Probably prototype or salesman's sample.   4"   **$100**

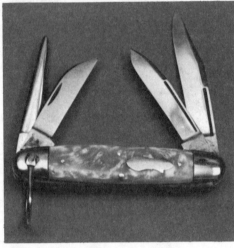

Utility Knife, 4 Blade, Clip, Large Pen, Wharncliffe and Punch - Cracked Ice handles w/shield and bale   3¼"   **$75**

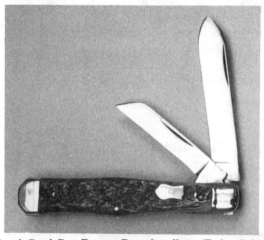

Jack, Peach Seed Cut, Rogers Bone handles w/Federal shield - semi hex rear   3½" bolsters   **$65**

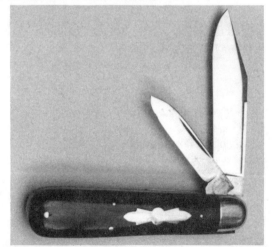

Heavy, 2 Blade Jack, large clip blade tang stamped Shapleigh Haweco - Blade etching "Stumpp & Walter Co."; Pen blade tang stamped same and overstamped Western States, Boulder Colo. There is a T under both of these tang stampings; Ebony handles, large bowtie shield.   3⅝"   **$75**

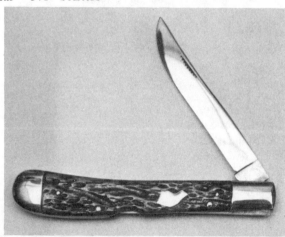

Lockback, Bone handle with Dog head shield, long skinning blade. Made by Union Cutlery for Western States - 1911-1919.   5⅜"**$450**

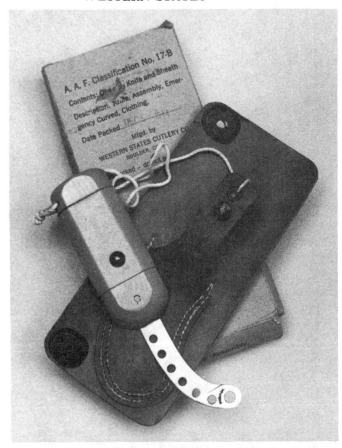

Raft Knife, floatable, Army Air Force WW II, w/packing box dated Nov. 1944, Shroud Cutter (utility)   3¾" $25

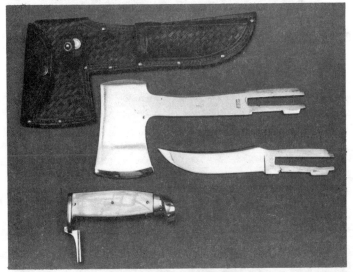

Knife-Axe Combo, Pearl Comp. handles, 2nd model $150

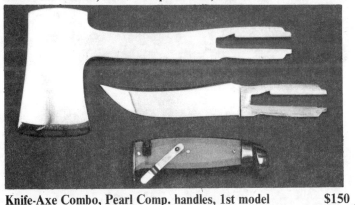

Knife-Axe Combo, Pearl Comp. handles, 1st model $150

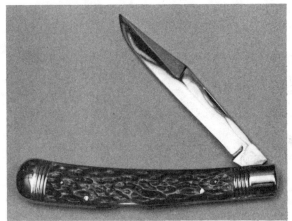

Lockback, Bone   5¼" $400

Christmas Tree handles, Garden of the Gods   2⅝" $50

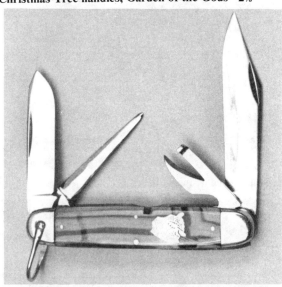

7400   Bull Head Pattern, Heavy Utility Knife, 4 blade, Butter & Molasses handles w/Bull Head shield, 4¾" $500

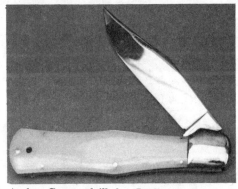

A100BH   Amber Cream, drilled   5¼" $125

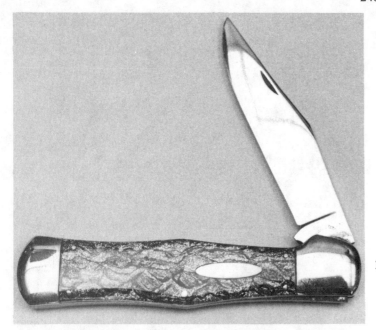

A100   Folding Hunter, Christmas Tree handles, 1 blade, Clip, Flat ground w/oval shield.   5⅜" $250

100   Christmas Tree handles, drilled   5¼" $200

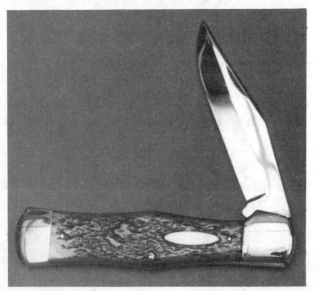

6100   Bone Stag handles, regular blade & backsprings, shield, Rogers Bone, Western, Boulder   5¼" $250

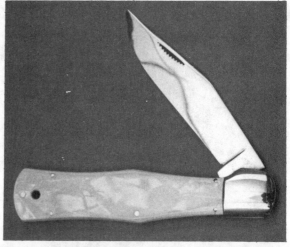

2100BH   Pearl Overlay Comp. drilled   5¼" $100

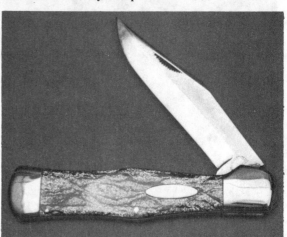

2100   Christmas Tree handles, white liner, Buffalo skull etching   5⅜" $300

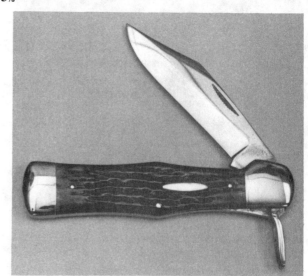

6100L   Lockback, bone, small shield, sab. ground   5⅜" $350

6100 Bone, heavy blade, Buffalo skull etching 5⅜" $300

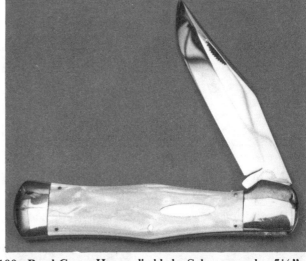

2100 Pearl Comp. Heavy clip blade, Saber ground 5¼" $100

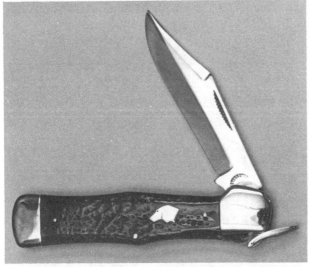

6100L Lockback, Bone, regular jig "Dog Head" shield 5⅜" $400

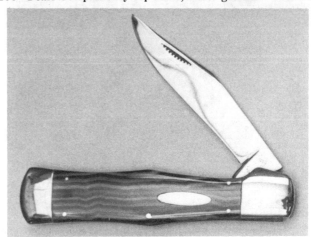

3100 Pearl Comp. Ceylon type 5¼" Waterfall $250

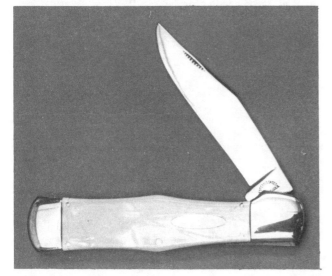

3100 Pearl overlay Comp. handles, flat ground blade 5¼" $125

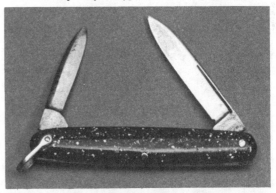

S203B Green sparkle handles w/bale 2½" $25

2203SB Pearl Comp. handles w/bale 2½" $20

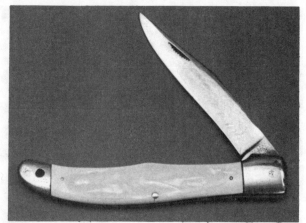

2106V Pearl Overlay Comp. handles, drilled, no shield (1 blade rare)
5⅛" $75

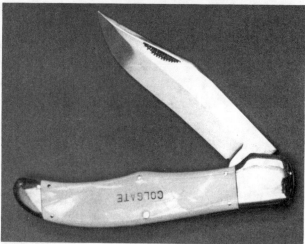

2106BH Pearl Overlay handles   5¼" $150

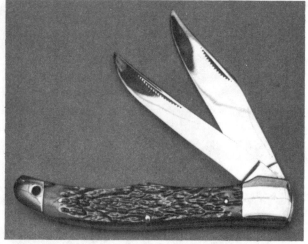

6206 Bone, no shield, black iron blade & cap pins, war years 5⅛"
$65

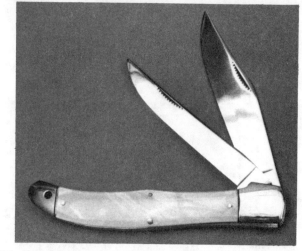

2206 Imi. Pearl handles, drilled   5⅛" $65

6206 5¼" closed Folding Hunter, Honey Bone handles no shield
(Top to bottom) $90

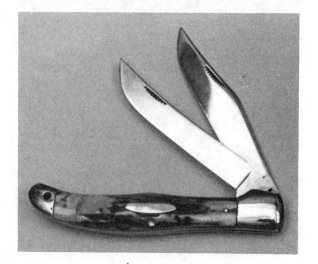

5206 Genuine Stag, drilled, Buffalo skull etching, 5⅛" $75

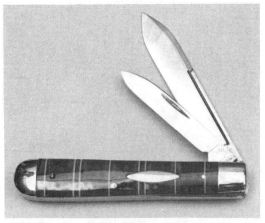

C208   Jack, Candy Stripe Pyralin handle 3⅝"   **$75**

13208½GS   Goldstone Comp. handles   Jack 3⅜"   **$60**

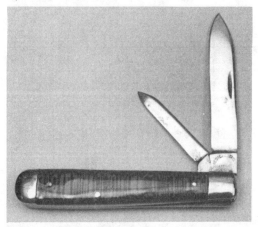

13208   Brown & Black Swirl Comp. Handles   3⅜"   **$25**

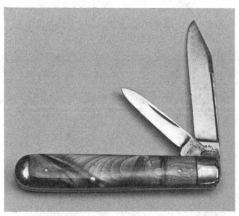

13208½   Golden shell pyralin LP Jack   3¼"   **$30**

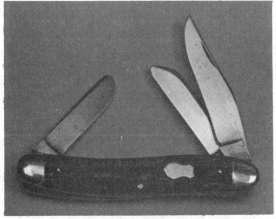

16208   Bone   3¼"   Western States overstamped with: Thomaston Knife Co. Conn - Both 3½" blades stamped $40

13208½   Mottled Pyralin Jack, Buffalo Skull etching 3⅜"   **$30**

13228½   Dogleg Jack, Christmas Tree handles   3"   **$75**

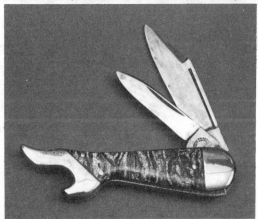

9210   Ladies Leg, Christmas Tree handles, both blades stamped Western States, Boulder Col., Made in U.S.A. Buffalo skull etching on M.B.   3¼" $125

252

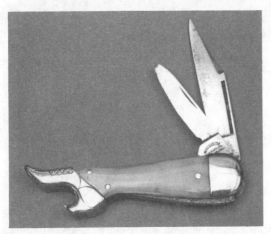

9210   ladies Leg, Rainbow Pearl "Waterfall" handles, both blades stamped Western States Cut & Mfg Co., Boulder Col.; 1st etching (tested temper) barely visible on M.B.   3¼" $125

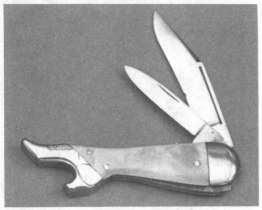

9210   Master blade tang stamping; Western States Cut & Mfg Co., Master Blade etching Valley Forge, secondary blade tang stamping: Valley Forge Cutlery Co., Newark NJ, Made in USA.   3¼"$125

Daddy Barlow, Green Bone handles. Listed in 1921 catalog as No. 2111, in '41 sheets as 6111½   5" $100

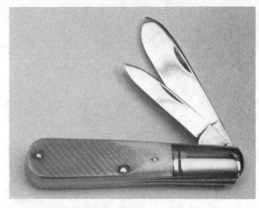

6211   Barlow, Bone (Spear)   3⅜" $125

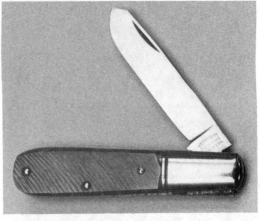

6111SP   Barlow, Bone, very rare   3⅜" $100

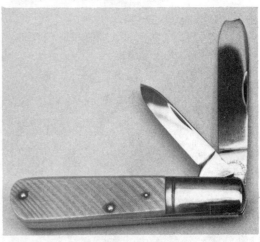

6211R   Barlow, Bone w/Razor blade   3⅜" $150

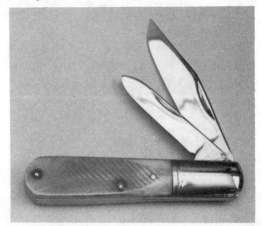

6211½   Barlow, Bone, clip   3⅜" $100

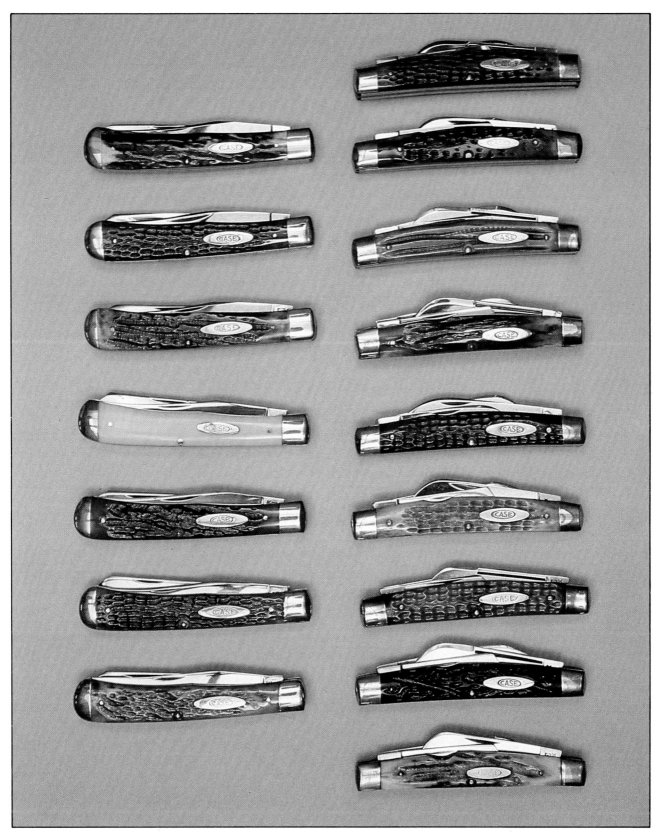

(left, top to botton)
CASE
#54 patterns Trappers...Genuine Stag, Red Bone, 2nd Cut Stag, Yellow Composition, Red Stag, Green Bone,
Rogers Bone.

(right, top to bottom)
CASE
#88 patterns Congress...Green Bone, Bone, Winterbottom Bone, Genuine Stag, Red Bone, 2nd Cut Stag, Green
Bone, Rough Black, Genuine White Stag.
Courtesy Joe Chance & Barney Hightower

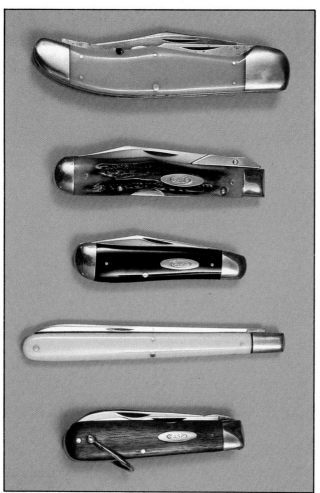

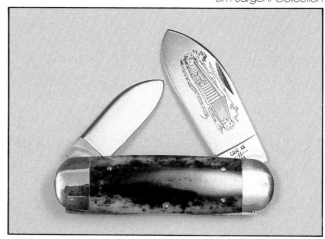

(top to bottom)
CASE
#3465 4 blade Folding Hunter (flat blade) with Yellow Composition handle, #5111½ L Cheetah with Genuine Stag handle, #22028 Dog Leg Jack with Black Composition handle, #4100SS Citrus Knife with White Composition handle, #12031LR Electrician's Knife with Walnut handle.
Jim Sargent Collection

(top to bottom)
QUEEN
NKCA 10th Anniversary (1972-1982) with emblem with Genuine Stag handle (1200 made), #58 Cokebottle with Red Imitation Winterbottom Bone handle, #11 (knife shown is upside down) Winterbottom Bone handle, Serpentine Jack with Imitation Red Winterbottom Bone handle.
Jim Sargent Collection

(top to bottom)
CASE
#6254SSP Trapper with Delrin handle, #61011 Hawlbill with Pakkawood handle, #6488 Congress with Bone handle.
Jim Sargent Collection

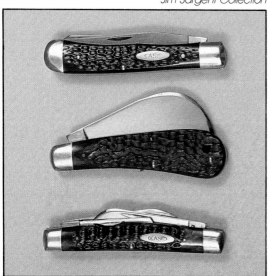

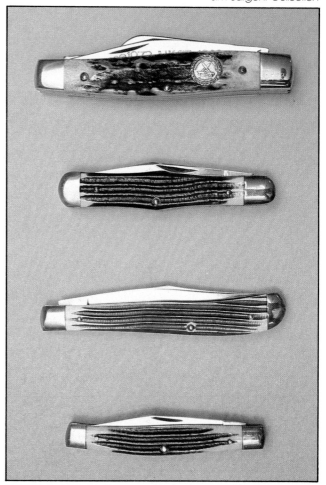

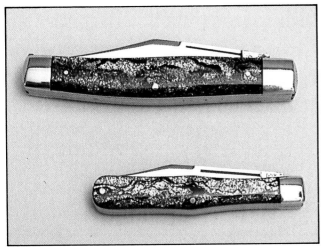

(top to bottom)
Standard Knife Co., 3 blade Stockman, 4", Christmas Tree, $400.
Case Tested XX, B2025½, 2 blade Coke Bottle, 3", Christmas Tree, $300.

(top to bottom)
Case, Red Winterbottom Bone.
Case, Green Swirl Celluloid.

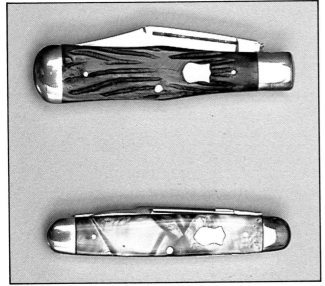

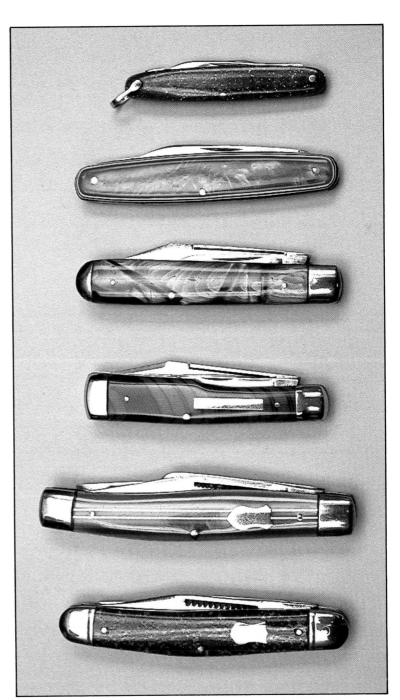

Western States Cutlery,
Boulder, Co., assorted multi-color handles.

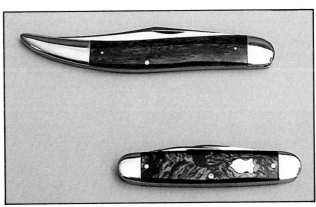

(top to bottom)
Case Tested XX, BM1095, 5" Toothpick,
Brown Mottled Scales (rare handle), $350.
Winchester, 3⅜", 3 blade, Blue & Black Swirl,
Punch, $150.

(top to bottom)
QUEEN
These Queens exhibit older handle materials. #35 small Serpentine with Rough Black handle, rare Q Stainless stamp, #15 Congress with Brown Rogers Bone, rare Q Stainless stamp, #20 Folding Outdoors Knife with Green Rogers Bone, rare Q Stainless stamp.

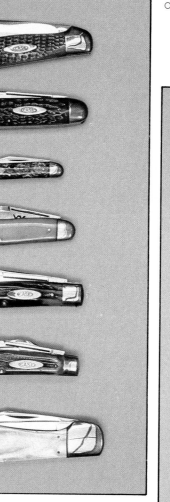

WINCHESTER
#1920 Folding Hunter (Cokebottle) with bone handle.
Jim Sargent Collection

(top to bottom)
REMINGTON
Teardrop Easy Opener Jack with Brass handle, Equal End Jack with Candy Stripe handle, Pruner with Imitation Ivory handle, Serpentine with Christmas Tree handle, Serpentine with Nickel Silver handle, Jack with Multi-Color handle, Serpentine Jack with Candy Stripe handle.
Jim Sargent Collection

(top to bottom)
CASE
#6100 Honeycomb Green Bone, #6394½ Cigar with Red Bone, #B2020 Peanut with Christmas Tree handle, B239½ Sowbelly with Waterfall handle, #5375 Stockman with Red Stag handle, #6488 Congress with Winterbottom Bone handle, #9265 Folding Hunter with Cracked Ice handle.
Courtesy Joe Chance & Jim Sargent

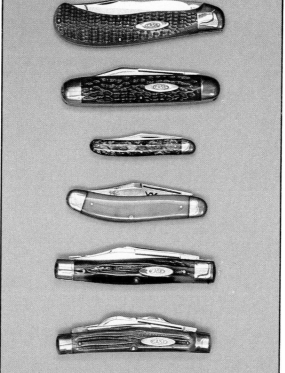

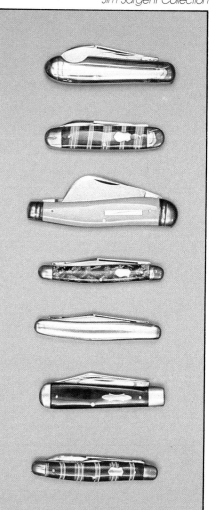

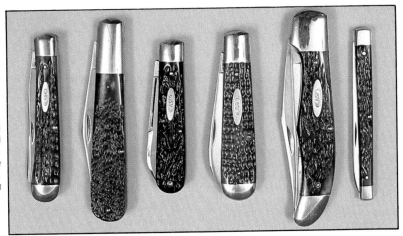

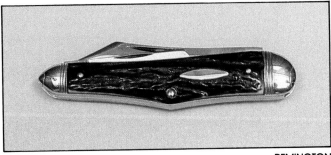

REMINGTON
#R6836 Humpback Whittler, Genuine Stag handle.
Jim Sargent Collection

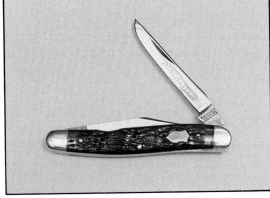

WINCHESTER
Improved Muskrat with Bone handle.
Courtesy Joe Chance

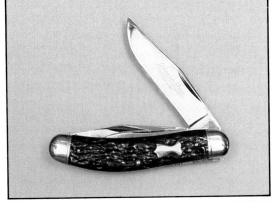

REMINGTON
#R4283 5 blade Sowbelly with Bone handle.
Jim Sargent Collection

(top to bottom)
QUEEN
These Queens exhibit older handle material. #9 Stockman's with Green Winterbottom Bone, rare Q Stainless stamp, #19 Heavy Duty Trapper with White & Brown Winterbottom Bone, rare satin finished blades, Q Steel stamp, #46 Folding Fishing Knife with rare, light brown winterbottom bone, blade etched (no tang stamp).

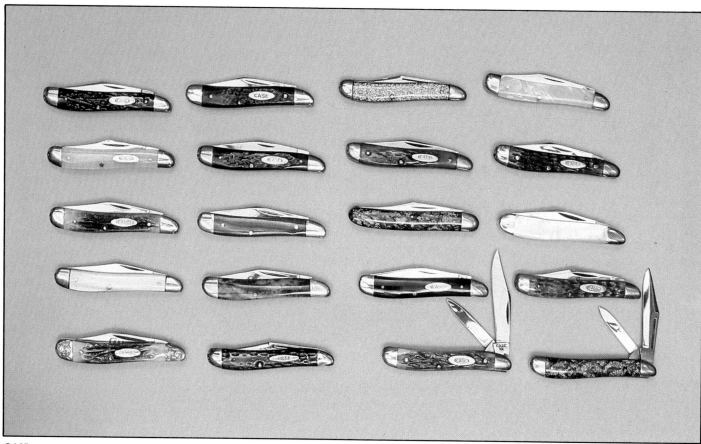

CASE
This particular display of Case Peanuts shows 20 variations of handle
materials, stampings and pulls.
Courtesy Joe Chance

REMINGTON
Handsomely boxed assortment of Scout Knives which were introduced in the
late 20's to early 30's.

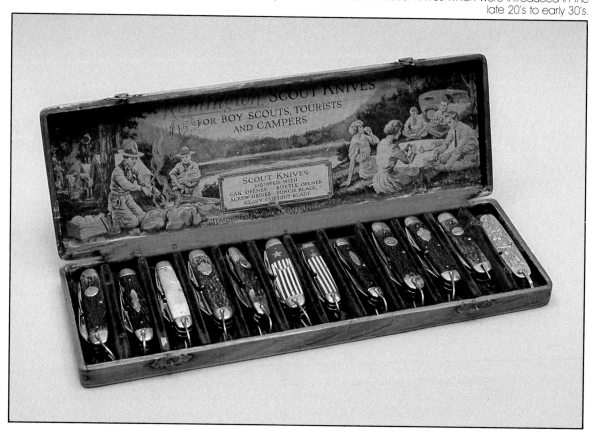

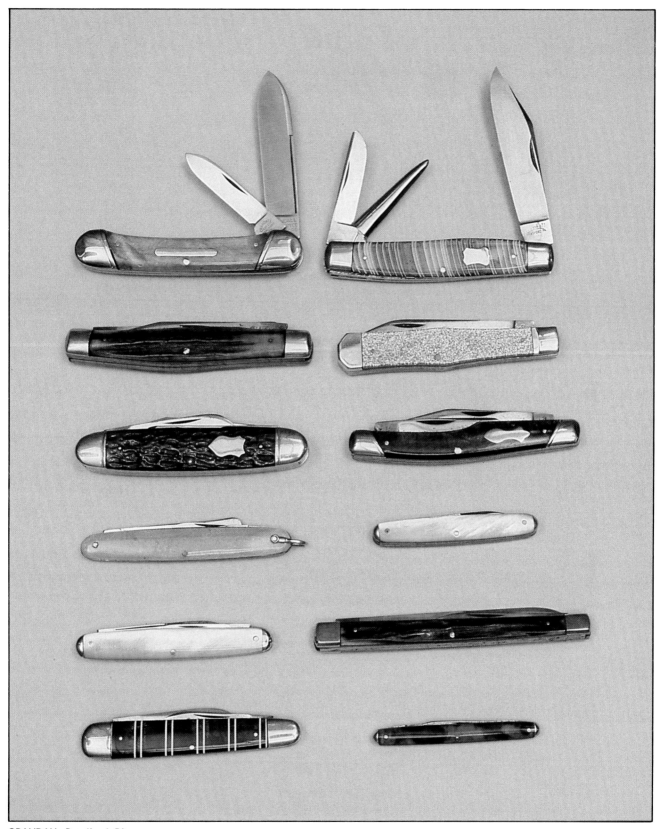

CRANDALL, Bradford, PA
This collection of 12 knives is the most complete collection of Crandall knives known.
Courtesy Joe Chance

IMPERIAL
An attractive display of Toothpicks showing multi-colored handles.
Courtesy Herman Williams

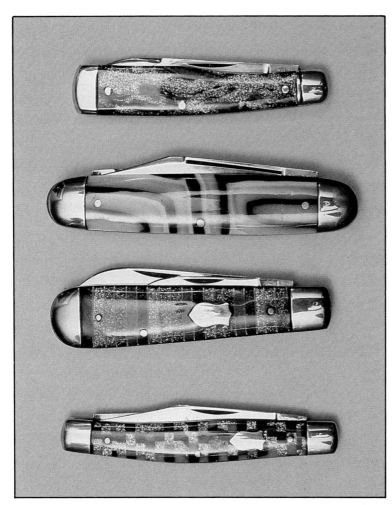

(top to bottom)
SCHRADE
Gunstock with Christmas Tree handle, Equal End with Butter and Molasses handle, Jack with Multi-Stripe handle, Serpentine with Checkerboard handle.
Courtesy Herman Williams

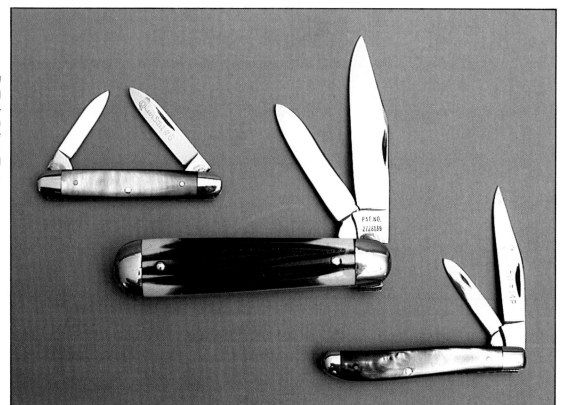

(top to bottom)
QUEEN
Smoked Pearl Pen.
center: Orange Composition
Imitation Winter Bottom (made
1969 only).
Smoked Pearl Peanut (smoked
pearl is very scarce).

Queen, #57, 3¼", 3 blade, Smoked Pearl,
(rare) $140

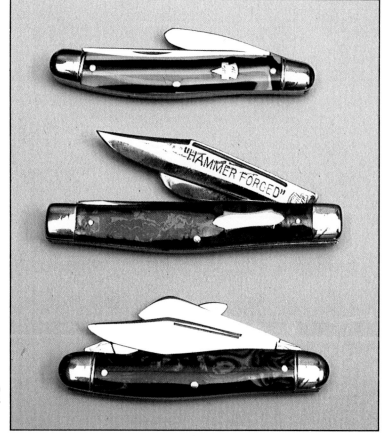

Keen Kutter & Shapleigh
showing assorted multi-color handles

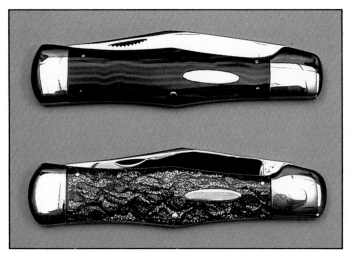

(top to bottom)
WESTERN STATES CUTLERY, BOULDER, CO.
Folding Hunter, Stripe Waterfall (rare).
Folding Hunter, Christmas Tree.

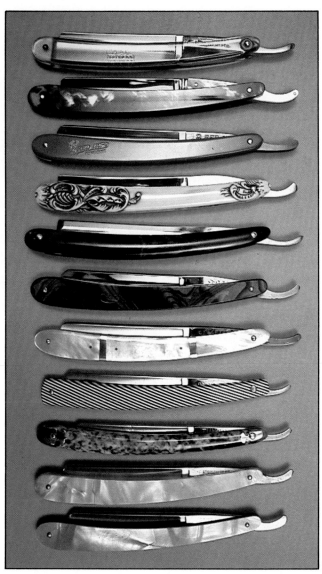

Case razors shown here exhibit the exotic and fanciful handle materials and designs that has made razor collecting so popular through the years.

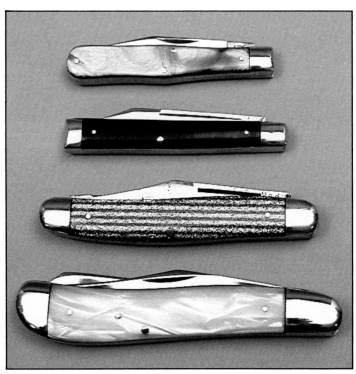

(top to bottom)
Case Tested XX, M2025½, 2 blade Coke Bottle, 3″, Green Swirl, (rare) $300. W. R. Case & Sons, Bradford, Pa. M2086, 2 blade Phys. Knife, 3⅛″, Tortoise (rare) $600. Standard Knife Co., 3⅞″, 3 blade, Green & Gold Stripe, (rare) $350. Case Tested XX, 9240SP, 2 blade Trapper, 4½″, French Pearl $650.

Western States Cutlery, Boulder, Co., Clasp Knife, Butter & Molasses Folding Hunter.

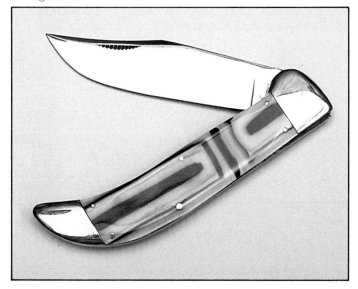

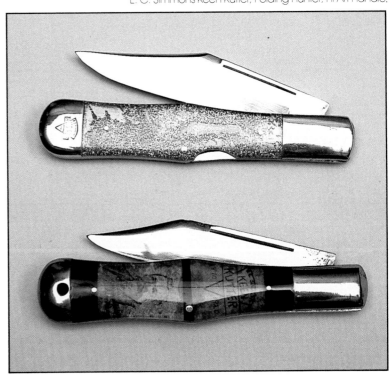

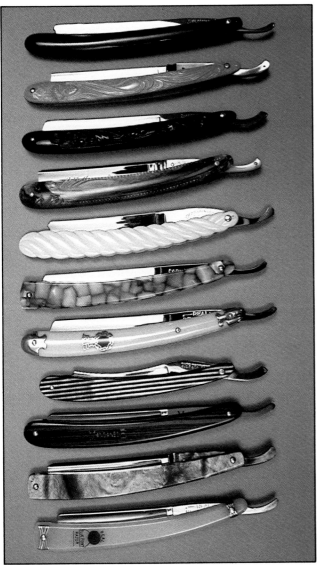

Case razors shown here exhibit the exotic and fanciful handle materials and designs that has made razor collecting so popular through the years.

Western States Cutlery, Boulder, Co., large utility, Butter & Molasses celluloid handle, large Buffalo head shield.

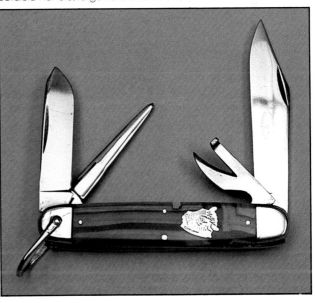

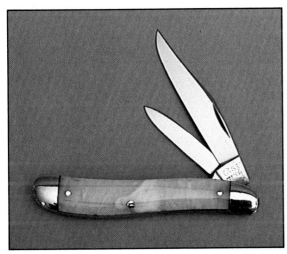

Case Tested XX, B220, 2 blade Peanut,
2⅞", Imitation Onyx, (rare) $250

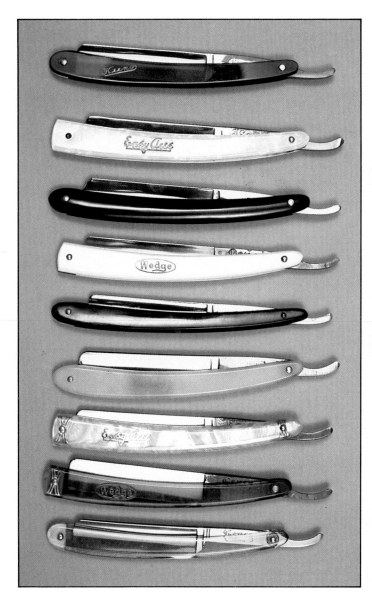
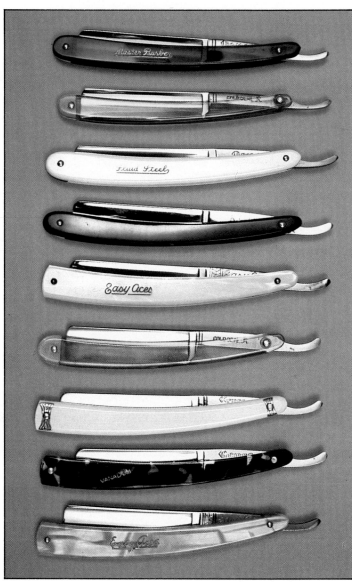

Case razors shown here exhibit the exotic and fanciful handle
materials and designs that has made razor collecting so popular through the years.

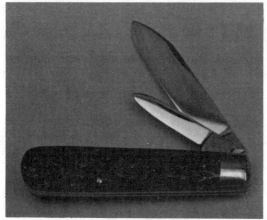

6212   Jack   Bone   3¼" $30

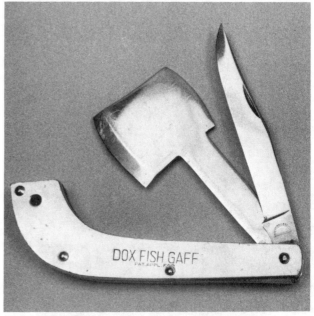

S219H   Hatchet Knife, Cherry Tree Chopper 5" $85

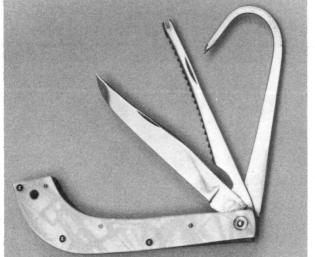

P319   Gaff Knife, Pearl Comp. handles 5" $60

17220   Buffalo Horn Pyralin handles, Coke Bottle   3" $40

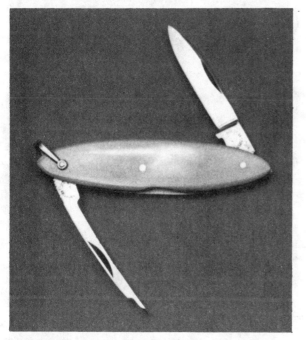

819   Pearl handles, Lobster pattern, 2½" $45

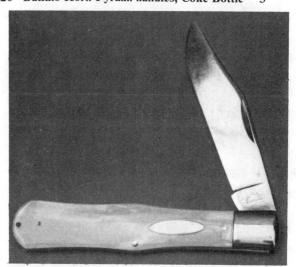

X2121BH   Pearl Comp. handles not drilled, shield   Westaco   5⅛"
$75

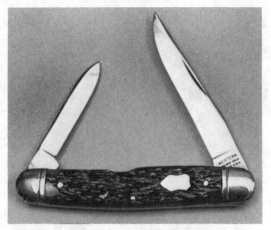

422   **Bone, shield   3⅝"**   **$50**

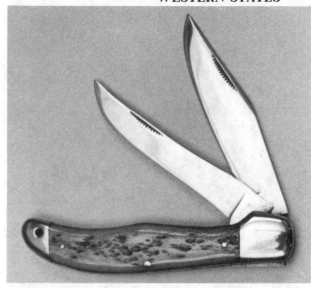

6227   **Saber, Rogers Bone, drilled, Black Iron pins, liners & bolsters**
      5¼"   **$75**

17224½   **Gunstock Grey horn pyralin handles, Buffalo skull etching**
(enclosed)   **3"**   **$60**

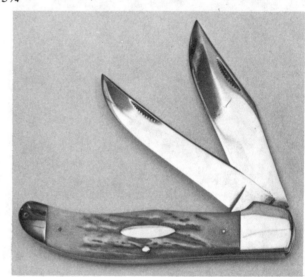

5227   **Genuine Stag, not drilled, shield in center   5¼"**   **$90**

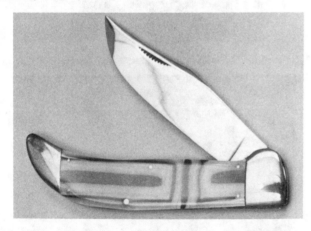

A125   **Heavy Clasp, Agate (Butter & Molasses) handles 5½"$800**

251325   **Bone, Utility, 5 blade, Prototype or Salesman's Sample on
back of M. Blade, extremely rare   3¼"**   **$475**

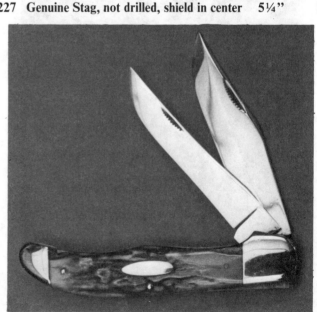

5227   **Genuine Buckhorn handles, not drilled, Buffalo skull etching**
      5¼"   **$125**

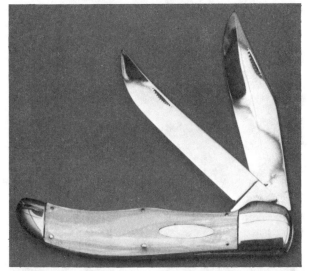

2227   Heavy Pearl Comp. handles, not drilled   5¼" $100

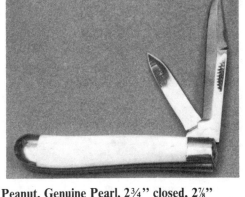

18229   Peanut, Genuine Pearl, 2¾" closed, 2⅞" $60

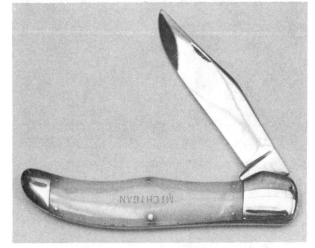

A127   Amber Cream Comp.   5¼" clasp $65

16229   Peanut, Bone, Reg. M.S. Pull   2⅞" $45

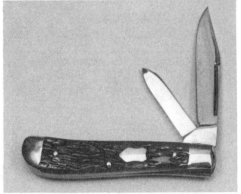

16228½   Peanut, Bone   3" $60

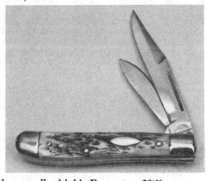

16229   Bone, long pull, shield, Peanut   2⅞" $45

A229GS   Peanut Goldstone handles $60
6229   Peanut Rogers Bone   2⅞" $50

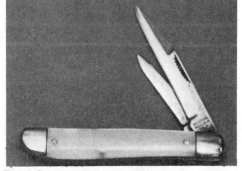

12229½   Pearl Comp. handles Peanut   2⅞" $20

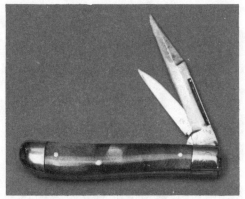

13229½ Golden Shell handles Peanut 2⅞" $30

17233 Pyralin Handles, Candy Stripe, Teardrop 3⅜" $50

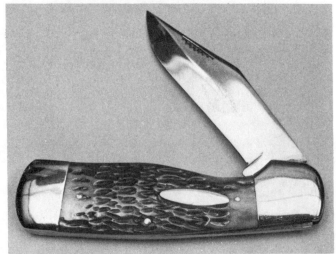

6130 Bone, oval shield 4½" $250

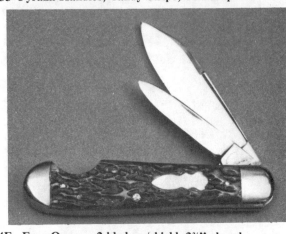

6234E Easy Opener, 2 blade w/shield, 3⅜" closed $65

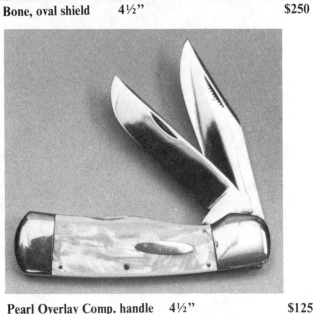

2230 Pearl Overlay Comp. handle 4½" $125

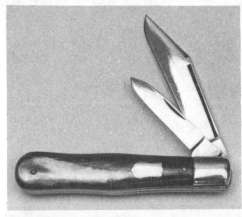

1235 Genuine Horn Handles 3½" $45

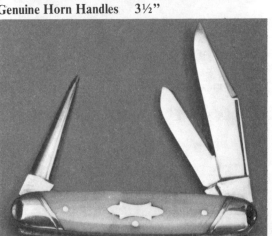

9336P Surveyor pattern, Waterfall handle, 3⅜", clip (long pull) Spey
& Punch blades, 1st etching $200

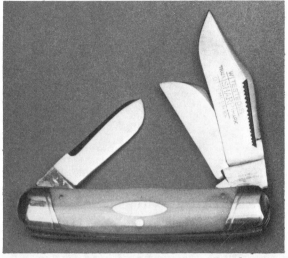

9337 Heavy Surveyer, Waterfall handles, 3½", clip w/long m. striker pull, Sheep Foot and Spey, Salesman's Sample, 1st blade etching $400

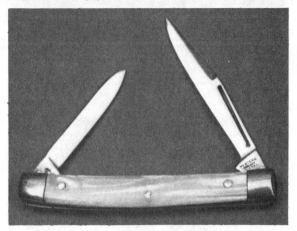

241 2 Blade Pen, Imi. Pearl handles   2⅝" $25

6342   Bone   Jack   3¼" $35

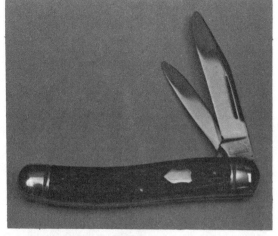

6242   Serpentine Jack Bone   3⅜" $30

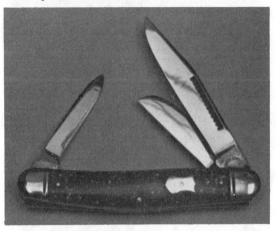

342   Red Sparkle Celluloid handles   3⅝" $45

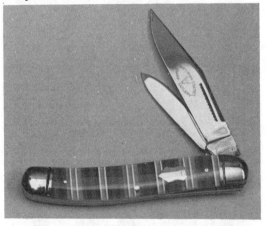

C3242   Candy Strip Comp Handle, Serpentine Jack   3⅝" $85

742   Bone, Shield, Stockman   4" $50

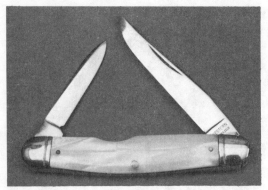

02242C Pearl Comp. (cracked ice) handles   3⅝" $30

2343-P   Whittler, Bullhead pattern, Cracked Ice handles w/White liner   3⅜" $75

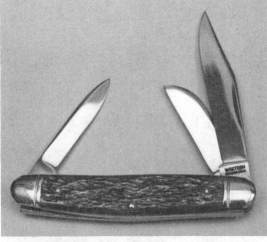

6342   Bone Stockman   3⅝" $40

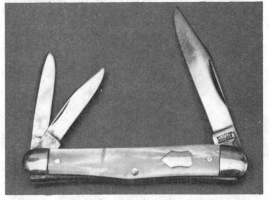

643   Whittler, Pearl Comp. (cracked ice)   3¼" $35

SO2243BB   Pearl Comp. handle w/bale, Buffalo skull etching   3¼" $25

SO2243B   Green Comp handles w/White Flecks   3¼" $30

02243T   Pearl Comp. (cracked ice) handles   3¼" $25

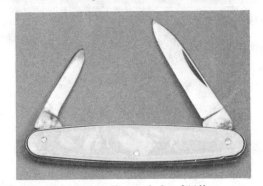

SO2243B   Pearl comp handles no bale   3¼" $25

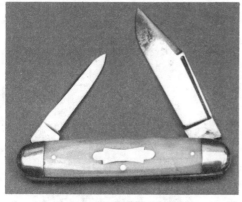

09243½   **Equal End, Waterfall handles 3¼" closed**   **3⅜"**   **$65**

8344   **3 Blade, Genuine Pearl handles**   **2⅞"**   **$40**

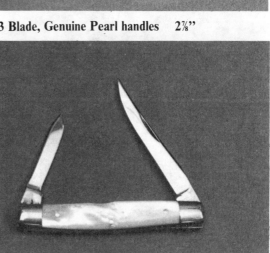

C243½P   **Candy Stripe Pyralin, Cigar Pattern**   **3⅜"**   **$125**

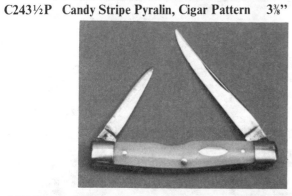

OY244C   **2 Blade, Yellow Comp. handles, Shield**   **3"**   **$20**

8244   **2 Bl. Pearl, etched 2nd**   **3"**   **$40**

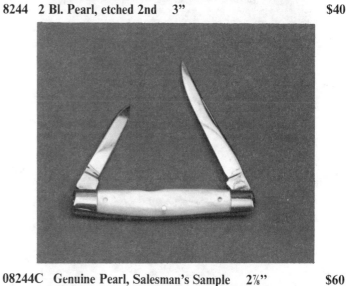

08244C   **Genuine Pearl, Salesman's Sample**   **2⅞"**   **$60**

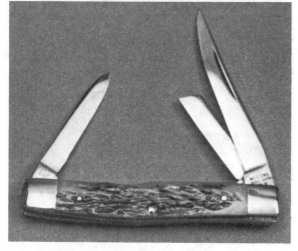

6344C   **3 Blade Rogers Bone handles**   **2⅞"**   **$40**

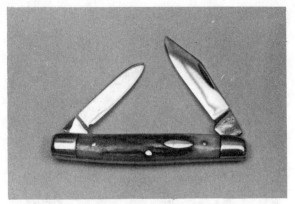

05244   **Genuine Buck Horn handles   3"** $25

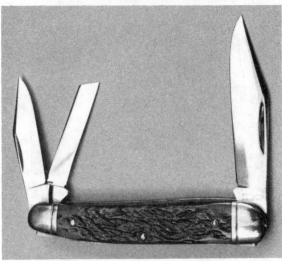

6346   **Whittler, Bone, B.I. Bolsters & blade pins   3⅞"** $125

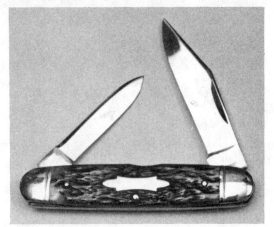

06245½   **Bone, Cigar pattern   3⅝"** $150

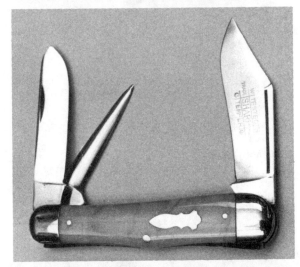

9346P   **Whittler, 3 backsprings, Waterfall   3⅝"** $500

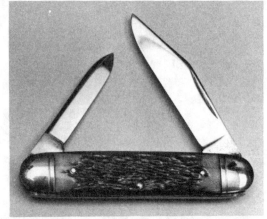

06245½   **2 Bl. Bone   3⅝"** $45

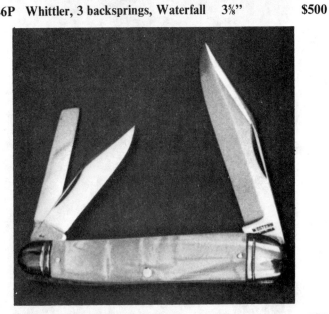

2346   **Whittler, Pearl Comp. handles   3⅞"** $75

6345½   **Cattle Knife, Rogers Bone handle w/Shield   3⅝"** $150

6346   Whittler, Green Bone, no shield   3⅞" $75

6346   Whittler Rogers Bone 3⅞"   Shield $85

6346½ P   Whittler, 3 backsprings, bone handles, Eureka Pattern
     3⅝" $300

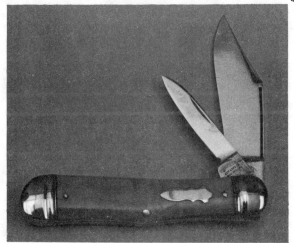

9246½   Rainbow Pearl Pyralin   3⅝" $45

A33047   Whittler, Agate Comp. handles   3⅝" $90

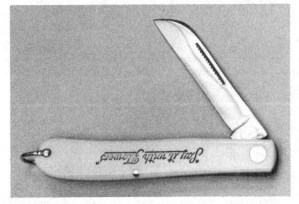

4149F   Florist Knife, Imi. Ivory handles   3⅞" $40

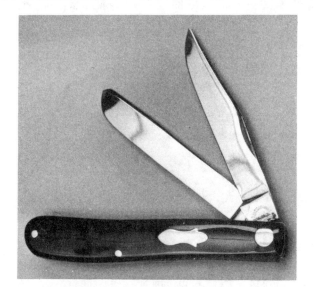

B249S   Trapper, Black Comp. handles   3⅞" $75

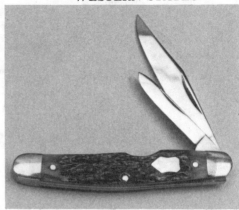

653   2 Blade Jack, Bone handles   3⅜" $45

A349KFS   Combination Knife, fork & spoon, amber non breakable handles   3⅞" $225

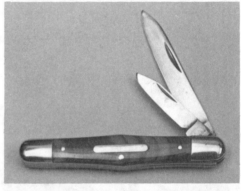

7256   Ceylon Pearl Pyralin handles 3"   Swell center $40

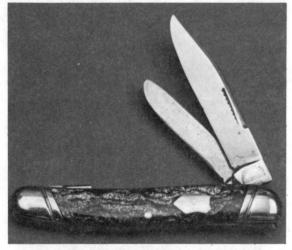

03350   Christmas tree Comp. handles, pen blade broken   3¼"$60

**2356F   File, Small Clip w/pen blade in other end. Pearl Comp. handles
      2⅞" $45**

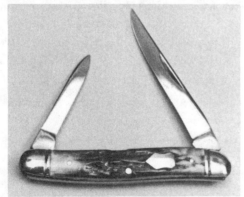

05251C   Genuine Stag handles w/shield, Buffalo skull etching on Calif. Clip blade, Pen Blade on other end.   3⅛" $60

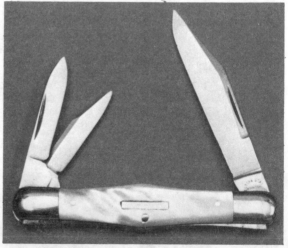

8356   Whittler, Genuine Pearl handles   3" $60

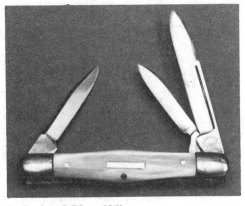

2356   Pyralin Scales, 3 Bl.   2⅞"   **$45**

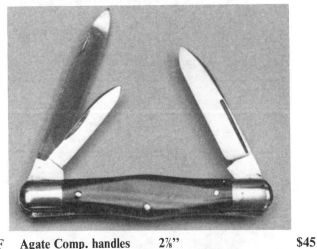

7356F   Agate Comp. handles   2⅞"   **$45**

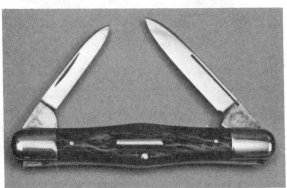

06256   Bone 3"   Swell center   **$30**

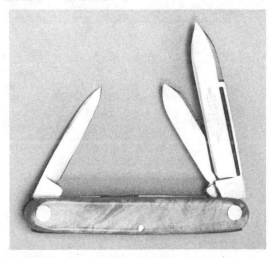

A357   Bulls Eye Pattern, Golden Shell Comp. handle   3¼" $40

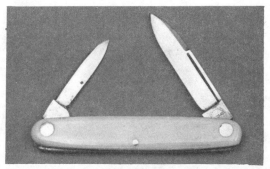

4257   Ivory Comp. Handle, Bulls eye, 1st etching (sharp temper) 3⅜"
                                                                          $30

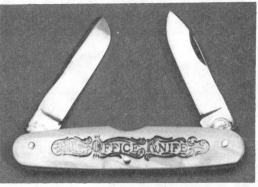

7258   "Office Knife"   Ivory Comp. handles   3⅝"   **$30**

658   Bone Serpentine 3 Bl   3⅜"   **$30**

461   Whittler, Walnut handle "Carpenter's Special   3⅞"   **$45**

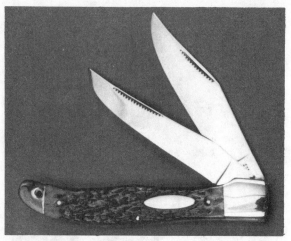

062 Bone, drilled, sheild   5⅛" $75

2363 Whittler Pearl Comp. handles   3" $40

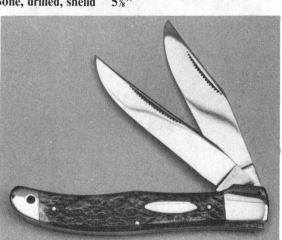

062 Bone, Drilled, Shield   5⅛" $65

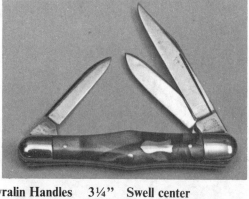

6364 Whittler, Rogers Bone, no shield   3¼" $50

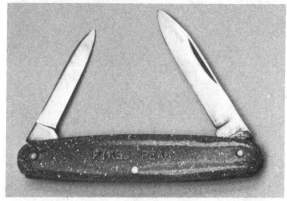

02263GS, Goldstone Shadow w/Pikes Peak stamped on handle   3"
$25

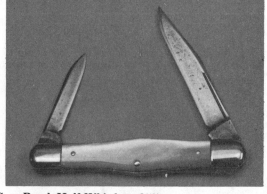

1364 Pyralin Handles   3¼"   Swell center $45

6363 Whittler, Rogers Bone handles   3" $85

8264 Gen. Pearl Half Whittler 3⅛" $45

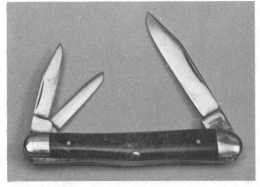

A364   Whittler, Agate Comp. handles   3¼" $45

B364   Whittler, Black Comp. handles   3¼" $45

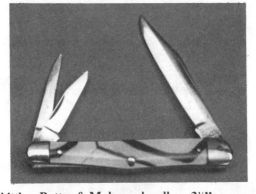

A364   Whittler, Butter & Molasses handle   3⅛" $45

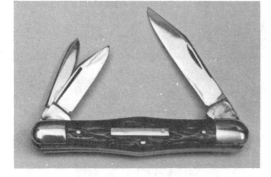

06364   Whittler, Bone   3⅛" $45

06265C   Green Bone handles   3⅜" $35

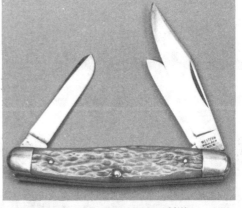

6365   Bone, B.I. blade pins, no shield   3⅜" $30

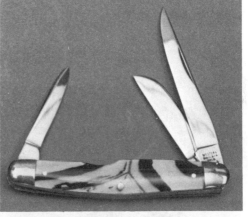

A365C   Agate comp. handles   B.I. Blade pins   3⅜" $45

SO2265C   Pearl Comp. "Cracked Ice" handles   3⅜" $25

266

WESTERN STATES

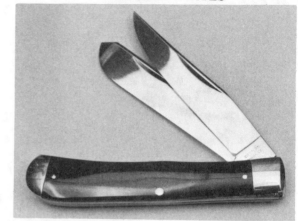

06265C Bone   3⅜" $30   **2269S   Trapper   4⅛"** $45

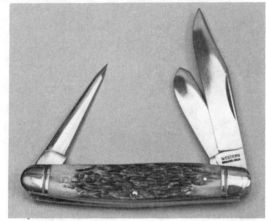

6365P   Bone no shield   3⅝"   No. 2 Case $50

6269S   Trapper, Bone, no shield 4⅛" $125

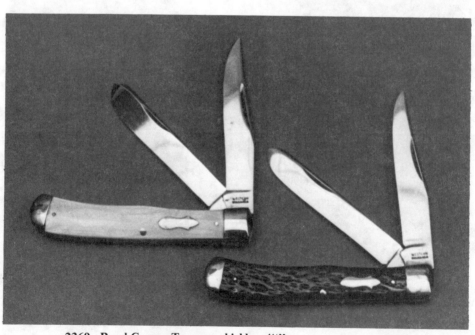

2369   Pearl Comp., Trapper, shield   4⅛" $85
6269   Bone, shield   4⅛" $75

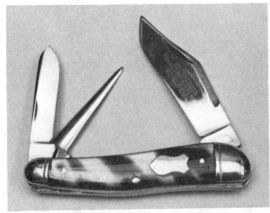

7372P   Whittler, Imi. Horn handles   3¼"   **$125**

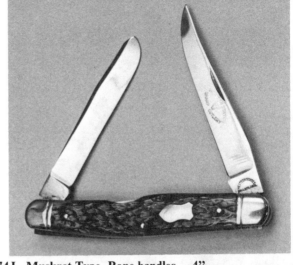

6274J   Muskrat Type, Bone handles   4"   **$225**

G372½   Whittler, Christmas Tree handles   3¼"   **$275**

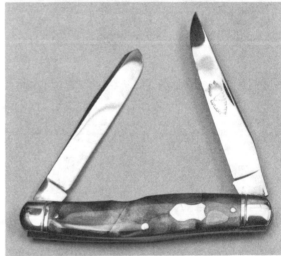

3274J   Muskrat Type, Imi. Shell handles   4"   **$200**

6374   Bone, etched "Premium Stock"   4"   **$175**

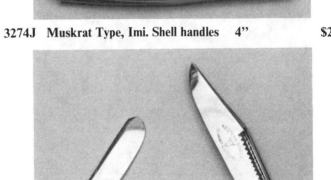

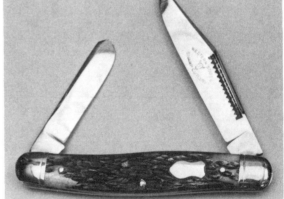

6274S   Bone handle, 2nd etching   4"   **$200**

268 WESTERN STATES

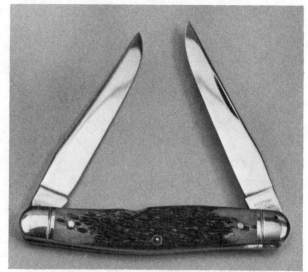

6274C Bone, Muskrat, no shield   4"   **$75**

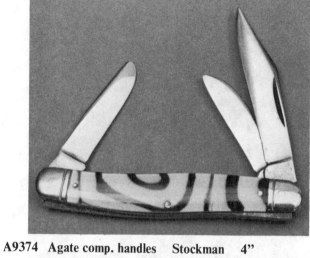

A9374   Agate comp. handles   Stockman   4"   **$50**

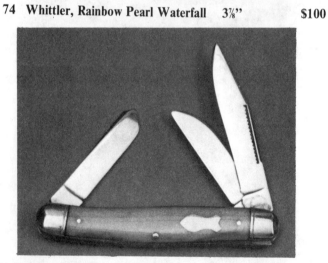

74   Whittler, Rainbow Pearl Waterfall   3⅞"   **$100**

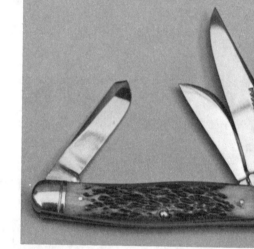

6374   Bone Match Striker Pull   Stockman   4"   **$60**

9374, Rainbow Pearl Waterfall handles, Stockman, pinched bolster, 1919 catalog, earlier knife than above and larger yet same pattern   4"
$125

6374S   Stockman, Long Spay MB, Bone shield, 4", Sheep foot & Punch 2nd blade etching
$225

269

6374P Premium Stock etched on master blade with Buffalo skull, Green Bone handles   4" $175

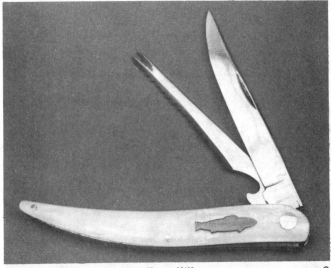

S22075D Pearl Comp. handles   4⅜" $45

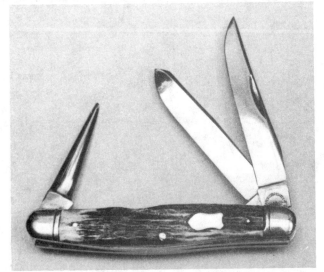

5374C-P Skinning Blade, Long Spey and Punch, Genuine Stag w/shield   4" $200

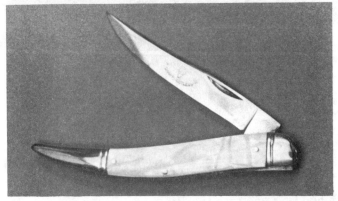

71075 Texas Toothpick, Imi. Pearl (Cracked Ice) handles, Buffalo skull etching on blade, pull on rear of blade   4¼" $65

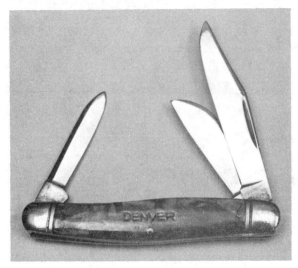

9374 Celluloid handles, Green Stockman   4" $45

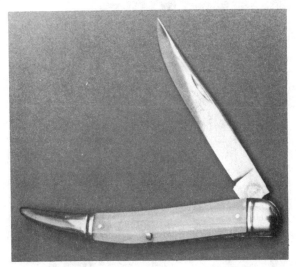

Y175 Texas Toothpick, Yellow Comp. handles, Western States blade stamping   4¼" $75

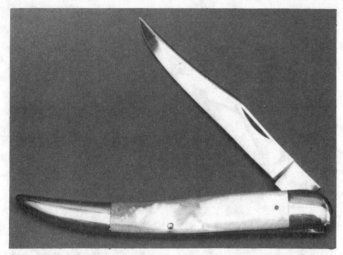

8175 Texas Toothpick, Gen. Pearl handles, Stainless Steel blade
   5" $100

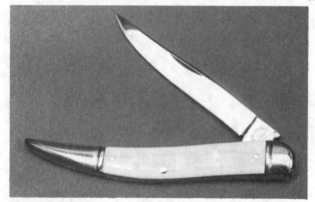

71075 Texas Toothpick, Imi. Pearl overlay handles, Buffalo skull
etching on blade   4¼" $75

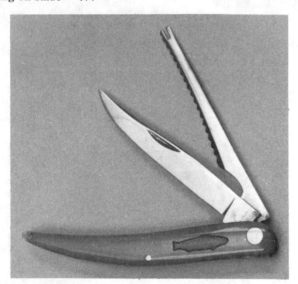

SR2075F Fish Knife, 4¼" closed, Red handles $35

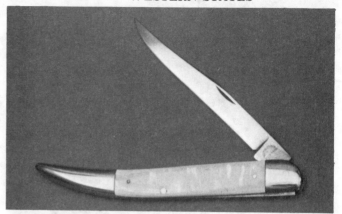

2175V Fish Knife, "Toothpick"   5" $50

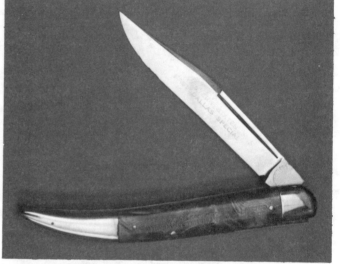

3175 Texas Toothpick   5⅛"   Etching on blade: "Western States
East Dallas Special" $300

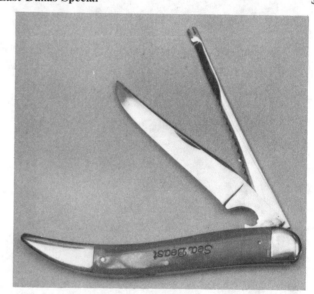

R276D   Fish Knife, Red Comp. handles   5½" $50

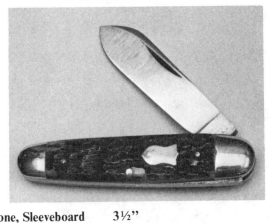

6176 Bone, Sleeveboard   3½" $65

9278-T   İmi. Pearl handles 3⅛"   Sleeveboard, tip bolsters, Buffalo skull etching $25

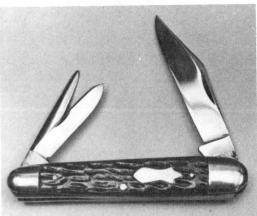

6376½   Bone 3 Bl. Whittler   3⅝" $65

378GS   Whittler, Goldstone handles   3⅜" $65

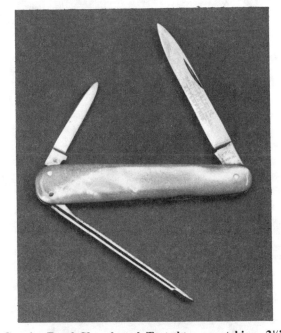

8378   Genuine Pearl, Sleeveboard, Tested temper etching   3⅛" $40

6379   Whittler, Bone, Heavy Surveyor pattern   3⅝" $475

5283B   Gen. Stag, Lobster pattern   3" $35

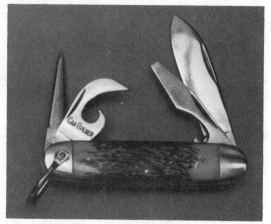

6490   **Bone, small stamp, utility**   ¾" $45

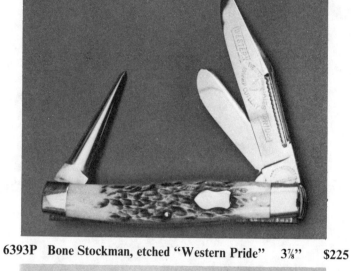

6393P   **Bone Stockman, etched "Western Pride"**   3⅞" $225

0093   **Bone Jack**   3¾" $55

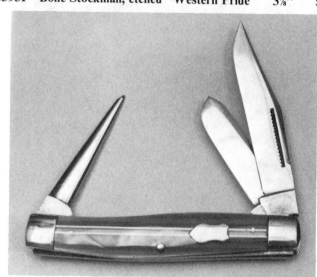

C393P   **Stockman, Cornelia Stripe handle**   3⅞" $125

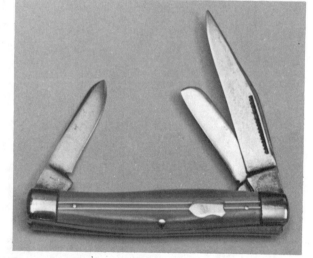

C33093   **Candy Stripe Comp. handles, Stockman**   3⅞" $65

32093   **2 Blade w/2nd etching, Golden Shell Pyralin handles**   3⅞"
$100

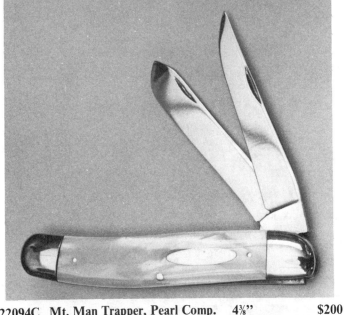

22094C   Mt. Man Trapper, Pearl Comp.   4⅜" $200

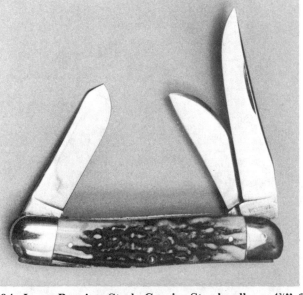

53094   Large Premium Stock, Genuine Stag handles   4⅜" $275

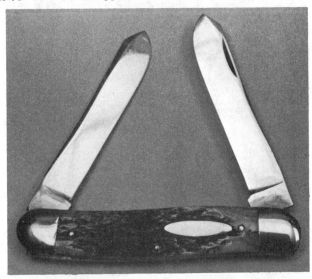

06294S   2 Bl. Rogers Bone, Mtn. Man Pattern   4¼" $250

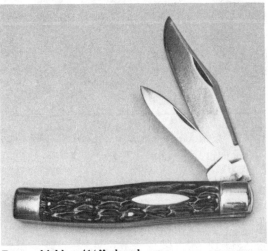

6294   Bone, shield   4¼" closed $50

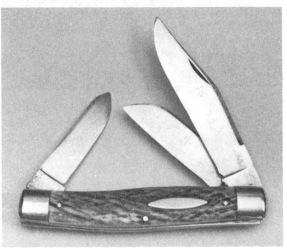

5394   Sec. Cut stag on Front, regular stag on back handle   4¼" $85

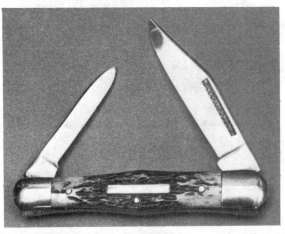

**6296½   Half Whittler, Bone, Barshield, long match striker pull, 2nd
blade etching   3½" $95**

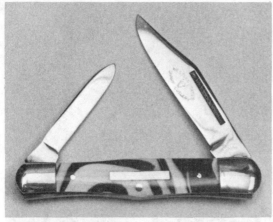

A296½   Half Whittler, Agate Comp. handles   3½"   **$90**

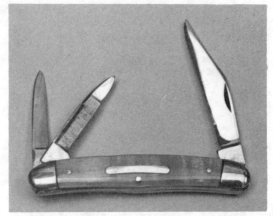

9399½   Whittler, Sway back, Rainbow Pearl Pyralin handles   3¼"
$65

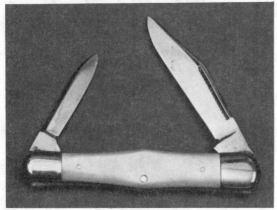

8296½ Genuine Pearl handles   3½"   **$40**

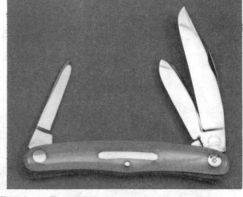

99½   Rainbow Pearl (Waterfall) Comp. handles   3¼" $80
1st etching on blade

A125
Rare Waterfall handle, 5½"   (Clasp) $1200
Courtesy Curtis Walker

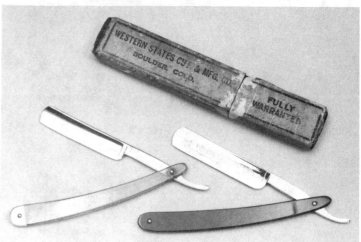

$20 each Razor

KEEN KUTTER
HEADQUARTERS

"The recollection of QUALITY remains long after the PRICE is forgotten" TRADE MARK REGISTERED.
TRUE OF KEEN KUTTER GOODS.

ST. LOUIS　　　　1904

A. F. SHAPLEIGH, 1810-1902

E. C. SIMMONS, 1839-1921

KEEN KUTTER
SIMMONS HARDWARE CO.

C. 1868-1960   This firm was founded in about 1868. Their firm was located in St. Louis, Missouri. The trademark Keen Kutter was used from the first beginnings of this firm. This hardware grew to be one of the giants in the industry. Simmons eventually gained control over several manufacturing firms. One of these was the Walden Knife Co. of Walden, New York. In 1922 this firm merged with the Winchester Arms Co. forming what was known as the Winchester-Simmons Company. At this time all of the manufacturing firms Simmons had acquired were turned over to the Winchester management. The hardware outlets Winchester owned, were taken over by the Simmons management. In 1929 the Winchester-Simmons firm was dissolved and each firm again went its own way. In 1940 the Shapleigh Hardware Co., also of St. Louis, purchased the E.C. Simmons Company. Shapleigh continued to use the trademarks Simmons had used, this time as a second line of goods to their own Diamond Edge line. In 1960 Shapleigh was in turn sold, and the Simmons and Shapleigh trademarks were discontinued.

STAMPINGS

E. C. Simmons
  Hornet on back of tang

Simmons Boss

Silver Tip
  c. 1927-1928 (Novelty Cut.)

E. C. Simmons St. Louis Mo.
  c. 1868-1960

Simmons Hdwe, Co.
  c. 1868-1960 Keen Kutter stamped out on blade. England on back of tang.

Simmons Hdwe. Co. Germany
  c. 1868-1960

R. A. Simmons Chicago Ill.

Simmons, Warden, White Co. Dayton O. USA
  c. 1937-1946 This firm was located at 1101 Negley Place, Dayton.

Shapleigh Hardware Company

C. 1846-1960 This company had its start in 1843 when A. F. Shapleigh, then a junior partner of Rogers Bros. & Co. of Philadelphia, brought to St. Louis a stock of goods to open a branch of that company. This branch was named the Rogers Shapleigh & Company. In 1847 the company became Shapleigh, Day & Co. This name was used until 1863 when the firm became A. F. Shapleigh & Co. The next year, 1864, Diamond Edge was adopted as the trademark for their tools and cutlery. The exact marking on these early knives is unknown at this time. In 1880 the name was the A. F. Shapleigh and Cantwell Hardware Co. This firm continued until 1888, when it became the A. F. Shapleigh Hardware Company. The next change in the company occurred in about 1902. At this time the company became the Norvell-Shapleigh Hardware Co. Saunders Norvell started with the E.C. Simmons Hardware in the late 1800's as a clerk. He was still a clerk in 1898, but by 1900 was a Vice-President of the Simmons firm. By 1902 he had changed to Shapleigh, and was President by 1907 of the Norvell-Shapleigh Hardware Co. The name once more reverted to A. F. Shapleigh Hardware Co. in about 1920. On July 1, 1940 Shapleigh purchased the E. C. Simmons Hardware. From this time until about 1960, they used the old Simmons trademarks on their products, as a second line to the Diamond Edge trademark. This business continued to do business until 1960 when the firm was sold. The knives produced by this firm were marked on all blades up until the middle 1940's. After this, they were marked on the master blade only. Some of the markings sold by Shapleigh were:

Berkshire
Bridge Cutlery Co.
Enders Oak Leaf
Diamond Edge (c. 1864-1960)
Keen Kutter (c. 1940-1960)
Empire Knife Co.
NorShap (c. 1902-1920)
Norvell-Shapleigh (c. 1902-1920)

S. Norvell (c. 1902-1920)
Norvell's Best (c. 1902-1920)
G. W. Putman & Co. Germany
Enterprise Cutlery Co.
Simmons Hardware Co. (c. 1940-1960)
Simmons Sonny (c. 1940-1960)
J. Koester's Sons Germany

Harry King with his vast Keen Kutter collection.

K1058 E.C. Simmons, Lock Back, Brown Bone 4¼"   **$225**

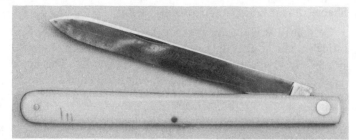

A102 Diamond Edge, Melon Tester, Ivory Type   5¾"   **$25**

**Simmons Hardware, Swell End Jack, 1 Blade, Gray and Red Celluloid
3"**   **$25**

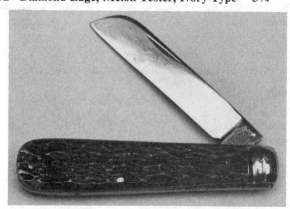

E.C. Simmons, 1 Blade, Brown Bone   4" Sheep Foot   **$45**

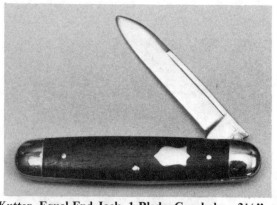

Keen Kutter, Equal End Jack, 1 Blade, Cocobola   3¼"   **$25**

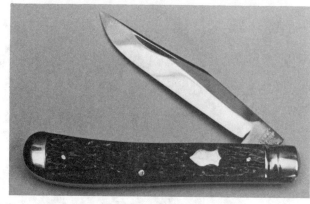

E.C. Simmons, Trapper, One Blade, Brown Bone   **$90**

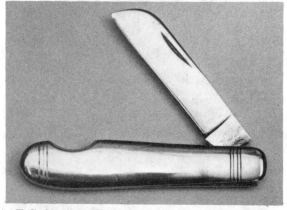

1719½ E.C. Simmons, Easy Opener Jack, Metal   3⅜"   **$55**

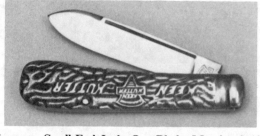

E.C. Simmons, Swell End Jack, One Blade, Metal   3½"   **$45**

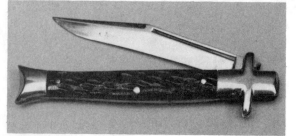

E.C. Simmons, Bow Tie, Bone   3⅞"   **$80**

E.C. Simmons, Keen Kutter, 3½", 1 Blade Barlow, Bone   **$85**

279

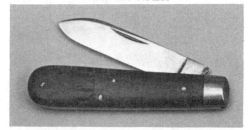

Simmons Boss, Germany Equal End Jack, 1 Blade Walnut   3"$35

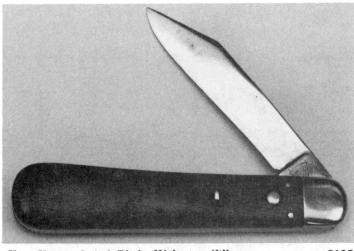

Keen Kutter, Switch Blade, Walnut   4⅞" $125

E.C. Simmons, Lock Back, S.A.B. Brown Bone, Punch Bols, 3½"
$150

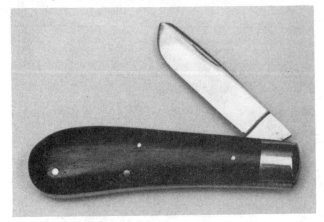

E.C. Simmons, Maize, Walnut   4" $65

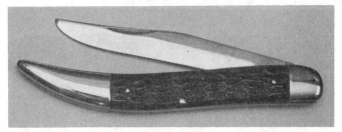

1898¾   E.C. Simmons, Texas Toothpick, Brown Bone   5"$175

E.C. Simmons, Hawkbill, Walnut   4" $40

K1998¾   Keen Kutter, Texas Toothpick, Cracked Ice Celluloid   5"
$75

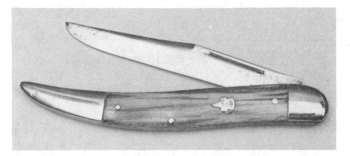

K100   Keen Kutter, Texas Toothpick, Butter and Molasses   5"
$150

E.C. Simmons, Trapper, One Blade, Brown Bone, Spear   4½"$125

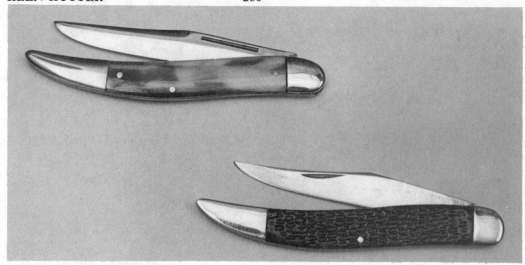

E.C. Simmons, Texas Toothpick, Yellow and Brown Celluloid 5" $175

Simmons Hardware, Texas Toothpick, Black Imi. Bone 5" $65

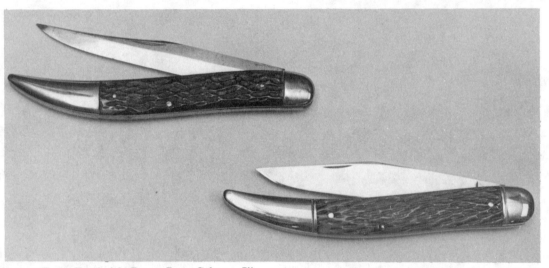

K1898¾ E.C. Simmons, Texas Toothpick, Brown Bone, Sabor 5" $175

802 Keen Kutter, Texas Toothpick, Peach Seed Bone 5" $175

1881 Keen Kutter, Barlow, 1 Blade, Brown Bone 3⅜" $40

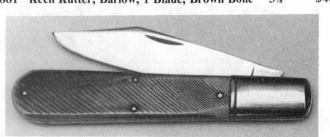

801 Keen Kutter, Daddy Barlow, Brown Bone 5" $125

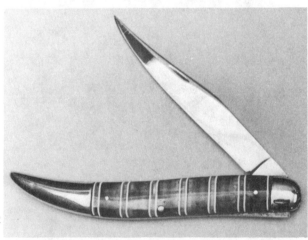

E. C. Simmons, Texas Toothpick, Candy Stripe 5" $175

281

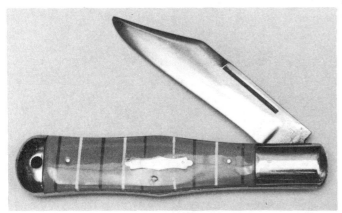

Keen Kutter, Folding Hunter, Swell Center, Orange, Green and White Celluloid   5¼"   **$250**

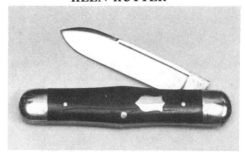

E. C. Simmons, Swell Center Jack, 1 Blade, Walnut   3⅜" $30

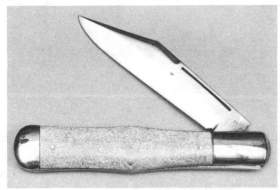

E. C. Simmons, Folding Hunter, Swell Center, S.A.B., Gold Stone 5¼"   **$250**

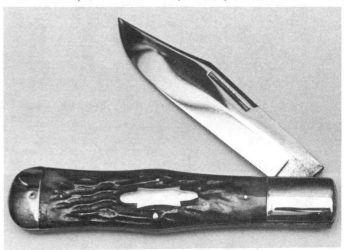

E. C. Simmons, Coke Bottle, 1920 Brown Bone   5¼" $250

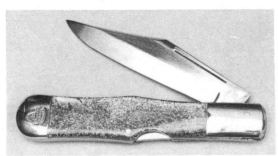

E. C. Simmons, Hunter Lock Back, S.A.B., Gold Tone   5⅛"$350

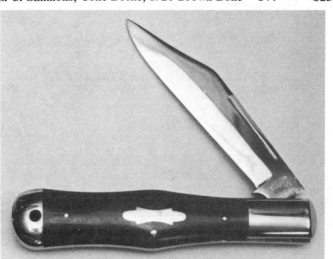

E. C. Simmons, Coke Bottle, Ebony   5⅛" $150

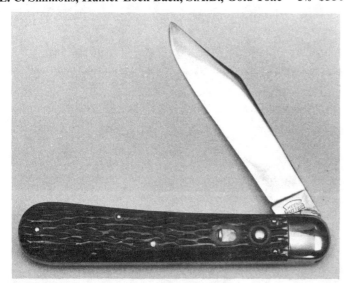

Keen Kutter, Switch Blade, Patented June 6, 1916, Peach Seed Bone 4⅞" $300

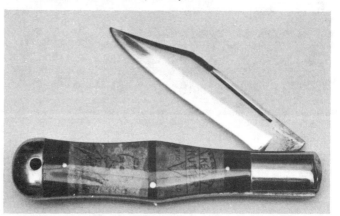

E. C. Simmons, Coke Bottle with Simmons picture in handle, Clear Celluloid, 1870-1920   5¼" $225

Simmons Hardware Germany, Switch Blade, Brown Bone, Rare S/B 3⅜"; $150

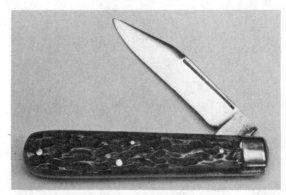

E. C. Simmons, Jack, 1 Blade, Brown Bone 3¼" $40

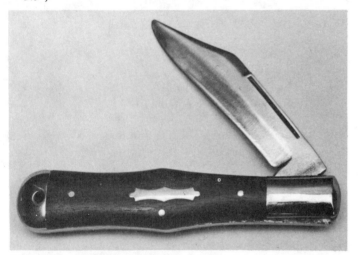

Keen Kutter, Coke Bottle, Ebony 5¼" $150

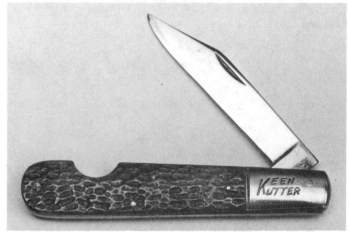

1773¾ E. C. Simmons, Daddy Barlow, Easy Opener, Pick, Bone 5" $225

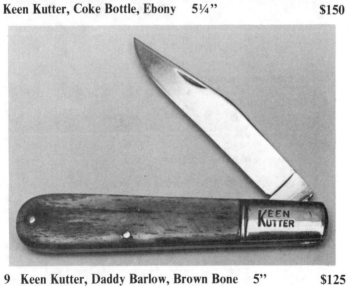

9 Keen Kutter, Daddy Barlow, Brown Bone 5" $125

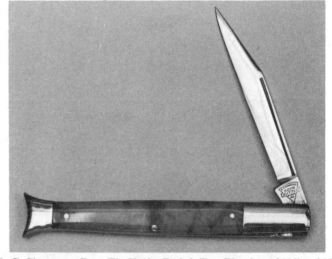

E. C. Simmons, Bow Tie Knife, Red & Tan Plastic 3¾" $100

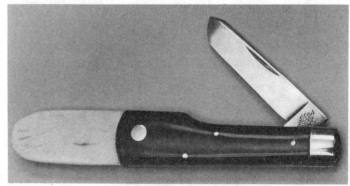

Shapleigh Hardware, Grafting Knife, Ebony 3⅛" $50

Simmons Hardware, Hornet Dogleg, Metal   2⅞" $30

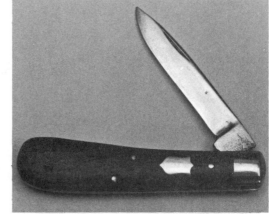

Keen Kutter, Dogleg Jack, One Blade, Walnut   3⅜" $30

E. C. Simmons, Pen, One Blade Jack, Ebony   2½" $30

E. C. Simmons, Corn Razor, Pearl   3" $100

2 BLADE

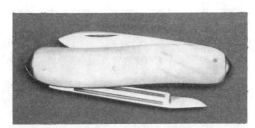

0154   E.C. Simmons, Lobster Pen, Pearl   3" $35

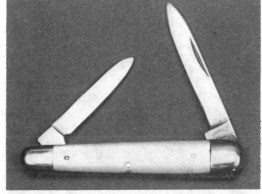

E.C. Simmons, Sleeveboard Pen, Pearl   2⅞" $45

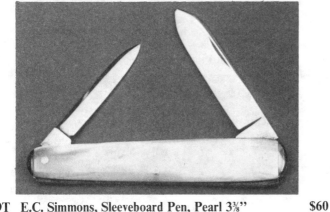

099T   E.C. Simmons, Sleeveboard Pen, Pearl 3⅜" $60

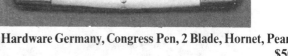

Simmons Hardware Germany, Congress Pen, 2 Blade, Hornet, Pearl
2⅞" $50

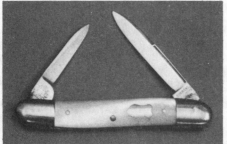

Simmons Hardware Germany, Serpentine Pen, Pearl 2⅝" $40

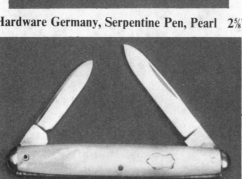

0388 E.C. Simmons, Senator Pen, 2 Blade, Pearl 2⅞" $35

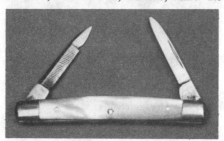

E.C. Simmons Congress, 2 Blade, Pearl 2½" File $45

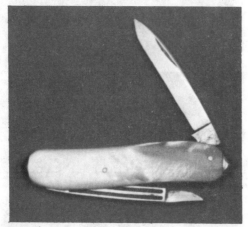

E.C. Simmons, Sleeveboard Lobster Pen, Pearl 3⅛" $40

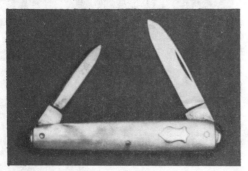

E.C. Simmons, Sleeveboard Pen, Pearl 2¾" $40

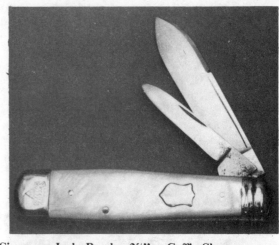

E.C. Simmons, Jack, Pearl 3⅝" Coffin Shape $125

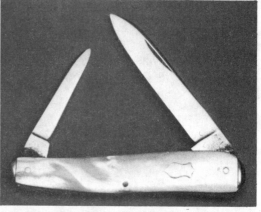

02339 E.C. Simmons, Dogleg Pen, Pearl 3¼" $60

E.C. Simmons, Swell End Jack, Pearl WPC 3" $45

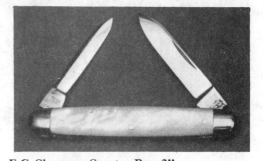

R0209 E.C. Simmons, Senator Pen, 3" $40

285

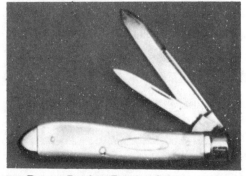

E.C. Simmons, Peanut Dogleg, Pearl   3" $50

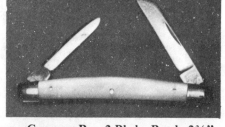

E.C. Simmons, Congress Pen, 2 Blade, Pearl   2¾" $45

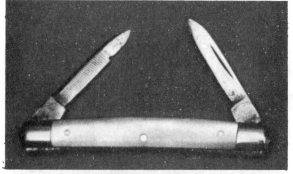

E.C. Simmons, Congress Pen, 2 Blade, Pearl   2½" $50

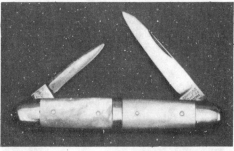

Simmons Hardware Germany, Senator Pen, Hornet, Pearl   3"$60

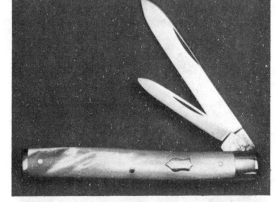

26004   E.C. Simmons, Doctor Pill Buster, 2 Blade, Pearl   3⅜"$150

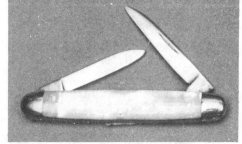

Keen Kutter, Senator Pen, Pearl   3" $40

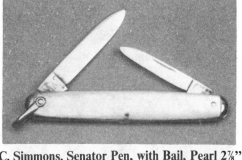

0488   E.C. Simmons, Senator Pen, with Bail, Pearl 2⅞" $40

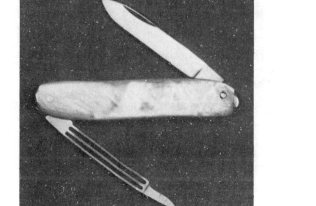

E.C. Simmons, Lobster Pen, Pearl   3" $45

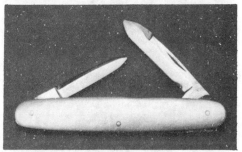

E.C. Simmons, Senator Pen, Pearl   3⅛" $45

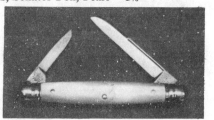

E.C. Simmons, Senator Pen, Hornet, Pearl   2½" $60

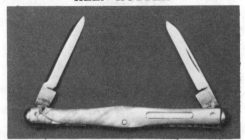

E.C. Simmons, Swell Center Pen, Rare, Pearl   3" $90

K715   Keen Kutter, Dogleg Pen, Cracked Ice   3" $30

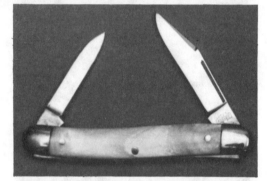

E.C. Simmons, Whittler, Aluminum Bolster, Rare, Pearl   3⅛" $100

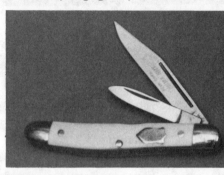

218   Keen Kutter, Peanut, Ivory Type   2⅞" $20

K236   Keen Kutter, Serpentine Pen, 2 Blade, Cracked Ice   3¼"
$30

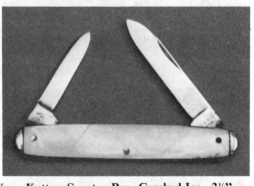

K8   Keen Kutter, Senator Pen, Cracked Ice   3⅛" $20

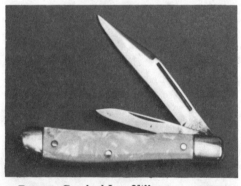

Keen Kutter, Peanut, Cracked Ice, 2⅞" $25

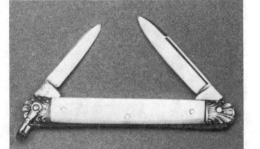

K42   Keen Kutter, Senator Pen, Cracked Ice   3⅛" $20

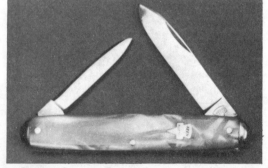

Simmons Hardware, Germany, Hornet, Pen Senator, fancy bolster with bail, Pearl   2½" $150

840   Keen Kutter, Senator Pen, 2 Blade, Cracked Ice   3⅜" $25

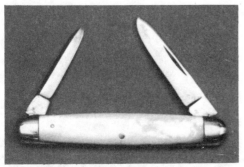

E.C. Simmons   Senator 2 Blade, Pearl   3" $40

G2235   E.C. Simmons, Sleeveboard Dogleg, Goldstone 3" $60

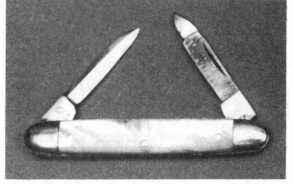

013   E.C. Simmons, Pearl Senator   2⅜" $40

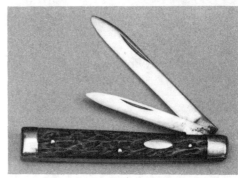

K196   Keen Kutter, Doctor Pill Buster, Brown Bone 2⅞" $150

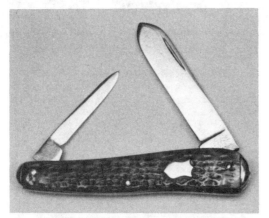

E.C. Simmons, Sleeveboard Dogleg, Brown Bone 3¼" $55

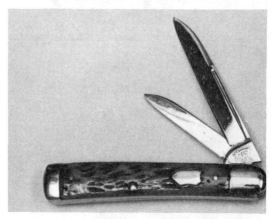

E.C. Simmons, Doctor Pill Buster, Brown Bone 3¼" $175

K187   Keen Kutter, Moose, Brown Bone   4" $175

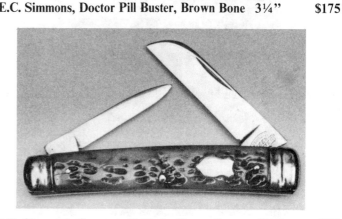

E.C. Simmons, Congress, 2 Blade, Brown Bone   3¾" $85

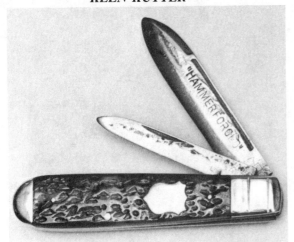

K2226 E.C. Simmons, Jack, Brown Bone 3⅞"   **$100**

E.C. Simmons, Swell End Jack, White Bone 3⅝"   **$65**

E.C. Simmons, Equal End Jack, Cocobola 3¼"   **$40**

53¾ E.C. Simmons, Jack, Brown Bone 3⅜"   **$50**

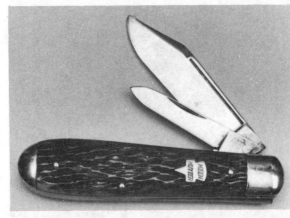

Keen Kutter, Swell End Jack, Peach Seed Bone 3⅝"   **$65**

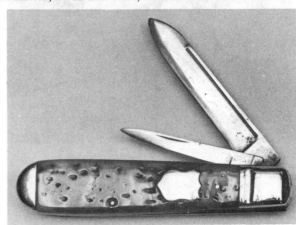

2203 E.C. Simmons, Jack, Brown Bone 3⅞"   **$50**

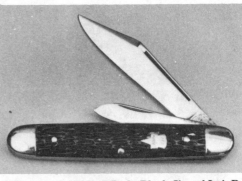

833 Keen Kutter, Equal End Jack, Black Jigged Imi. Bone 3⅛"$25

E.C. Simmons, Swell End Jack, Rough Black 3⅝"   **$45**

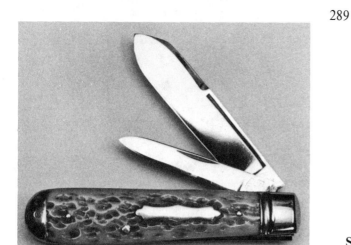

E.C. Simmons, Swell End Jack, Brown Bone 3¾" $55

Simmons Hardware, Equal End Jack, Rare, Banana Bone   3½"
$60

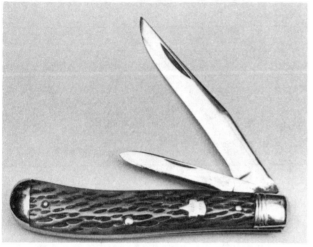

841   Keen Kutter, Trapper, Peach Seed Bone 3⅞" $90

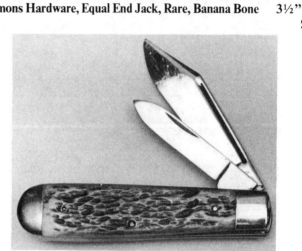

K3   Keen Kutter, Jack, Brown Bone   3½" $40

Simmons Hardware, Trapper, Black Imi. Bone 3¾" $75

Keen Kutter, Trapper, Peach Seed Bone   3⅞" $125

Diamond Edge, Trapper, Peach Seed Bone   3⅞" $90

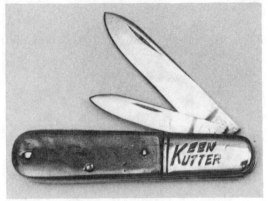

2881   E.C. Simmons, Barlow, Brown Bone   3⅜" $45

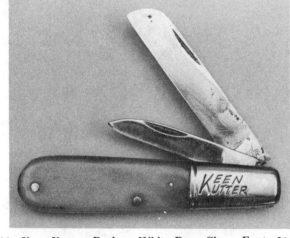

288½   Keen Kutter, Barlow, White Bone Sheep Foot   3½" $60

828   Keen Kutter, Barlow, Yellow Bone   3⅜" $45

K254   Keen Kutter, Barlow, Brown Bone   3⅜" $45

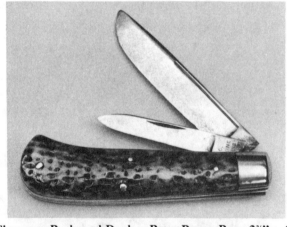

E.C. Simmons, Backward Dogleg, Rare, Brown Bone 3⅜" $125

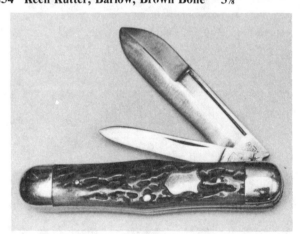

2498   E.C. Simmons, Swell Center Jack, Sab. Blade, Brown Bone
3⅝" $100

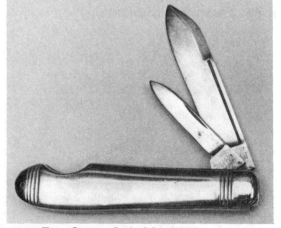

E.C. Simmons, Easy Opener Jack, Metal 3⅜" $75

04527   E.C. Simmons, Congress, 2 Blade, Brown Bone   3¼"$45

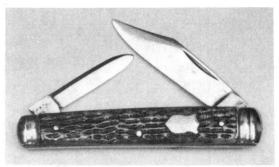

E.C. Simmons, Pen, 2 Blade, Brown Bone   3¼" $65

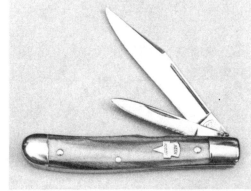

K233   Keen Kutter, Peanut, Butter and Molasses   2⅞" $30

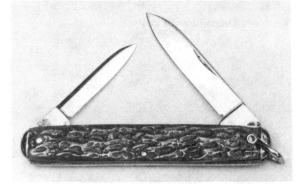

S03471   E.C. Simmons, Senator Pen, with Bail, Brown Bone   3⅜" $40

Keen Kutter, Dogleg Pen, Brown Imi. Bone   3¼" $20

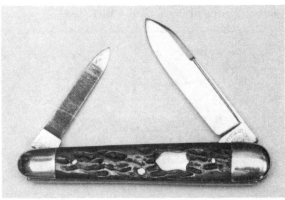

E.C. Simmons, Sleeveboard Pen, Brown Bone   3⅜" $50

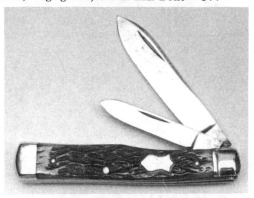

5328   E.C. Simmons, Brown Bone Gunstock   3" $125

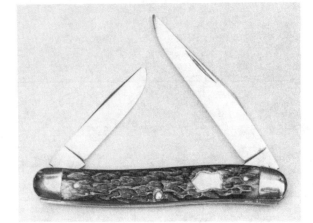

K03706½   Keen Kutter, Dogleg Pen, Brown Bone   3¼" $45

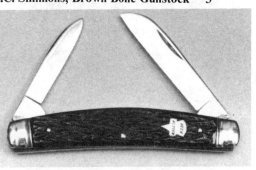

790   Keen Kutter, Congress, 2 Blade, Black Celluloid   3⅛" $25

0198   E.C. Simmons, Sleeveboard Pen, 2 Blade, ¾ Brown Bone   3⅜" $45

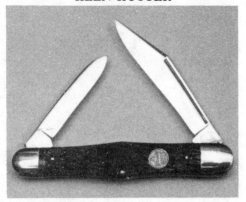

K29 Keen Kutter, Swell Center Pen, Salesman Sample, Black Celluloid 3" **$30**

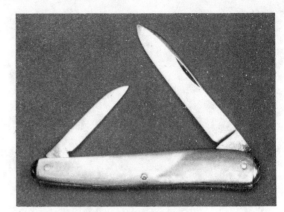

E.C. Simmons, Dogleg Pen, Pearl 3" **$50**

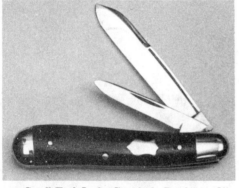

E.C. Simmons, Senator Pen, Brown Bone 3⅜" **$40**

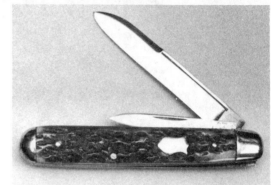

E.C. Simmons, Senator Jack, Brown Bone 3⅜" **$45**

E.C. Simmons, Swell End Jack, Cocobola Dogleg 3" **$40**

E.C. Simmons, Sow Belly, Black Plastic 3⅞" **$65**

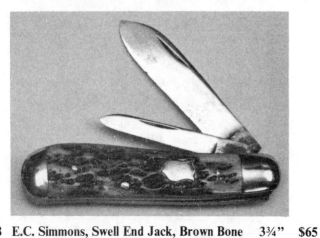

2728 E.C. Simmons, Swell End Jack, Brown Bone 3¾" **$65**

843 Keen Kutter, Folding Hunter, Brown Jig Bone 5¼" $125

E.C. Simmons, Jack, Brown Bone, Coffin Bols, 3½" **$90**

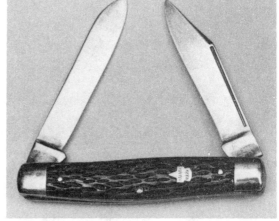

K231 Keen Kutter, Moose, Peach Seed Bone 4" **$90**

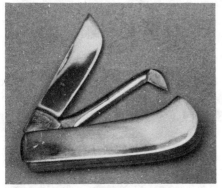

E.C. Simmons, Veterinarian, Metal 2⅝" **$50**

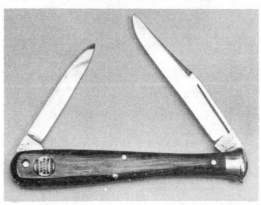

Shapleigh Hardware, St. Louis, Half Whittler Official League Bat, Brown and Tan 3⅞" **$100**

K713S Keen Kutter, Peanut, Brown Bone 2⅞" **$35**

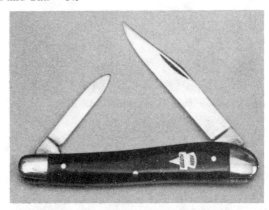

Keen Kutter, Dogleg Pen, Black Celluloid 3" **$40**

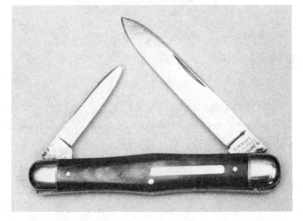

Simmons Hardware, Half Whittler, Swell Center Hornet, Horn Handle 3⅝" **$75**

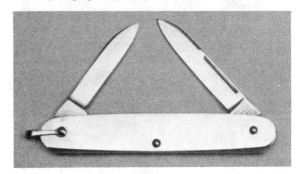

Keen Kutter, Senator Pen, Metal 3⅛" **$20**

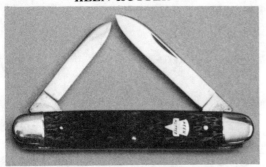

Keen Kutter, Senator Pen, Black Celluloid   3⅛" $20

K733¾C   Keen Kutter, Peanut, Yellow Celluloid   2¾" $25

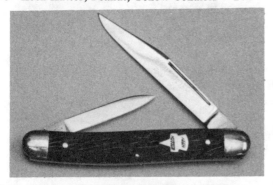

Keen Kutter, Senator Pen, Black Imi. Bone   2¾" $20

Keen Kutter, Pen, 2 Blade, Black Celluloid   2⅝" $20

Keen Kutter, Senator Pen, Brown Imi. Bone   3⅛" $20

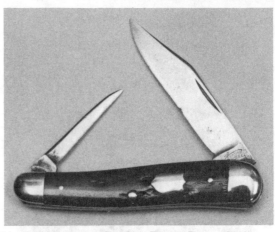

02467¾   E.C. Simmons, Dogleg, Brown Bone   3¼" $50

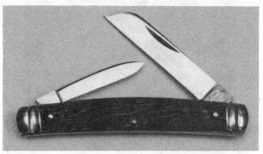

811   Keen Kutter, Congress, 2 Blade, Pen, Black Plastic   3" $25

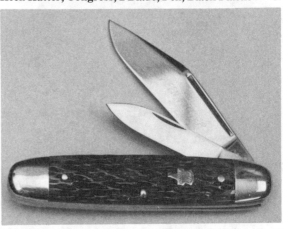

K238   Keen Kutter, Equal End Jack, Peach Seed Bone   3⅜"$40

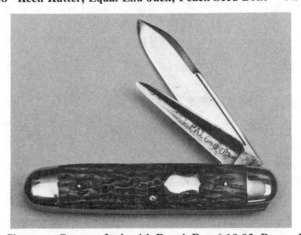

E.C. Simmons, Senator Jack with Punch Pat. 6-10-02, Brown Bone
    3⅝" $60

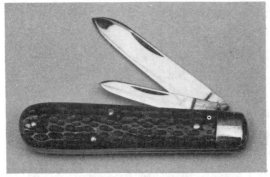

Diamond Edge, Equal End Jack, Brown Bone   3⅜" $25

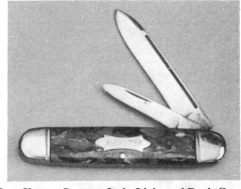

K68C   Keen Kutter, Senator Jack, Light and Dark Green Celluloid   3⅜" $35

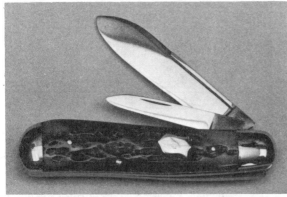

E.C. Simmons, Jack, Brown Bone 3¾" $75

E.C. Simmons, Swell End Jack, Metal   3½" $50

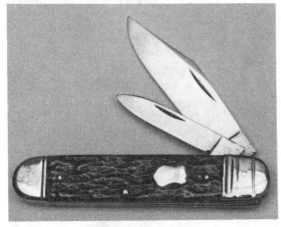

E.C. Simmons, Equal End Jack, Brown Bone   4¼" $125

Keen Kutter, Pen, 2 Blade with Bail, Cracked Ice   2½" $20

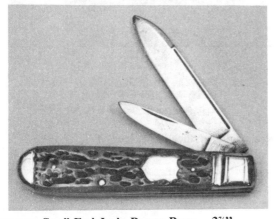

E.C. Simmons, Swell End Jack, Brown Bone   3⅞" $65

KS323   Keen Kutter, Pen, 2 Blade, Ivory   3" $40

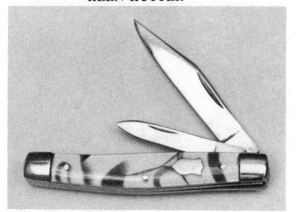

807   Keen Kutter, Senator Jack, Butter and Molasses   3¼"$35

Simmons Hardware Germany, Office Knife, Hornet, Ivory Type
3¾" $45

K765   Keen Kutter, Serpentine Jack, Cracked Ice   3⅜" $30

K7WCS   E.C. Simmons, Equal End Jack, Brown Bone   3" $45

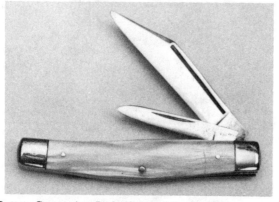

Keen Kutter, Serpentine Jack, Cracked Ice   3¼" $30

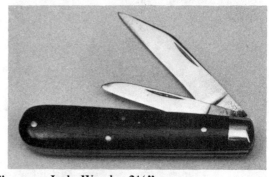

E.C. Simmons, Jack, Wood   3¼" $40

794   Keen Kutter, Office Knife, Ivory Type   3⅜" $40

E.C. Simmons, Jack, Brown Bone   3⅞" $45

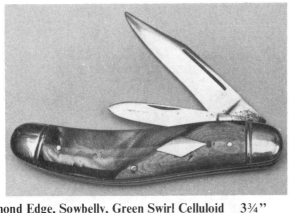

Diamond Edge, Sowbelly, Green Swirl Celluloid   3¾" $125

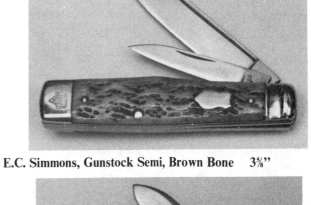

E.C. Simmons, Gunstock Semi, Brown Bone   3⅝" $125

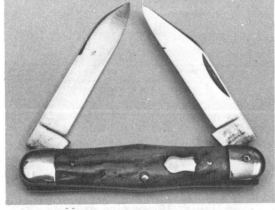

Shapleigh Hardware, Swell Center Equal End, Brown Bone   3⅜" $65

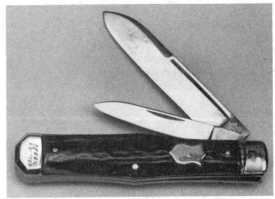

E.C. Simmons, Swell Center Jack, Stag Coffin Bols.   3½" $125

Keen Kutter, Moose, Peach Seed Bone   3⅞" $75

K34C   Keen Kutter, Equal End, Black Plastic   3⅜" $40

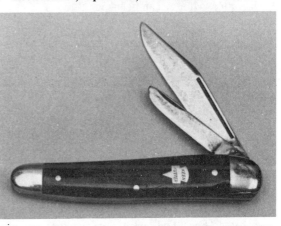

847   Keen Kutter, Sleeveboard Jack, Black Plastic   3⅝" $40

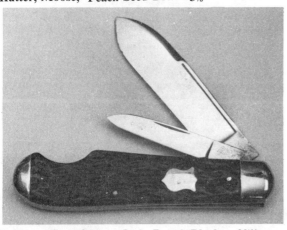

E.C. Simmons, Easy Opener Jack, Rough Black   3⅝" $45

Keen Kutter, Equal End Jack, Brown Bone   3⅜" $40

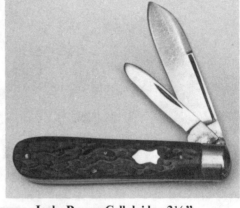

E.C. Simmons, Jack, Brown Celluloid   3¼" $40

K53¾   Keen Kutter, Equal End Jack, Rough Black,   3⅜" $35

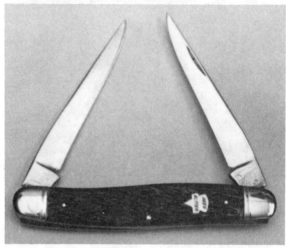

781   Keen Kutter, Muskrat, Black Imi. Bone   3⅞" $75

K345   Keen Kutter, Moose, Tan Celluloid   3⅜" $40

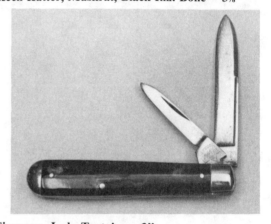

E.C. Simmons, Jack, Tortoise   3" $75

K68C   Keen Kutter, Equal End Jack, Cream and Red Celluloid   3⅜"
$40

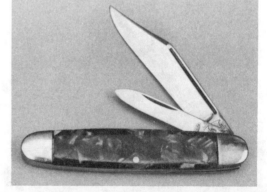

Keen Kutter, Equal End Jack, Mingle Green Celluloid   3⅜" $40

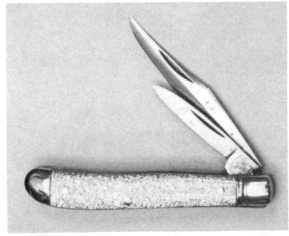

E.C. Simmons, Peanut, Goldstone   2⅞" $85

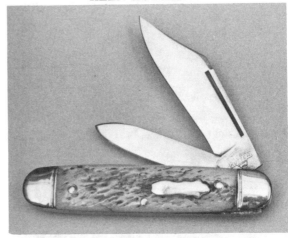

E.C. Simmons, Equal End, Yellow Bone   3¾" $55

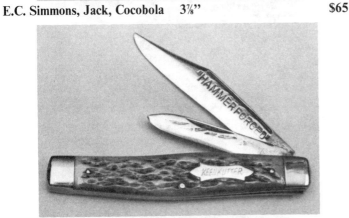

E.C. Simmons, Jack, Cocobola   3⅞" $65

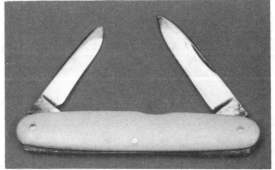

E.C. Simmons, Senator, Senator, Office Knife, White Plastic   3⅝"
                                                          $35

K2825   E.C. Simmons, Serpentine Jack, Yellow Bone   3⅞" $85

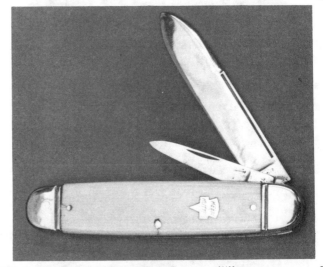

E.C. Simmons, Jack, Heavy, Imi. Ivory   4⅛" $75

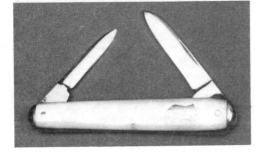

E.C. Simmons, Pen Sleeveboard, Pearl   2¾" $55

E.C. Simmons, Swell Center Jack, Brown Bone   3⅝" $85

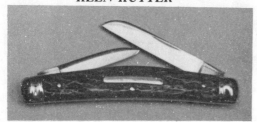

E.C. Simmons, Congress, 2 Blade, Brown Bone   3¼" $40

E.C. Simmons, Backward Dogleg, Black Bone   3⅜" $85

72288¾   E.C. Simmons, Jack with Punch, Rough Black   3½" $45

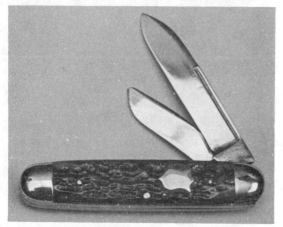

E.C. Simmons, Equal End Jack, Brown Bone   3⅝" $60

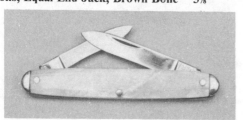

K20   Keen Kutter, Senator Pen, White Celluloid   2¾" $20

K34   Keen Kutter, Congress, 2 Blade, ® in Shield, Black   3⅛"$45

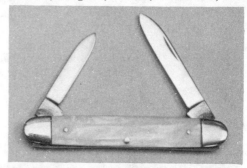

K8   Keen Kutter, Senator Pen, Cracked Ice   3⅛" $20

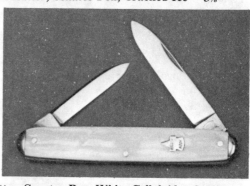

Keen Kutter, Senator Pen, White Celluloid   3¼" $25

Keen Kutter, Easy Opener Jack, White Plastic   3⅛" $65

Keen Kutter, Senator Pen, Gray Celluloid   3⅛" $35

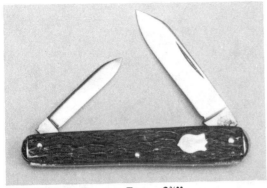

K281T   Keen Kutter, Senator Pen   3⅜" $40

828   Keen Kutter, Barlow, Brown Bone   3⅜" $50

Shapleigh Hardware, Equal End, 2 Blade, Brown Bone, Milled Liners   3½" $35

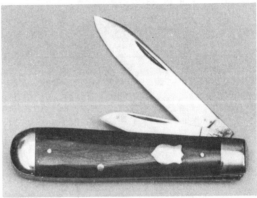

K50K   Keen Kutter, Jack, Red Celluloid   3⅜" $45

E.C. Simmons, Barlow, White Celluloid   3⅜" $45

E.C. Simmons, Barlow, Yellow Bone   3⅜" $50

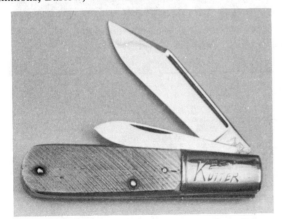

K2881¾   Keen Kutter, Barlow, Brown Bone   3½" $50

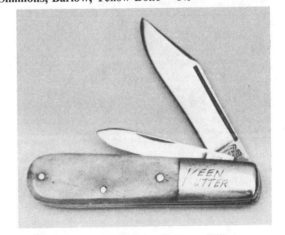

K254   Keen Kutter, Barlow, Brown Bone   3⅜" $50

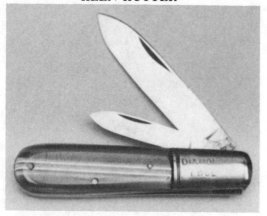

Diamond Edge, Barlow, Longways Candy Stripe   3⅜" $95

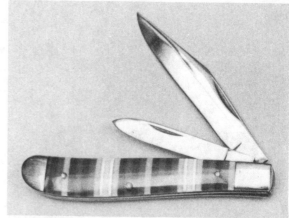

K22   Keen Kutter, Peanut, Candy Stripe   2⅞" $75

Diamond Edge, Barlow, Candy Stripe, LP   3⅜" $95

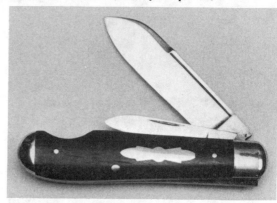

E. C. Simmons, Easy Opener Jack, Ebony   3⅝" $50

Keen Kutter, Swell Center Pen, Candy Stripe   3⅜" $60

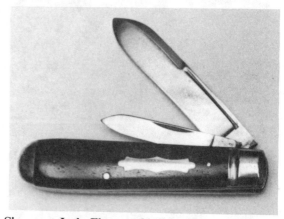

E. C. Simmons, Jack, Ebony   3¾" $40

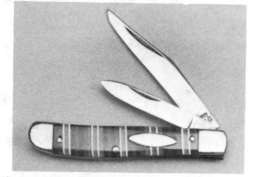

30   E. C. Simmons, Peanut, Candy Stripe   2⅞" $75

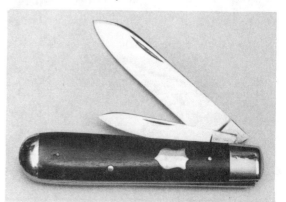

2621   E. C. Simmons, Jack, Ebony   3¾" $45

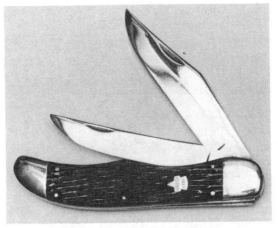

843   Keen Kutter, Folding Hunter, S.A.B., Black Celluloid   5¼'$60

KS279   E. C. Simmons, Equal End Jack, Peach Seed Bone   4¼"
$150

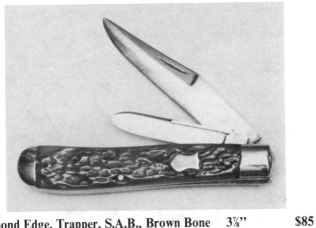

Diamond Edge, Trapper, S.A.B., Brown Bone   3⅞" $85

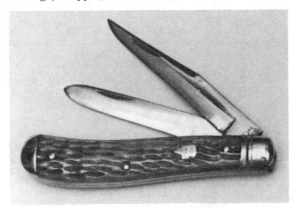

KS276   Keen Kutter, Trapper, Peach Seed Bone   3⅞" $85

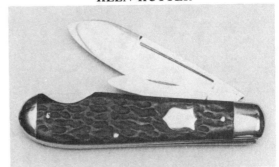

E. C. Simmons, Easy Opener Jack, Black Celluloid   3⅝" $45

E. C. Simmons, Senator Pen, Brown Bone   3⅛" $35

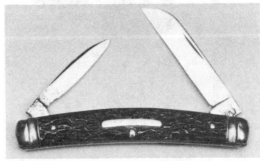

Keen Kutter, Congress, 2 Blade, Brown Bone   3½" $45

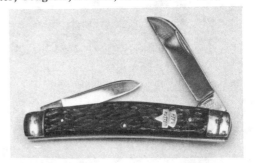

K7   Keen Kutter, Congress, 2 Blade, Salesman Sample, Black Celluloid   3½" $35

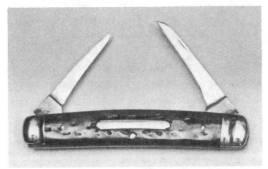

Keen Kutter, Congress, 2 Blade, Brown Bone   3¾" $50

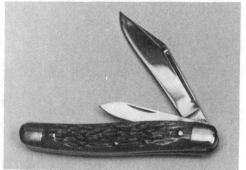

K234   Keen Kutter, Serpentine Jack, Brown Bone   3¼"   **$35**

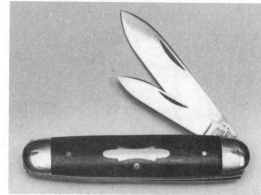
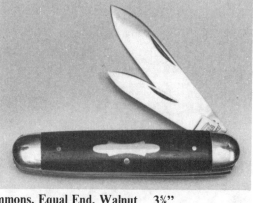

E. C. Simmons, Equal End, Walnut   3⅝"   **$45**

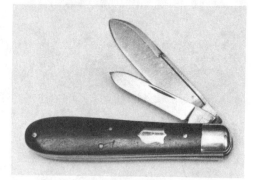

22443   E. C. Simmons, Dogleg Jack, Brown Bone   3¼"   **$65**

K6   Keen Kutter, Equal End Jack, Black Plastic   3⅝"   **$20**

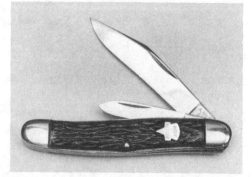

E. C. Simmons, Swell End Jack, Walnut   3⅜"   **$40**

B579   Diamond Edge, Muskrat, Peach Seed Bone   3⅞"   **$150**

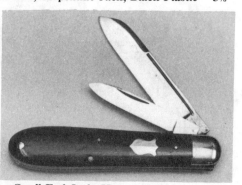

K1   Keen Kutter, Serpentine Jack, Black Plastic   3⅜"   30

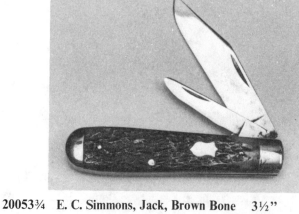

20053¾   E. C. Simmons, Jack, Brown Bone   3½"   **$45**

Keen Kutter, Swell End Jack, Horn   3⅜"   **$45**

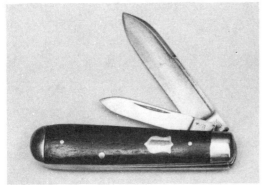

E. C. Simmons, Jack, Walnut   3⅜" $40

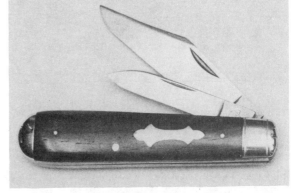

22369   E. C. Simmons, Jack, Redwood,   3½" $40

934   Keen Kutter, Serpentine Jack, Stag   3⅝" $125

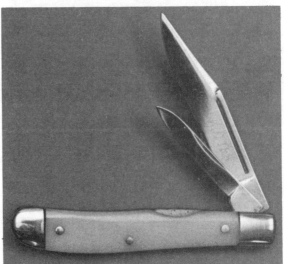

305   Keen Kutter, Peanut, Yellow Celluloid   2⅞" $20

E. C. Simmons, Brown Bone, Moose   3⅞" $150

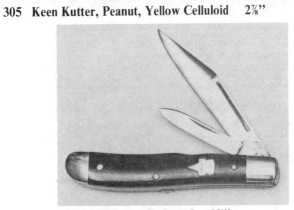

315   Keen Kutter, Peanut, Redwood   2⅞" $20

E. C. Simmons, Jack, Brown Bone   3¼" $40

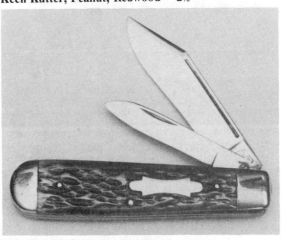

K3   Keen Kutter, Jack, Brown Bone   3½" $40

Diamond Edge, Equal End Jack, Brown, Yellow Mingle Celluloid
3⅜" $40

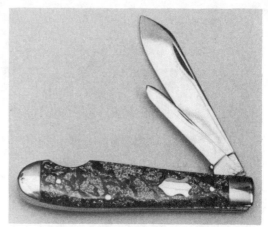

E. C. Simmons, Easy Opener Jack, Green and Black Celluloid 3⅜"
$45

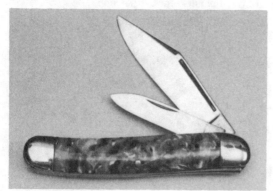

Keen Kutter, Serpentine Jack, Brown, Yellow Mingle Celluloid
3½" $35

E. C. Simmons, Serpentine Jack, Fancy Scalloped Bolsters, S.A.B.,
Brown Bone   3½" $125

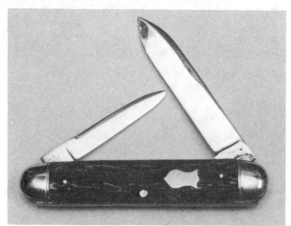

E. C. Simmons, Stag, Equal End   3¾" $55

E. C. Simmons, Jack, Brown Bone   3⅝" $125

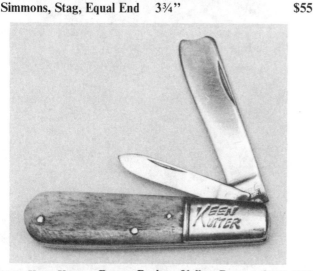

K2881½   Keen Kutter, Razor, Barlow, Yellow Bone   3½" $65

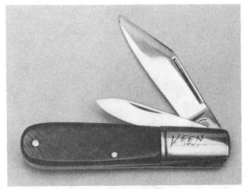

Keen Kutter, Barlow, Slick Black Comp.   3⅜" $35

53   E. C. Simmons, Jack, Equal End, Sale Sample, Brown Bone
    3½" $45

7763   E.C. Simmmons, Jack, Swell End, Brown Bone   3⅝" $75

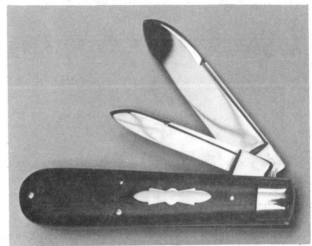

E. C. Simmons, Jack, Walnut   3⅞" $65

Diamond Edge, Jack, Serpentine, Fluted Bolster, Brown Bone   3¾"
                                              $150

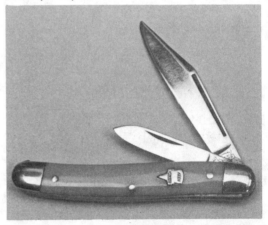

K235   Keen Kutter, Jack, Serpentine, Yellow Celluloid   3¼" $40

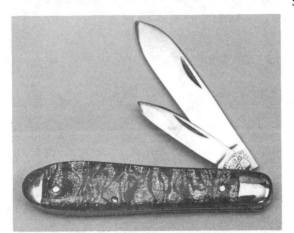

E. C. Simmons, Jack, Swell End, Red and Black Celluloid   3⅜" $60

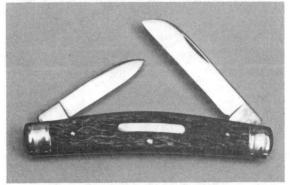

K7   E. C. Simmons, Congress, 2 Blade, Brown Bone   3½" $40

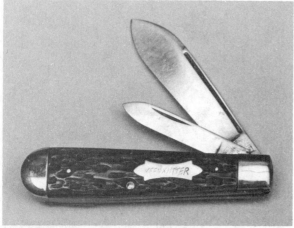

K53 E. C. Simmons, Jack, Equal End, Brown Bone   3⅜" $60

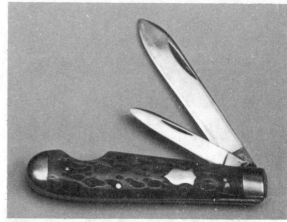

981B E. C. Simmons, Jack Easy Opener, Brown Bone,   3¼"$60

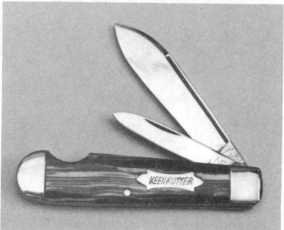

**K98C   Keen Kutter, Easy Opener Jack, Black and White Celluloid
3⅜" $60**

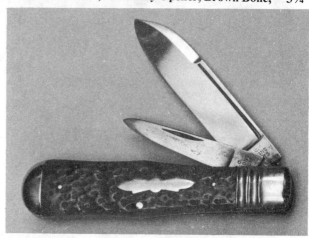

**E.C. Simmons, Jack Swell Center, Threaded Bolster, Brown Bone
3¾" $125**

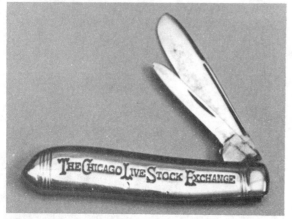

**730   E. C. Simmons, Dogleg Jack, Chicago Livestock Exchange,
Nickel Silver   3½" $60**

Simmons Hardware, Hornet, Ring Opener, Brown Bone   3¼"$75

E. C. Simmons, Sleeveboard Pen, Brown Bone   3⅜" $45

E. C. Simmons, Equal End Jack, Stag   3½" $65

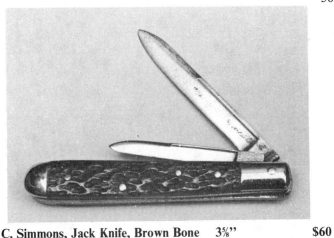

E. C. Simmons, Jack Knife, Brown Bone   3⅝" $60

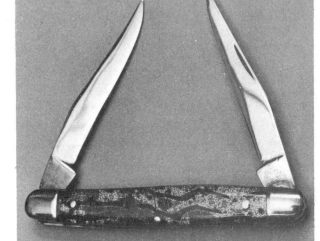

E. C. Simmons, Muskrat, Christmas Tree   4" $200

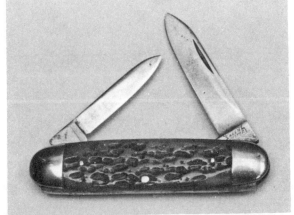

01111   E. C. Simmons, Equal End, Unusual, Green Bone   3"$45

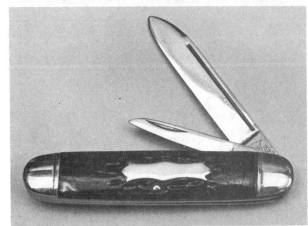

K6   Keen Kutter, Equal End Jack, Black Plastic   3⅝" $40

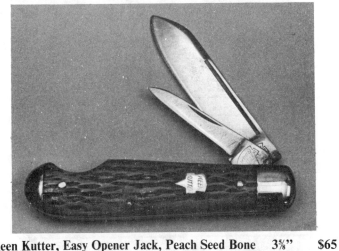

Keen Kutter, Easy Opener Jack, Peach Seed Bone   3⅝" $65

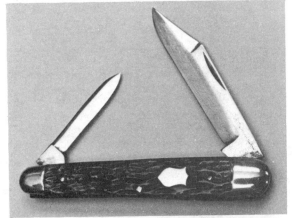

E. C. Simmons, Sleeveboard Pen, Peach Seed Bone   3½" $45

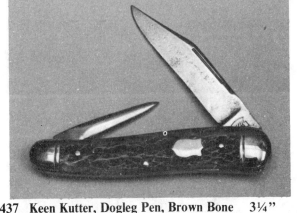

K02437   Keen Kutter, Dogleg Pen, Brown Bone   3¼" $45

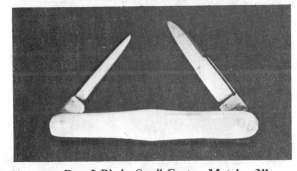

E. C. Simmons, Pen, 2 Blade, Swell Center, Metal   3" $30

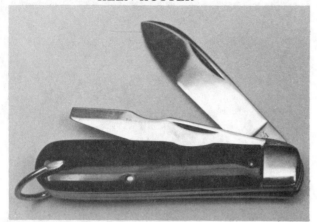

Keen Kutter, Electrician Knife, Slick Black   3¾" $40

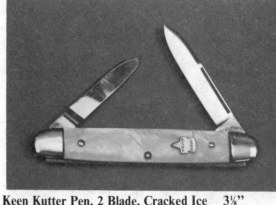

768   **Keen Kutter Pen, 2 Blade, Cracked Ice**   3⅛" $20

50K   **E. C. Simmons, Equal End Jack, Red and Black Plastic**   3½"
$45

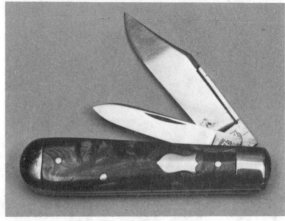

E. C. Simmons, Jack, Swell End, Green Swirl   3⅜" $60

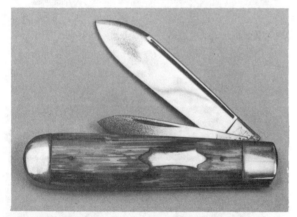

K4   **Keen Kutter, Equal End Jack, Red and Tan Plastic**   3½"$45

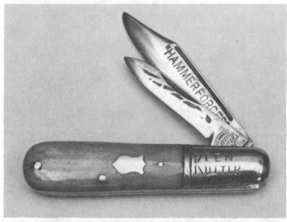

K2825   **E. C. Simmons, Sunday Barlow, Hammer Forged, Yellow Bone**   3⅜" $100

E. C. Simmons, Jack, Metal   3½" $30

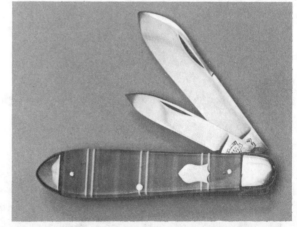

E. C. Simmons, Jack Tear Drop, Candy Stripe   3¼" $75

311   *KEEN KUTTER*

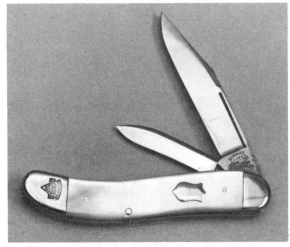

E. C. Simmons, Jack, Backward Dog Leg, Pearl   3⅜" $150

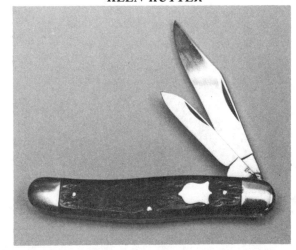

944SPL   E.C. Simmons, Jack Serpentine, Black Plastic   3⅜"$35

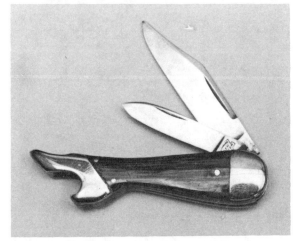

E. C. Simmons, Leg Knife, Brown and Tan Plastic   3⅛" $125

713 E.C. Simmons, Peanut, Brown Bone   2⅞" $60

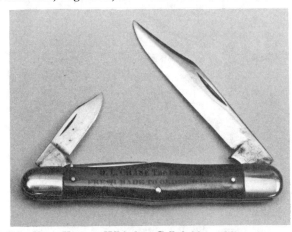

3315/CC   Keen Kutter, Whittler, Celluloid   3⅝" $75

E. C. Simmons, Jack Senator, Rough Black   3¼" $35

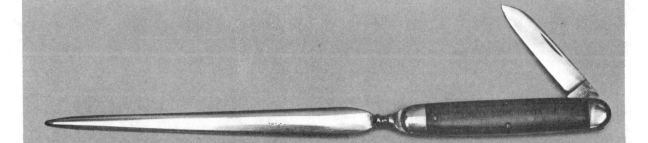

Keen Kutter, Letter Opener, Knife, Clear Celluloid   9" overall $30

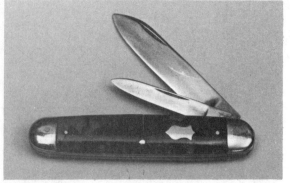

2420C   E. C. Simmons, Equal End Jack,   3¼"   **$85**

3 BLADE

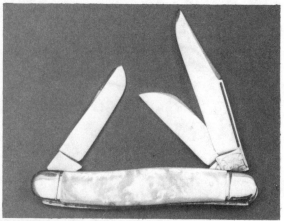

Keen Kutter Premium Stockman Pearl   3⅝" Pat. Applied for $85

K3463   E.C. Simmons Whittler Pearl 3⅜"   **$80**

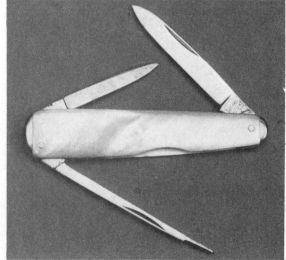

K3037T   Keen Kutter, Lobster Sleeveboard Pen, Pearl   3⅛" $45

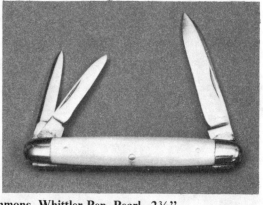

E.C. Simmons, Whittler Pen, Pearl   2¾"   **$50**

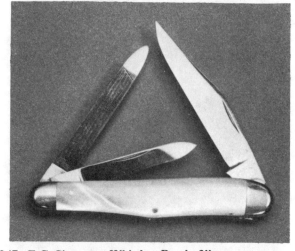

K33247   E.C. Simmons, Whittler, Pearl   3"   **$80**

E.C. Simmons, Whittler, Pearl 3¼"   **$65**

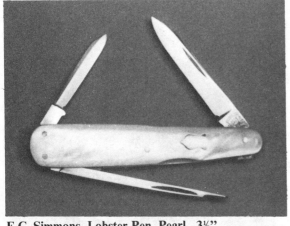

3037   E.C. Simmons, Lobster Pen, Pearl   3⅛"   **$50**

788   Keen Kutter, Premium Stockman, Cracked Ice   3¼"   **$35**

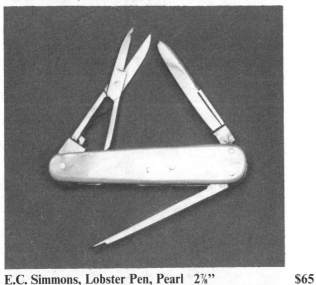

5443   E.C. Simmons, Lobster Pen, Pearl   2⅞"   **$65**

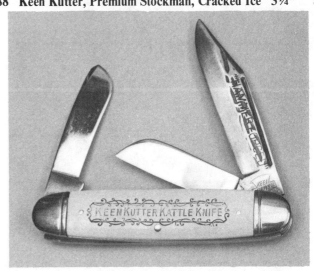

K8465   Keen Kutter, Kattle Stockman, Ivory Type   3⅝"   **$150**

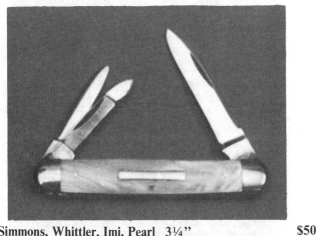

E.C. Simmons, Whittler, Imi. Pearl   3¼"   **$50**

3071   E.C. Simmons, Whittler, Brown Bone   3⅜"   **$60**

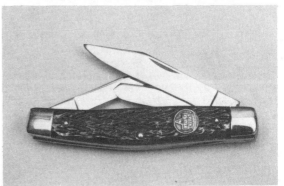

E.C. Simmons, Lobster, 3 Blade, Pearl   2½"   **$45**   Keen Kutter, Serpentine Stockman® , Black Celluloid   3¼" $55

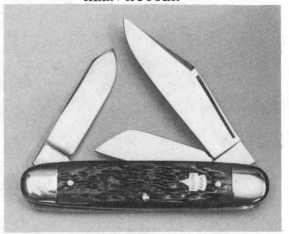

869 Keen Kutter, Kattle Stockman, Brown Bone 3⅜" **$85**

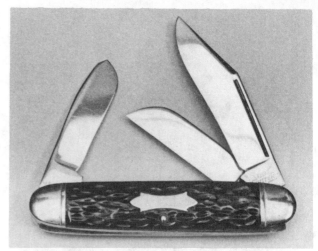

K14 Keen Kutter, Kattle Stockman, Black Imi. Bone 3⅝" **$30**

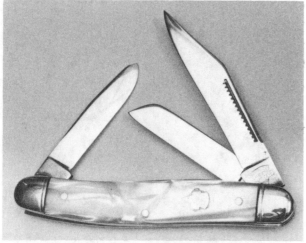

861 Keen Kutter, Premium Stockman, Cracked Ice 4" **$60**

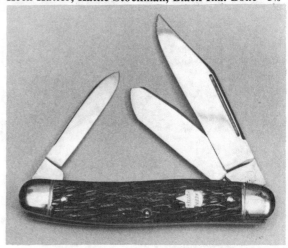

876 Keen Kutter, Serpentine Stockman, Peach Seed Bone 3½"
$60

E.C. Simmons, Whittler, Rare, Pink Bone 3¼" **$75**

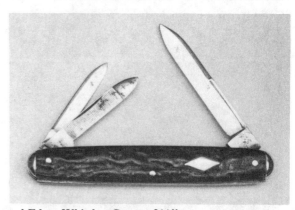

Diamond Edge, Whittler, Stag 3¼" **$50**

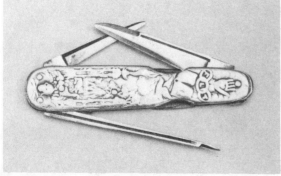

E.C. Simmons, Sleeveboard Lobster, Metal, Sterling Silver 3"$75

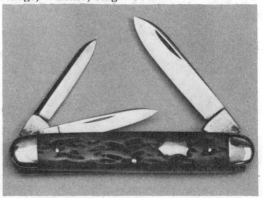

E.C. Simmons, Whittler, Brown Bone 3¼" **$60**

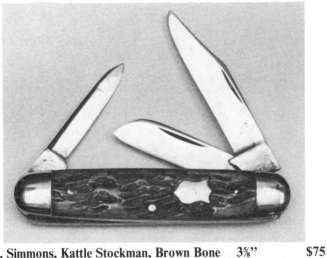

E.C. Simmons, Kattle Stockman, Brown Bone　　3⅝"　　　$75

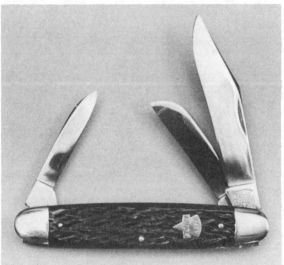

E.C. Simmons, Senator Serpentine, Salesman Sample, Black Plastic
　3¼"　　　　　　　　　　　　　　　　　　$35

8307R　E.C. Simmons, Whittler, Brown Bone　　3"　　　$60

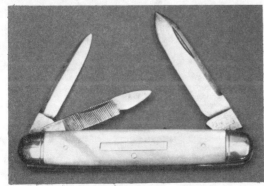

E.C. Simmons, Whittler Senator, Pearl　　3⅜"　　　$85

E.C. Simmons, Serpentine Stockman, Butter and Molasses　　3½"
　　　　　　　　　　　　　　　　　　　　　　$65

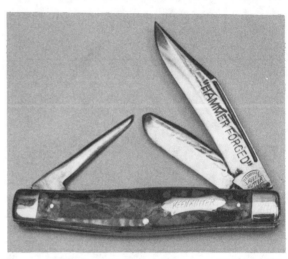

E.C. Simmons, Premium Stockman, Hammer Forged, Black and
Orange Celluloid　　3⅞"　　　　　　　　　　　$125

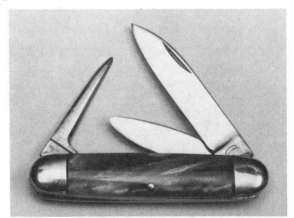

Keen Kutter, Cattle Stockman, Tan and Green Celluloid　3⅜"$50

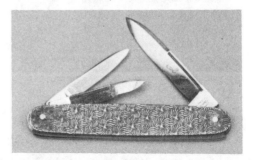

Simmons Hardware Germany, Whittler, Salesman Sample, Hornet,
Mill Worked Handles　2⅝"　　　　　　　　　　$150

E.C. Simmons, Whittler, Swell Center, Stag   3¾" $110

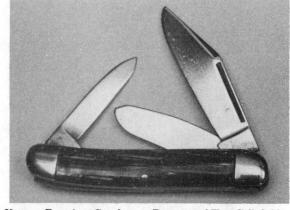

Keen Kutter, Premium Stockman, Brown and Tan Celluloid   3½" $45

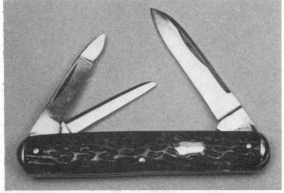

E.C. Simmons, Whittler Pen, Brown Bone   3⅜" $65

865   Keen Kutter, Premium Stockman, Brown Bone   3¼" $45

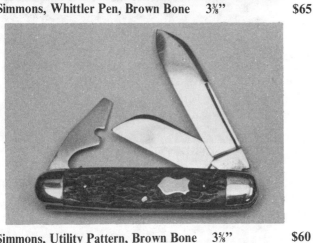

E.C. Simmons, Utility Pattern, Brown Bone   3⅝" $60

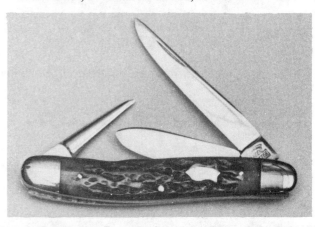

73733   E.C. Simmons, Premium Stockman, Brown Bone   3½" $60

879   Keen Kutter, Premium Stockman, Peach Seed Bone   3½" $45   K78465   Keen Kutter, Kattle Stockman, Ivory Type   3⅝" $100

317 *KEEN KUTTER*

874 Keen Kutter, Premium Stockman, Black Celluloid 3¼" $40

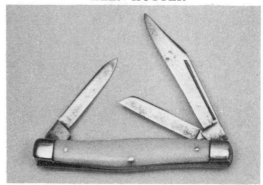

Keen Kutter, Premium Stockman, Yellow Celluloid   2⅝" $20

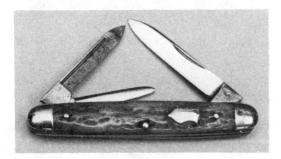

E.C. Simmons, Whittler Pen, Bone   3" $55

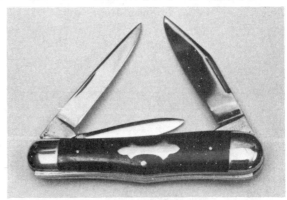

E.C. Simmons, Whittler, Ebony, 3 Backspring   3⅝" $125

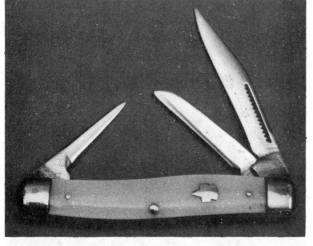

Keen Kutter, Premium Stockman, Yellow Celluloid, Punch   3⅞"$65

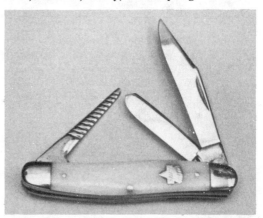

769 Keen Kutter, Serpentine Stockman, Yellow Composition, Spiral Punch   3⅜" $50

861   Keen Kutter, Stockman Pen, Cracked Ice   4" $55

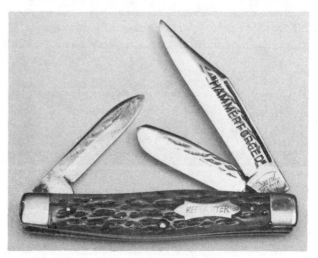

K3935 Keen Kutter, Premium Stockman, Hammer Forged, Brown Bone   3⅞" $125

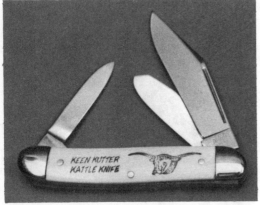

894   **Keen Kutter, Kattle Stockman, Ivory Type**   **3½"**   **$60**

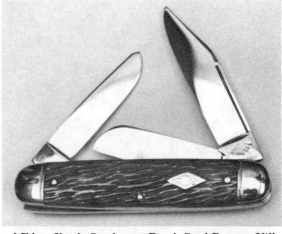

Diamond Edge, Kattle Stockman, Peach Seed Bone   **3⅝"**   **$60**

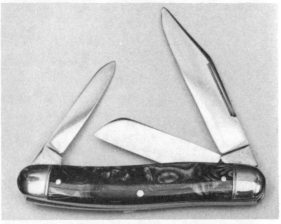

Diamond Edge, Premium Stockman, Blue Swirl Celluloid   **3½"** **$60**

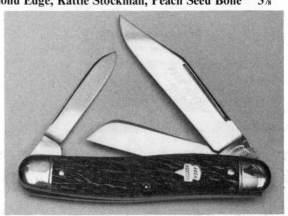

Keen Kutter, Premium Stockman, Salesman Sample, Peach Seed Bone   **3½"**   **$50**

873   **Keen Kutter, Serpentine Stockman, Butter and Molasses**   **3½"**   **$35**

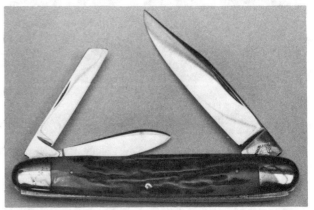

5391   **Diamond Edge, Whittler, Stag**   **4½"**   **$250**

Shapleigh Hardware, Kattle Stockman with Punch, Brown Bone   **3⅝"**   **$50**

786   **Keen Kutter, Swell Center, Imi. Bone.**   **3⅜"**   **$35**

860   Keen Kutter, Premium Stockman, Matchstriker, Peach Seed Bone   3⅞" $75

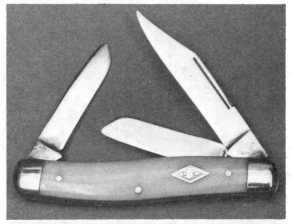

1020   Diamond Edge, Premium Stockman, Waterfall   3⅞" $150

853   Keen Kutter, Premium Stockman, Waterfall   3⅞" $150

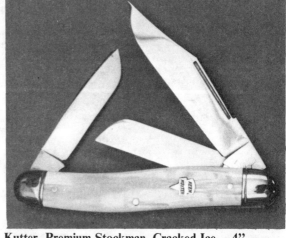

Keen Kutter, Premium Stockman, Cracked Ice   4" $60

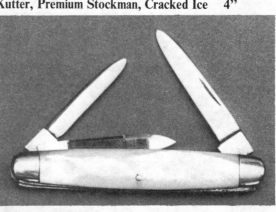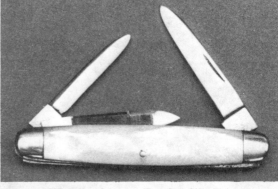

E.C. Simmons, Whittler, Senator, Pearl   3" $75

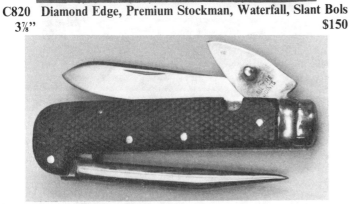

C820   Diamond Edge, Premium Stockman, Waterfall, Slant Bols 3⅞" $150

Keen Kutter, Military Knife, Gutta-Percha   4⅞" $90
Can Opener, Marlin Spike

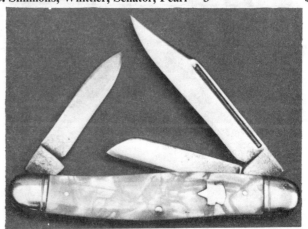

Keen Kutter, Serpentine, Stockman, Cracked Ice   3⅞" $60

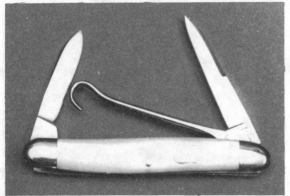

E.C. Simmons, Serpentine with Button Hook, Pearl   3¼" $110

855   Keen Kutter, Serpentine Stockman, Peach Seed Bone   3½"
$45

854   Keen Kutter, Premium Stockman, Yellow Composition   3⅞"
$60

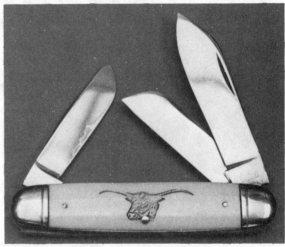

E.C. Simmons, Kattle Stockman, Ivory Type   3⅝" $100

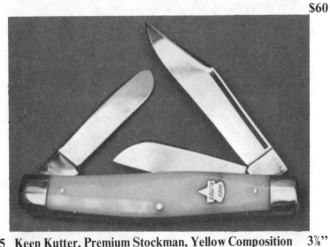

795   Keen Kutter, Premium Stockman, Yellow Composition   3⅞"
$60

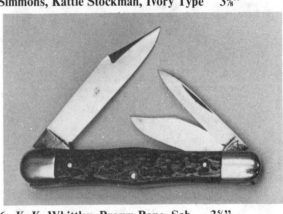

K3316   K. K. Whittler, Brown Bone, Sab.   3⅝" $75

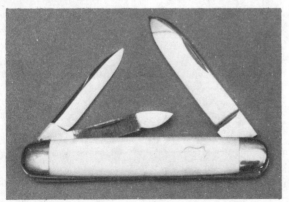

K3073   E.C. Simmons, Whittler, Etched, Pearl   3⅜" $75

Simmons Hardware, Whittler, Swell Center, Black Plastic   3⅝"$90

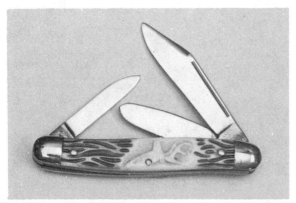

835 Keen Kutter, Premium Stockman, Deer Head in Handle, Yellow and Brown Celluloid 3¼" $25

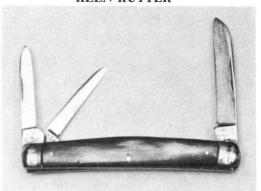

Simmons Hardware, Whittler, Hornet, Horn Handle, Congress Pattern 3¼" $125

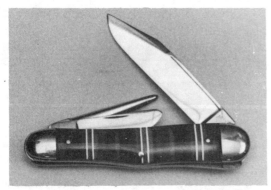

E. C. Simmons, Whittler, 3 Back Spring with Punch, Candy Stripe 3⅝" $225

Keen Kutter, Premium Stockman, Black Plastic 3¼" $45

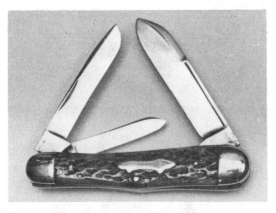

E. C. Simmons, Whittler, 3 Back Spring, Brown Bone 3⅝" $225

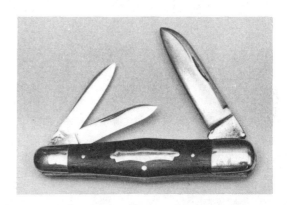

Keen Kutter, Swell Center Whittler, Cocobola 3⅝" $90

E. C. Simmons, Cabinet Maker Knife, Ebony 3⅝" $85   861 Keen Kutter, Premium Stockman, Cracked Ice 4" $50

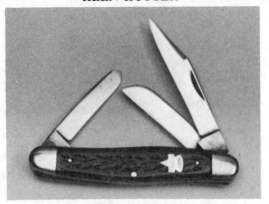

770   Keen Kutter, Premium Stockman, Black Plastic   3⅜" $40

874   Keen Kutter, Premium Stockman, Brown Plastic   3⅜" $45

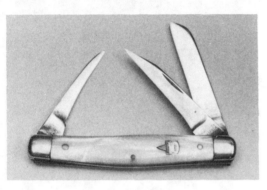

885   Keen Kutter, Premium Stockman, Cracked Ice   3¼" $35

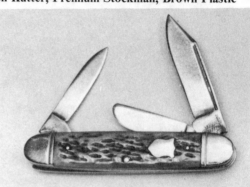

Keen Kutter, Kattle Stockman, Brown Bone   3⅜" $60

Simmons Hardware, Kattle Stockman, Brown Bone   3⅜" $60

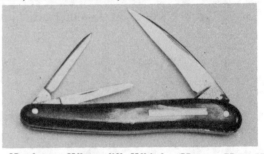

Simmons Hardware, Wharncliffe Whittler, Hornet, Horn Handle
2⅞" $100

3827   E.C. Simmons, Congress Whittler, Brown Bone   3¼"$125

K3433¼   E. C. Simmons, Premium Stockman, Brown Bone   3⅜"
$75

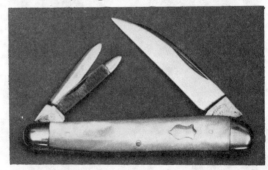

E. C. Simmons, Sleeveboard Pen, with Scissors and File, Pearl   2¾"
$90

323 KEEN KUTTER

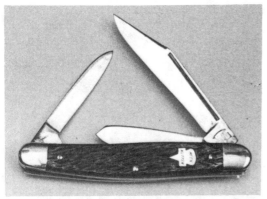

792 Keen Kutter, Stockman Pen, Black Plastic   3" $30

881   Keen Kutter, Stockman, Serpentine, Stag   4" $100

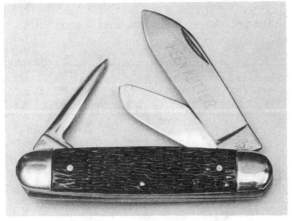

Keen Kutter, Stockman with Punch, Black Plastic   3⅝" $35

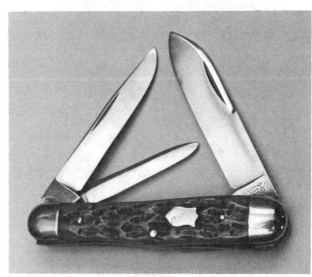

E. C. Simmons, Whittler, Brown Bone   3⅝" $125

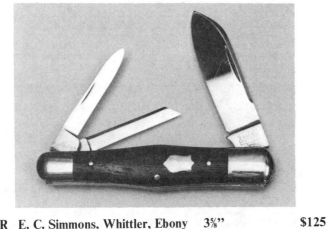

366R   E. C. Simmons, Whittler, Ebony   3⅝" $125

Keen Kutter, Stockman, Bird Eye, Yellow Composition   3⅞"$45

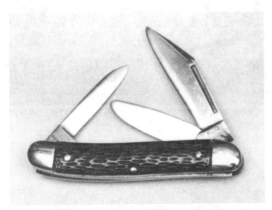

Keen Kutter, Serpentine Stockman, Black Plastic   3½" $20

947   Keen Kutter, Premium Stockman, Peach Seed Bone, Concave
   4" $125

Keen Kutter, Stockman, Black Imi. Bone, Punch   3¾" $25

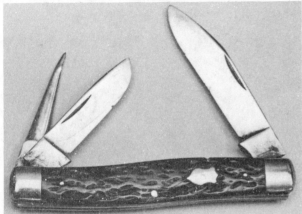

73828   E.C. Simmons, Whittler, Rare, Brown Bone   3⅞" $125

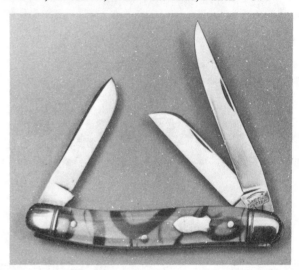

873   Keen Kutter, Serpentine Stockman, Butter and Molasses 3½"
                                                $45

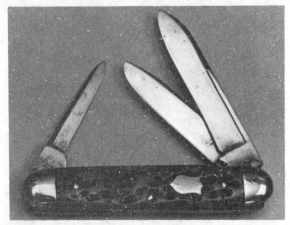

Keen Kutter, Kattle Stockman, Brown Bone   3⅜" $65

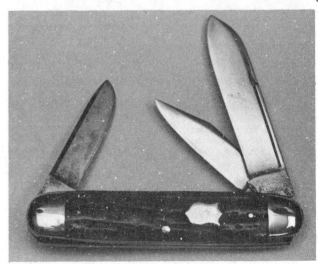

E. C. Simmons, Kattle Stockman Stag   3⅝" $90

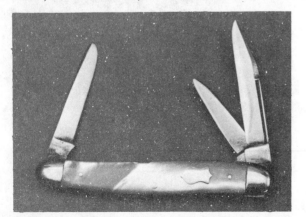

E. C. Simmons, Serpentine, Stockman, Pearl   3¼" $90

325

KEEN KUTTER

K241   Keen Kutter, Whittler Tip Bolster, Brown Bone   3" $65

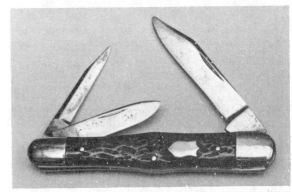

E. C. Simmons, Whittler, Swell Center, Brown Bone   3⅝" $90

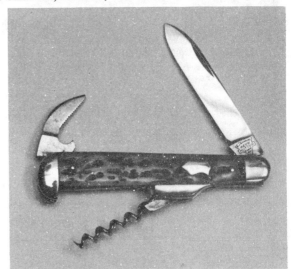

Bar Tender Knife, Brown Bone   3¼" $85

K25   Keen Kutter, Stockman, Master ® in Shield, Sale Sample, Brown Bone   4" $125

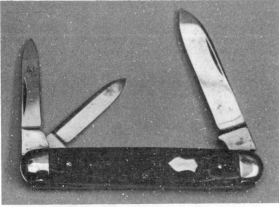

3071   E. C. Simmons, Whittler, Brown Bone   3¼" $90

E. C. Simmons, Bar Tender Knife, Brown Bone   3¼" $85

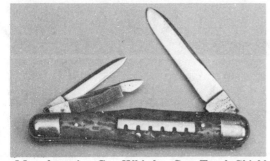

Simmons Manufacturing Co., Whittler, Saw Tooth Shield, Yellow Bone   3⅛" $125

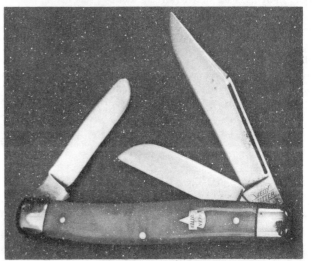

K11   Keen Kutter, Stockman Serpentine, Waterfall   3⅞" $150

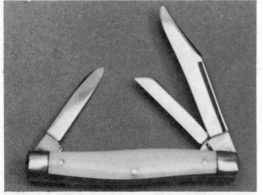

793   Keen Kutter, Stockman Pen, Yellow Celluloid   2⅝" $25

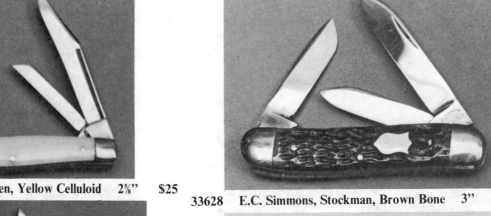

33628   E.C. Simmons, Stockman, Brown Bone   3" $65

889   Keen Kutter, Stockman Senator, Cracked Ice   3⅛" $65

E. C. Simmons, Whittler, Sleeveboard, Brown Bone   3½" $200

E. C. Simmons, with Punch, Brown Bone   3⅜" $65

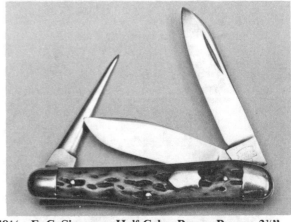

738/48¼   E. C. Simmons, Half Coke, Brown Bone   3⅜" $85

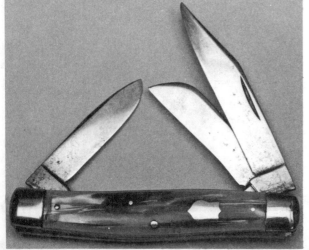

K3825H   E. C. Simmons, Stockman Premium, Red and Orange Celluloid   3⅞" $100

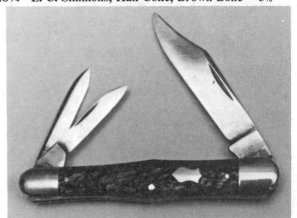

3310   E. C. Simmons, Whittler, Swell Center, Brown Bone   3⅝" $125

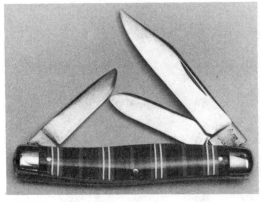

E.C. Simmons, Premium Stockman, Candy Stripe   4"   **$150**

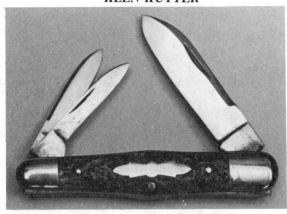

E. C. Simmons, Whittler, Swell Center, Brown Bone   3⅝"   **$125**

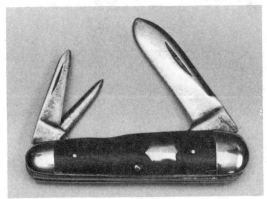

73266¼   Keen Kutter, Sleeveboard Whittler, Walnut   3½"**$110**

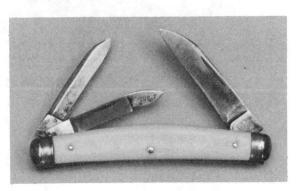

E. C. Simmons, Whittler Congress, Ivory Type   3¼"   **$125**

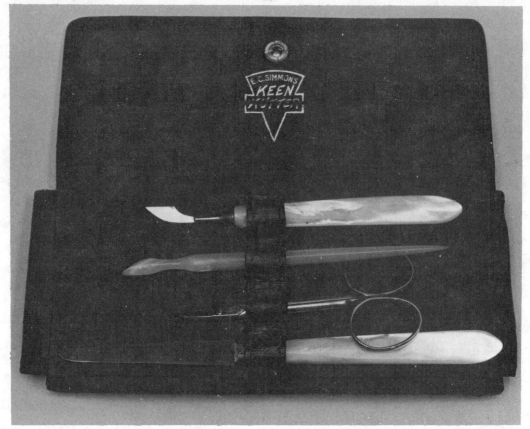

E. C. Simmons, Manicure Set, Pearl, 4 Piece & Holder $100

Meat Cleaver $35

E. C. Simmons, Sheath Knife, Overall Bone   9¾" $125

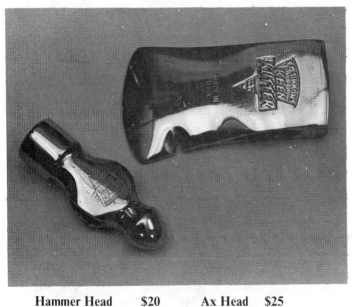

Hammer Head $20   Ax Head $25

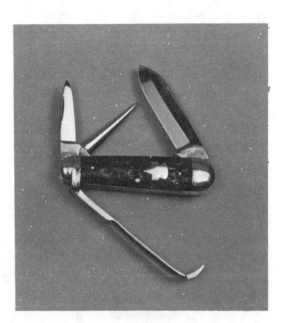

**E.C. Simmons, Keen Kutter, St. Louis, MO, 3½"   3 bl. Whittler
with Hoof Pick, Sab. Spear blade, bone handle $400**

4 BLADE

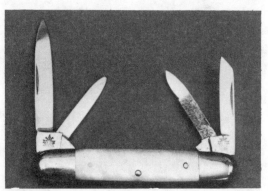

Simmons Hardware Germany, Senator Pen, 4 Blade, Hornet, Pearl 2⅝" $85

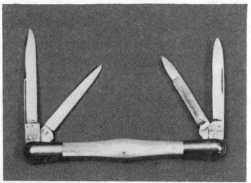

Simmons Hardware, Swell Center Pen, 4 Blade, Hornet, Pearl 2⅞" $90

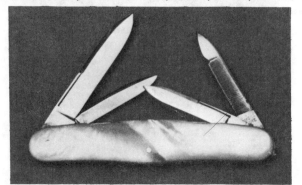

E.C. Simmons, Congress, Closed Backspring, 4 Blade, Pearl 3½"
$200

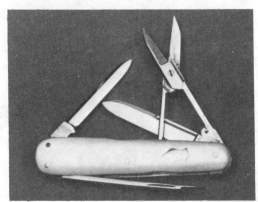

4843   E.C. Simmons, Lobster Sleeveboard, Scissors, Pick and Pen, 2¾"   Pearl $110

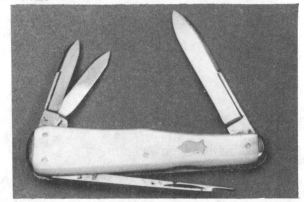

357   E.C. Simmons, Lobster, Gunstock Whittler, Pearl 3" with file $150

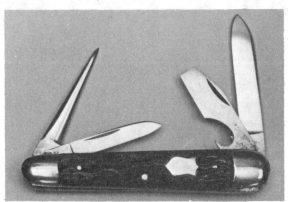

E. C. Simmons, Pen, Utility, Brown Bone, Sleeveboard   3⅜" $150

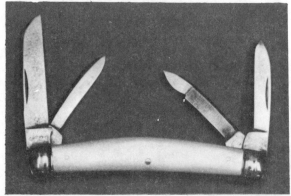

4529   E.C. Simmons, Congress, 4 Blade, 3¼" $125

331   KEEN KUTTER

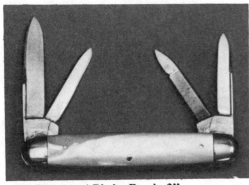

E.C. Simmons, Senator, 4 Blade, Pearl   3"   **$90**

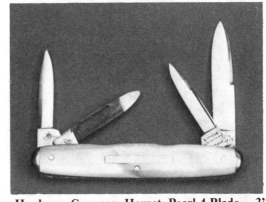

Simmons Hardware Germany, Hornet, Pearl 4 Blade   3" $125

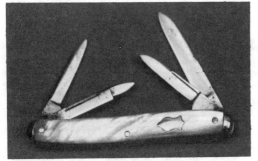

4849   E.C. Simmons, Senator Pen, 4 Blade, Pearl   3" $125

KS450   Keen Kutter, Congress, 4 Blade, Black Imi. Bone   3"$65

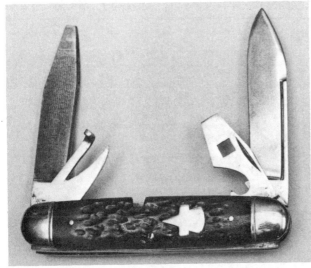

E.C. Simmons, Scout, Rare, Brown Bone, Skate Wrench, File   3⅝"
$150

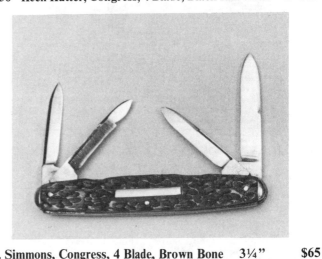

E.C. Simmons, Congress, 4 Blade, Brown Bone   3¼" $65

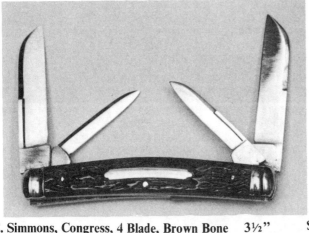

E.C. Simmons, Congress, 4 Blade, Brown Bone   3½" $90

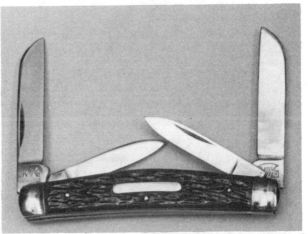

K16   Keen Kutter, Congress, 4 Blade, Brown Bone   3½" $65

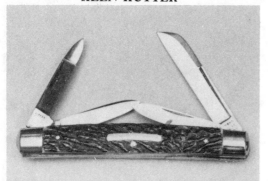

E.C. Simmons, Magnatic Cutlery Co., Congress, 4 Blade, Hornet, Very Rare, Brown Bone   3⅛" $225

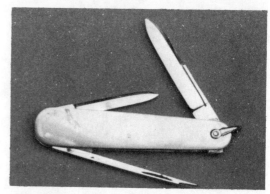

0643 E.C. Simmons, Lobster Pen, Pearl   2¾" $45

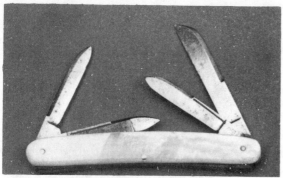

E.C. Simmons, Congress, 4 Blade, Pearl   3⅜" $150

E.C. Simmons, Congress, 4 Blade, Brown Bone, File   3½" $125

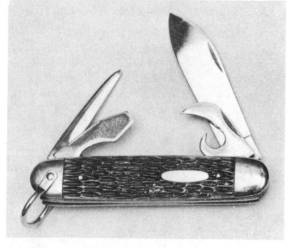

899   Keen Kutter, Scout, Brown Celluloid   3¾"   25

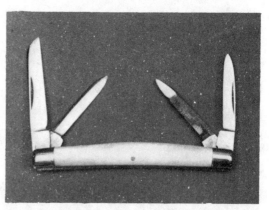

K4733 E.C. Simmons, Congress, Pen, 4 Blade Pearl   2¾" $100

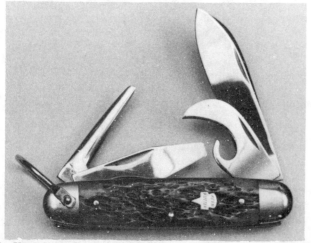

899   Keen Kutter, Scout, Brown Bone   3¾" $85

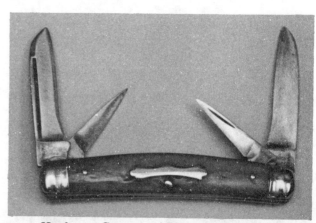

Simmons Hardware, Congress, 4 Blade, Light Bone   4⅛" $100

333

KEEN KUTTER

4843   E.C. Simmons, Lobster, Pen Sleeveboard, Pearl   2¾" $90

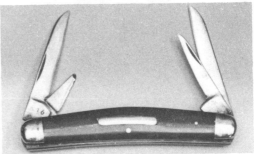

Keen Kutter, Congress, 4 Blade, Green Bone   3½" $100

773   Keen Kutter, Congress, 4 Blade, Black Plastic   3⅜" $45

Keen Kutter, Senator, 4 Blade, Brown Jig Bone   3⅛" $65

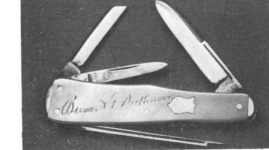

Keen Kutter, Gunstock Whittler, Mayor of St. Louis, Pearl, File   3"
$150

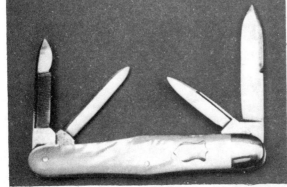

E.C. Simmons, Enclosed Back, Pearl, 4 Blade, Swell Center   3⅛"
$150

K41   Keen Kutter, Congress, 4 Blade, Black Plastic   4⅛" $45

6559   E. C. Simmons, Scout, S.A.B. Brown Bone, Sab. Spear   3⅝"
$125

K6558   Keen Kutter, Scout Camp, Brown Bone   3⅝" $90

18 K Solid Gold; Inlaid
Platinum center. Hand
engraved. Ring for at-
taching to watch chain.
$50.00

"How did you know I wanted a Remington Pocket Knife?"

IT doesn't take a mind-reader to know *that!* Fifty times during the past year you've asked him for his penknife.

And he always answered—"Sure—take it. But it won't *cut* anything."

And because every man he knew had the same trouble with his own knife, it didn't seem worth while to buy a new one.

But about a year ago, the *Remington Pocket Knives* came out.

People said—"Remington, eh! Must be pretty good."

Men everywhere bought the knives. Tried them. Found them *more* than "pretty good" —*the very finest pocket knives in America today.*

* * *

So this year at least *his* gift is the easiest part of your Christmas shopping.

He expects a *Remington Pocket Knife.* Don't disappoint him!

There are more than 700 patterns of Remington Knives to choose from. A knife for every purpose—in all combinations of blades and handles, ranging in price from 50 cents to $50.

Remington

THE AUTHORITY IN FIRE ARMS, AMMUNITION AND CUTLERY

REMINGTON ARMS COMPANY, Inc.—New York City.

Remington

DUPONT

REG. U.S. PAT. OFF.

When Eliphalet Remington started his arms manufacturing plant in 1816, he had no idea that this new venture would lead to the eventual production of some of the most highly prized and sought after knives in the world. Upon his death, the arms company passed to his sons who soon sold to Marcellus Hartley, of Union Metallic Cartridge Company. When Hartley died, his grandson Marcellus Dodge took over both the Remington Arms Co. and the Union Metallic Cartridge Company and merged them into one, the Remington Union Metallic Cartridge Company. Since the Remington name was better known, the Union Metallic Cartridge name was dropped; however, most of the knives will have the UMC stamped within the Remington circle on the tang.

It took over a century and WWI to spur the company into manufacturing these highly prized knives.

Remington was a major manufacturer of bayonets for WWI and upon the war's end, the company found itself with a tremendous production capability but no contracts; hence the decision to enter the pocket knife market and this they did in February 1920.

From this beginning things progressed well with an ever increasing number of patterns. In 1929, Remington felt the crunch of the depression and sold controlling interest to the DuPont Company in 1933.

With the war looming ever larger in Europe, the US Government began gearing up and increasing arms contracts pushed the pocket knives aside.

Pal Cutlery Company bought the cutlery equipment in approximately 1940.

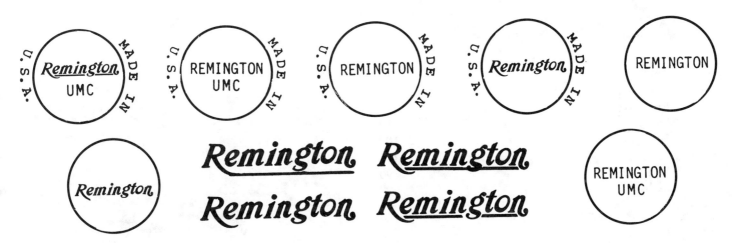

REMINGTON PATTERN NUMBERS

The Remington pattern number was stamped on the reverse side of the tang with either the circle stamp or the straightline. The "circle" was reserved for the higher quality knives. Some stamps were inked on.

The "R" preceding a number denotes that it is a pocket knife and the last digit reveals the handle material.

1. Redwood
2. Black Composition
3. Bone
4. Pearl
5. Pyremite
   CH. - designates knife with chain.

6. Genuine Stag
7. Ivory or White Bone
8. Colobolo Wood
9. Metal - Stainless, Nickel, Brass, etc.
0. Horn - Buffalo, Cow

Note From The Author . . .

Remington manufactured advertising knives for many companies. The author has never seen a Remington advertising knife with a pattern number.

REMINGTON

Nr.	Handle	Lgth.	Mint Value
RA1	Redwood	3⅜	
R1	Redwood	3⅜	70
R2	Black	3⅜	80
R3	Bone	3⅜	
R5	White Pyremite	3⅜	
R01	Redwood	3⅜	70
R02	Black	3⅜	70
R03	Bone	3⅜	70
RC5	Pyremite		70
RC6	Gen. Stag		70
RC7	Ivory		70
RC8	Cocobolo		70
RC9	Metal		70
R15	Pyremite (leg)	3¼	225
R015	Pyremite		100

BARLOW (Clip)

RB44	**Brown Bone**	**3⅜"**	**$125**
RB44W	White	3⅜	110

SWITCHBLADE/PULL BALL

R17	**White Comp.**	**2¾"**	**$110**
R21	Redwood		80
R21CH	Redwood	3⅜	100
R22	Black	3⅜	90
R23	Bone	3⅜	100
R23CH	Bone	3⅜	110
R25	White Pyremite	3⅜	90
R31	Redwood	3⅜	90
R32	Black	3⅜	90
R33	Bone	3⅜	100
R35	Pyremite		100
RB040	Brown Bone	3⅜	90
RB041	Brown Bone	3⅜	90

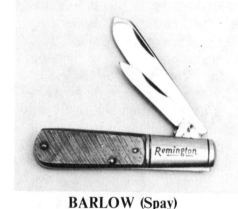

BARLOW (Spay)

RB45	**Brown Bone**	**3⅜"**	**$135**

BARLOW (L.P. Spay)

RB45	**Brown Bone, upside down stamp long pull**	**3⅜"**	**$150**

BARLOW SPEAR

RB43	**Brown Bone**	**3⅜"**	**$125**
RB43	Brown Bone LP	3⅜"	$125

BARLOW (Sheep Foot)

RB46	**Brown Bone**	**3⅜"**	**$150**

BARLOW

RB47　Brown Bone　　　3⅜"　$165

R100R　Brown Bone, Long Pull, Punch
Blade Enclosed, Back Spring　　3⅜"　125

Nr.	Handle	Lgth.	Mint Value
R51	Redwood		90
R52	Black		160
R53	Bone		180
R55	Pyremite		170
R63	Bone		170

Nr.	Handle	Lgth.	Mint Value
R102	CH Black	3½	140
R103	CH Bone	3½	150

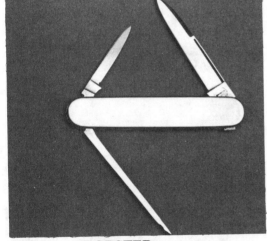

LOBSTER

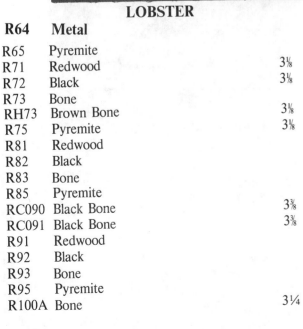

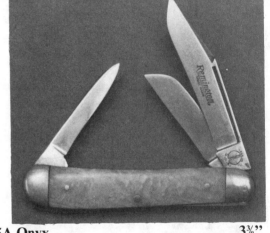

R105A　Onyx　　　3⅜"　125

Nr.	Handle	Lgth.	Mint Value
R64	**Metal**		**$75**
R65	Pyremite		90
R71	Redwood	3⅛	100
R72	Black	3⅛	100
R73	Bone		140
RH73	Brown Bone	3⅛	130
R75	Pyremite	3⅛	115
R81	Redwood		100
R82	Black		115
R83	Bone		150
R85	Pyremite		115
RC090	Black Bone	3⅜	75
RC091	Black Bone	3⅜	75
R91	Redwood		130
R92	Black		140
R93	Bone		165
R95	Pyremite		130
R100A	Bone	3¼	160

Nr.	Handle	Lgth.	Mint Value
R105B	Pyremite	3¼	120
R108	CH Cocobolo	3½	100
R111	Redwood		100
R112	Black		100
R113	Bone		145
R115	Pyremite		115
R122	Black	3½	135
R123	Bone	3½	150
R125	Pyremite	3½	140
R131	Redwood		135
R132	Black		135
R133	Stag		160
R135	Pyremite		150
R141	Redwood		115
R142	Black		115
R143	Bone		150
R145	Pyremite		130
R151	Redwood		115
R152	Black		115
R153	Bone	3½	160
R155	Pyremite	3½	130
R161	Redwood		115
R162	Black		115
R163	Bone	3½	160

Nr.	Handle	Lgth.	Mint Value
R175	Pyremite		150
R181	Redwood		150
R182	Black		150
R183	Bone	3⅝	180
R185	Pyremite		155
R191	Redwood		140
R192	Black		140
R193	Bone		180
R195	Pyremite		160
R201	Redwood		150
R202	Black		150

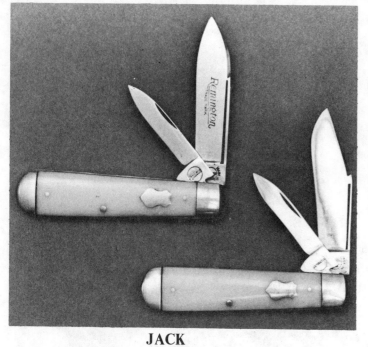

JACK

R165 Yellow Scale   3½" $100

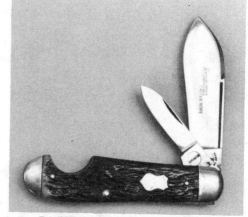

JACK/EASY OPENER

R203 Brown Bone   3⅝" $200

R205	Pyremite	175
R211	Redwood	150
R212	Black	150
R213	Bone	180

JACK

R165 Pyremite   3½" $125

Nr.	Handle	Lgth.	Mint Value
R171	Redwood		130
R172	Black		130

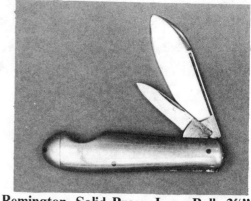

R219 Remington, Solid Brass, Long Pull 3⅝" $175

R222	Black	130
R223	Bone	180
R225	Pyremite	150
R228	Cocobolo	140
R232	Black	140
R233	Bone	180
R235	Pyremite	160
R238	Cocobolo	130
R242	Black	180
R243	Bone	200
R245	Pyremite	180
R248	Cocobolo	160
R252	Black	150

JACK

R173 Brown Bone, Teardrop   3¾" $150

Nr.	Handle	Lgth.	Mint Value
R253	Bone		180
R255	Pyremite		170
R258	Cocobolo		150
R262	Black	4	140
R263	Bone	4	180
R265	Pyremite	4	180
R272	Black		170

Nr.	Handle	Lgth.	Mint Value
R275	Pyremite		180
R282	Black		170
R283	Bone		220
R303	Bone	3¾	170
R305	Pyremite	3¾	150

TEXAS JACK

R273   Brown Bone, Acorn Shield   4" $190

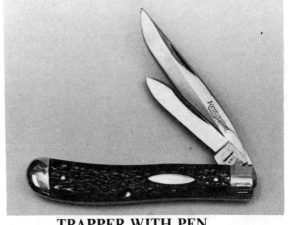

TRAPPER WITH PEN

R313   Brown Bone, Saber   3⅞" $225

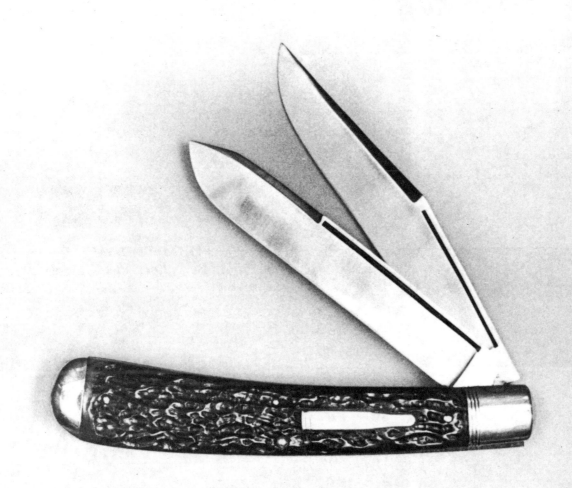

R293   **FIELD & STREAM BULLET**, Brown Bone, Long Pull, Bullet Shield   5¼" $1800

Nr.	Handle	Lgth.	Mint Value
R315	Pyremite	3⅞	170
R322	Black		160
R323	Bone		180
R325	Pyremite		170
R328	Cocobolo		160
R341	Redwood		170
R342	Black		170
R343	Bone		200
R352	Black	3¾	150
R353	Bone	3¾	200
R355	Pyremite	3¾	170
R358	Cocobolo	3¾	160
R363	Bone	3¾	200

Nr.	Handle	Lgth.	Mint Value
R412	Black		150
R413	Bone		185
R415	Pyremite		170
R423	Bone		170
R432	Black	3½	250
R435	Pyremite	3½	250
R443	Bone		235
R444	Pearl		375
R453	Bone		360
R455	Pyremite		250
R463	Bone		170
R465	Pyremite		150
R473	Bone	3¼	170
R475	Pyremite	3¼	150
R482	Black	3½	150
R483	Bone	3½	180
R485	Pyremite	3½	150
R488	Cocobolo	3½	150
R493	Bone		180
R495	Pyremite		150
R503	Bone		180
R505	Pyremite		150
R512	Black		150
R513	Bone		170
R515	Pyremite		150
R523	Bone		200
R525	Pyremite		150
R551	Redwood	3¼	120
R552	Black	3¼	120

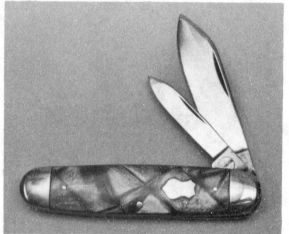

JACK

R365	**Gold Swirl Pyremite**	3¾"	**$150**
R372	Black		160
R373	Bone		200
R375	Pyremite		170

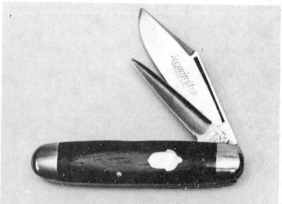

EQUAL END JACK

R378	**Cocobolo, Acorn Shield**	3¾"	**$150**
R383	Bone	3¾	200
R391	Redwood	3⅜	160
R392	Black	3⅜	160
R393	Bone	3⅜	200
R395	Pyremite	3⅜	170
R402	Black		150
R403	Bone		185
R405	Pyremite		170
R410	Buffalo horn		150

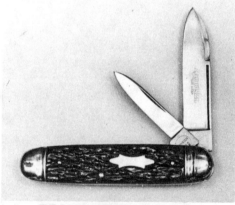

EQUAL END JACK

R553 **Brown Bone, Long Pull, Grooved Bolster**   3¼"   **$140**

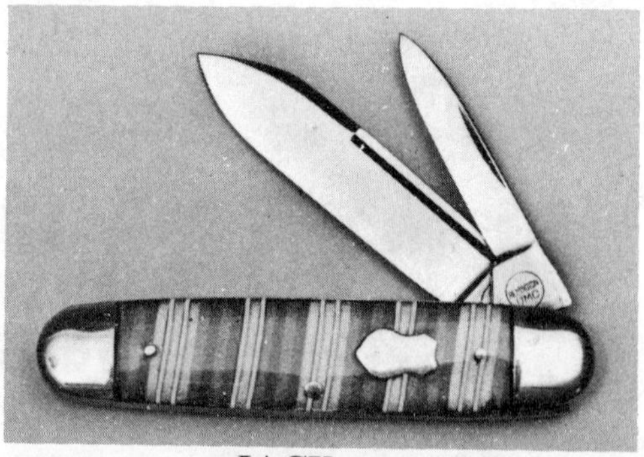

JACK

R555 **Remington Circle UMC, Candy Stripe Scales**   3¼"   **$175**

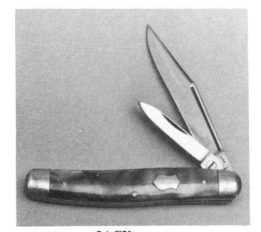

Nr.	Handle	Lgth.	Mint Value
R563	Brown Bone, Acorn Shield	3¼"	$110
R572	Black		150
R575	Pyremite		140
R583	Bone		170
R585	Pyremite		150
R590	Buffalo horn	3¼	250
R593	Bone	3¼	160
R595	Pyremite	3¼	140

JACK
R605 Gold Swirl Pyremite   3⅜" $125

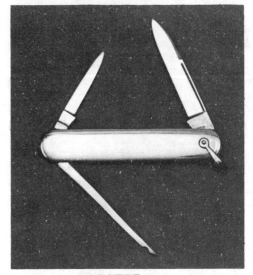

LOBSTER
R629 Metal, with Bail   2¾" $90

SMALL SERPENTINE JACK
R603 Bone   3⅜" $110

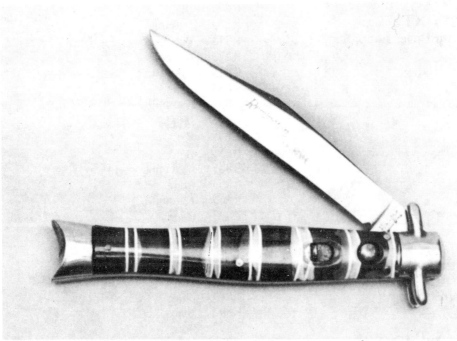

R645 Switchblade, Candy Stripe   4" $350

Nr.	Handle	Lgth.	Mint Value
R605	Pyremite	3⅜	130
R609	Metal		160
R613	Bone		185
R615	Pyremite		150
R622	Black		160
R623	Bone	4	185
R625	Pyremite	4	225
R633	Bone		180
R635	Pyremite		150
R643	Bone		250
R645	Pyremite		220
R655	Pyremite		450
R653F	Black		230
R653	Bow Tie		300
R663	Bone		300
R668	Cocobolo		275
R672	Black	3	150
R673	Bone	3	170
R674	Pearl	3	275
R675	Pyremite	3	175
R677	Ivory		3-200
R679	Metal	3	150
R682	Black	3	300

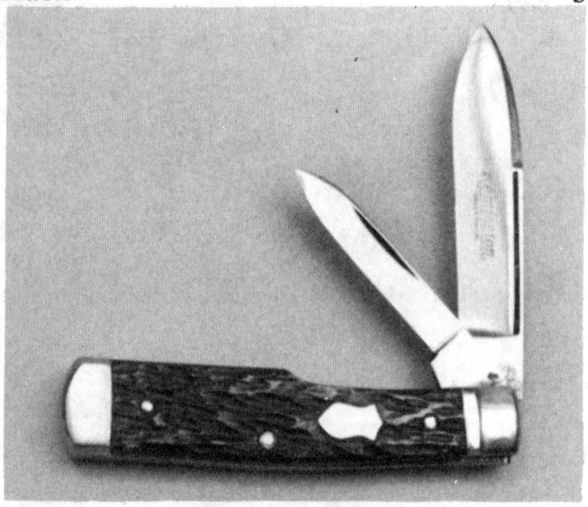

GUNSTOCK

R683	**Remington, Brown Bone, Long Pull**	**3"**	**$400**
R684	Pearl	3	500
R685	Pyremite	3	400
R693	Bone	4	150

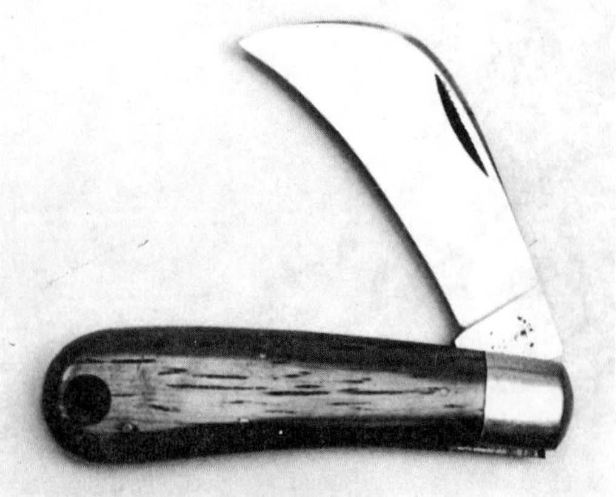

HAWKBILL

R698	**Cocobolo**	**4"**	**$110**

Nr.	Handle	Lgth.	Mint Value
R703	Bone	3⅝	100
R706	Gen. Stag		80

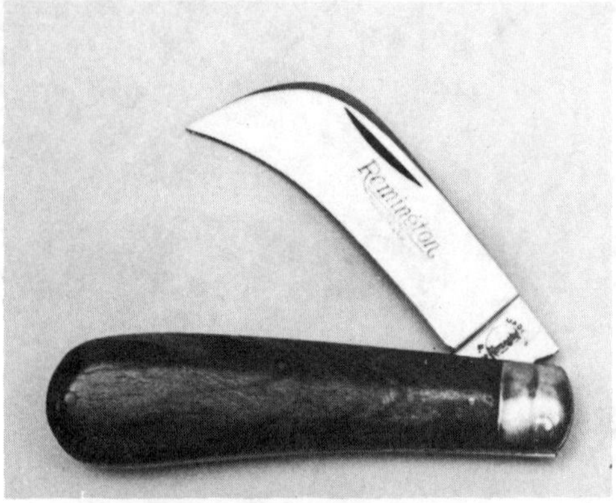

HAWKBILL

R708	**Cocobolo**	**3⅝"**	**$90**
R713	Bone	3¾	170
R718	Cocobolo	3¾	150
R723	Bone	4½	250
R728	Cocobolo	4½	175
R732	Black		120
R733	Bone		160
R735	Pyremite		140
R738	Cocobolo		120
R743	Bone		160
R745	Pyremite		135
R753	Bone		150
R755	Pyremite		135
R756	Gen. Stag		175
R763	Bone		150
R772	Black		150
R773	Bone		175
R775	Pyremite		155
R783	Bone		190
R793	Bone		230
R803	Bone	3	100
RC803	Bone	3	50
R805	Pyremite		100
R813	Bone		220
R823	Bone		170
R825	Pyremite		135
R833	Bone	3⅝	170
R835	Pyremite	3⅝	130
R843	Bone		170
R845	Pyremite		140
R853	Bone		175
R855	Pyremite		150
R863	Bone		210
R865	Pyremite		170
R873	Bone	3⅛	90
R874	Pearl	3⅛	110
R875	Pyremite	3⅛	100
R881	Redwood		120
R882	Black		125
R883	Bone		160
R892	Black		140
R893	Bone		200
R895	Pyremite		170

Nr.	Handle		Lgth.	Mint Value
R901	Redwood			140
R913	Bone	# Front Tang		200
R921	Redwood	1 Blade Maize	4⅛	120
R932	Black			200
R935	Pyremite			285
R942	Black			235
R943	Bone		5	285
R945	Pyremite			250
RC953	Bone		5	250
R953	Bone Toothpick Round Bullet Shield		5	700
R955	Pyremite		3	235
R962	Black		4¼	130
R965	Pyremite		4¼	150
R971	Redwood			235

Nr.	Handle		
R1002	Black	3⅝	115
R1003	Bone	3⅝	125
R1005	Pyremite	3⅝	115
R1012	Black	3⅝	150
R1013	Bone	3⅝	150
R1022	Black	4¼	325
R1023	Bone	4¼	325
R1032	Black	3⅜	100
R1033	Bone	3⅜	115
R1035	Pyremite	3⅜	100
R1042	Black	3⅜	150
R1043	Bone	3⅜	160
R1045	Pyremite	3⅜	150
R1051	Redwood	3½	90
R1053	Bone	3⅜	90
R1055	Pyremite	3⅜	90
R1061	Redwood	3⅜	90
R1062	Black	3⅜	100
R1063	Bone	3⅜	130
R1065	White Pyremite	3⅜	90

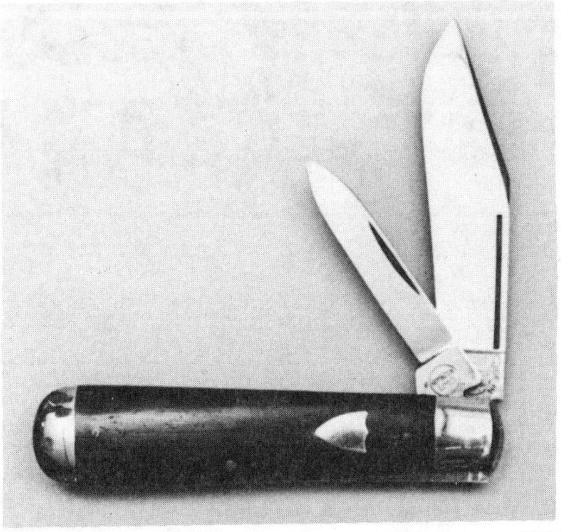

JACK

R973 Imitation Bone, 4¼" $225

Nr.	Handle	Lgth.	Value
R982	Black	2⅞	100
R983	Bone	2⅞	130
R985	Pyremite	2⅞	100
R992	Black	3¼	115
R993	Bone	3¼	130

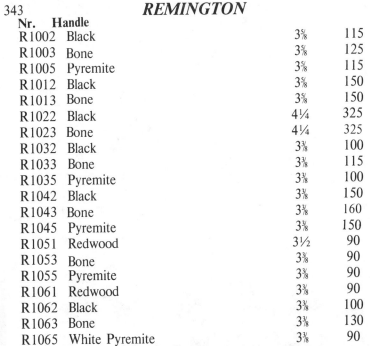

R1071 Cocobolo (shows 2 blade styles) 3⅜" $100

Nr.	Handle	Lgth.	Value
R1072	Black		90
R1073	Bone	3⅜	125
R1075	Pyremite	3⅜	100
R1082	Black		60
R1083	Bone		80
R1085	Pyremite	3⅜	70
R1092	Black		50
R1093	Bone		75
R1102	Black		95

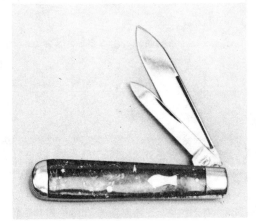

JACK

R995 Blue & White Comp. 3¼" $110

JACK

R1103 Brown Bone 3⅜" $135

R1123 Brown Bone, Bullet Shield   4½" $900

Nr.	Handle	Lgth.	Mint
R1112	Black		95
R1113	Bone	3⅜	125
R1128	Cocobolo Bullet (rare)		1,600
R1133	Bone		160
R1143	Bone	4⅜	160

R1173 Brown Bone, Baby Bullet   3½" $2000

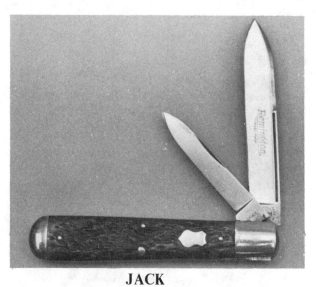

JACK

R1163 Brown Bone   4½" $ 350

JACK

R1153 Brown Bone   4½" $350

Nr.	Handle	Lgth.	Mint
R1182	Black		125
R1183	Bone		160
R1192	Black		100
R1193	Bone		125
R1202	Black		140
R1203	Bone		150
R1212	Black		235
R1213	Bone		300
R1222	Black		250
R1223	Bone		285

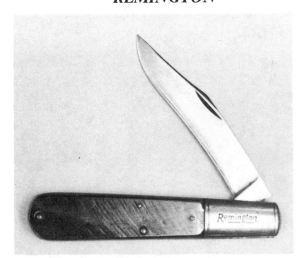

BARLOW
R1240 Remington, Brown Bone   5" $250

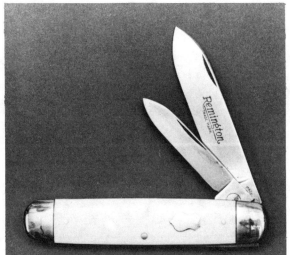

JACK

R1225 White Comp.   4½" $275

R1232	Black		150
R1233	Bone		175
R1241	Redwood		285
R1242	Black		300
R1243	Bone		350

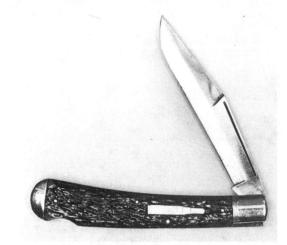

**R1253L Remington, Brown Bone, Long
Pull, Lockback, Bullet Shield   5¼" $1200**

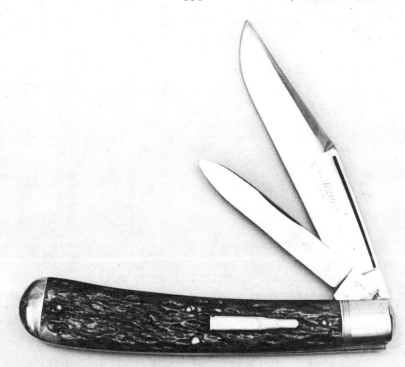

R1263 Remington Bullet, Brown Bone   5⅜" $1200

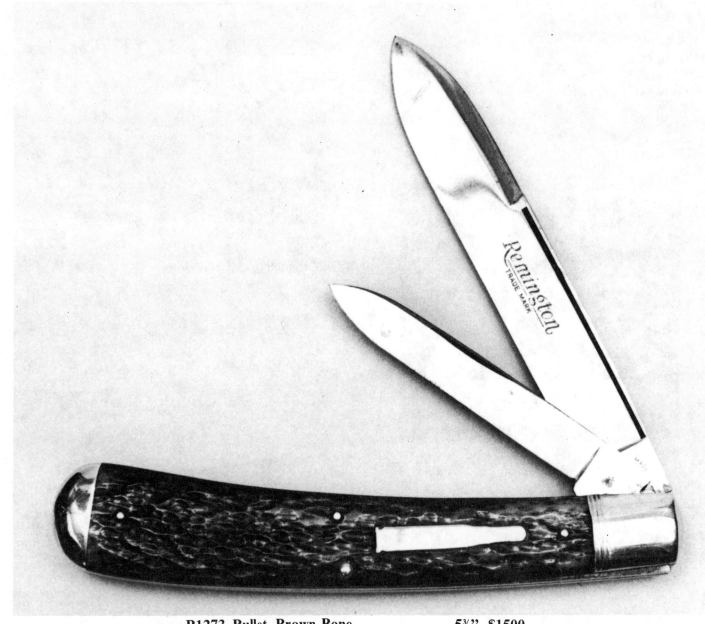

R1273 Bullet, Brown Bone   5⅜" $1500

Nr.	Handle	Lgth.	Mint	Nr.	Handle	Lgth.	Mint
R1283	Bone	3	125	R1293	Bone		200
R1284	Pearl		190	R1295	Pyremite		215

SWELL CENTER

R1285 Tortoise Shell   3" $160

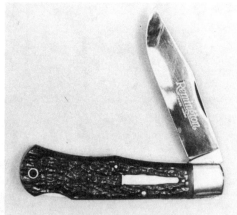

R1303 Remington Bullet, Brown Bone, Lockback, Bullet Shield   4½" $1200

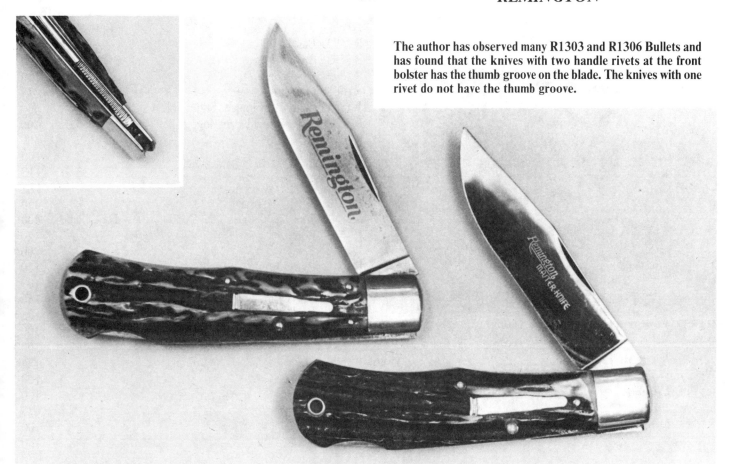

The author has observed many R1303 and R1306 Bullets and has found that the knives with two handle rivets at the front bolster has the thumb groove on the blade. The knives with one rivet do not have the thumb groove.

R1306 Remington Bullet, Stag, Thumb Groove on Top of Blade (inset)   4⅝" $1000

Nr.	Handle	Lgth.	Mint
R1315	Pyremite		160
R1323	Bone	3	160
R1324	Pearl		215
R1325	Pyremite	3	130
R1333	Bone		90

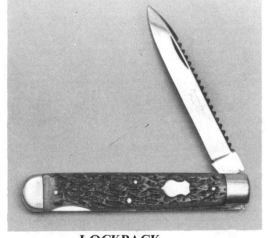

LOCKBACK
R1383 Fish Scaler, Brown Bone   4¼" $350

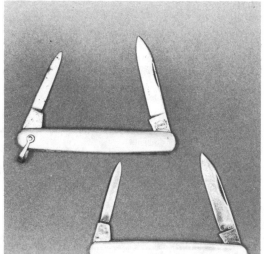

R1339 Remington, All Metal,   3" $65

Nr.	Handle	Lgth.	Mint
R1343	Bone	4¼	285
R1353	Bone		215
R1363	Bone		215
R1373	Bone		285
R1379	Metal		250

Nr.	Handle	Lgth.	Mint
R1389	Metal		200
R1399	Metal		100
R1409	Metal		100
R1413	Bone		115
R1423	Bone		115
R1437	Ivory		140
R1447	Ivory		140
R1457	Ivory		160
R1465	Pyremite Budding Knife	3⅝	165
R1477	Ivory		120
R1483	Bone		140

Nr.	Handle	Lgth.	Mint
R1485	Pyremite		115
R1493	Bone		140
R1495	Pyremite		140

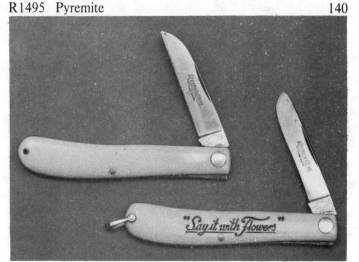

R1535 Florist Knife, Imitation Ivory   3¾"   **$80**

R1545 Florist Knife, Imitation Ivory, With Bail   3¾"   **$80**

Nr.	Handle	Lgth.	Mint
R1555	Pyremite		140
R1568	Cocobolo		120
R1572	Black	3	100
R1573	Bone	3	100

R1573CH Remington, Imitation Bone, Reg. Pull, with Chain   3"   **$125**

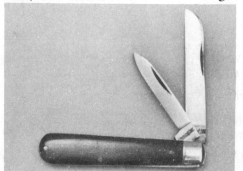

R1582 Slick Black   3"   **$90**

Nr.	Handle	Lgth.	Mint
R1592	Black		100
R1593	Bone		100
R1595	Pyremite		100
R1608	Cocobolo		75
R1613	Bone BL. Emblem Bullet Shield		900
R1613	Bone Round Cartridge Sh.	5	700
R1615	Pyremite	5	300
R1622	Black	3	100
R1623	Bone	3	115
R1623CH	Imi. Bone		125
R1630	Buffalo Horn		400
R1630	Bone Fish Scaler Top, Daddy Barlow Lock Blade		400
R1643	Bone		120
R1644	Pearl		200
R1645	Pyremite		100
R1655	Pyremite		100
R1668	Cocobolo		160
R1671	Redwood		75
R1673	Bone		100
R1685	Pyremite	3¾	100
R1687	Ivory		125
R1688	Cocobolo		100
R1707	Ivory		100
R1715	Pyremite	4¼	75
R1717	Ivory		100
R1723	Bone	3½	150
R1751	Redwood		80
R1752	Black		80
R1753	Bone	3½	100
R1755	Pyremite		80
R1763	Bone		115
R1772	Black		115
R1773	Bone		115
R1782	Black		150
R1785	Pyremite	3½	125
R1803	Bone		100

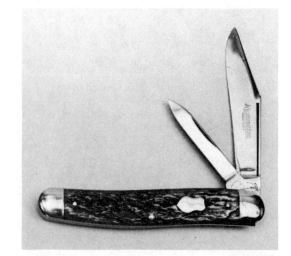

R1823 Brown Bone, Long Pull   3⅝" **$110**

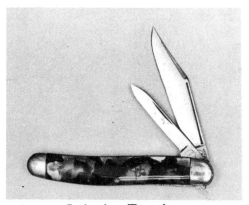

R1825 Remington, Imitation Tortoise, Long Pull 3⅝" $125

Nr.	Handle	Lgth.	Mint
R1833	Bone		150
R1853	Bone	3⅜	125
R1855	Pyremite	3⅜	100
R1863	Bone	3⅜	115
R1873	Bone	3⅝	100
R1882	Black	3	150
R1903	Bone		100
R1905	Pyremite		80
R1913	Bone		140

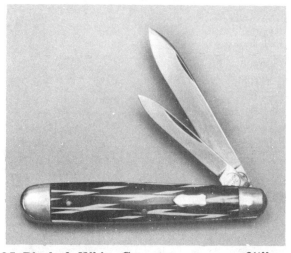

R2095 Black & White Comp. 3⅛" $75

Nr.	Handle	Lgth.	Mint
R2103	Bone	3⅛	70
R2105	Pyremite	3⅛	60
R2111	Redwood		120
R2203	Bone	3⅜	100
R2205	Pyremite	3⅛	75
R2213	Bone	3⅜	75

JACK

R2215 Red & Black Pyremite 3⅜" $90

R2223	Bone	3⅜	55
R2303	Bone Switch Blade	4⅛"	500
R2403	Bone Switch Blade	5"	600
R2503	Bone		55
R2505B	Pyremite		55
2505M	Pyremite		55
2505R	Pyremite		55
R2603	Bone		80

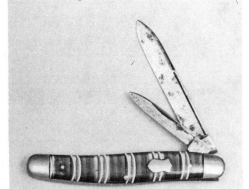

R1915 Remington, Candy Stripe, Long Pull 3⅜" $150

R1962	Black		100
R1973	Bone		185
R1995	Pyremite	4¼	115
R2043	Bone	3¼	55
R2045	Pyremite	3¼	55
R2053	Bone		55
R2055	Pyremite		55
R2063	Bone	3⅛	55
R2065	Pyremite	3⅛	55
R2073	Bone	3⅛	55
R2075	Pyremite	3⅛	55
R2083	Bone	3¼	60
R2085	Pyremite		60
R2093	Bone	3⅛	70

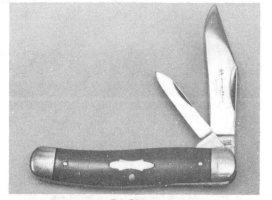

JACK

R2605 Red Scale 3³" $110

Nr.	Handle	Lgth.	Mint
R3003	Bone		285
R3005	Pyremite		250
R3013	Bone		285
R3015	Pyremite		250
R3033	Bone		330
R3035	Pyremite		250
R3050	Buffalo Horn	4	300
R3053	Bone	4	285

Nr.	Handle	Lgth.	Mint
R3062	Black	4	250
R3063	Bone	4	285
R3064	Pearl	4	400
R3065	Pyremite	4	250
R3070	Buffalo Horn		250
R3073	Bone		235
R3075	Pyremite		285
R3083LP	Bone		400
R3085	Pyremite		330
R3093	Bone		250
R3095	Pyremite		185
R3103	Bone		285
R3105	Pyremite		235
R3113	Bone	4	180
R3115G	Pyremite	3⅞	150
R3115W	Pyremite	3⅞	150

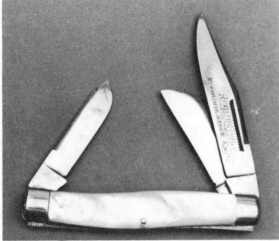

STOCKMAN

R3054	**Genuine Pearl**	**4"**	**$400**
R3055	Pyremite	4	250
R3056	Gen. Stag	4	350

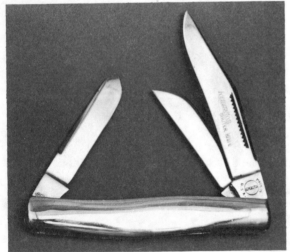

STOCKMAN

R3059	**All Metal**	**4"**	**$250**

STOCKMAN

R3065	**Yellow, Long Pull, Punch Blade**	**4"**	**$225**

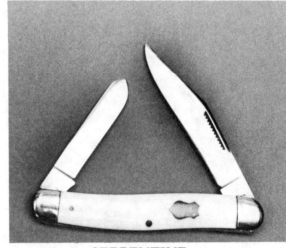

SERPENTINE

R3115	**Imitation Ivory**	**4"**	**$135**
R3123	Bone	3⅞	250
R3133	Bone	4	300
R3143	Bone	4	1200

EQUAL END

R3153	**Brown Bone, Acorn Shield**	**3½"**	**$250**
R3155	Pyremite		200
R3155B	Pyremite		185
R3163	Bone	3½	285
R3165	Pyremite	3½	225

Nr.	Handle	Lgth.	Mint	Nr.	Handle	Lgth.	Mint
R3173	Bone		265	R3274	Pearl	3¾	400
R3183	Bone	3½	265	R3275	Pyremite	3¾	275
R3185	Pyremite	3½	260	R3283	Bone		275
R3193	Bone		265	R3285	Pyremite		250
R3202	Black		260	R3293	Bone		275
R3203	Bone	3½	265	R3295	Pyremite		250
R3212	Black		260	R3302	Black	3¾	360
R3213	Bone		300	R3303	Bone	3¾	360
R3215	Pyremite		260	R3305	Pyremite	3¾	350
R3222	Black		190	R3312	Black		300
R3223	Bone		250	R3313	Bone	3¾	385
R3225	Pyremite		225	R3315B	Pyremite		360
R3232	Black		190	R3322	Black		200
R3233	Bone		260				
R3235	Pyremite		260				
R3242	Black	3¾	260				
R3243W	Pyremite	3¾	240				
R3253	Bone		300				
R3255	Pyremite		260				
R3263	Bone		300				
R3265	Pyremite		260				

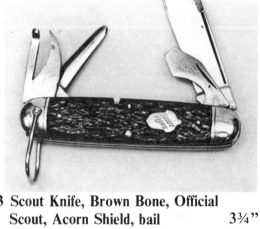

R3333 Scout Knife, Brown Bone, Official
Scout, Acorn Shield, bail   3¾" $250

CATTLE
R3273 Brown Bone, Equal End   3¾" $250

CATTLE
R3273 Brown Bone, Long Pull, Equal
End, Grooved Bolster   3¾" $275

RS3333 Brown Bone, with Bail, Official
Scout Shield, "Be Prepared"   3¾" $200

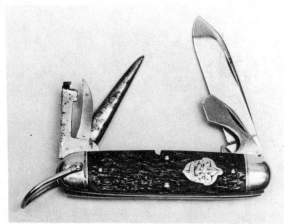

RS3333 Scout Knife, Brown Bone, Scout Shield,
Acorn Shape   3¾"   **$250**

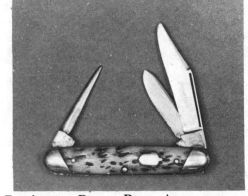

R3413 Remington, Brown Bone, Acorn
Shield, Long Pull, Slant Bolsters   3⅜"   **$185**

Nr.	Handle	Lgth.	Mint
R3414	Pearl		290
R3415	Pyremite	3⅜	200
3415H	Pyremite	3⅜	200

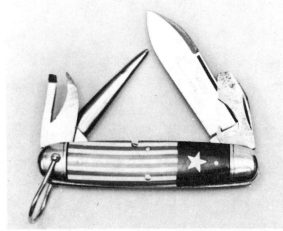

R3335 Scout Knife, Red, White, & Blue   3¾"   **$285**

Nr.	Handle	Lgth.	Mint
3352	Black	3¾	170
3353	Bone	3¾	225

EQUAL END

R3423 Slant Bolsters Bone   3¼"   **$225**

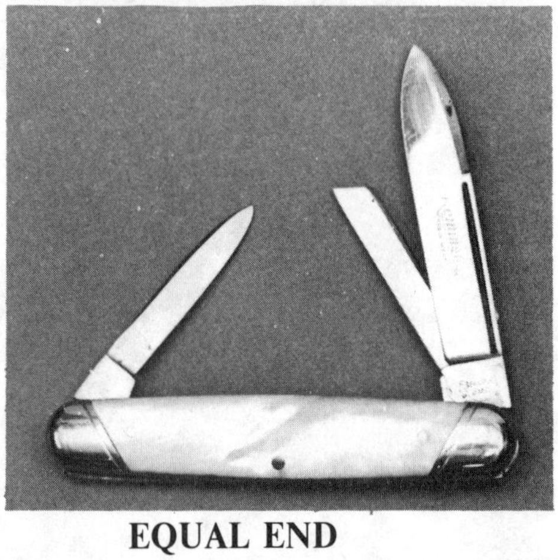

R3363 Remington, Brown Bone, Long
Pull   3¾"   **$250**

Nr.	Handle	Lgth.	Mint
R3372	Black	3¾	170
R3373	Bone	3¾	150
R3375	Pyremite	3¾	200
R3382	Black		200
R3383	Bone		215
R3385S	Pyremite		200
R3393	Bone	3¾	200
R3395T	Pyremite	3¾	185
R3403	Bone		250
R3405J	Pyremite		215

EQUAL END

R3424 Pearl, Slant Bolsters   3⅜"   **$350**

Nr.	Handle	Lgth.	Mint
R3425P	Pyremite		215
R3432	Black		170
R3433	Bone		190
R3435	Pyremite		170
R3442	Black	3¼	170
R3445	Pyremite	3¼	170
R3453	Bone		190
R3455	Pyremite		170
R3463	Bone		260

Nr.	Handle	Lgth.	Mint	Nr.	Handle	Lgth.	Mint
R3465B	Pyremite		225	R3533	Bone	3⅜	175
R3475K	Pyremite		225	R3535	Pyremite	3⅜	150
R3475J	Pyremite		200	R3545	Pyremite		150
R3480	Buffalo Horn		200				
R3483	Bone		225				
R3484	Pearl		300				

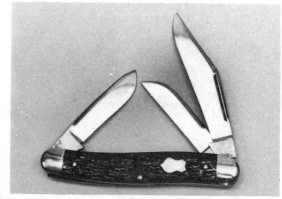

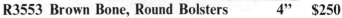

R3553 Brown Bone, Round Bolsters   4"   **$250**

EQUAL END
R3485 Gold Swirl Pyremite   3⅜"   **$200**

R3489	Metal		175
R3493	Bone		225
R3494	Pearl		275
R3495M	Pyremite		150
R3499	Metal		250
R3500BU	Buffalo Horn		200
R3503	Bone		215
R3504	Pearl		300
R3505	Pyremite		240

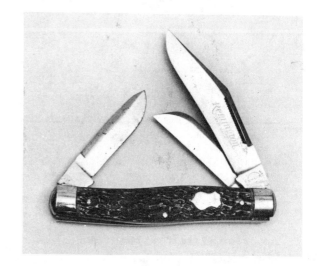

R3553 Brown Bone, Square Bolsters   4"   **$275**
R3554   Pearl   350

SERPENTINE
R3513 Brown Bone, Acorn Shield   3⅜"   **$150**

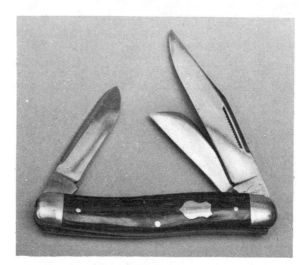

R3514	Pearl		200
R3515	Pyremite		190
R3520BU	Buffalo Horn	3⅜	225
R3523	Bone	3⅜	230
R3524	Pearl	3⅜	330
R3525	Pyremite	3⅜	200

STOCKMAN
R3555 Mingled Red Scale   4"   **$250**
R3555G   Pyremite   3⅞   250

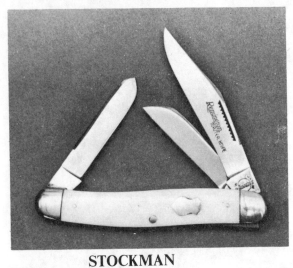

Nr.	Handle	Lgth.	Mint
R3593	Bone		300
R3595	Pyremite		285
R3596	Gen. Stag		350
R3600	Buffalo Horn		200
R3603	Bone		215
R3604	Pearl		300
R3605	Pyremite		200
R3613	Bone		215
R3615	Pyremite		200
R3620BU	Buffalo Horn		140
R3623	Bone		150
R3625	Pyremite		140
R3633	Bone		150
R3635	Pyremite		140
R3643	Bone	4	375

STOCKMAN

R3557 Imitation Ivory   4" $225

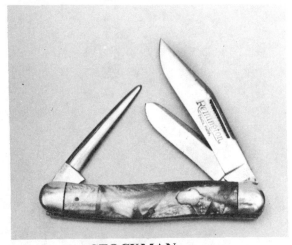

STOCKMAN

R3565 Brown Swirl Pyremite, Acorn Shield   4" $250

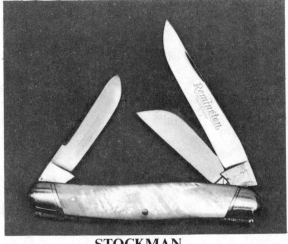

STOCKMAN

R3644 Pearl Scale, Slant Bolster   4" $450

Nr.	Handle	Lgth.	Mint
R3645	Pyremite	4	350
R3653	Bone	3⅞	250
R3655	Pyremite		225
R3665	Pyremite		300
R3675	Pyremite		300
R3683C	Bone		230
R3685C	Pyremite		170

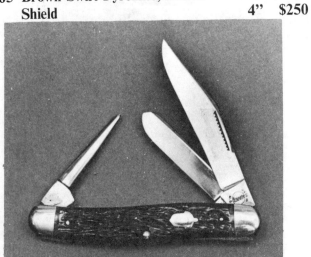

R3563 Bone, Acorn Shield   4" $250

Nr.	Handle	Lgth.	Mint
R3565D	Pyremite	3⅞	200
R3573	Bone		240
R3575	Pyremite		200
R3580BU	Buffalo Horn		125
R3583	Bone		150
R3585	Pyremite		140

WHITTLER

R3693 Brown Bone, Acorn Shield, Saber Blade, Slant Bolsters   3½" $550

Nr.	Handle	Lgth.	Mint
R3695G	Pyremite		500
R3700BU	Buffalo Horn	4	230
R3703	Bone	4	250
R3704	Pearl	4	350
R3705	Pyremite	4	225
R3710BU	Buffalo Horn		225
R3713	Bone	3⅞	260
R3714	Pearl		400
R3715	Pyremite		260
R3722	Black		280
R3723	Bone		500
R3725	Pyremite		330
R3732	Black		330
R3733	Bone		385
R3735	Pyremite		330

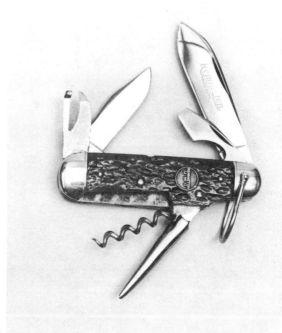

UTILITY KNIFE
R3843 Brown Bone   3⅝" $350

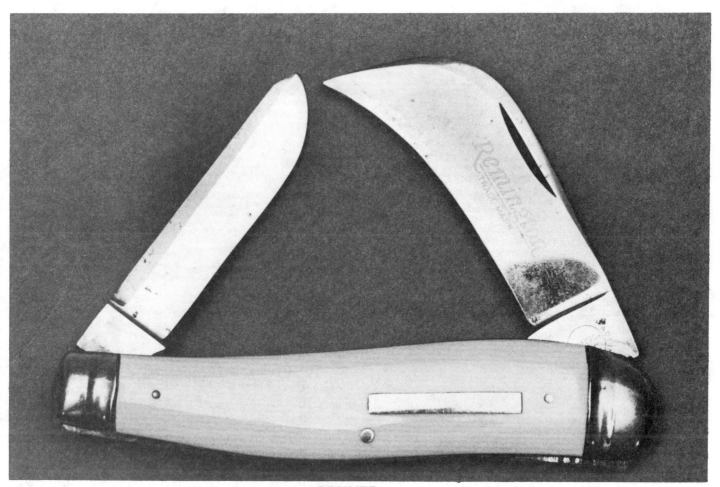

PRUNER
R3855 Remington, Imitation Ivory   4" $250

Nr.	Handle	Lgth.	Mint
R3853	Bone	4	215
R3858	Cocobolo		200
R3870BU	Buffalo Horn	4	215
R3873	Bone	4	240
R3874	Pearl	4	350
R3875A	Pyremite	4	215
R3883	Bone		275
R3885	Pyremite		240
R3893	Bone	3⅞	150
R3895	Pyremite		150
R3903	Bone	3⅞	225
R3926	Gen. Stag		400
R3932	Black		350
R3933	Stag		400
R3935	Pyremite		350

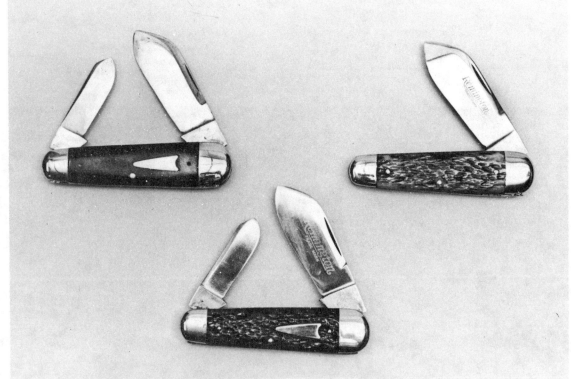

R3863 Scout Knife, Brown Bone, Acorn
     Shield   3¾" **$225**

LARGE SLEEVEBOARD   **SLEEVEBOARD**
R3942 Ebony   3⅝" **$250**   **R3943 Rogers Bone**   3⅝" **$250**

SLEEVEBOARD
R3943 Brown Bone   3⅝" **$275**

Nr.	Handle	Lgth.	Mint
R3952	Black		175
R3953	Bone		200
R3955	Pyremite		190
R3962	Black		190
R3963	Bone		215
R3705	Pyremite	4	225
R3710BU	Buffalo Horn		225
R3713	Bone	3⅞	260
R3714	Pearl		350
R3715	Pyremite		260
R3722	Black		280
R3723	Bone		400

Nr.	Handle	Lgth.	Mint
R3725	Pyremite		330
R3732	Black		330
R3733	Bone		385
R3735	Pyremite		330
R3853	Bone	4	215
R3858	Cocobolo		200
R3870BU	Buffalo Horn	4	215
R3873	Bone	4	240
R3874	Pearl	4	350
R3875A	Pyremite	4	215
R3883	Bone		275
R3885	Pyremite		240

Nr.	Handle	Lgth.	Mint
R3893	Bone	3⅞	150
R3895	Pyremite		150
R3903	Bone	3⅞	225
R3923	Bone 3 Bl. Stockman		400
R3926	Gen. Stag		400
R3932	Black		385
R3933	Bone		400
R3935	Pyremite		385
R3952	Black		175
R3953	Bone		200
R3955	Pyremite		190
R3962	Black		190
R3963	Bone		215
R3965	Pyremite		190
R3973	Bone	3⅝	215
R3975	Pyremite	3⅝	175
R3983	Bone		200
R3985	Pyremite		150
R3993	Bone	3⅝	200
R3995	Pyremite		200
R4003	Bone		150
R4005	Pyremite	3⅝	125
R4013	Bone		200
R4015	Pyremite		150
R4023	Bone		240
R4025	Pyremite		200
R4033	Bone	3⅝	240
R4035	Pyremite	3⅝	185
R4043	Bone		215
R4045	Pyremite		185
R4053	Bone		215
R4055	Pyremite		200
R4063	Bone		240
R4065	Pyremite		200

Nr.	Handle	Lgth.	Mint
R4103	Bone	3⅜	150
R4105	Pyremite	3⅜	125
R4113	Bone	3⅞	250
R4114	Pearl		325
R4123	Bone		300
R4124	Pearl		325

STOCKMAN

R4133 Bone   3⅜" **$175**

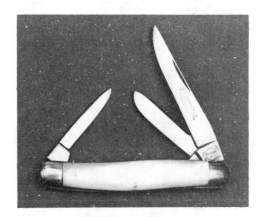

STOCKMAN

R4134 Pearl   3⅜" **$250**

Nr.	Handle	Lgth.	Mint
R4135	Pyremite	3⅜	200
R4143	Bone	3⅜	135
R4144	Pearl		240
R4145	Pyremite		200
R4163	Bone		215
R4173	Bone		200
R4175	Pyremite		200
R4200	Buffalo Horn		215
R4203	Bone		240
R4213	Bone		240
R4223	Bone	3¼	240
R4225	Pyremite		215
R4233	Bone		200

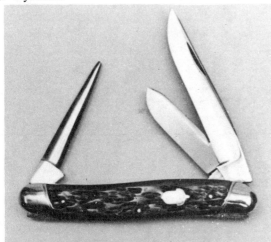

SERPENTINE

**R4073 Brown Bone, Saber Blade, Acorn
Shield, Slant Bolsters**   4" **$250**

Nr.	Handle	Lgth.	Mint
R4075	Pyremite		200
R4083	Bone	3⅞	240
R4085	Pyremite		215
R4093	Bone		215
R4095	Pyremite		185

RS4233 Little Scout Knife, Brown Bone, Scout Shield, Pinched Bolsters 3⅜" **$225**

Nr.	Handle	Lgth.	Mint
R4234	Pearl		300
R4235	Pyremite		225

R4243 Camp Bullet, Remington, Brown Bone, Long Pull, Bullet Shield 4¾" **$1100**

Nr.	Handle	Lgth.	Mint
R4253	Bone		235
R4263	Bone		290
R4273	Bone	3¾	500
R4274	Pearl	3¾	600

R4283 Sowbelly, Remington, Brown Bone 3¾" $2000

Nr.	Handle	Lgth.	Mint
R4293	Bone		215
R4303	Bone		215
R4313	Bone	3⅞	215

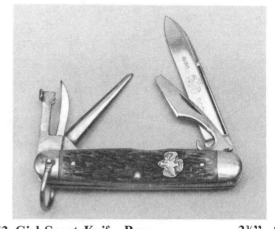

R4373 Girl Scout Knife, Bone   3⅜" $225

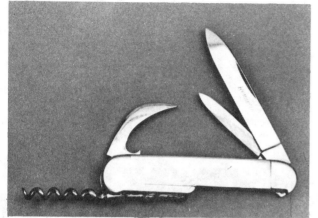

BARTENDER'S KNIFE

R4334 Pearl   3½" $250

Nr.	Handle	Lgth.	Mint
R4375	Pyremite		225
R4383	Bone	3⅜	225
R4384	Pearl		300
R4394	Pearl		350
R4403	Bone		215

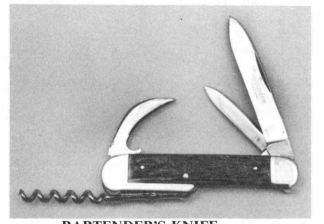

BARTENDER'S KNIFE

R4336 Stag   3½" $225

R4343	Bone		285
R4345	Pyremite		285

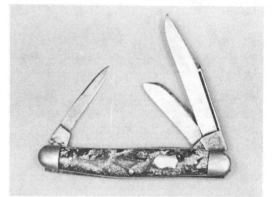

R4405 Remington, Christmas Tree, Long Pull   3⅜" $250

R4413	Bone		200
R4423	Bone	3¼	200

R4353 Bullet/Big Muskrat, Remington, Brown Bone, Bullet Shield   4¼" $1400

R4425 Remington, Pyremite, Long Pull, Acorn Shield, Slant Bolsters   3⅜" $200

R4363	Bone		285
R4365	Pyremite		285

R4433	Bone	3¼	285
R4443	Bone		200
R4466	Bone Baby Bullet	3¾	2,000

R4473 Slant Bolsters   3¼" **$140**
R4483 Bone   3½   285
R4493 Bone   200

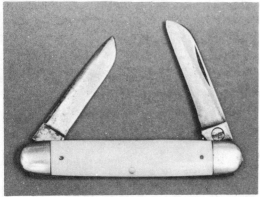

R4497 Florist's Knife, Remington, Imitation Ivory,   3¾" **$110**

Nr.	Handle	Lgth.	Mint
R4505	Pyremite	3⅞	215
R4506	Gen. Stag		250

R4513 Brown Bone, Acorn Shield, Etched "Great Western"   4" **$300**

Nr.	Handle	Lgth.	Mint
R4523	Bone		200
R4533	Bone		200
R4548	Cocobolo		250
R4555	Pyremite		215
R4563	Bone	4¼	330
R4573	Bone		250
R4583	Bone		160

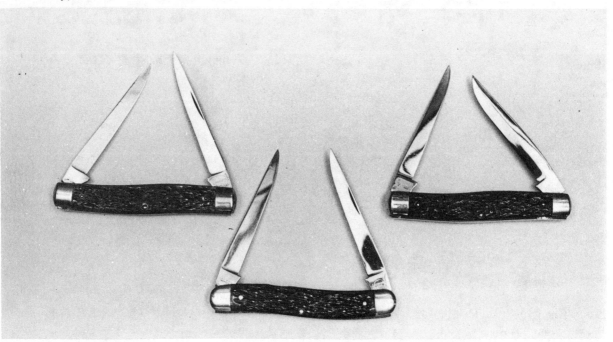

MUSKRAT
R4593 Remington, Brown Bone, Square Bolsters   4" **$225**

MUSKRAT
R4593 Remington, Brown Bone, Sq. Bolster, Sabre Blade   4"   **$275**

MUSKRAT
R4593 Remington, Brown Bone, Round Bolsters   4" **$250**

EQUAL END

R4603 Brown Bone, Acorn Shield   3¼" **$225**

Nr.	Handle	Lgth.	Mint
R4605	Pyremite	3¼	200
R4613	Bone		150

EQUAL END

R4623 Brown Bone   3⅜" **$150**

R4625	Pyremite		160
R4633	Bone	3⅜	150
R4635	Pyremite	3⅜	185
R4643	Bone	3⅝	145

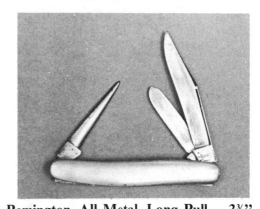

R4679 Remington, All Metal, Long Pull   3⅜" $125

R4683	Bone	3¼	170
R4685	Pyremite	3¼	140
R4695	Pyremite		165
R4702	Black Moose		250

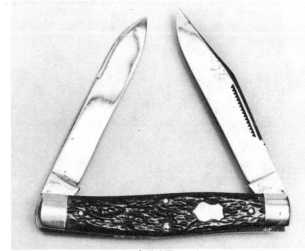

MOOSE

R4703 Brown Bone   4¼" **$250**

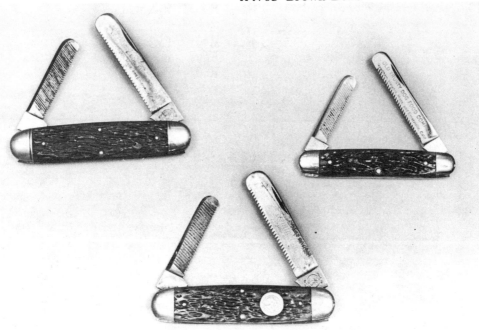

Bottom: Dog Grooming Knife, Brown Bone, Airdale Doghead Shield 3¾" $275; Top Left: R4733 Dog Grooming Knife, Remington, Brown Bone, No Shield, 3¾", $225; Top Right: No. Nr. Dog Grooming Knife, Remington, Brown Bone, No Shield, 3⅜", $250.

Nr.	Handle	Lgth.	Mint
R4713	Bone		150
R4723	Bone	3⅜	80

R4833	Bone		95
R4835	Pyremite		95

RS4773 Scout Knife, Brown Bone 3⅜" **$175**

R4843 Imitation Bone 3¼" **$90**

RS4783 Scout Knife, Brown Bone, With Emblem 3½" **$175**

R4813	Bone		125
R4815	Pyremite		115
R4823	Bone		100
R4825	Pyremite		100

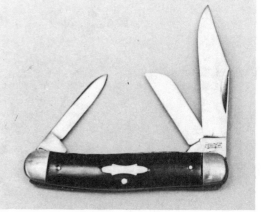

STOCKMAN

R4845	**Straightline, Slick Black**	**3⅜"**	**$90**
R4853	Bone		100
R4855	Pyremite		95
R4863	Bone		95
R4565	Pyremite		90
R6014	Pearl	3⅜	235
R6015	Pyremite	3⅜	150
R6023	Bone		235
R6024	Pearl		300
R6025	Pyremite		170

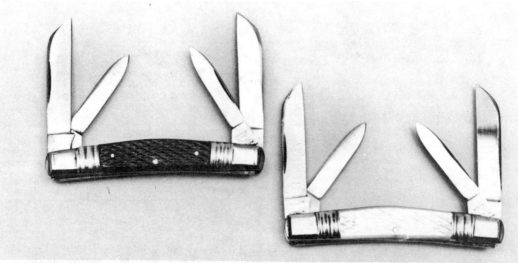

CONGRESS: Left: R6032, Black Comp. Scale, Extended Grooved Bolsters, 3½", $350; Right: R6034, Pearl, Extended Grooved Bolsters, 3⅜", $450.

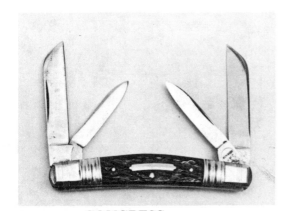

CONGRESS

R6033 Brown Bone, Extended Grooved Bolsters 3½" **$250**

Nr.	Handle	Lgth.	Mint
R6083	Bone	3⅝	275
R6093	Bone		140
R6103	Bone	3	140

CONGRESS

R6104	**Pearl**	**3⅛"**	**$150**
R6105	Pyremite	3	125
R6113	Bone		260

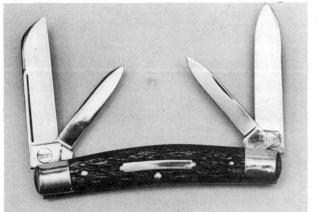

CONGRESS

R6043 Brown Bone 4⅛" **$600**
R6053 Bone 4⅛ 385

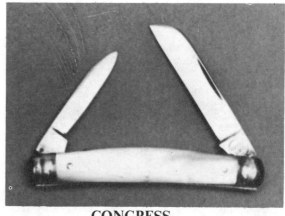

CONGRESS

R6123 Brown Bone, Grooved Bolsters 3½" **$200**

CONGRESS

R6063 Brown Bone 4¼" **$225**

WHITTLER

R6133 Remington, Brown Bone, Threaded Bolsters

3½" **$275**

R6143	Bone	3½	150
R6145	Pyremite	3½	115
R6153	Bone		150
R6155	Pyremite		115

R6073 Brown Bone, Long Pull 3¾" **$275**

CONGRESS

R6163 Bone   4" $150

Nr.	Handle	Lgth.	Mint
R6175	Pyremite	3¾	125
R6182	Black	3¼	75
R6183	Bone	3¼	100
R6184	Pearl	3¼	150
R6185	Pyremite	3¼	100
R6192	Black	3⅜	100
R6193	Bone	3⅜	130

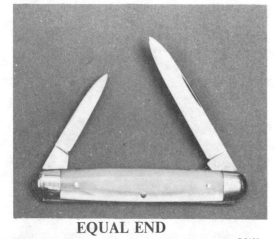

EQUAL END

R6194 Pearl   3⅜" $175

EQUAL END

R6195 Brown Mottled   3¼" $110

6203   Remington, Bone, File Blade   3¼" $110

Nr.	Handle	Lgth.	Mint
R6204	Pearl		150
R6205	Pyremite		75
R6213	Bone	3¼	115
R6214	Pearl	3¼	200
R6215	Pyremite	3¼	90
R6223	Bone	3¼	185
R6224	Pearl		225

WHITTLER

R6225 Remington, Green Swirl Pyremite,
**   Long Pull & Reg. Pull   3¼" $225**

Nr.	Handle	Lgth.	Mint
R6233	Bone	3¼	160
R6234	Pearl	3¼	190
R6235	Pyremite	3¼	100
R6243	Bone		100
R6244	Pearl	3⅛	100
R6245	Pyremite		80
R6249	Metal		75
R6255	Pyremite		70
R6259	Metal		70
R6265	Pyremite		150
R6275	Pyremite		335
R6285	Pyremite		335
R6295	Pyremite		330
R6303	Bone		150
R6313	Bone		225
R6323	Bone		240
R6325	Pyremite		200
R6330	Buffalo Horn		175
R6333	Bone		175
R6334	Pearl		215
R6335	Pyremite		175
R6340	Buffalo Horn	3½	175

Nr.	Handle	Lgth.	Mint
R6343	Bone	3½	250
R6344	Pearl	3½	340
R6345	Pyremite	3½	200
R6350	Buffalo Horn		200
R6353	Bone		250
R6355G	Pyremite		250
R6362	Black	3½	100
R6363	Bone	3½	125
R6365	Pyremite	3	100
R6390	Buffalo Horn	3⅜	140

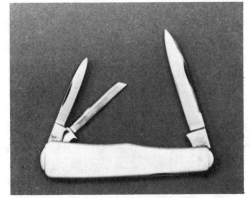

GUNSTOCK WHITTLER

R6454	Pearl	3"	$300

WHITTLER

R6393	**Brown Bone, Blood Groove**	**3⅜"**	**$500**
R6394	Pearl	3⅜	550
R6395	Pyremite	3⅜	500
R6400	Buffalo Horn		130
R6403	Bone		130
R6404	Pearl		200
R6405	Pyremite		175
R6423	Bone		80

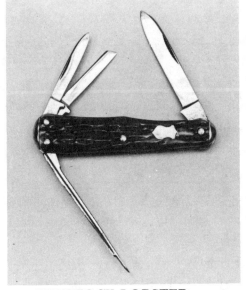

GUNSTOCK LOBSTER

R6456	**Genuine Stag, Shows Grooved File**	**3"**	**$275**
R6463	Bone	3	75
R6464	Pearl	3	100

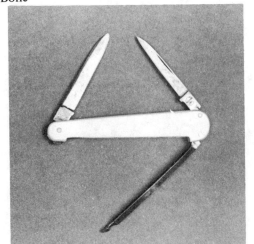

SLEEVEBOARD/LOBSTER

R6424	**Remington, Pearl**	**2¾"**	**$110**
R6429	Metal		65
R6433	Bone		100
R6434	Lobster, Pearl	2¾	115
R6439	Metal		75
R6443	Bone	2¹¹⁄₁₆	75
R6444	Pearl		125
R6445	Pyremite		75
R6448	Cocobolo		50

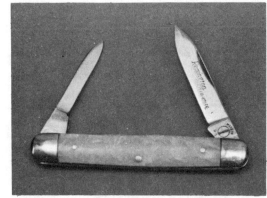

R6465	**Onyx**	**3"**	**$90**

Nr.	Handle	Lgth.	Mint
R6473	Bone		100
R6474	Pearl		125
R6483	Bone	3	100
R6484	Pearl	3	125
R6494	Pearl	3	100
R6495	Pyremite	3	60

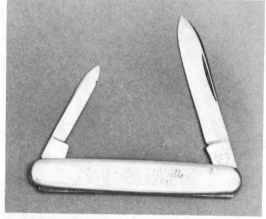

R6499 Remington, All Metal   3"   **$60**

SWELL CENTER

R6563 Remington, Brown Bone, Long Pull   3⅝"   **$125**

Nr.	Handle	Lgth.	Mint
R6565	Pyremite		100

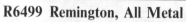

R6504 File, Pearl, Tip Bolsters, With Bail   3"   **$125**

Nr.	Handle	Lgth.	Mint
R6505	Pyremite		70
R6513	Bone	3⅛	75
R6514	Lobster, Pearl	3⅛	125
R6519	Metal		100
R6520	Buffalo Horn	3	150
R6523	Bone	3	150
R6524	Pearl	3	215
R6534	Pearl		175

SLEEVEBOARD

R6573 Brown Bone, Tip Bolsters   3½"   **$125**

R6575	Pyremite		100

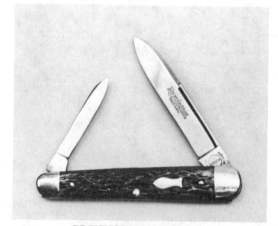

SLEEVEBOARD

R6583 Bone   3½"   **$150**

WHITTLER

R6533 Remington, Brown Bone   3"   **$175**

Nr.	Handle	Lgth.	Mint	Nr.	Handle	Lgth.	Mint
R6535	Pyremite		125	R6585	Pyremite	3½	125
R6543	Bone		200	R6593	Bone		135
R6545	Pyremite		150	R6595	Pyremite		100
R6554	Pearl	3	100	R6603	Bone		115
R6559	Metal		80				

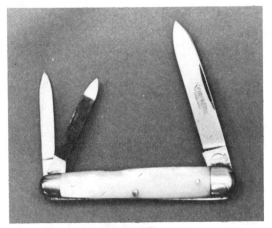

WHITTLER

R6604 Pearl   3½" $250

Nr.	Handle	Lgth.	Mint
R6605	Pyremite		200
R6613	Bone		140
R6615	Pyremite		130
R6623	Bone	3⅛	100
R6624	Pearl		150

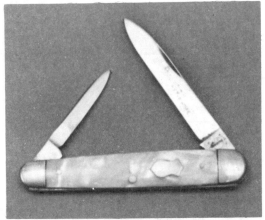

SLEEVEBOARD

R6625 Cracked Ice   3⅛" $90

R6633	Bone		100
R6634	Pearl		100
R6635	Pyremite		100
R6643	Bone	3⅛	115

SLEEVEBOARD

R6644 Pearl   3⅛" $150

SLEEVEBOARD

R6645 Cracked Ice, Tip Bolsters   3⅛" $100

WHITTLER

R6653 Brown Bone   3⅛" $150

Nr.	Handle	Lgth.	Mint
R6654	Pearl	3⅛	180
R6655	Pyremite	3⅛	125
R6663	Bone		140
R6664	Pearl		185
R6673	Bone		175
R6674	Pearl		230
R6683	Bone		175

CONGRESS

R6693 Remington, Brown Bone   3⅛" $200

R6694	Pearl		225
R6695	Pyremite		175
R6703	Bone	3	150
R6704	Pearl	3	160
R6705Q	Pyremite	3	125

EQUAL END
R6713 Remington, Brown Bone   **3"** **$150**

Nr.	Handle	Lgth.	Mint
R6714	Pearl	3	175

WHITTLER
R6723 Remington, Brown Bone, Long Pull **3⅛"** **$200**

Nr.	Handle	Lgth.	Mint
R6724	Pearl		300
R6725	Pyremite		200
R6733	Bone	3¼	125
R6735	Pyremite	3¼	75
R6744	Pearl		100
R6745F	Pyremite		75
R6754	Pearl		200
R6755A	Pyremite		140
R6763	Bone		175
R6764	Pearl		275
R6765A	Pyremite		150
R6773	Bone		235
R6775	Pyremite		175
R6781	Redwood		100
R6785	Imi. Ivory Office Knife		125

R6787 Ivory   **3¼"** **$150**

Nr.	Handle	Lgth.	Mint
R6793	Bone		125
R6795	Pyremite		100
R6803	Bone		150
R6805	Pyremite		150
R6816	Gen. Stag		1100

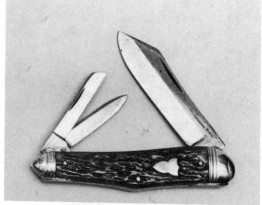

HUMPBACK WHITTLER
Nr.	Handle	Lgth.	Mint
R6823	**Grooved Bolsters**	**3⅝"**	**$900**
R6825	Pyremite		650
R6834	Pearl		475
R6835	Pyremite	3⅛	450

HUMPBACK WHITTLER
R6836 Remington, Stag, Grooved Bolsters **3⅛"** **$450**

Nr.	Handle	Lgth.	Mint
R6843	Bone	3¾	75
R6844	Pearl		85
R6845	Pyremite		50
R6854	Pearl	2⅞	85
R6859	Metal	2⅞	50
R6863	Bone	2⅝	50
R6864	Pearl	2⅝	75
R6865	Pyremite	2⅝	50
R6872	Black	3	60
R6873	Bone	3	75
R6874	Pearl	3	100
R6875	Pyremite	3	75
R6883	Bone	3	150
R6885	Pyremite	3	125
R6893	Bone	3⅛	200
R6894	Pearl	3⅛	275
R6895	Pyremite	3⅛	150
R6903	Bone	2½	50

REMINGTON

R6904 Pen, Pearl, With Bail   2½" **$75**

R6905 Pen, Onyx   2½" **$60**

R6914	Pearl	60
R6919	Metal	50
R6923	Bone	115
R6924	Pearl	175

CONGRESS

R6925 Imitation Ivory, Threaded Bolsters   3" $125

R6933	Bone	175
R6934	Pearl	225
R6949	Metal	50
R6954	Pearl	325
R6956	Gen. Stag	325
R6964	Pearl	325
R6973	Bone	185
R6974	Pearl	375

R6984 Pearl, Worked Backspring   3¼" **$700**

Nr.	Handle	Lgth.	Mint
R6993	Bone		175
R6994	Pearl		250
R6995	Pyremite Sway Back Congress		225
R7003	Bone		250
R7004	Pearl		285
R7005	Pyremite		200
R7023	Bone		150
R7024	Pearl		200
R7026	Gen. Stag		175
R7034	Pearl		75
R7045	Pyremite		70
R7039/5	Metal		75
R7039/6	Metal		75
R7039/7	Metal		75
R7039/8	Metal		75
R7044	Pearl		100
RG7049/21	Metal		75
RG7049/22	Metal		75
RG7049/23	Metal		75
RG7049/24	Metal		75
RG7054	Pearl		75
RG7059/17	Metal		75
RG7059/18	Metal		75
RG7059/19	Metal		75
RG7059/20	Metal		75
RG7064	Pearl		75
R7069/25	Metal		75
R7069/26	Metal		75
R7069/27	Metal		75
R7069/	Metal		75
R7073	Whittler		400
R7074	Pearl		75
RG7079/10	Metal		75
RG7079/11	Metal		75
RG7079/12	Metal		75
RG7079/35	Metal		75
RG7079/36	Metal		75
RG7079/37	Metal		75
RG7084	Pearl		170
RG7089/13	Metal		75
RG7089/14	Metal		75
RG7089/15	Metal		75
RG7089/16	Metal		75
RG7089/32	Metal		75
RG7089/33	Metal		75
RG7089/34	Metal		75
R7090	Buffalo Horn		100
R7091	Redwood		100
R7094	Lobster, Pearl		100
RG7099/1	Metal		100
RG7099/2	Metal		100
RG7099/3	Metal		100
RG7099/4	Metal		100
RG7099/29	Metal		100
RG7099/30	Metal		100
RG7099/31	Metal		100
RT7099	Metal		100
R7103	Bone		70
R7104	Pearl		100
R7114	Pearl		115

Nr.	Handle	Lgth.	Mint
R7116	Gen. Stag		75
R7120	Buffalo Horn		75

Nr.	Handle	Lgth.	Mint
R7233	Bone	3	75
R7234	Pearl		85
R7236	Gen. Stag		75
R7243	Bone		200

SLEEVEBOARD

Nr.	Handle	Lgth.	Mint
R7124	**Circle UMC, Pearl, Long Pull**	**3¼"**	**$250**
R7126	Gen. Stag		200
R7134	Pearl		150
R7144	Pearl		250
R7146	Gen. Stag		200
R7153	Bone		150
R7163	Bone		135
R7176	Gen. Stag		175
R7183	Bone		250
R7196	Gen. Stag		230
R7203	Bone		270

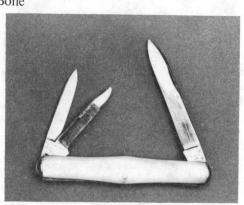

SWELL CENTER WHITTLER

Nr.	Handle	Lgth.	Mint
R7244	**Genuine Pearl**	**3"**	**$225**
R7246	Gen. Stag		250
R7254	Pearl		75
R7264	Pearl		75
R7274	Pearl		75

SWELL CENTER

Nr.	Handle	Lgth.	Mint
R7216	**Genuine Stag, Tip Bolsters**	**3½"**	**$275**
R7223	Bone	3	100
R7224	Pearl		115

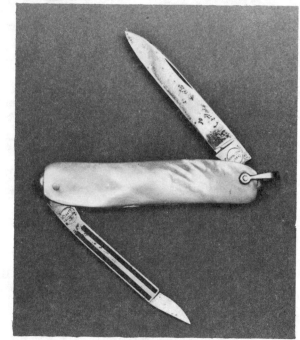

LOBSTER

Nr.	Handle	Lgth.	Mint
R7284	**Pearl, With Bail**	**3"**	**$80**

SWELL CENTER

Nr.	Handle	Lgth.	Mint
R7225	**Green Swirl Pyremite, Long Pull**	**3"**	**$110**

WHITTLER

Nr.	Handle	Lgth.	Mint
R7293	**Brown Bone, Long Pull, Grooved**		
	Sabre Blade	**3⅜"**	**$400**

Nr.	Handle	Lgth.	Mint
R7309	Metal		90
R7319	Metal		75
R7324	Pearl		100
R7329	Metal		50
R7335	Pyremite		60
R7339	Metal	3	60

CORKSCREW

R7343	**Brown Bone**	3⅛"	**$125**
R7344	Pearl		100
R7353	Bone		100
R7363	Bone	2⅝	100

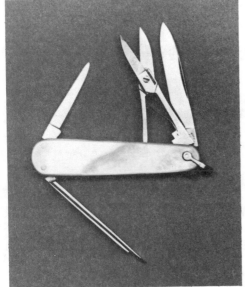

SLEEVEBOARD/LOBSTER

R7364	**Pearl, With Bail, Scissors & File**	2⅝"	**$150**
R7366	Gen. Stag		150
R7374	Pearl		100
R7375	Pyremite		100
R7384	Pearl		100
R7394	Lobster, Pearl	2⅝	100
R7396	Gen. Stag		100
R7403	Bone		85
R7404	Pearl		115
R7414	Pearl		115

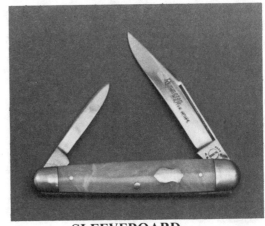

SLEEVEBOARD

R7425	**Onyx**	3⅛"	**$95**

Nr.	Handle	Lgth.	Mint
R7433	Bone		150
R7443	Bone		110
R7453	Bone		110
R7463	Bone		110
R7465	Pyremite		100
R7473	Bone		110
R7475	Pyremite		100
R7483	Bone		200
R7485	Pyremite		200
R7493	Bone		300
R7495	Pyremite		275

WHITTLER

R7500	**Horn**	3⅜"	**$225**
R7503	Bone		235
R7513	Bone		235
R7526	Gen. Stag		150
R7536	Gen. Stag		150
R7543	Bone		100
R7544	Pearl		125
R7546	Gen. Stag		125
R7554	Pearl		100
R7564	Pearl		100
R7566	Gen. Stag		100
R7573	Bone		75

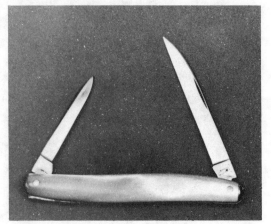

R7574 Wharncliffe, Pearl, Tip Bolsters 3¼" **$150**

Nr.	Handle	Lgth.	Mint
R7576	Gen. Stag		125
R7584	Pearl		200
R7586	Gen. Stag		150
R7593	Bone	3¼	115
R7594	Pearl		175
R7596	Gen. Stag		140

SERPENTINE

R7603 Bone, Tip Bolsters 3¼" **$175**

R7604	Pearl		175
R7606	Gen. Stag		175
R7613	Bone		75
R7614	Pearl		75
R7623	Bone		75
R7624	Pearl		100
R7633	Bone	3⅛	150
R7643	Bone		90
R7645	Pyremite		75
R7653	Bone		175
R7654	Pearl		200
R7663	Bone		175
R7664	Bone		250
R7674	Pearl		75
R7683	Bone		65
R7684	Pearl		100

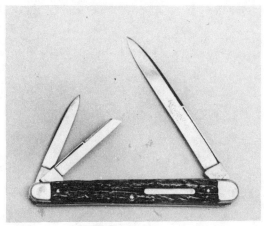

WHITTLER

R7696 Stag, Flat Bolsters 3⅝" **$250**
R7706 Gen. Stag 150

R7713 Bone, With Bail 2½" **$65**

R7725	Pyremite		75
R7734	Pearl		75
R7744	Pearl		75
R7756	Gen. Stag		750

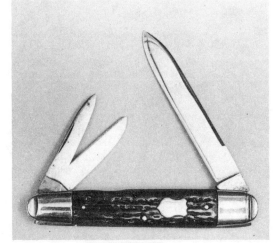

WHITTLER

R7766 Remington, Genuine Stag, Pinched Bolsters 4½" **$1000**

R7772	Black		50
R7773	Bone	3⅛	65
R7775	Pyremite		65
R7783	Bone		100
R7785	Pyremite		125

Nr.	Handle	Lgth.	Mint
R7793	Bone		75
R7795	Pyremite		75
R7803	Bone		125
R7805	Pyremite		150
R7813	Bone		75
R7814	Pearl		115
R7823	Bone		100
R7825	Pyremite		100

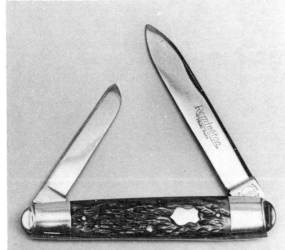

R7833 Brown Bone, Pinched Bolsters   4½"   **$550**

R7853	Bone	3	100

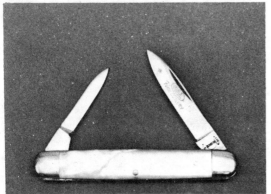

EQUAL END

R7854 Pearl, Blade Etched "Pal Fine Cutlery"   3"   **$150**

RC7853	Bone	3	75
R7857	Ivory		75
R7863	Bone		75
R7873	Bone		75
R7895	Pyremite		50
R7925	Pyremite	2¹³⁄₁₆	40
R7985	Pyremite		100
R7993	Bone	3⅜	50
R7995	Pyremite	3⅜	120
R8003	Bone	3	60
R8004	Pearl		75
R8013	Bone		50
R8023	Bone	3⅜	175

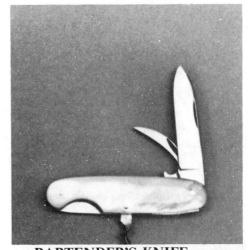

BARTENDER'S KNIFE

R8034 Pearl   2⅞"   **$225**

R8044 File & Scissors   2¾"   **$225**

R8055	Pyremite		100
R8059	Metal	3	65

R8063 Switchblade, Bone   3¼"   **$350**

R8065 Double Switchblade, Pyremite   3½"   **$350**

R8069	Metal		125
R9003SS	Bone		150

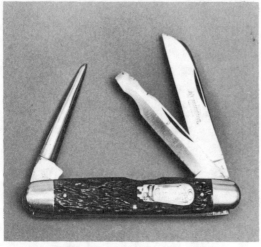

Cunningham Radio Tube, Rem-mington, Brown Bone, Reg. Pull, Radio Tube Shield, Electrician's Blade & Punch $500

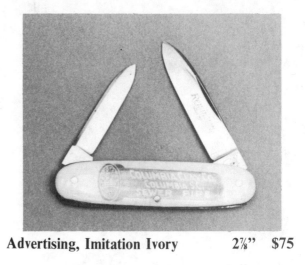

Advertising, Imitation Ivory   2⅞" $75

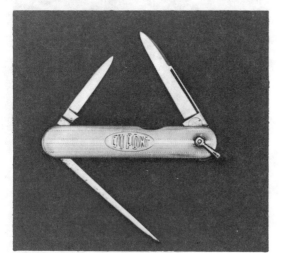

LOBSTER
Advertising Display Knife
Gold Scale, With Bail   2¾" $110

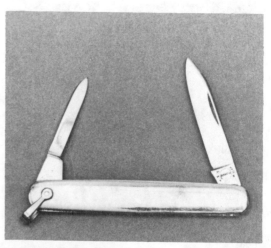

Advertising, Imitation Ivory   2⅞" $85

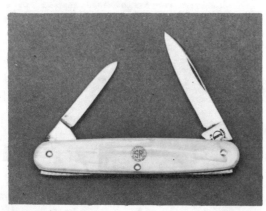

Pen, Imitation Pearl, (Southern Railroad Emblem)   3¼" $85

All Metal, With Bail   3" $50

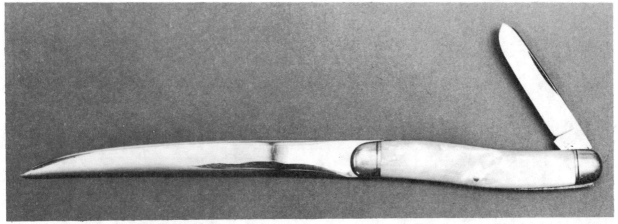

Letter Opener, Pearl, 4" Knife Handle   9" $325

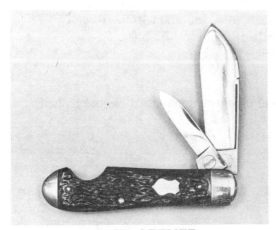

EASY OPENER
Remington Bone, Long Pull   3⅝" $140

STOCKMAN
Remington, Imitation Tortoise,
Long Pull   4" $275

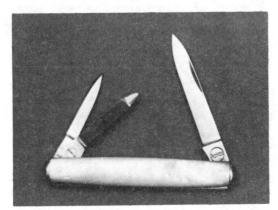

WHITTLER

Pearl   3" $200

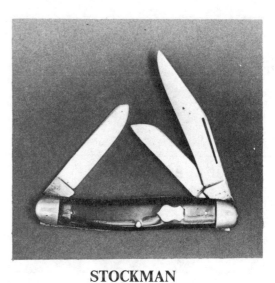

STOCKMAN
Remington, Slick Black   4" $175

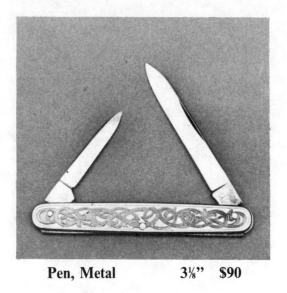

Pen, Metal   3⅛" $90

EASY OPENER
Remington, Imitation Bone, Round
Endicott Johnson Emblem, Screw
Driver/Cap Lifter   3½" $110

The remaining Remington photos arrived too late to include them in the normal numerical sequence; hence, this small special appendix to the Remington section.

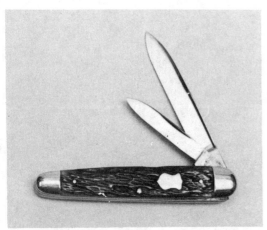

JACK
RH73, 2 bl., Br. Bone   3⅛" $110

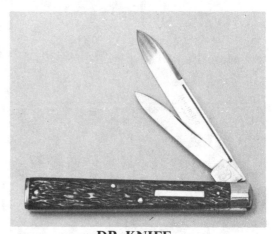

DR. KNIFE
Br. bone, 2 blade   3½" $350

EQUAL END
R333   Brown Bone   3¾" $175

BOWTIE
R653, Bone   3⅞" $250

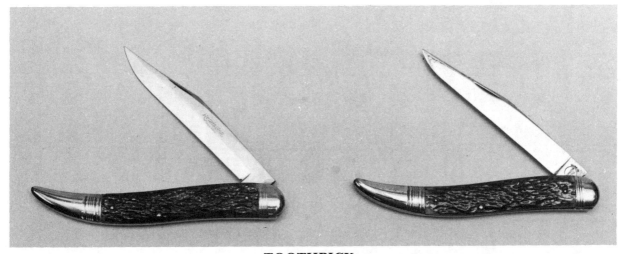

TOOTHPICK

R953   **Brown Bone, Grooved Bolster,**   R953   **Brown Bone, Grooved Bolster,**
        Saber Blade   5" $300   **Flat Blade, No Shield**   5" $250

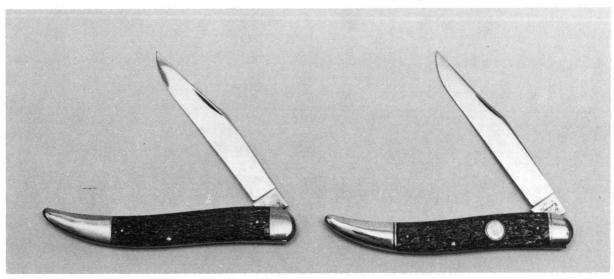

R953   **Brown Bone**   5" $225   R953   **Remington UMC, Brown Bone,**
                                                      Round Bullet Shield   5" $700

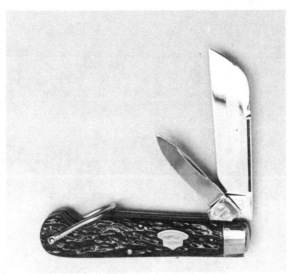

SCOUT/EASY OPENER
R963   **Imitation Bone, Spear Blade**   4¼" $350

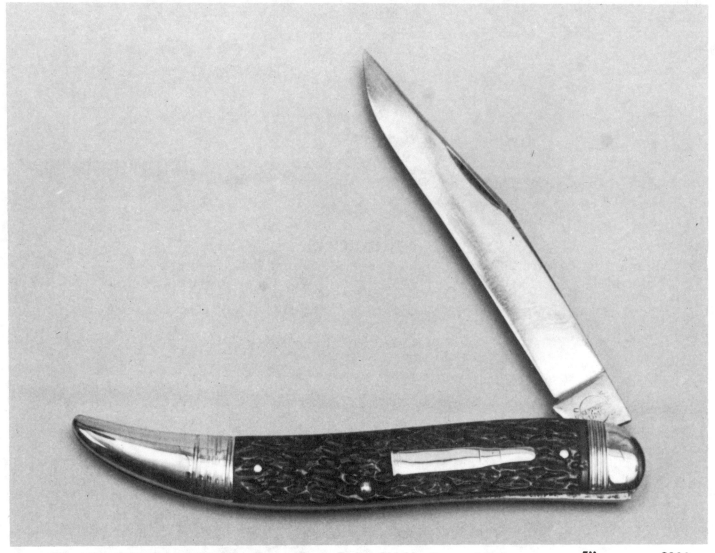

R1613BL TOOTHPICK BULLET   Brown Bone, Bullet Shield, Grooved Bolsters   5" $900

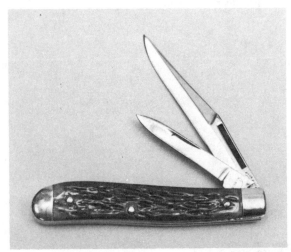

PEANUT

R1653 Brown Bone   2⅞" $125

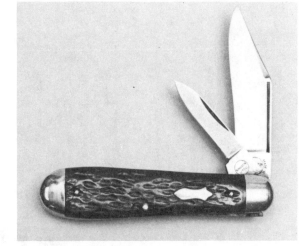

JACK TEARDROP

R1783 Brown Bone   3½" $125

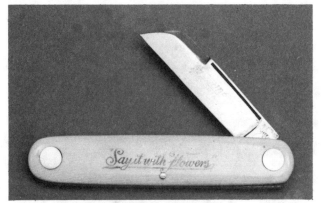

R1957 Florist Knife, Imitation Ivory   4¼" $85

**R2403 1 blade, Br. Bone, Straight-Line
(stamp)**   5" $500
**R2303 Br. Bone, Straight-Line (stamp),
1 blade**   4⅛" $600

R3443, 2 blade, Br. Bone   3¼" $110

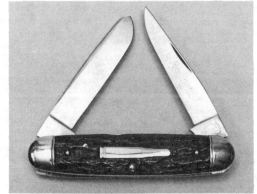

BABY MUSKRAT
R4466 Stag, Shield   3¾" $2,000

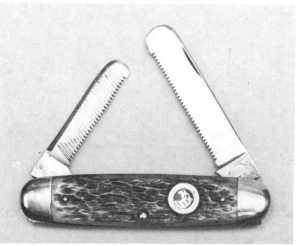

DOG GROOMING
**R4733, Br. Bone, Airdale Doghead
Shield**   3¾" $225

R6013 Br. Bone, Fluted Bolsters   3⅜" $325

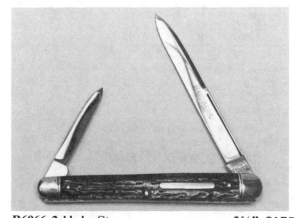

R6966 2 blade, Stag   3¾" $175

**R7423, 2 blade, Blade Etched Pal
Fine Cutlery**   3⅛" $100

R8623 Brown Bone   3⅛" $85

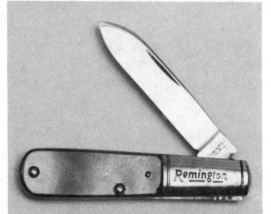

BARLOW
1 blade, Black Bone, Straighted lined,
no number   3⅜" $175

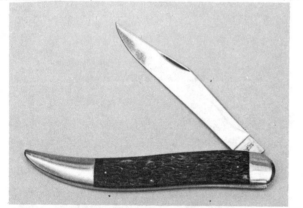

1 blade, Straight lined, no number, Imi.
Bone $150

2 blade, Imi. B., Bone, Hanover Shoe
Emblem   3½" $125

EASY OPENER
Brown Bone, Chain   3½" $175

R233   Remington 7.65MM Cartridge Case
        Custom Made, Price Varies

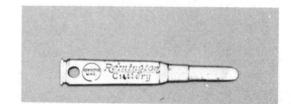

R234   Remington Knife Opener $20

R4273	Sowbelly 3 Bl.	3¾" Brown Bone	$500
R4274	Sowbelly 3 Bl.	3¾ Gen. Pearl	600

Additional Remington knives discovered and made available for this second edition.

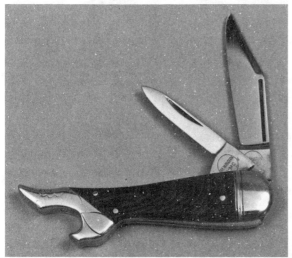

R15 3¼", 2 Bl. small leg, Grey Swirl Pyremite,3¼", Remington Circle UMC $225

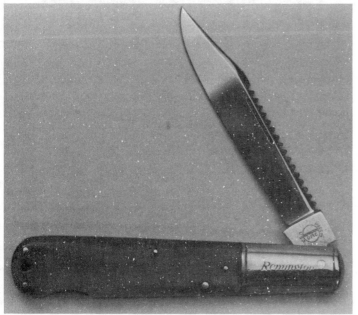

R1630 Fish Scaler Daddy Barlow, Brown Bone, 5", Lock Back, Remington Cir., UMC, Rare $400

R23CH Imi. Black Bone 3⅜" Remington, UMC $110 2 Bl. with Chain

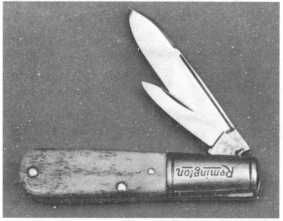

RB43 2 Bl. Barlow, LP 3⅜" Remington Circle UMC $125

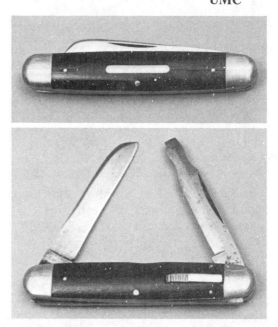

R4548 Remington Circle, U.M.C., 3¾" 2 Blade, Electrician Knife with Lock-Blade, Release in handle Rare, Coco Bolo Wood $275

R1073 Brown Bone, 3⅜" Remington Circle, UMC, 2 Bl. Jack $125

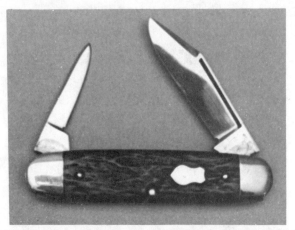

R4473 Brown Bone 2 Bl. LP 3¼" Remington, Straight Bolsters
$125

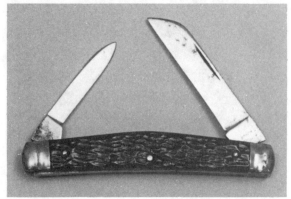

R6143   Brown Bone, 2 Bl   3½" Remington Circle $125
Congress, UMC

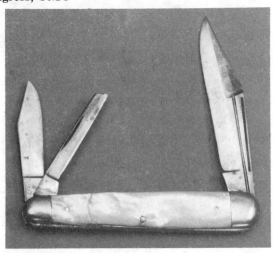

R6394 Pearl Whittler, Blood Groove, 3½", Rare, Remington,
Circle, UMC $700

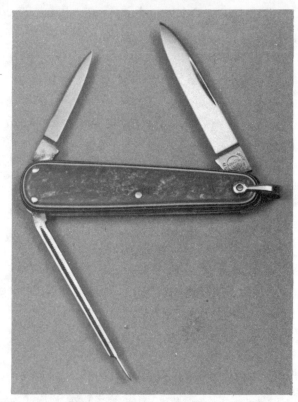

R7385   2 Bl. File, Lobster Green Pyremite, Bail   2⅝"
Remington Circle UMC $85

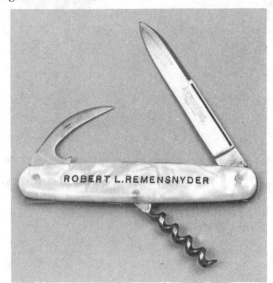

R7995   Pyremite, Bartender, 3⅜", 3 Bl. Remington Circle UMC
$120

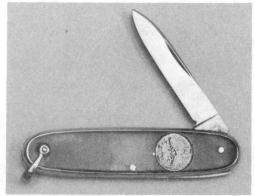

1 Bl. Black Comp. Scales with Cloisonne Emblem Adv. Vacuum
Oil Co., New York (Gorgoyle), 2⅞", Remington, UMC $75

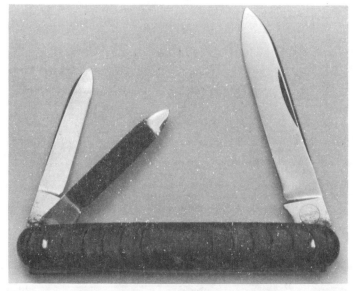

No Number, 3 Blade, Black Comp. Scalloped Handles, Whittler, 3¼", Rem. Circle, Rare Handle $225

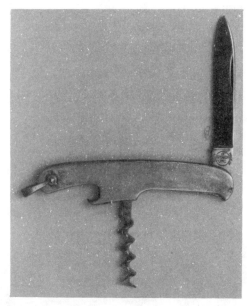

Blade & Corkscrew, Bottle Opener, All metal, Bail, Stainless, No Number, 3⅛", Remington, Circle UMC $75

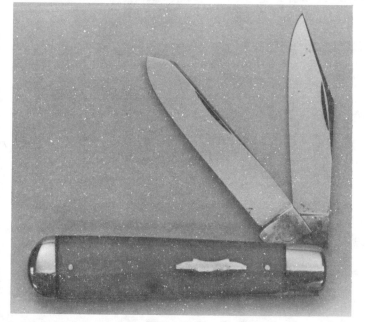

2 Blade Jack, Long Spay Blade, Yellow Scales w/sh. No number, 3⅜", Remington, Circle, UMC $150

ABBREVIATIONS	
½	master blade is clip blade
B	Budding
EO	Easy Opener
F	File
J	Long Spay Blade
K	Corkscrew
LR	Electrician's Knife
M	Metal
PEN	Pen Blade
PU	Punch Blade
R	Bail in handle
RAZ	Razor Blade
SAB	Sabor Blade
SC/SCI	Scissors
SH	Sheepfoot Blade
SP	Spay Blade
SSP	Stainless Steel, Polished Blade Edge
SS	Stainless Steel
T	Tip Bolsters

Remington Totum Pole Mastadon Ivory scales handles   Rare$700

R A1 - $70

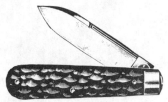

R 3 - $80

R03 - $70

R105-B - $120

R02 - $70

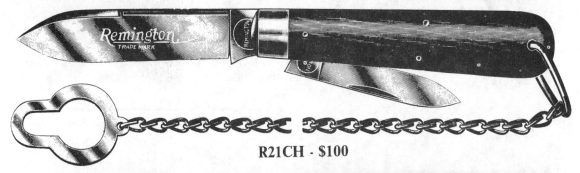

R21CH - $100

R23 - $100

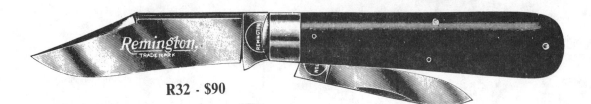

R32 - $90

RLO 24 - $80

RLO 35 - $75

RLO 70 - $125

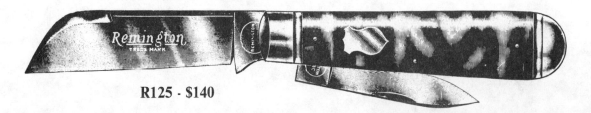

R125 - $140

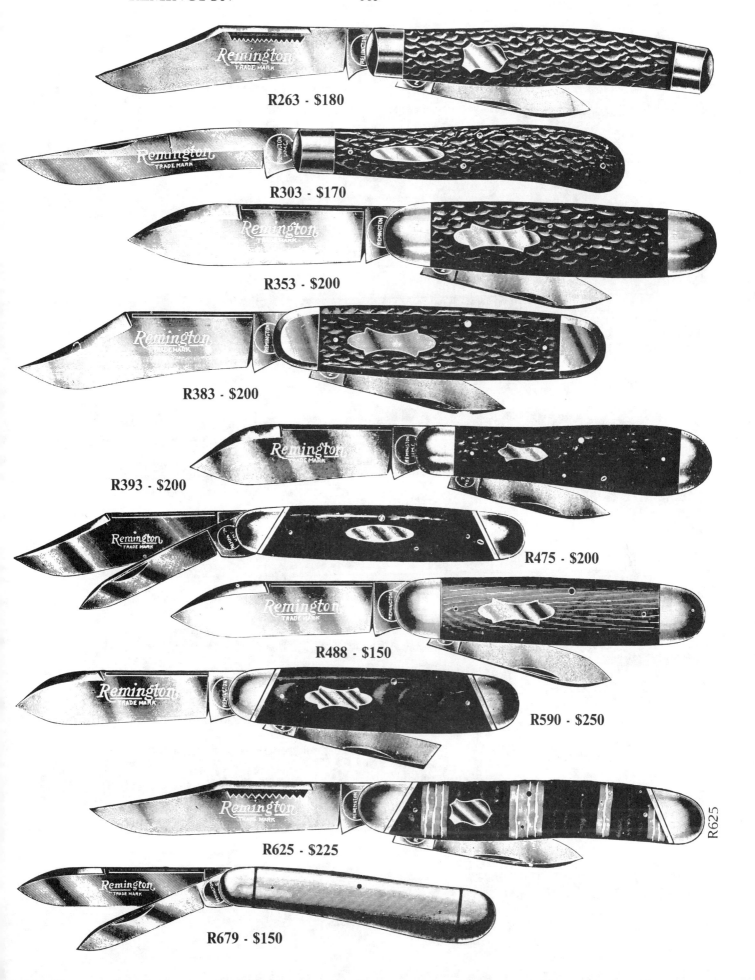

R263 - $180

R303 - $170

R353 - $200

R383 - $200

R393 - $200

R475 - $200

R488 - $150

R590 - $250

R625 - $225

R679 - $150

R625

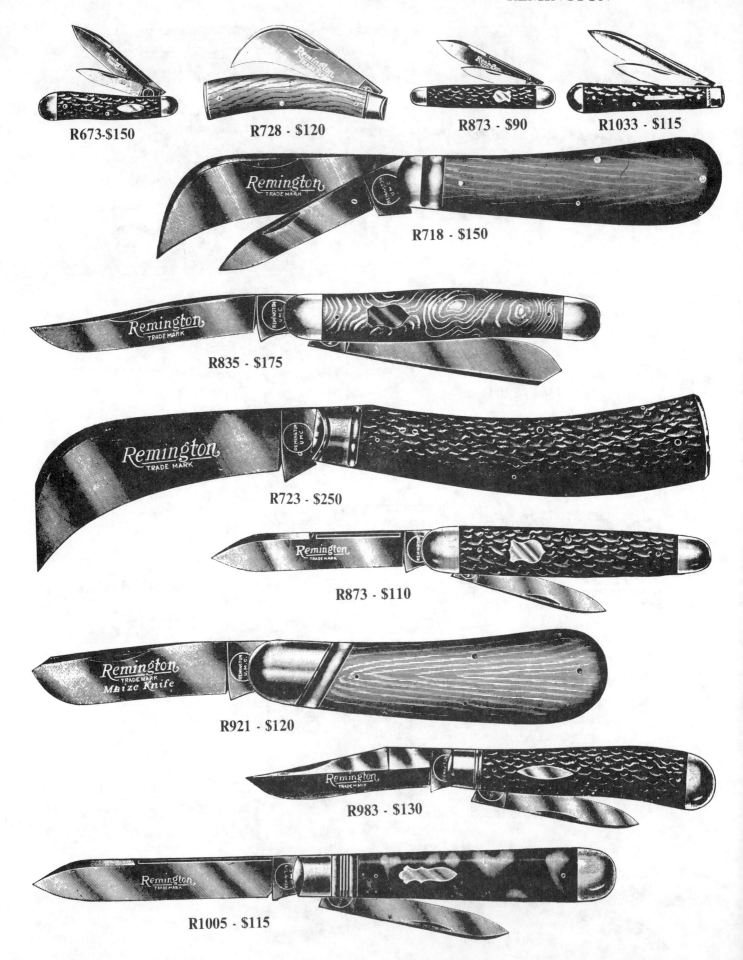

R673-$150

R728 - $120

R873 - $90

R1033 - $115

R718 - $150

R835 - $175

R723 - $250

R873 - $110

R921 - $120

R983 - $130

R1005 - $115

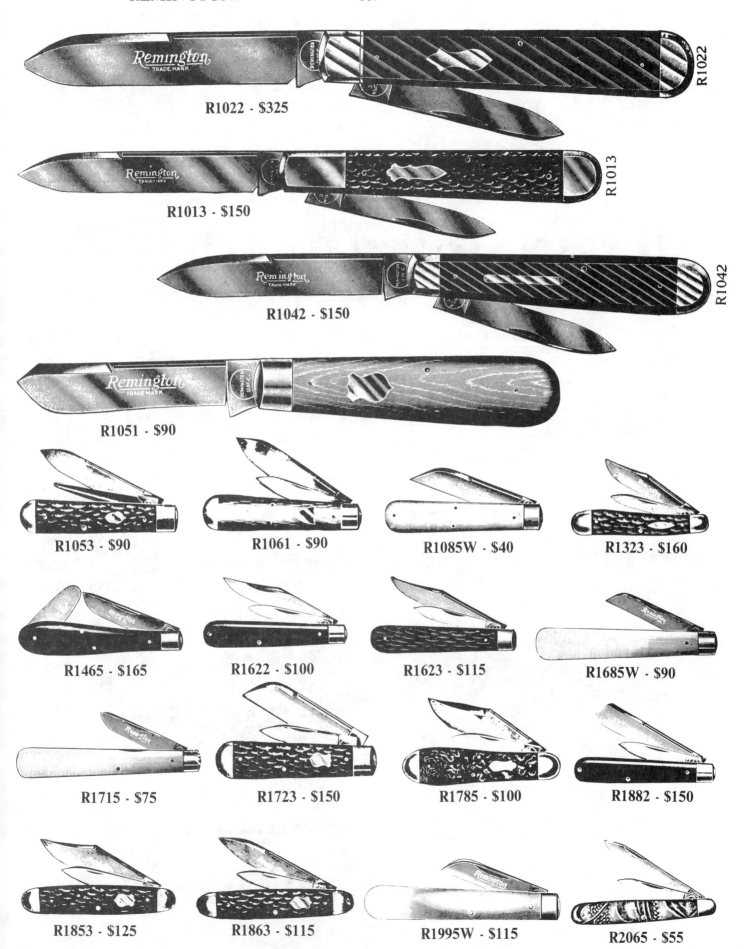

R1022

R1022 - $325

R1013

R1013 - $150

R1042

R1042 - $150

R1051 - $90

R1053 - $90

R1061 - $90

R1085W - $40

R1323 - $160

R1465 - $165

R1622 - $100

R1623 - $115

R1685W - $90

R1715 - $75

R1723 - $150

R1785 - $100

R1882 - $150

R1853 - $125

R1863 - $115

R1995W - $115

R2065 - $55

R2075 - $55

R2103 - $70

R2105 - $60

R3056 - $350

R3123 - $250

R3163 - $285

R3185 - $260

R33373 - $150

R3535 - $150

R3873 - $240

R3903 - $225

R3973 - $215

R3975 - $175

R3993 - $200

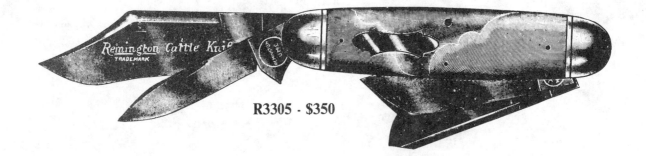

R3305 - $350

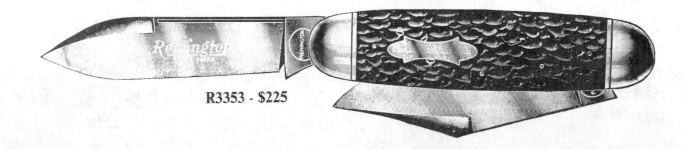

R3353 - $225

R3395 - $185

R3520 - $225

R4033 - $240

R4143 - $135

R6083 - $275

R4005 - $125

R4103 - $150

R4143 - $135

R4223 - $240

R4483 - $285

R4505 - $215

R4563 - $330

R4633 - $100

R4635 - $115

R4643 - $145

R4685 - $140

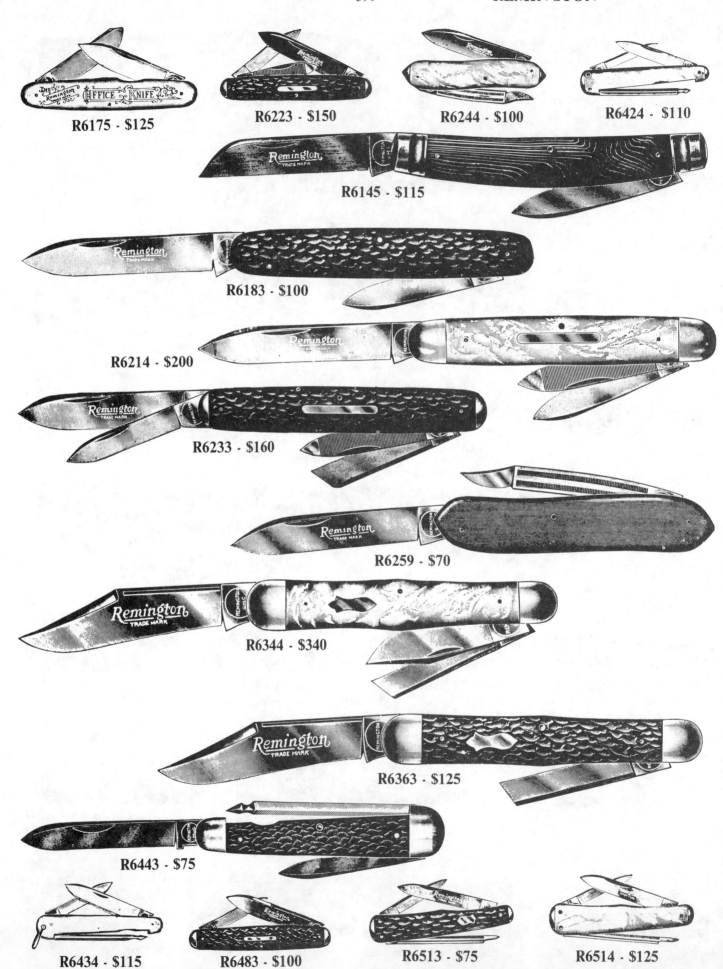

R6175 - $125

R6223 - $150

R6244 - $100

R6424 - $110

R6145 - $115

R6183 - $100

R6214 - $200

R6233 - $160

R6259 - $70

R6344 - $340

R6363 - $125

R6443 - $75

R6434 - $115

R6483 - $100

R6513 - $75

R6514 - $125

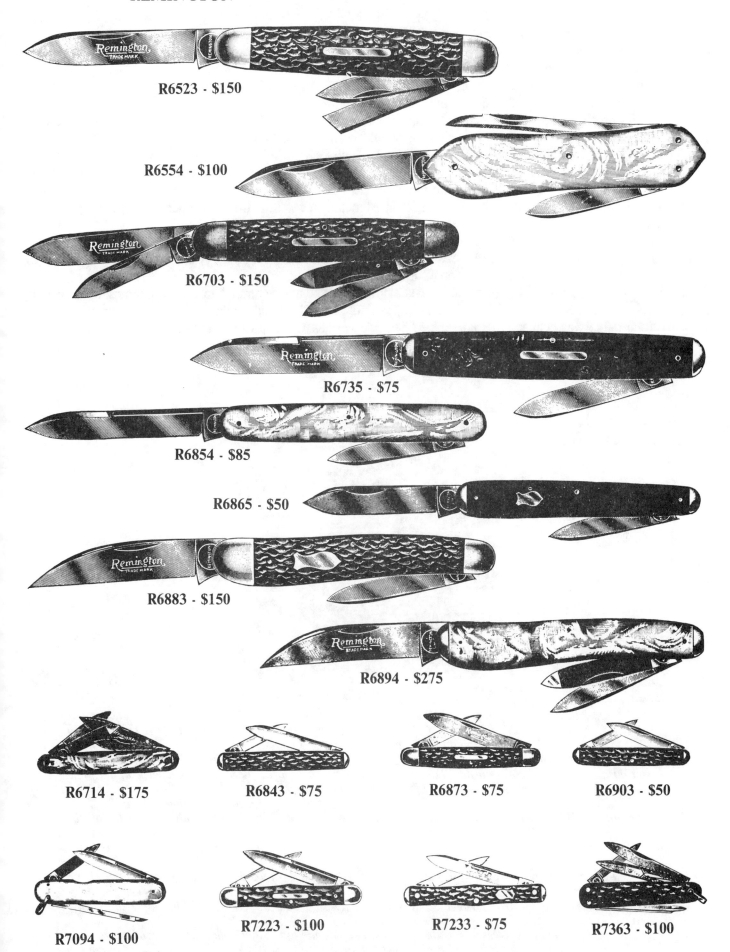

R6523 - $150

R6554 - $100

R6703 - $150

R6735 - $75

R6854 - $85

R6865 - $50

R6883 - $150

R6894 - $275

R6714 - $175

R6843 - $75

R6873 - $75

R6903 - $50

R7094 - $100

R7223 - $100

R7233 - $75

R7363 - $100

SCHRADE-WALDEN

In 1892, George and William Schrade came to Walden, New York. George had perfected the Push Button Knife and had secured his first patent. With the knife and the patent in hand, he approached the Walden Knife Company who agreed to establish a Press Button Knife Dept. in their plant.

As George became more skilled in knife manufacturing, he began planning his own plant which would eliminate the duplication of parts and install a fine quality control system.

In 1903, his brother Louis returned from Europe and the decision was made to start their own factory. The Push Button Knife with a new innovation, a safety lock, would be their first knife.

The Schrade Cutlery Company was incorporated in 1904 with George, William and Louis taking part in the management. Their plans were to produce a line of pocket knives with interchangeable components. To do this, much new equipment was designed which eliminated many hand operations. A system of dies, jigs and gauges were installed in order to maintain a high standard of quality. This insistence of high standards continued through the years with new improvements.

In 1910, George left the company and Louis bought his interest. In 1918, Middletown encouraged the Schrade Cutlery Company to purchase a vacant factory and establish a branch factory. Another brother, Joseph, was brought in to run this branch until the depression forced its closing in 1932.

The company continued under the same management until 1946 and Schrade Cutlery Company sold controlling interest to the Imperial Knife Associated Companies, owners of the Imperial Knife Company and the Ulster Knife Company. The name was changed at that time to Schrade-Walden Cutlery Corporation.

HERMAN WILLIAMS

The story of Herman's unusual collection started around 1978, when he visited his first knife show. It was love at first sight, but the exorbitant prices gave him cause to pause.

"I stood there admiring those beautiful knives, knowing many were not in reach. Then I thought, if they can do it, so can I." Upon returning home he began doing customized file work and repairs on old junk knives, taking several of the same patterns and brands, making one presentable knife.

While at a knife show in Louisville, Kentucky he was introduced to a representative of Schrade Cutlery Corporation. When Herman's work was inspected, he was invited to visit the Schrade Cutlery factory in Ellenville, New York. There he was interviewed by "Uncle Henry" Baer, and also became close friends with Mr. Dave Swinden, who at that time was manager of the Ellenville facility. Herman was given the opportunity to learn the art of knifemaking from the old timers who worked in the Schrade factory. Since then he has developed a very close relationship with the people at the Imperial-Schrade Corporation and through his visits to the factory he has gained valuable knowledge of the cutlery industry.

Collecting is his first love, however, and is a continuous pastime. Frequently visiting knife shows helps keep his collection current.

"I usually find my little treasures at these shows and at trade lots, other collectors are good sources, too.

"Knives are not only a passion with me, but they are a really good investment, also. I hope to continue collecting as long as the Good Lord sees fit to keep me on this earth."

Original factory of the Schrade Cutlery Co., Walden, N.Y.

Current plant site on Canal Street, Ellenville, N.Y.

No. 1 — 1904 - Louis, William and George Schrade incorporated the Schrade Cutlery Company in 1904. The earliest stamping to be found on Schrade is the rarest. It is the "Schrade Cut. Co. Walden N.Y. Germany," used around 1904. Schrade was unable to meet their cutlery demands and imported some of these German-made knives to meet their sales demand.

No. 2 — 1904-1928 - The second stamping used by Schrade is known as the "half-moon circle." Schrade Cutlery Company marked over Walden, N.Y. These knives were made from Schrades inception up to World War I. This is a most sought-after stamping by Schrade collectors. One in mint condition is a rare find.

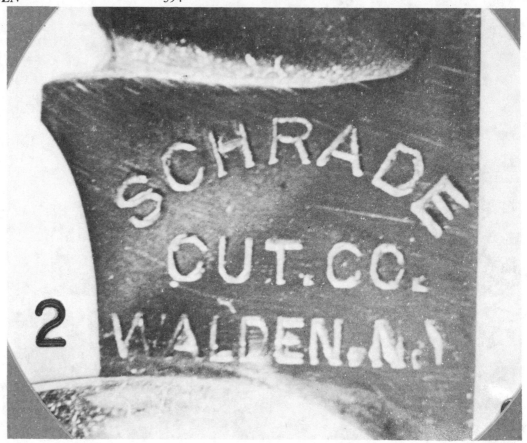

No. 3 — 1930-1948 - The straight-line Schrade Cut. Co. marking was adopted after World War I, and was used through 1948.

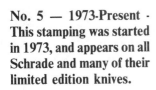

No. 4 — 1948-1973 - The "Schrade Walden, N.Y. USA" was started in 1948 with a few not bearing the USA stamp. This stamping was used until 1973.

No. 5 — 1973-Present - This stamping was started in 1973, and appears on all Schrade and many of their limited edition knives.

KEY TO SCHRADE CUTLERY CO. NUMBERING SYSTEM

The number of blades is denoted by the first figure.

1 represents a 1 blade knife

2 represents a 2 blade knife (both blades in one end)

3 represents a 3 blade knife (3 blades in one end)

7 represents a 2 blade knife (1 blade in each end)

8 represents a 3 blade knife (2 blades in one end and 1 blade in the other end)

9 represents a 4 blade knife (2 blades in each end)

The second and third figures of a number indicate the pattern or style of knife:

The handle material is denoted by the last figure.

1. Cocobola
2. Ebony
3. Bone Stag
4. Celluloid
5. White Bone

6. Mother of Pearl
7. Stained Bone
8. Buffalo Horn
9. Miscellaneous

Following are the letters indicating celluloid colors:

AC—Assorted Colors
AP—Abalone Pearl
B—Black (Ebony)
BLUE—Blue Pearl
BP—Black Pearl
BRNZ—Bronze
C— Cocobolo
GL—Goldaleur
GP—Golden Pearl
G—Green Pearl
H—Black and White Striped
HORN—Horn

J—Red-White-Amber Striped
K—Brown Lined Cream
M—Marine Pearl
MB—Mottled Blue
MR—Mottled Red
O—Onyx
P—Smoked Pearl
PP—Persian Pearl
S—Tortoise Shell
US—Red-White-Blue Striped
W—(White) Ivory
X—Mottled Green

Miscellaneous handles are indicated by a letter or letters after the figure 9, as follows, 2019BR, indicates a brass handle.

The following is a list of miscellaneous handles, with letters indicating same:

BR—Solid Brass
GM—Gun Metal
GOLD—12 Karat Gold Plate

GS—Genuine Stag
GSIL—Nickel Silver
SS—Sterling Silver

A fraction at the end of a number indicates the kind of blade substituted for a spear pocket blade, as follows:
Example: No. 1543½ would indicate our regular No. 1543 with a Sheepfoot blade substituted for a Spear blade.

The following is a list of fractions used:

¼—Spay Pocket
½—Sheepfoot Pocket

¾—Clip Pocket
⅞ — Razor Point Pocket

NOTE:

Schrade Cutlery Co.'s numbering system started approx. 1904 and ran through 1946. Schrade Walden numbering system started in 1946 and ran through 1973. In 1974 the company name changed to Schrade, NY. U.S.A. and in 1985 changed to Imperial Schrade Corporation. Most Schrade Walden knives were stamped with only 3 numbers, therefore the numbering system does not correspond with Schrade Cut Co.'s numbering system.

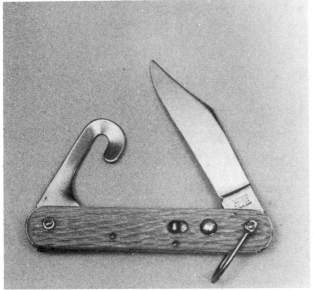

No Nr. Jigged Orange Comp   4¼" $75
Var. with shroud cutter
      Black Comp.   4¼" $100
Var. with shroud cutter (rare)
      Black Comp.   4¼" $75
Var. without shroud cutter
(Note...some knives may be found with different handles on each side (ex. bone front, composition back). These were possibly made up as salesmen's samples or perhaps just by mistake)

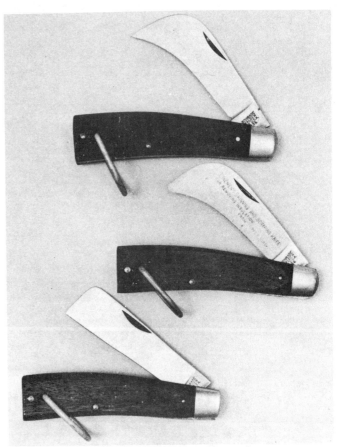

Three knives showing differences in blades:
#186, 4⁷⁄₁₆, Cocobolo Scales, Sharp point pruner, $20.00
#136, 4⁷⁄₁₆, Cocobolo, Lineman's knife, $25.00;
#163, 4⁷⁄₁₆, Cocobolo, Navy rope knife, $30.00;

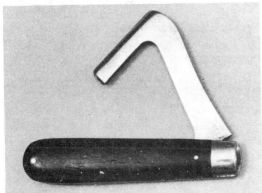

No Nr. Timberscribe, Ebony   3¾" $35

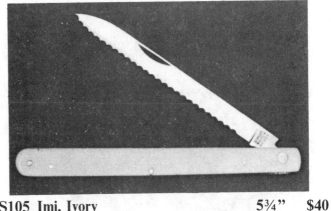

SS105 Imi. Ivory   5¾" $40
Var. also in Black Comp. $30

SS102 Imi. Ivory   4¹¹⁄₁₆" $20
Var. also in Black Comp. $25.00, Marine Pearl $20.00

110   Imi. Ivory   2¾" $25
Var. also in Black Comp. $25

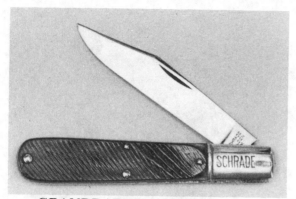

GRANDDADDY BARLOW

114   Saw Cut Green Bone also in
Brown Bone   5" $150
Var. Black Comp. $100

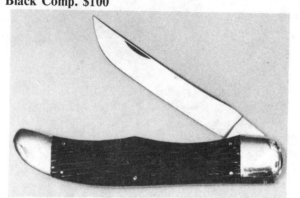

115   Peachseed Black Comp.   5¼" $150
Var. Skinning Knife, Turkish clip, also in Marine
Pearl, 2nd Peachseed Bone,

121   Walnut   4" $22

139   Sheepfoot, Black Comp.   3" $30

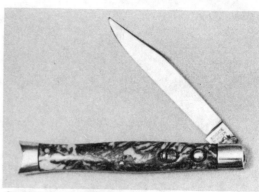

151   Switchblade, Black & White
Mottled Celluloid   4" $125
Var. also in assorted celluloids

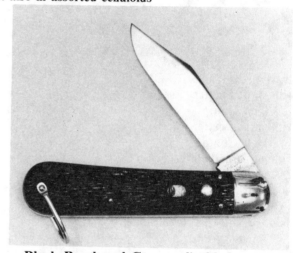

155   Black Peachseed Comp., clip blade
with shackle   4¼" $85
Var. Bone handle, $140

G155   Orange Comp.   4¼" $200
Var. Paratrooper Knife with guard, (very rare)

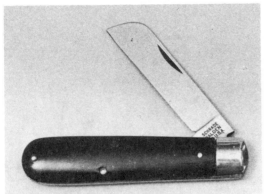

175   Sheepfoot, Mottled celluloid   3¾" $20
also in Imi. Ivory

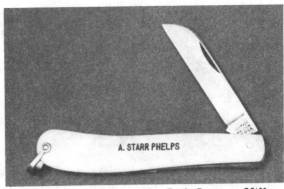

195   Sheepfoot with shackle, Imi. Ivory   3⅞" $30
also in Black Comp.

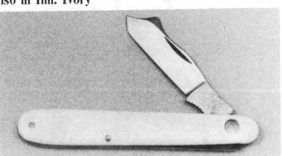

181   Bark loosener, Imi. Ivory   4" $35

PRUNING BLADE

196   Imi. Ivory   3⅞" $22

2 BLADE

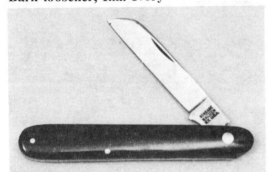

182   Sheepfoot, Black Comp.   4" $30
also in Imi. Ivory

190   Black Composition, also in Imi. Ivory   4⅝" $40
and Black Peachseed Comp.

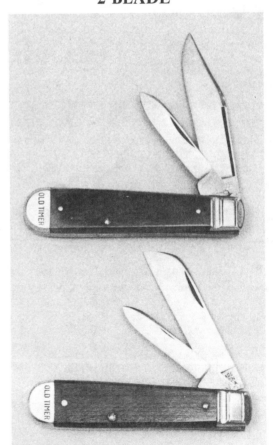

2 O.T. Smooth Brown Bone, clip & pen
blades   3½" $100
same with sheepfoot blade, approx. 25 made as salesmen's
samples, $200

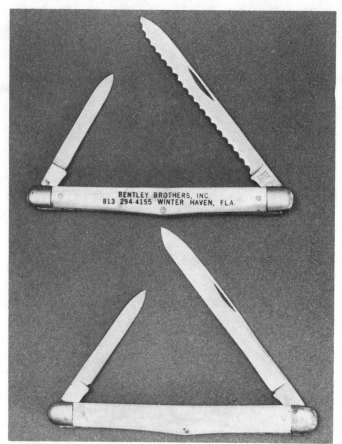

SS700 Marine Pearl, serrated edge   4½" $45
Var. with plain edge $30

20T   2 Bl. LP Jack, Brown Bone with Craftsman
Emblem, Old Timer Bols., Schrade Walden, NY USA,
3½" $150

708
Jigged Delrin, blade etched "Craftsman
Custom made", hollowground 2¾" $40
also in Peachseed Bone, $60; Black Peachseed
Comp., $40; Yellow Comp., $50; Imi. Ivory, $40;
Delrin with Scout Shield, $40; Black Comp. with
Cadillac Shield, $40.
also in Delrin, $40; Cocobolo, $40

204   Cocobolo, with shackle   3¾" $40

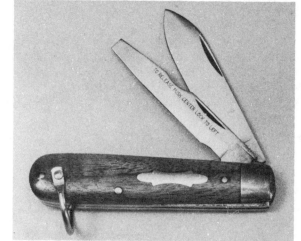

204S   Walnut, Electrician's Knife   3¾" $50

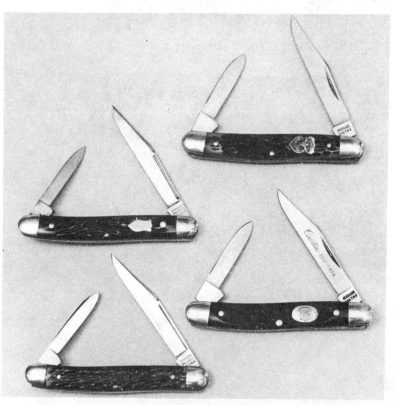

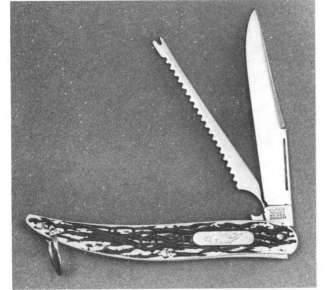

209   **Staglon, Old Lunker**   5" $30

SS709   **Metal, file blade**   3¹/₁₆" $25

BARTENDER'S KNIFE
712   **Nickle Silver**   3" $25
Also in Marine Pearl, $25

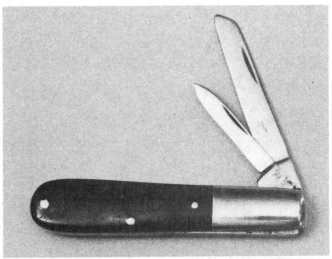

BABY BARLOW
214   **Slick Black**   2¾" $40
also in Imi. Ivory, $40

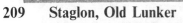

716   **Grafting Knife, Imi. Ivory**   3¹¹/₁₆" $35

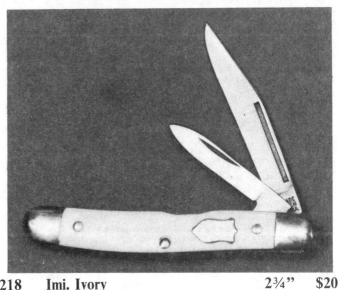

218   **Imi. Ivory**   2¾" $20

FOLDING HUNTER
225   Jigged Brown Bone   5¼" $150
     also in Marine Pearl, $110; (older Folding
Hunters are saber ground with numbers on back of
tang

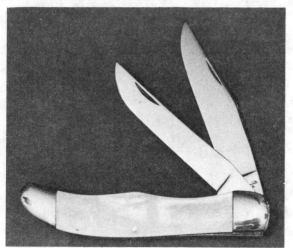

FOLDING HUNTER
225   with flat blade, Marine Pearl   5¼" $100
     also in Yellow Scales, $100; Brown Delrin, $40;
Jigged Bone, $125

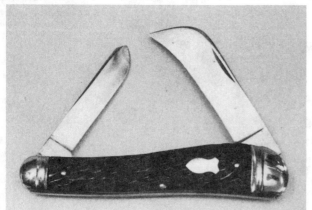

730   Peachseed Bone   4⅛" $100
     also in Black Jigged Peachseed, $100

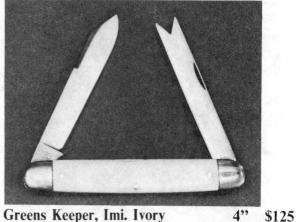

733   Greens Keeper, Imi. Ivory   4" $125

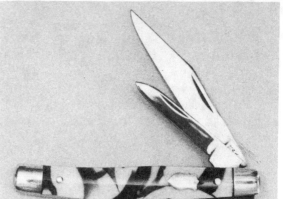

234K   Celluloid   3⁵⁄₁₆" $40
     Peachseed Bone, $50

735   Sailor's Knife, Brown Jigged
        Peachseed Comp.   4⅛" $40
Black Jigged Peachseed, $40

236   Black Peachseed Comp.   3⁹⁄₁₆" $75
     Peachseed Bone, $125; Brown Delrin
Peachseed, $40; Slick Black, $60

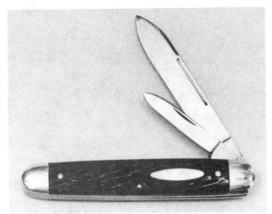

242   Black Peachseed Bone   3⅛" $40
Assorted Celluloid, $40; Peachseed Bone, $55; Pearl, $65

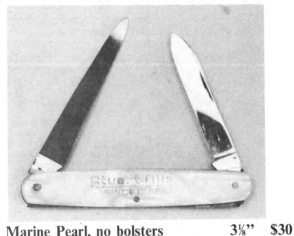

742   Marine Pearl, no bolsters   3⅛" $30
     with extended bolsters, $30

742   Genuine Stag   3⅛" $40
Assorted Celluloids, $30; Genuine Pearl, $50; Nickle
Silver, $40

742   Propwood   3⅛" $25

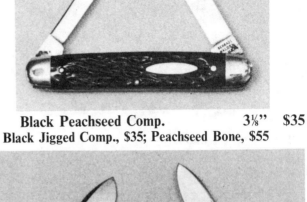

742   Black Peachseed Comp.   3⅛" $35
Black Jigged Comp., $35; Peachseed Bone, $55

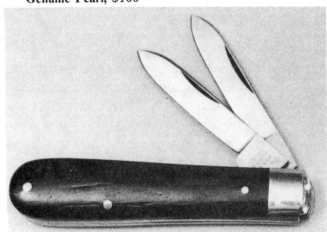

749   Imprinted Office Knife, Imi. Ivory   3⅜" $50
Genuine Pearl, $100

SB2151 Cocobolo, Grafting Knife   3⅜" $75

**752   Aluminum Scales, Advertising
Knife**   3⅜" $20

760   Asst. Celluloids   3⅛" $40
Genuine Pearl, $50

272   Peachseed Bone   2⅞" $50
Slick Black, $25; Brown Delrin, $25; Black Jigged
Peachseed, $30

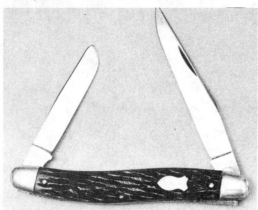

761   Peachseed Bone   4" $90
Turkish Clip & Spay

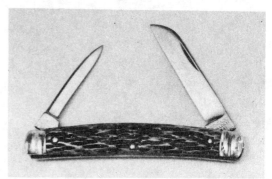

774   Peachseed Bone   3" $40
Black Jigged Peachseed, $40

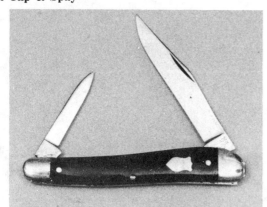

766   Slick Black   3" $35
Peachseed Bone, $65; Assorted Celluloids, $35

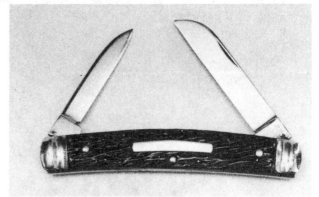

775   Black Jigged Peachseed,   3½" $45
Peachseed Bone, $60; Stag, $75

F770   Black Jigged Peachseed, pen & file 3" $25
Peachseed Bone, $40; Marine Pearl, $25; Genuine
Pearl, $40; K-Horn, $25; (770 same as above with
spear & pen)

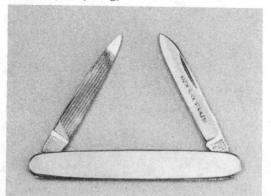

778RB Stainless Steel   2⅞" $25
"UNCLE HENRY" TRAPPER

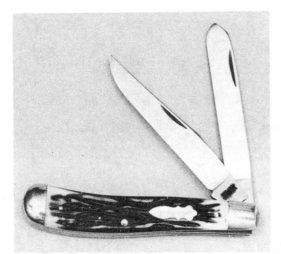

285UH Staglon   3⅞" $35

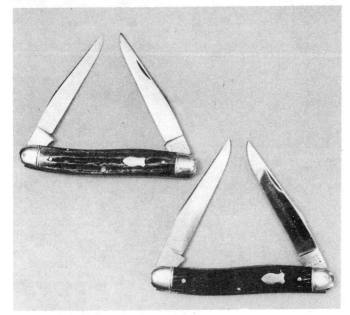

IMPROVED MUSKRAT
787   Stag   4" $200
Peachseed Bone, $150; Marine Pearl, $150;
Improved Muskrat/Bone, $200

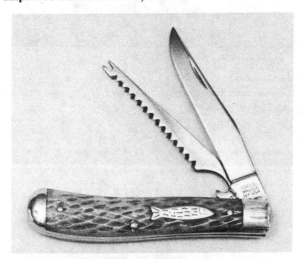

TRAPPER/FISH KNIFE
SS292   Peachseed Bone   3⅞" $250

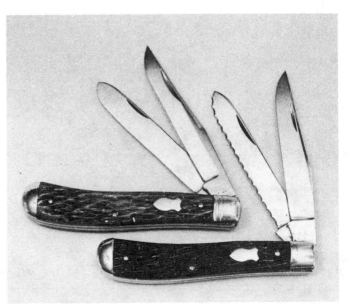

293   Peachseed Bone   3⅞" $125
Peachseed Bone with flat blade (serrated long
spay), $160

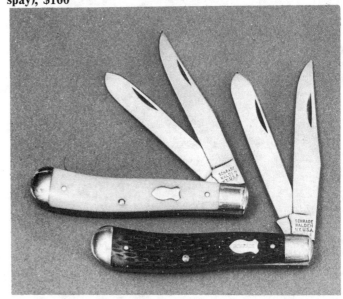

293 & 293Y   Full Trappers   3⅞" $35

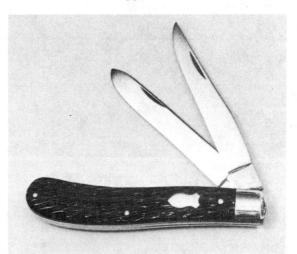

S294   Black Peachseed Comp.   3⅞" $125
no lower bolsters

406   *SCHRADE WALDEN*

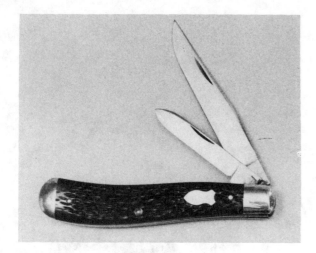

294   Brown Jigged Delrin   3⅞" $50
(94 O.T., $30

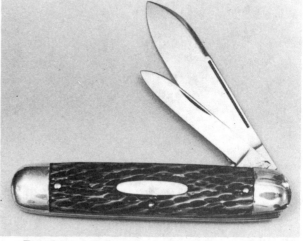

297   Peachseed Bone   4¼" $150

294   Peachseed Bone, with shield   3⅞" $100
without shield $110

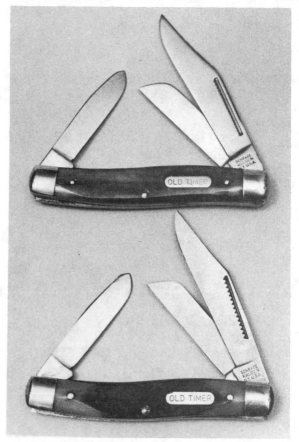

8 O.T. Slick Brown Bone   4" $75
     Brown Saw-Cut Delrin, $30; (885 U.H.,
Staglon, $35)

295   Assorted Celluloids   3" $45
     Peachseed Bone, $70; K-Horn, $45; Marine
Pearl, $45; Pearl, $75

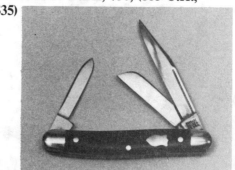

805   Cocobolo   2¾" $40
(805SW Brown Jigged Delrin, KON-KAV, $25)

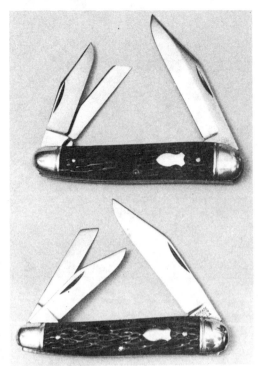

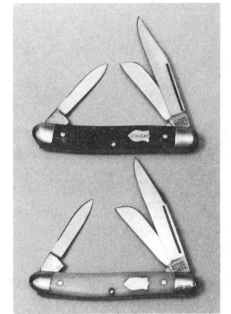

808   Brown Derlin   2¾"
bottom: 808Y Yellow Comp. 2¾", $25; top: Peachseed Bone, $40

804   Carpenters Knife   3⅞"
top: Peachseed Bone with saber, $150; bottom: Green Peachseed Bone with flat blade, $125; Black Jigged Peachseed Comp, $100; Brown Delrin, $45; Genuine Stag, $200

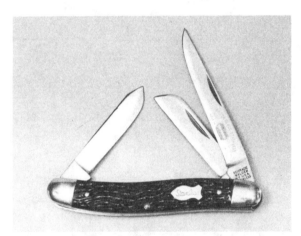

825RB Brown Delrin, blade is etched   3⁹⁄₁₆" $30

810   Black Peachseed Comp.   3⅛" $45
Peachseed Bone, $50; Asst. Celluloid, $40

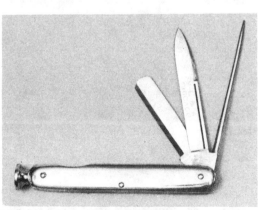

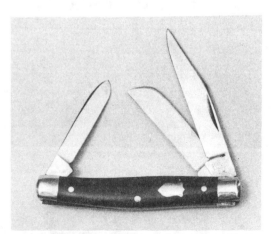

P308   Nickle Silver, Pipe Knife   3⅜" $65   832   Wonda-Wood   3⁵⁄₁₆" $40

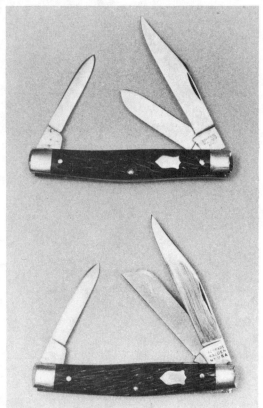

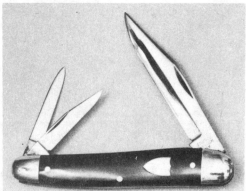

834   **Peachseed Bone**   3⁵⁄₁₆"   **$60**
        Yellow Comp.   3⁵⁄₁₆"   **$30**

836   **Slick Black, 3⁷⁄₁₆"**   **$80**
        Peachseed Bone, $125; Black Peachseed Comp.,
$110

S837   **Peachseed Bone**   3⁷⁄₁₆"   **$125**

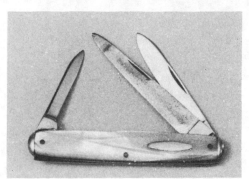

F842   **Marine Pearl**   3⅛"   **$40**
        Genuine Pearl, $65; Peachseed Bone, $60

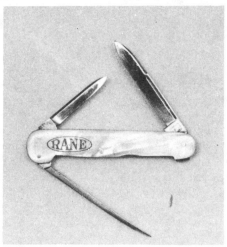

848   **Marine Pearl**   2¾"   **$25**
        Genuine Pearl, $40

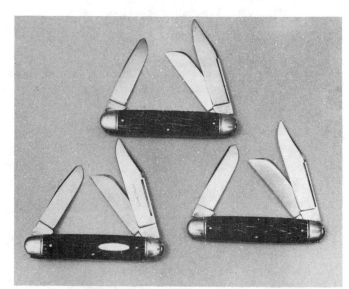

856   **Peachseed Bone**   3⅜"
        top: No shield, $60; left: With shield, $55; right:
Transition pattern, Schrade-Walden Master, Schrade-
Cut. Sheepfoot, $75

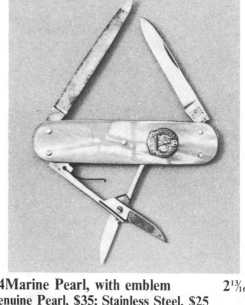

861   Brown Jigged Delrin   4" $35
Peachseed Bone with milled liners, $95; Marine
Pearl-milled liners optional, $75; Yellow Comp., $75

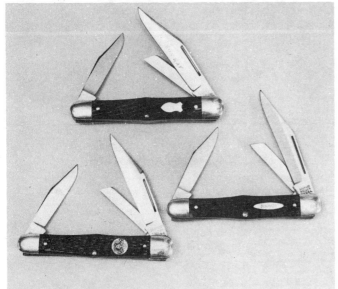

SS8764Marine Pearl, with emblem   2¹³⁄₁₆" $25
Genuine Pearl, $35; Stainless Steel, $25

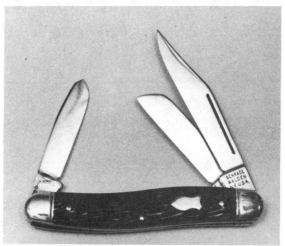

863   Peachseed Bone, blade etched
KON-KAV   3⅝" $110
Brown Jigged Delrin with Scout emblem and
saber ground blade, $50; Brown Delrin, $40; 863Y
Yellow Comp., $60

880   Peachseed Bone, blade etched
KON-KAV   4" $90
Var. Green Peachseed Bone, $100; Brown Delrin
with etching, $40

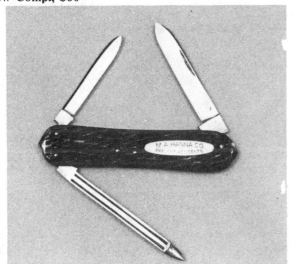

F865   Peachseed Bone   3¹⁄₁₆" $35
Var. Genuine Pearl, $40

881   Peachseed Bone, flat blade   4" $125
Var. Brown Delrin, $35

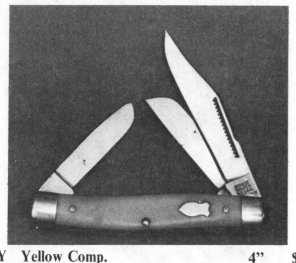

881Y   **Yellow Comp.**   4" $25

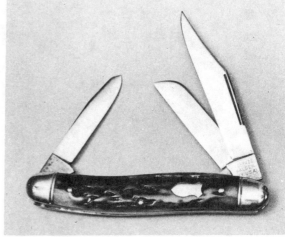

884   **Genuine Stag**   4" $140

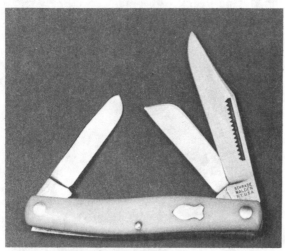

BIRDSEYE RIVETS

882Y   **Yellow Comp.**   4" $40

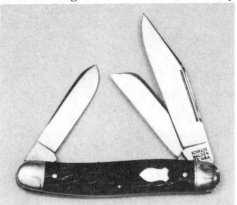

890   **Peachseed Bone**   3½" $65
Genuine Stag, $80

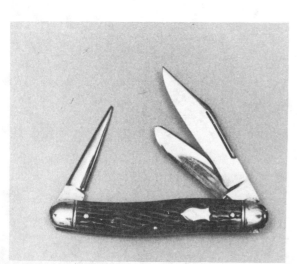

8823LB Peachseed Bone   4" $175
Transition with master blade Schrade-Cut and spay Schrade-Walden.

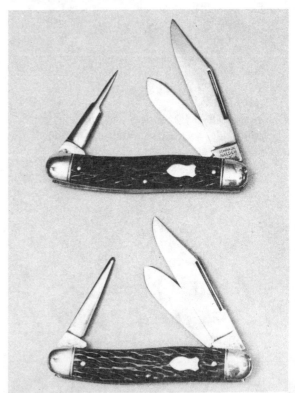

891   **Peachseed Bone**   3½"
top: Typesetter blade, $75; bottom: Punch, $65

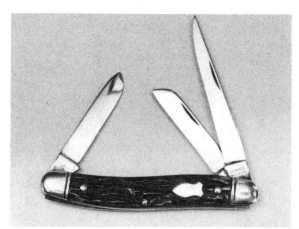

894 Genuine Stag 3%₁₆" $100

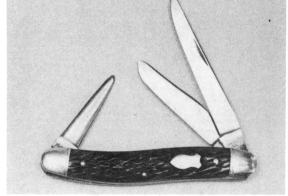

899LB Peachseed Bone, Leather borer 3%₁₆" $75

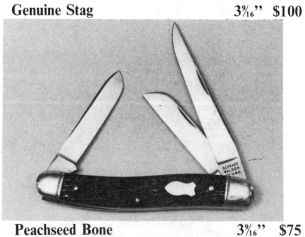

895 Peachseed Bone 3%₁₆" $75
Marine Pearl, $45; Yellow Comp., $45

F912 Nickle Silver 3" $40

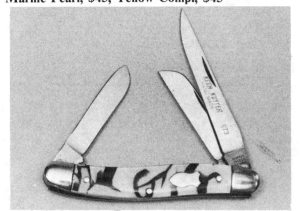

896K K-Horn Celluloid 3%₁₆"
Var. blade etched K.K., $45

898 Peachseed Bone 3%₁₆" $80

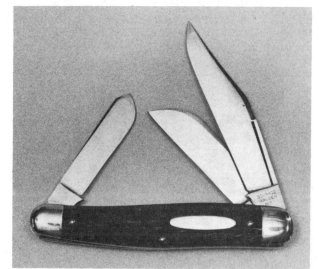

81043 4%₁₆" $400

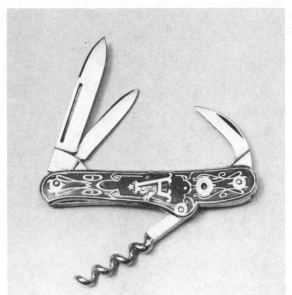

912   Cloissne   3¼" $150
Anhauser Busch, peep hole has Adolphus Busch's portrait

946   Peachseed Bone, Camp Knife   3⅝" $125

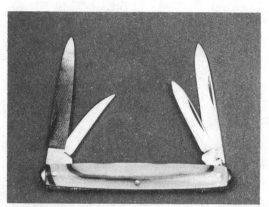

F970   K-Horn Celluloid   2⅞" $40
Genuine Pearl, $50; Marine Pearl, $35; Peachseed Bone, $50

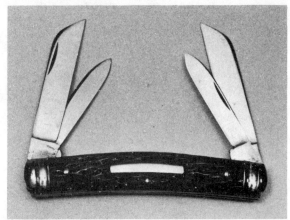

973   Peachseed Bone   3½" $85
Black Jigged Peachseed, $70; Genuine Stag, $125

974   Brown Jigged Delrin   3⅛" $30
Marine Pearl, $45; Peachseed Bone, $65

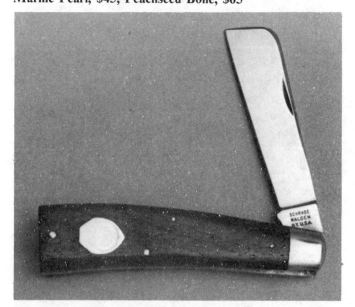

1 Bl. Rope Knife, Walnut Handle, Wall Rope Emblem, 4⅜",
Schrade, Walden, NY, Rare $85

SCHRADE CUTLERY CORP.

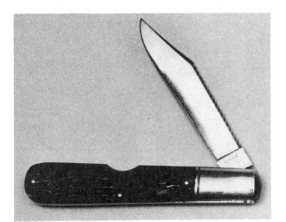

SSC114¾S Bone   5" $250

Nr.	Handle	Size	Mint
115S	Bone	3⅜	70

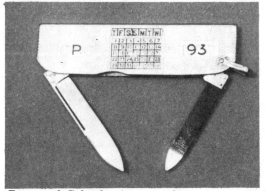

F170   Perpetual Calendar (very rare) $1,000

M1001	Cocobolo	4	65
1001	Cocobolo	4	65

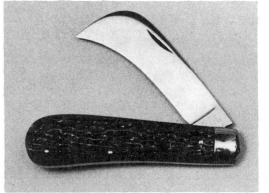

1003   Bone   4" $85

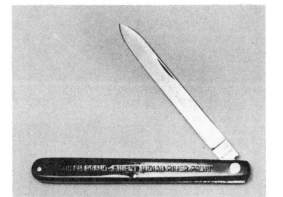

SS1024B Black Celluloid   4¹¹⁄₁₆" $50

Nr.	Handle	Size	Mint
SS1024W	Imi. Ivory	4¾"	$40

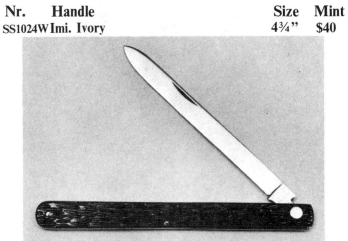

1054B	Rough Black	5¾"	$55
SS1054W	Imi. Ivory	5¾"	$45

1083	Bone	5"	$150
1083¾	Bone	5	150

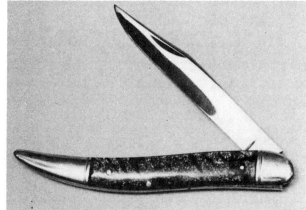

1083AC Christmas Tree   5" $160

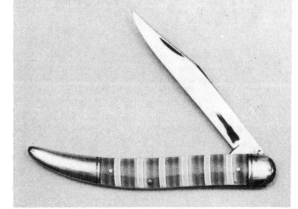

1084J   Pyralin, red-white-amber   5" $150

1147¾   Bone   5" $150

1084¾ Ivory Celluloid   5" $150

Nr.	Handle	Size	Mint
1091	Cocobolo	3⅝	35
1103⅝W	Ivory Celluloid	3⅝	40
1103⅛W	Ivory Pruning Blade		40
1104¾	Celluloid Stag	5¼	90

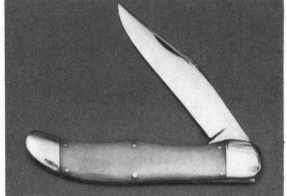

1153   Bone   3⅜" $45

Nr.	Handle	Size	Mint
1151	Cocobolo		35
1152	Ebony		35
1153¾	Bone		45
L1153	Bone	3⅜	45

1104⅜ Onyx Celluloid   5¼" $125

1104⅜M   Marine Pearl, Pyralin   125

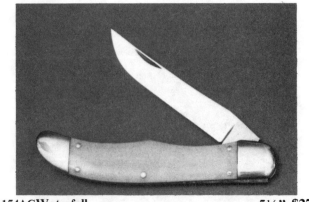

S1154AC Waterfall   5¼" $275

1121½ Cocobola $45

Nr.	Handle	Size	Mint
1131	Cocobolo	3½	50
1133	Bone		60
1131¾	Clip Blade Cocobolo		50
S135¼B	Black Celluloid	4	60

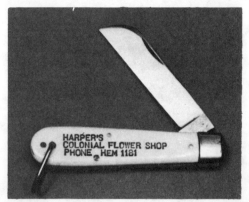

1154½ Celluloid   5¼" $50

1154½ W. White Celluloid 5¼" $45

Nr.	Handle	Size	Mint
1157	**Stained Bone**	**3⅜"**	**$65**
1157¼	Stained Bone	3⅜	75
1157½	Sheepfoot Blade		85
1157¾	Clip Blade		65
123EW	Walnut	4⁵⁄₁₆	75

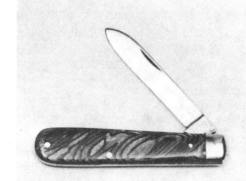

1254 Asst. Celluloids 5¼" $40

1251 Cocobolo 3¼" $40

1251 Cocobolo, with chain 3¼" $60

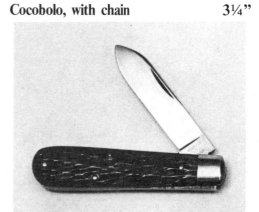

Nr.	Handle	Size	Mint
1253	**Bone**	**3¼"**	**$50**
1253	Bone, with chain		65

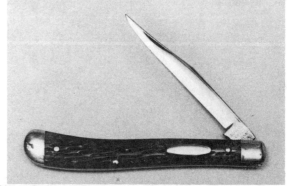

1293⅜ Bone 4⅛" $75

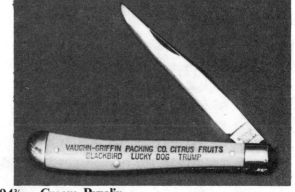

1294⅜ Cream Pyralin $60

1294⅜	Amber Striped Pyralin		75
1309GSIL	Silver	3⅛	30

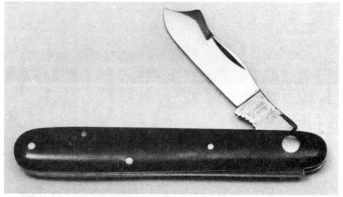

1354¼B Black Celluloid 4" $65

416   *SCHRADE CUTLERY CORP.*

Nr.	Handle	Size	Mint
1354½B	Black Celluloid	4	40
1354½W	Ivory Celluloid	4	40
1354½W	Ivory Celluloid	4	65

Nr.	Handle	Size	Mint
1361SHA	Cocobolo	4⁷/₁₆	50
SN1364	Stg, Shac, Fibestos	4⁷/₁₆	45

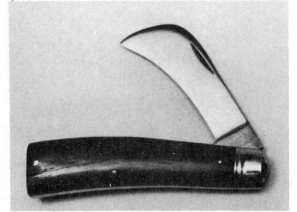

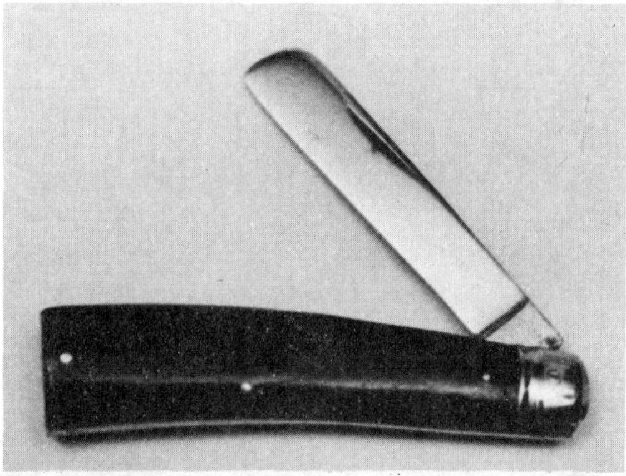

1361   Cocobolo   4⁷/₁₆" $45

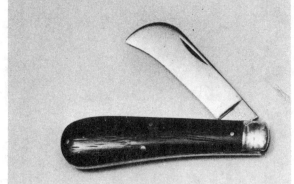

1391	**Cocobolo**	**3⁹/₁₆"**	**$45**
1392½	Ebony	3⁹/₁₆	45
L1404W	Ivory Celluloid (blade 3⅜")	8⅞	200
LR1429GSIL	Nickel Silver		225
1404¾W	Imi. Ivory Celluloid	3⅜	90
1404¾K	Cream & Brown Pyralin	3⅜	110
1404¾AC	Asst. Celluloid	3⅜	110
1504¾AC	Asst. Celluloid	3⅜	110
1514J	Red-White-Amber Pyralin	4	150
1514	Blue Celluloid	4	150
1514G	Green Jade Celluloid	4	150
1514K	Cream & Brown Pyralin	4	150
1514V	Black & White Celluloid	4	150
1514W	Ivory Celluloid	4	150
1514V	Black & White Celluloid	4	150

N1361   Cocobolo   4⁷/₁₆" $40

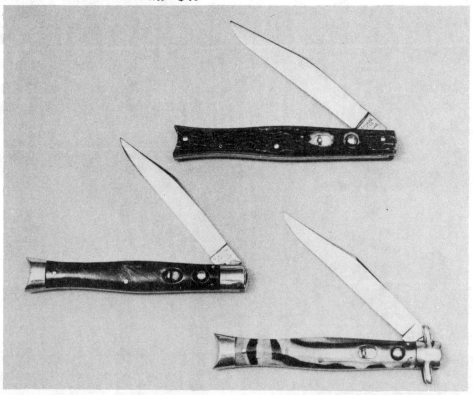

Left: G1514 Green Jade Celluloid   4" $150   Top: S1513   Bone   4" $150
Bottom: G1514K Cream & Brown Pyralin   4" $150

SCHRADE CUTLERY CORP.   417

Nr.	Handle	Size	Mint
1514A	Black & White Celluloid	4	150
1514B	Black Celluloid	4	150
1514C	Cocobolo Celluloid	4	150
1514E	Black & Pearl Celluloid	4	150
1514M	Marine Pearl Pyralin	4	150
1514P	Smoked Pearl Celluloid	4	150
1514Q	Black & White Celluloid	4	150

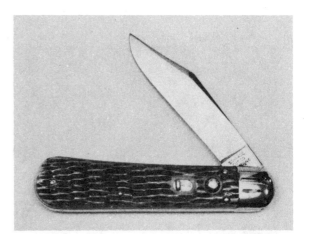

1553¾   Bone   4¼" **$150**

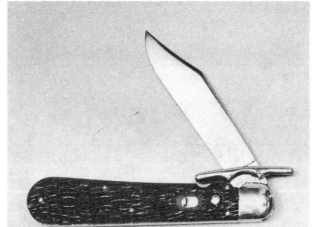

G1543¾ Bone   4⅞" **$375**

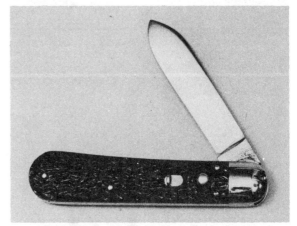

1553   Large Spearblade   4¼" **$150**
SS1564W Ivory Celluloid   3⅜   45

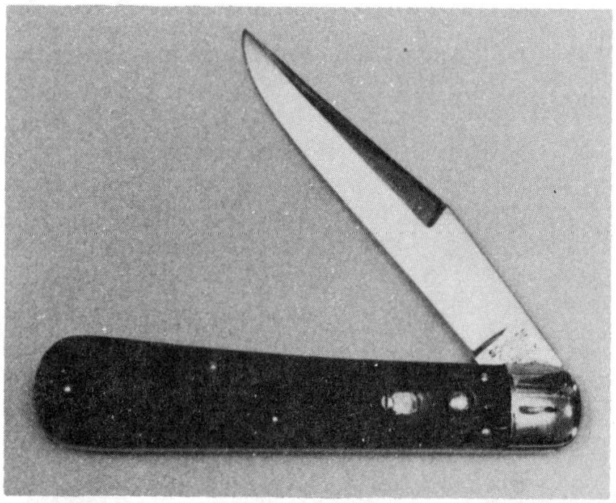

1543¾   Bone   4⅞" **$300**

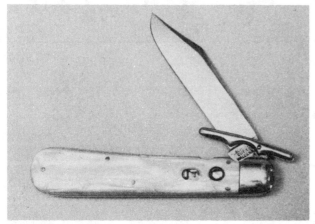

G1544¾M Marine Pearl Celluloid   4⅞" **$350**

G1544¾AC	Asst. Celluloid	4⅞	350
1544¾BM	Buttermilk Celluloid	4⅞	350
1544¾PO	Onyx Celluloid	4⅞	350

1613¾   Bone   4⅞" **$225**

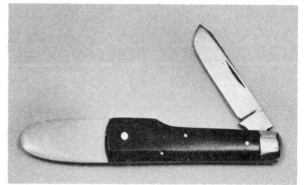

1694B   Black Celluloid   4⅝" **$60**

Nr.	Handle	Size	Mint
1693	Bone	4⅝	85
L1784M	Marine Pearl Pyralin		200

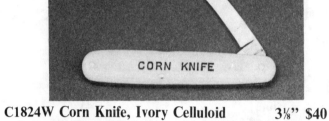

C1824W Corn Knife, Ivory Celluloid   3⅛" $40

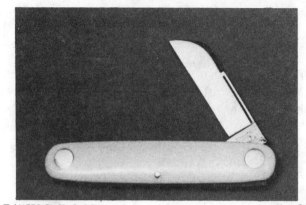

1974½W Celluloid   4¼" $35

1863¾ Bone   4½" $110

7004M Marine Pearl Rockwell Hardness Test $60

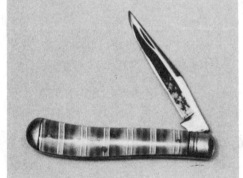

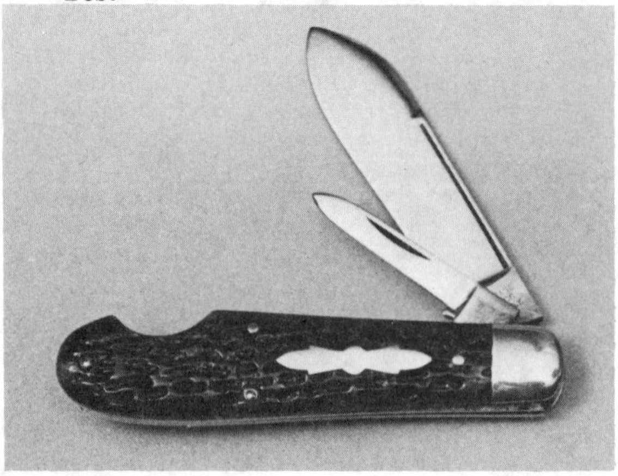

1944¾J Red-White-Amber Pyralin   3⅞" $125

C1944W	Ivory Celluloid	3⅞	45

S1944⅝ Ivory Celluloid   3⅞" $35

S1944½W	Ivory Celluloid	3⅞	35

2013 Bone   3⅝" $100

Nr.	Handle	Size	Mint
2011	Cocobolo	3⅝	70
2012	Ebony	3⅝	70
SS2013	Bone	3⅝	125
2014S	Tortoise Celluloid	3⅝	90
2014G	Green Pearl Pyralin	3⅝	90
2014P	Smoked Pearl Celluloid	3⅝	90
2014W	Ivory Celluloid	3⅝	80
2014X	Mottled Green Celluloid	3⅝	80
2014AC	Assorted Celluloid	3⅝	80

SCHRADE CUTLERY CORP.

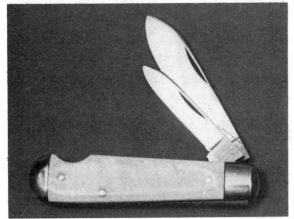

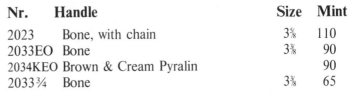

Nr.	Handle	Size	Mint
2023	Bone, with chain	3⅝	110
2033EO	Bone	3⅜	90
2034KEO	Brown & Cream Pyralin		90
2033¾	Bone	3⅜	65

2014M Marine Pearl   3⅝" $90

Nr.	Handle	Size	Mint
2022	Ebony	3⅝	70
2021	Cocobolo	3⅝	70
2023	Bone	3⅝	100

2019BR Brass   3⅝" $90

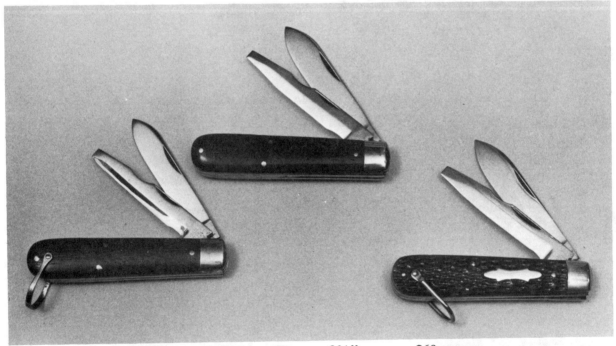

2312BSDC   Ebony   3¾" $60

2041SD   Cocobolo   3¾" $60   **2043SD   Bond, with Shackle   3¾" $80**

Nr.	Handle	Size	Mint
2042SD	Ebony	3¾	55
2042SD	Nickel Silver, Shackle	3¾	75
2043	Bone	3¾	75
2043¾	Bone	3¾	75
2043SD	Bone	3¾	75
C2043¾	Bone	3¾	90

Nr.	Handle	Size	Mint
2053½	Bone	3⅝	120
2054K	Brown & Cream Pyralin	3¹⁄₁₆	50
2053	Bone	3¹⁄₁₆	55
2054M	Marine Pearl Pyralin	3¹⁄₁₆	50
S2053	Fancy Bolsters	3¹⁄₁₆	65
2061¾	Cocobolo	3⅝	55
2061	Cocobolo	3⅝	60
2062	Ebony	3⅝	60
2062¾	Ebony	3⅝	55
2063½	Bone	3⅝	110

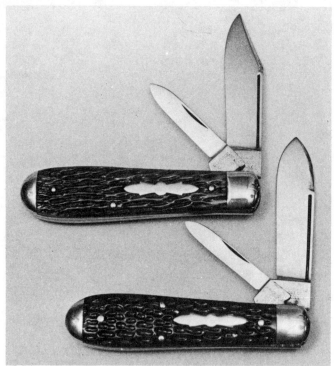

2063¾   Bone   **3⅝" $75**
2063   Bone   **3⅝" $75**

Nr.	Handle	Size	Mint
2064P	Celluloid	3⅝	90
2064S	Tortoise Celluloid	3⅝	90
2064W	Ivory Celluloid	3⅝	80
2064AC	Assorted Celluloid	3⅝	90

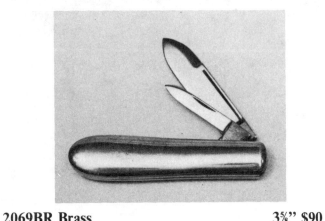

2069BR Brass   **3⅝" $90**

Nr.	Handle	Size	Mint
2069¾BR	Clip Pocket Blades	3⅝	90
2072	Ebony	3⅝	55
2071	Cocobolo	3⅝	55
2073	Bone	3⅝	75
2073¾	Bone	3⅝	75
2071¾	Cocobolo	3⅝	55
2072¾	Ebony	3⅝	55
7076Sha	Mother of Pearl	2⁵⁄₁₆	45

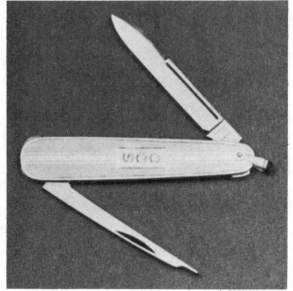

7079Sha   Nickel Silver   **2⁵⁄₁₆" $40**

Nr.	Handle	Size	Mint
2083B	Bone	3	45
7083B	Bone	3	40

2084AC· Asst. Celluloid   **3" $40**

7086B	Mother of Pearl	3	50
SSD2804PO	Onyx Celluloid	5	85

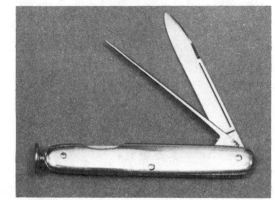

P2088   Nickel Silver, Pipe Knife   **3" $75**

SCHRADE CUTLERY CORP.

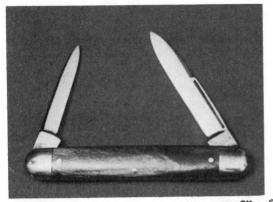

7084   Celluloid   5" $75

Nr.	Handle	Size	Mint
7089GM	Metal	3	40
SS7089GSIL	Nickel Silver	3	40

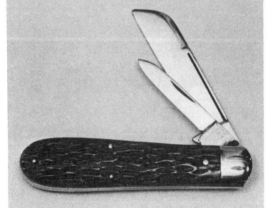

2093	**Bone**	**3⅝"**	**$75**
2091	Cocobolo	3⅝	55
2092	Ebony	3⅝	55

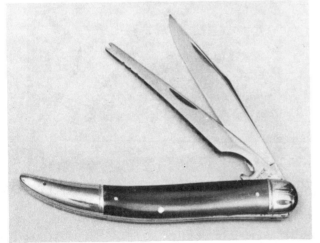

2098   Black Celluloid   5" $150

SS7099	I Shac, stainless metal engine turned	3¹⁄₁₆	40
SS7099I	Same as cut with smooth handle	3¹⁄₁₆	35
SS7099I	SHAC	3¹⁄₁₆	35
SSF7099SI	Shac. stainless steel	3¹⁄₁₆	40
SSM7099SI	Shac	3¹⁄₁₆	40
M7099GIL	Shac, Nickel Silver	3¹⁄₁₆	40

Nr.	Handle	Size	Mint
RM7099GSIL	Without shackle	3¹⁄₁₆	40
7099GM	Shac Metal	3¹⁄₁₆	40
7099GM	Without Shackle	3¹⁄₁₆	40
M7099GSIL	Shac Nickel Silver	3¹⁄₁₆	40
M7099GSIL	without shackle	3¹⁄₁₆	40
7099GSIL	Nickel Silver	3¹⁄₁₆	40

71043	**Bone (w/shield)**	**4¼"**	**$300**
	without shield		**250**

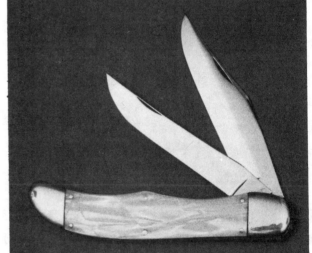

2104⅜POOnyx Celluloid   5¼" $325

2103⅜	Bone	5¼	140
2104⅜M	Marine Pearl Pyralin	5¼	125
2109⅜GS	Gen. Stag	5¼	200
7113	Bone	3⅜	45
S7113	Glaze Blades	3⅜	45
SS7113T	Bone	3⅜	65
SS7114ACT	Asst. Celluloid	3⅜	55
S7113T	Glaze Blades	3⅜	45
7113B	Bone	3⅜	40
S7113B	Glaze Blades	3⅜	40
7114P	Celluloid	3⅜	45
7114AP	Pearl Pyralin	3⅜	45
7114B	Black Celluloid	3⅜	45
7114	Horn Pyralin	3⅜	45

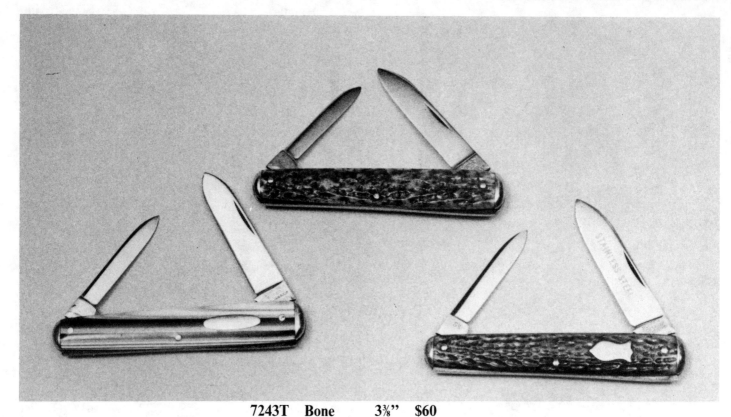

7243T Bone   3⅜" $60

7114RB Cream Pyralin with brown lines   3⅜" $40

7113T Bone   3⅜" $45

Nr.	Handle	Size	Mint
7114XT	Mottled Green Celluloid	3⅜	45
7114ACT	Assorted Celluloid	3⅜	45
7114SgMB	Marine Pearl Celluloid	3⅜	45
7113SgB	Bone	3⅜	50

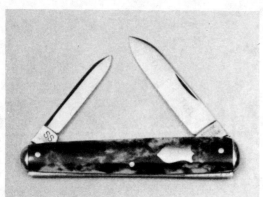

7114ST Tortoise Celluloid   3⅜" $45

Nr.	Handle	Size	Mint
7114GP	Golden Pearl Celluloid	3⅜	45
7114G	Green Pearl Pyralin	3⅜	45
71145	Tortoise Celluloid	3⅜	45
7114W	Ivory Celluloid	3⅜	45
7114AC	Assorted Celluloid	3⅜	45
7114PB	Smoked Pearl Celluloid	3⅜	40
7114BB	Black Celluloid	3⅜	40
7114GB	Green Pearl Pyralin	3⅜	40
7114	Horn B Pyralin	3⅜	40
7114SB	Tortoise Celluloid	3⅜	40
7114WB	Ivory Celluloid	3⅜	40
7114ACB	Assorted Celluloid	3⅜	40
7114WT	Ivory Celluloid	3⅜	45
7114BT	Black Celluloid	3⅜	45
7114GPT	Golden Pearl Celluloid	3⅜	45
7114	Horn T-Pyralin	3⅜	45
7114PT	Smoked Pearl Celluloid	3⅜	45

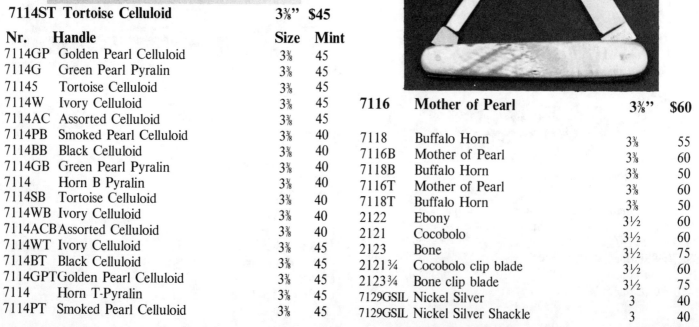

7116 Mother of Pearl   3⅜" $60

7118	Buffalo Horn	3⅜	55
7116B	Mother of Pearl	3⅜	60
7118B	Buffalo Horn	3⅜	50
7116T	Mother of Pearl	3⅜	60
7118T	Buffalo Horn	3⅜	50
2122	Ebony	3½	60
2121	Cocobolo	3½	60
2123	Bone	3½	75
2121¾	Cocobolo clip blade	3½	60
2123¾	Bone clip blade	3½	75
7129GSIL	Nickel Silver	3	40
7129GSIL	Nickel Silver Shackle	3	40

2133	**Bone**		3½"	$60

Nr.	Handle	Size	Mint
2133	Bone, chain	3½	65
2131	Cocobolo	3½	50
2132	Ebony	3½	50
7133	Bone	3¼	70
2134¾GP	Gold Pearl Pyralin	3¼	90
7143T	Bone	3⅛	40
7146T	Mother of Pearl	3⅛	50
7143B	Bone	3⅛	40

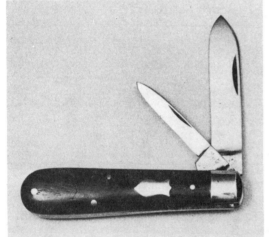

2151	**Cocobolo**	3⅜"	$45
21515D	Cocobolo		65

2152	**Ebony**	3⅜"	$45

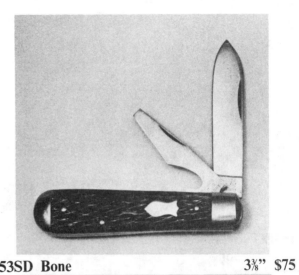

C2153SD	**Bone**	3⅜"	$75

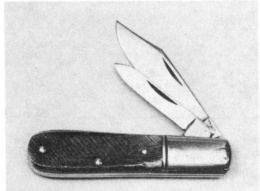

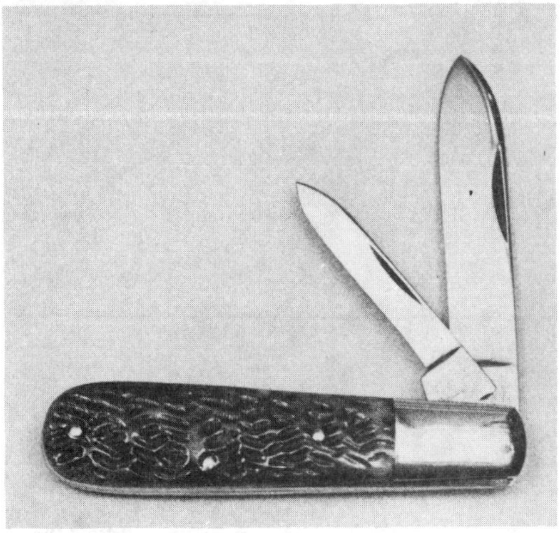

L2153	**Bone**		3⅜"	$65

Nr.	Handle	Size	Mint
L2153¾	Clip pocket blades	3⅜	60

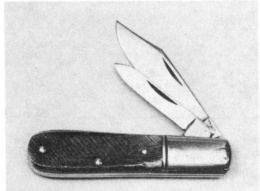

B2153½	**Bone**	3⅜"	$60
B2153¾	Bone	3⅜	50
B2151¾	Cocobolo	3⅜	45
B2152¾	Ebony	3⅜	45
S2151	Cocobolo	3⅜	45
S2152	Ebony	3⅜	45
S2153	Bone	3⅜	50
S2151LB	Cocobolo	3⅜	50
S2153LB	Bone	3⅜	65
2152½	Ebony	3⅜	60
2153½	Bone	3⅜	65

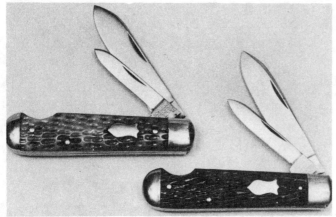

C2153EO Bone 3⅜" $60
C2153EO Bone 3⅜" $60

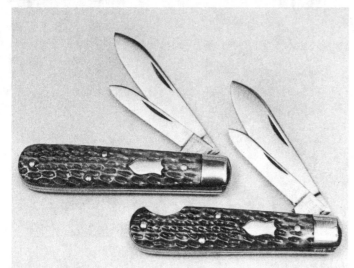

2153 Bone 3⅜" $50
2153 Bone, Easy Opener 3⅜" $60

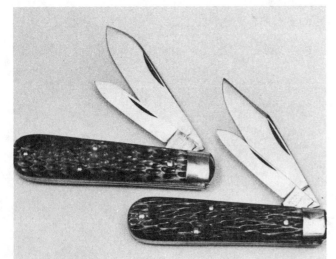

B2153 Bone 3⅜" $50
C2153¾ Bone 3⅜" $60

Nr.	Handle	Size	Mint
C2151	Cocobolo	3⅜	50
C2152	Ebony	3⅜	50
C21546G	Green Pearl Pyralin	3⅜	75

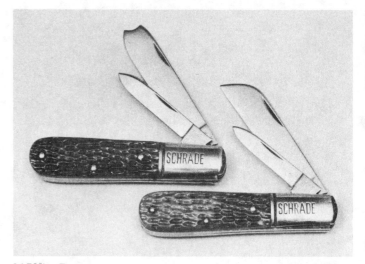

2153⅞ Bone 3⅜" $120
2153½ Bone 3⅜" $110

Nr.	Handle	Size	Mint
C2153½	Sheepfoot blade	3⅜	75
2153	Bone	3⅜	60
C2151¾	Cocobolo	3⅜	50
C2152¾	Ebony	3⅜	50
C2154¾AC	Assorted Celluloid	3⅜	65
B2151	Cocobolo	3⅜	45
B2152	Ebony	3⅜	45
B2152½	Ebony	3⅜	50
S2153¾	Bone	3⅜	50
S2152¾	Ebony	3⅜	45
2153¾	Bone	3⅜	50
2151¾	Cocobolo	3⅜	45
2152¾	Ebony	3⅜	45
C2154¾KLB	Cream & Brown Pyralin	3⅜	70
C2154¾APLB	Abalone Pearl Pyralin	3⅜	70
C2154¾ACLB	Asst. Celluloid	3⅜	70
C2152¾LB	Ebony	3⅜	60
C2151LB	Cocobolo	3⅜	60
C2154ACLB	Asst. Celluloid	3⅜	70
2157¼	Spay pocket blade	3⅜	85
2157½	Sheepfoot blade	3⅜	95
2157⅞	Razor point blade	3⅜	90

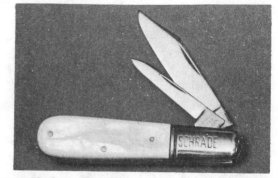

C2154¾AP Abalone Pearl 3⅜" $65

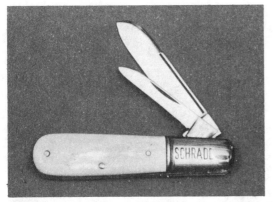

2154½ Marine Pearl   3⅜" $65

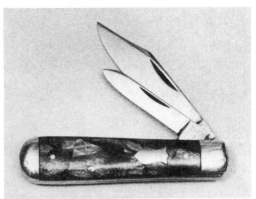

C2154AC Assorted Celluloid   3⅜" $70

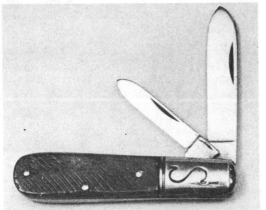

2157¾ Stained Bone   3⅜" $75

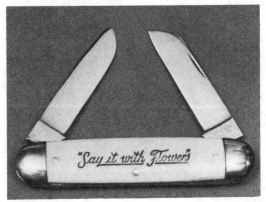

7164½ W Celluloid   3⅝" $55
7163   Bone   3⅝   85

2157   Stained Bone   3⅜" $75

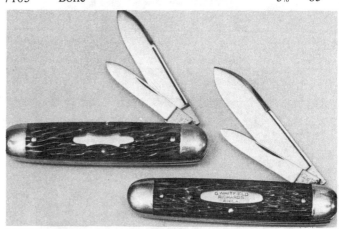

2173   Bone   3⅝" $80
7173   (bottom, has shield on both sides) 3⅝" $100

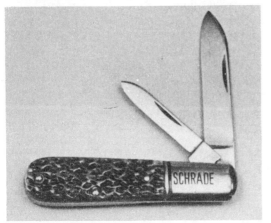

2155   Bone   3⅜" $100

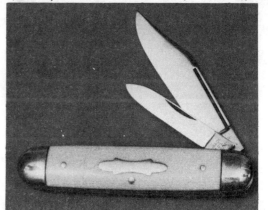

2174¾ W Celluloid   3⅝" $75

Nr.	Handle	Size	Mint
2172	Ebony	3⅝	65
2171	Cocobolo	3⅝	65
2172⅜	Ebony	3⅝	65
2174W	Ivory Celluloid	3⅝	80
2176	Mother of Pearl	3⅝	125
2179GS	Genuine Stag	3⅝	125
7173	Bone	3⅝	75
7171	Cocobolo	3⅝	60
7172	Ebony	3⅝	60
7173¾	Bone	3⅝	75
2173¾	Bone	3⅝	80
2171¾	Cocobolo	3⅝	65
2172¾	Ebony	3⅝	65
71745	Tortoise Celluloid	3⅝	65
2174¾AC	Assorted Celluloid	3⅝	75

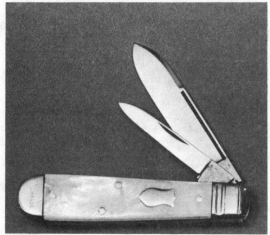

2204M   Marine Pearl   3½" $120

Nr.	Handle	Size	Mint
2211¾	Cocobolo	3½	65
2212¾	Ebony	3½	65
2213¾	Bone	3½	85

7193   Bone   3⅝" $85

2193¾	Bone	3⅝	85

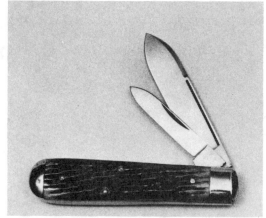

2213   Bone   3½" $65

SS2213	Bone	3½	75
2214¾	Ivory Celluloid	3½	75
2214¾AC	Asst. Celluloid	3½	85
2214P	Smoked Pearl Celluloid	3½	85
2214S	Tortoise Celluloid	3½	85
2214W	Ivory Celluloid	3½	75
2214X	Mottled Green Celluloid	3½	85
2219GS	Gen. Stag	3½	110
2214BSD	Black Celluloid	3⅝	60

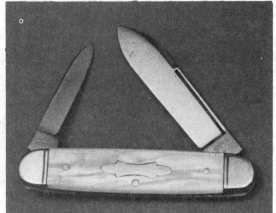

7194M   Marine Pearl   3⅝" $85

2202	Ebony	3½	90
2203	Bone	3½	110
2203¾	Bone	3½	110
2211	Cocobolo	3½	55
2212	Ebony	3½	55

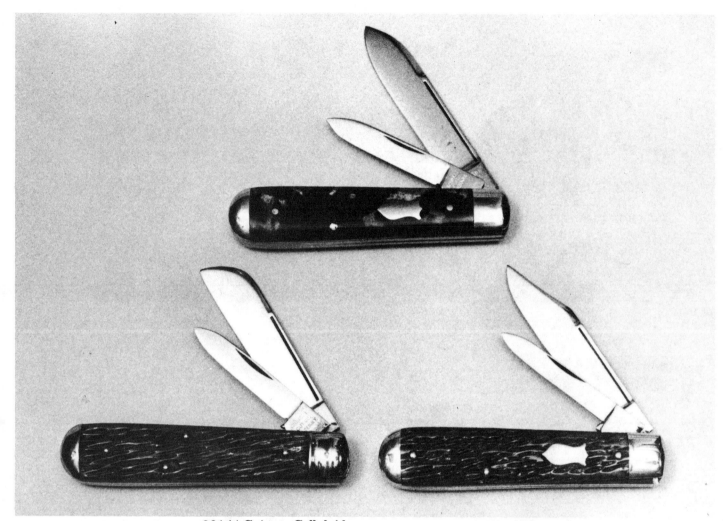

2213½	Bone		3½"	$95

2214AC Asst. Celluloid   3½" $95

3½" $85

2213½	Bone		3½"	$95

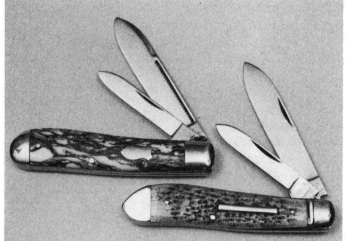

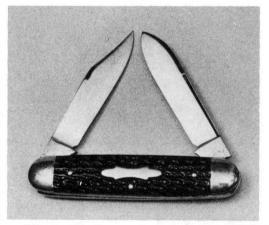

7233	Bone		3⅝"	$140

2224AC Asst. Celluloid   3½" $90

Nr.	Handle	Size	Mint
2221	Cocobolo	3½	85
2223	Bone	3½	100
2222	Ebony	3½	85
2224GP	Gold Pearl Pyralin	3	90
2223½	Bone	3½	110
2223¾	Bone	3½	100
2226	Mother of Pearl	3½	125

Nr.	Handle	Size	Mint
7236	Mother of Pearl	2½	40
7939GSIL	Nickel Silver	2½	30
7933T	Bone	2½	35
7936T	Mother of Pearl	2½	40
7243B	Bone	3⅜	60
7244HT	Black & White Pyralin	3⅜	50
7243¾	Bone	3⅜	60

Nr.	Handle	Size	Mint
2251	Cocobolo	3¼	50
B2253	Bone	3¼	60
B2251	Cocobolo	3¼	50
B2253½	Bone, Sheepfoot Blade	3¼	65

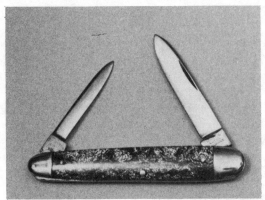

7244　　Christmas Tree　　　　3⅜"　$75

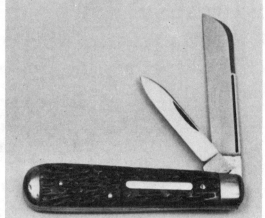

2263½　Bone　　　　　　　　3¼" $65

2252　　Ebony　　　　　　　　3¼"　$50

Nr.	Handle	Size	Mint
2253	Bone	3¼	60

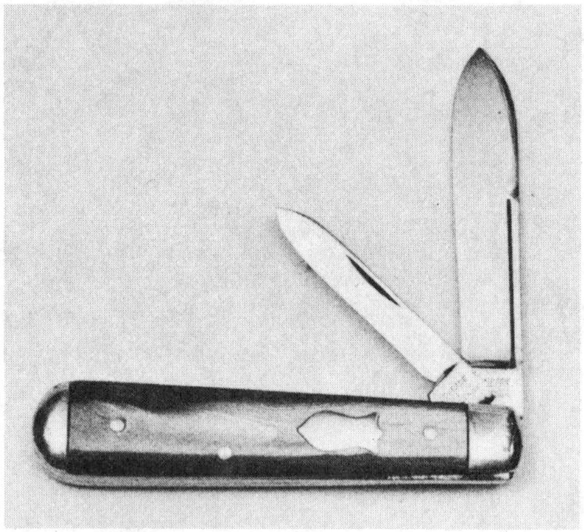

2261　　Cocobolo　　　　　　3¼"　$50

2262	Ebony	3¼	50
2263	Bone	3¼	60
2263¾	Bone Clip Blade	3¼	60
2264P	Smoked Pearl Celluloid	3¼	70
2264G	Green Pearl Pyralin	3¼	70
2264K	Cream & Brown Pyralin	3¼	70
2264S	Tortoise Celluloid	3¼	70
2264W	Ivory Celluloid	3¼	60
2264AC	Asst. Celluloid	3¼	70
2266	Mother of Pearl	3¼	75
2269BR	Brass	3¼	75
2271	Cocobolo	3½	65
2273	Bone	3½	85
2273	Bone	4⅛	110
S2282½	Ebony	3½	130
2283	Bone, chain	3½	95
2283	Bone	3½	85
2281	Cocobolo	3½	85
2283¾	Bone	3½	65
S2283½	Bone	3½	150
2293	Bone	3½	125

2253CH Bone　　　　　　　3¼" $75

2251	Cocobolo, chain	3¼	55
2251¾	Cocobolo	3¼	50
2253¾	Bone	3¼	60
B2251¾	Cocobolo	3¼	50
2252½	Ebony	3¼	50
2253½	Bone	3¼	60
2252⅞	Ebony	3¼	65
S2253EO	Bone, Chain	3¼	75

S7303	**Bone**	4⅛"	$200
Nr.	**Handle**	**Size**	**Mint**
7303	Bone	4⅛	175
RS7304W	Ivory Celluloid	4⅛	125
M2309GSIL	Silver	3⅛	40
7309GSIL	Silver	3⅛	35
7309GIL	without shackle	3⅛	35
7309SS	Shackle	3⅛	35
	Sterling Silver	3⅛	45
S7309F	Fibestos	4⅛	150
7309GM	Metal	3⅛	40
S7309GSIL	Silver	3⅛	65

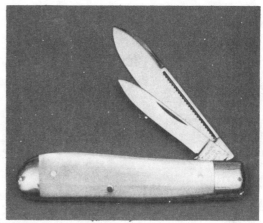

2336	**Pearl**	3⅜"	$150
Nr.	**Handle**	**Size**	**Mint**
2334AC	Asst. Celluloid	3⅜	85
2333¾	Bone	3⅜	75
2333½	Sheepfoot Blade	3⅜	85
7344M	Marine Pearl Celluloid	3⁵⁄₁₆	50
7343	Bone	3⁵⁄₁₆	50
7344K	Cream & Brown Pyralin	3⁵⁄₁₆	50
7344AC	Asst. Celluloid	3⁵⁄₁₆	50

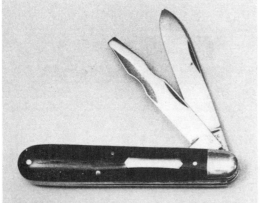

2311SD	**Cocobolo**	3⅝"	$60

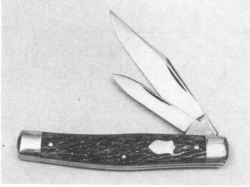

2343	**Bone**	3⁵⁄₁₆"	$60
2344AC	Asst. Celluloid	3⁵⁄₁₆	55

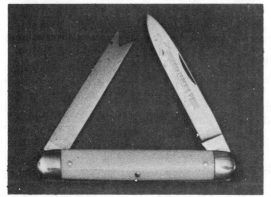

7324W	**Ivory Celluloid**	4"	$60
67324½W	Ivory Celluloid	4	125
7326	Mother Of Pearl		85
2333	Bone	3⅜	85
2331	Cocobolo	3⅜	75
2332	Ebony	3⅜	75
2334K	Cream & Bone Pyralin	3⅜	85
2334W	Ivory Celluloid	3⅜	75

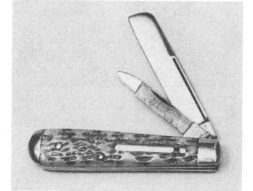

2353	**Bone**	3¼"	$75
7353	Bone	4⅛	85
SS7359GSIL	Nickel Silver	4⅛	65
7359GSIL	Nickel Silver	4⅛	65

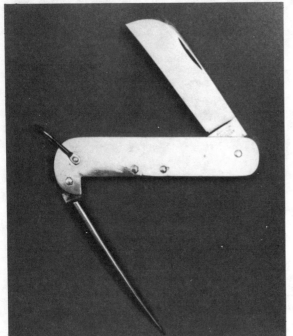

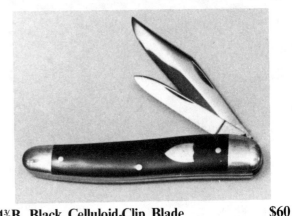

2364⅜B Black Celluloid-Clip Blade   **$60**

Nr.	Handle	Size	Mint
7364¾B	Black Celluloid	3⁹⁄₁₆	60
2364¾B	Black Celluloid	3⁹⁄₁₆	60

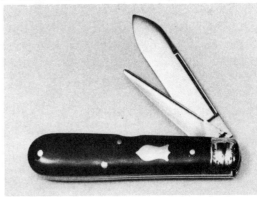

2392   Ebony   3½" $90

Nr.	Handle	Size	Mint
S2393	Bone	3½	135
2393	Bone	3½	100
2393¾	Bone Clip Pocket Blade	3½	100
2394½B	Black Celluloid	3⁹⁄₁₆	60
1394½B	Pen Blade	3⁹⁄₁₆	60
7403	Bone	3⅜	175
7404S	Tortoise Celluloid	3⅜	150
7404W	Ivory Celluloid	3⅜	150
7404X	Mottled Green Celluloid	3⅜	150
7404AC	Asst. Celluloid	3⅜	150
7404K	Cream & Brown Pyralin	3⅜	140
7404D	Black & Green Celluloid	3⅜	140
7404E	Black & Pearl Celluloid	3⅜	140
7404M	Marine Pearl Pyralin	3⅜	140
7404N	Blue & White Celluloid	3⅜	140
7404R	Red Celluloid	3⅜	140
7404V	Black & White Celluloid	3⅜	140
SS7404AC	Asst. Celluloid	3⅜	125
7404	Blue Pearl Celluloid	3⅜	150
7404AP	Abalone Pearl Pyralin	3⅜	150
7404B	Black Celluloid	3⅜	150
7404BP	Black Pearl Celluloid	3⅜	150
7404BRNZ	Bronze Celluloid	3⅜	150
7404C	Cocobolo Celluloid	3⅜	150
7404G	Green Pearl Celluloid	3⅜	150
7404GP	Green Pearl Celluloid	3⅜	150
7404GP	Gold Pearl Celluloid	3⅜	150

SS7359GSIL Nickel Silver (Marlin Spike) 4½" $200

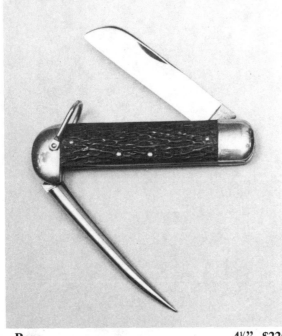

7353   Bone   4⅛" $225

2363   Bone   3½" $100

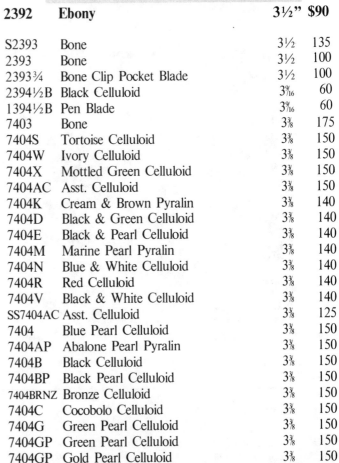

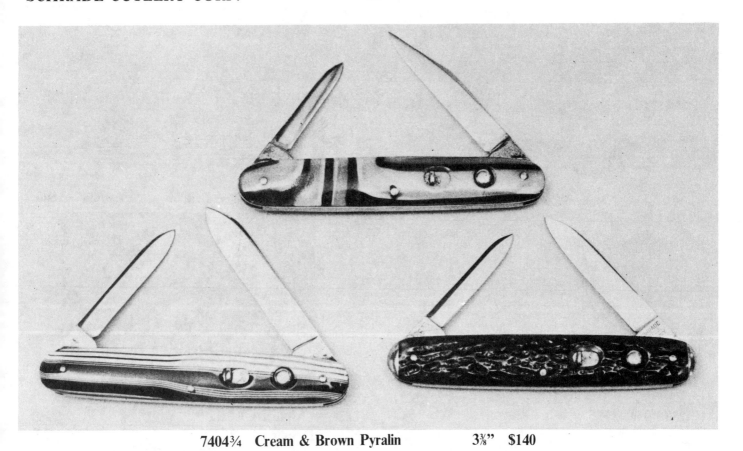

7404¾ **Cream & Brown Pyralin**   3⅜" $140

7404A **Black & White Celluloid**   3⅜" $140   **7403T** **Bone**   3⅜" $175

Nr.	Handle	Size	Mint	Nr.	Handle	Size	Mint
7404	Horn Celluloid	3⅜	150	7414G	Green Pearl Celluloid	3⅜	175
7404K	Cream & Brown Pyralin	3⅜	150	7414P	Smoked Pearl Celluloid	3⅜	175
74040	Onyx Celluloid	3⅜	150	7414W	Ivory Celluloid	3⅜	175
7404P	Smoked Pearl Celluloid	3⅜	150	7414BT	Black Celluloid	3⅜	175
07404W	Ivory Celluloid	3⅜	150	7413T	Bone	3⅜	175
7404GT	Green Pearl Celluloid	3⅜	150	7414ST	Tortoise Celluloid	3⅜	175
7404BT	Black Celluloid	3⅜	150	7414T	Ivory Celluloid	3⅜	175
7404BPT	Black Pearl Celluloid	3⅜	150	7416T	Mother Of Pearl	3⅜	425
7404BlueT	Blue Pearl Celluloid	3⅜	150	7416	Mother Of Pearl	3⅜	425
7404CT	Cocobolo Celluloid	3⅜	150	M7423TSha	With Shackle	3⅛	45
N07404W	Ivory Celluloid	3⅜	150	SS7423T	Bone	3⅛	65
7404PT	Smoked Pearl Celluloid	3⅜	150	SS7424GT	Green Jade Celluloid	3⅛	55
7404GPT	Gold Pearl Celluloid	3⅜	150	SS7424KT	Cream & Brown Pyralin	3⅛	55
7404HornT	Celluloid	3⅜	150	SS7424MT	Marine Pearl Celluloid	3⅛	55
7404KT	Cream & Brown Pyralin	3⅜	150	SS2423	Bone	3⅛	50
7404ST	Tortoise Celluloid	3⅜	150	SS2424AC	Asst. Celluloid	3⅛	45
7404WT	Ivory Celluloid	3⅜	150	SS2426	Mother Of Pearl	3⅛	55
7404ACT	Assorted Celluloid	3⅜	150	7424SqMB	Marine Pearl Celluloid	3⅛	40
7404¾E	Pearl & Black Celluloid	3⅜	140	7423T	Bone	3⅛	50
7404¾AC	Asst. Celluloid	3⅜	140	7424MB	Marine Pyralin	3⅛	40
7406	Mother Of Pearl	3⅜	400	7424WB	Ivory Celluloid	3⅛	40
7406T	Mother Of Pearl	3⅜	400	7424ACB	Asst. Celluloid	3⅛	45
7409GSIL	Nickel Silver	3⅜	125	F7423T	Bone	3⅛	45
7449GSIL	Nickel Silver	3⅜	125	F7426T	Mother Of Pearl	3⅛	50
7413	Bone	3⅜	165	2423	Bone	3⅛	50
7414S	Tortoise Celluloid	3⅜	175	2423EO	Bone	3⅛	60
7414B	Black Celluloid	3⅜	175	7423¾B	Bone	3⅛	50
7414C	Cocobolo Celluloid	3⅜	175	7424CT	Cocobolo Celluloid	3⅛	40

432	*SCHRADE CUTLERY CORP.*

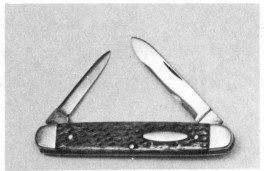

7423SqB Bone	3⅛"	$50

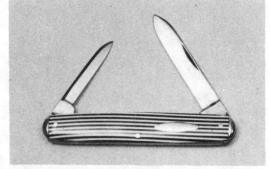

7424HT Black & White Pyralin	3⅛"	$40

M7423T Bone	3⅛"	$45

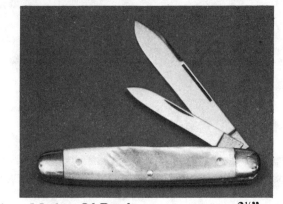

2426	Mother Of Pearl	3⅛"	$60
Nr.	**Handle**	**Size**	**Mint**
7424PT	Smoked Pearl Celluloid	3⅛	40
7424ST	Tortoise Celluloid	3⅛	40
7424WT	Ivory Celluloid	3⅛	40
7424ACT	Asst. Celluloid	3⅛	40
2424C	Cocobolo Celluloid	3⅛	45
2424B	Black Celluloid	3⅛	50
2424H	Black & White Pyralin	3⅛	50
2424J	Red-White-Amber Pyralin	3⅛	50
2424K	Cream & Brown Pyralin	3⅛	50
2424P	Smoked Pearl Celluloid	3⅛	50
2424S	Tortoise Celluloid	3⅛	50
2424US	Red-White-Blue Celluloid	3⅛	50
2424W	Ivory Celluloid	3⅛	50
2424AC	Asst. Celluloid	3⅛	50
2424WED	Ivory Celluloid	3⅛	45
2424CED	Cocobolo Celluloid	3⅛	45
2424PEO	Smoked Pearl Celluloid	3⅛	50
2424SEO	Tortoise Celluloid	3⅛	50
2424USEO	Tortoise Celluloid	3⅛	50

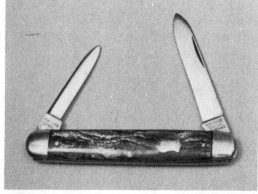

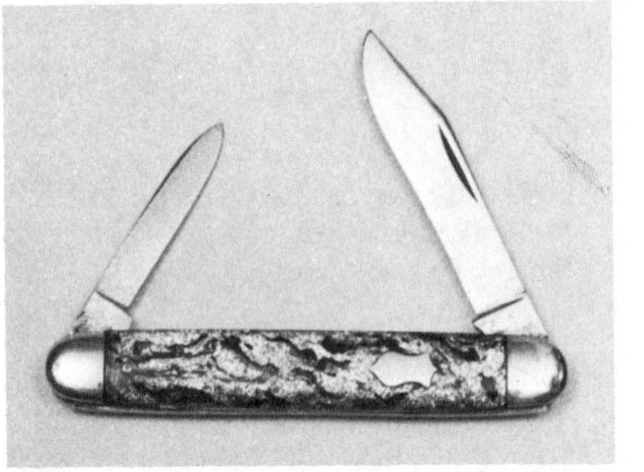

7424B Christmas Tree	3⅛"	$100

SS7424 Christmas Tree	3⅛"	$125

Nr.	Handle	Size	Mint
7424BT	Black Celluloid	3⅛	40
7424GLT	Goldaleur Celluloid	3⅛	40
7424GPT	Gold Pearl Pyralin	3⅛	40
7424KT	Cream & Brown Pyralin	3⅛	40
7424MT	Marine Pearl Pyralin	3⅛	40

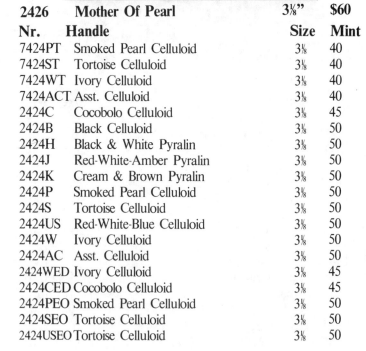

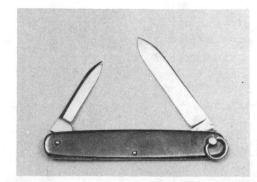

R7429GM Metal	3⅛"	$50

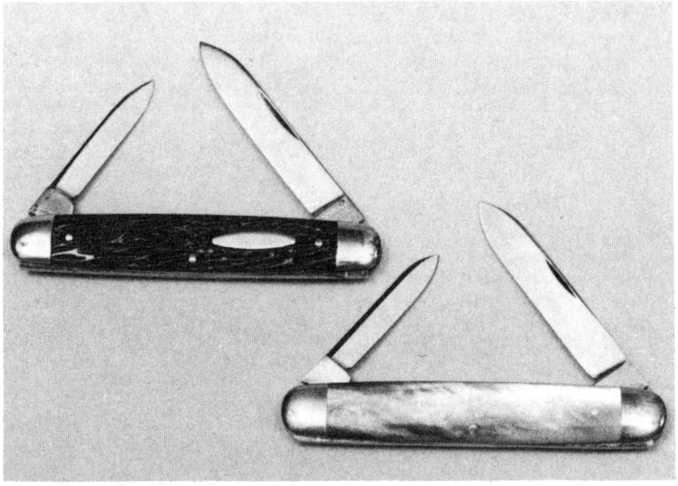

7423B Bone 3⅛" $50
7426B Mother Of Pearl 3⅛" $60

Nr.	Handle	Size	Mint
2424USED	Red-White-Blue Celluloid	3⅛	50
2424ACED	Asst. Celluloid	3⅛	50
2423¾	Bone	3⅛	50
2424¾J	Red-White-Amber Pyralin	3⅛	50
2424¾S	Tortoise Celluloid	3⅛	50
2424¾AC	Asst. Celluloid	3⅛	50
SS7426T	Mother Of Pearl	3⅛	60
SS7426B	Mother Of Pearl	3⅛	60
SS7423B	Bone	3⅛	55
F7426	Mother Of Pearl	3⅛	50
7426T	Mother Of Pearl	3⅛	50
7426	Mother Of Pearl	3⅛	50
7429GST	Gen. Stag	3⅛	55

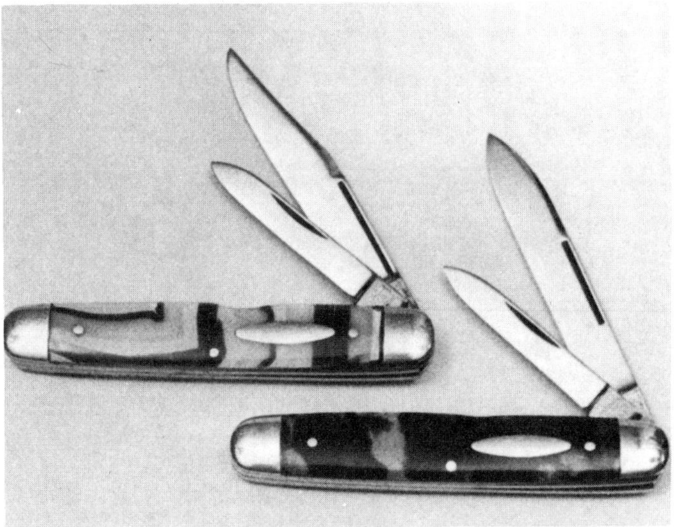

2424¾K Cream & Brown Pyralin 3⅛" $50
2424ST Tortoise Celluloid 3⅛" $50

7429GSIL	Nickel Silver	3⅛	35
SSR7429GSIL	Nickel Silver	3⅛	40
R7429GM	Metal	3⅛	35
R7429GSIL	Nickel Silver	3⅛	35
R7429SS	Sterling Silver	3⅛	45

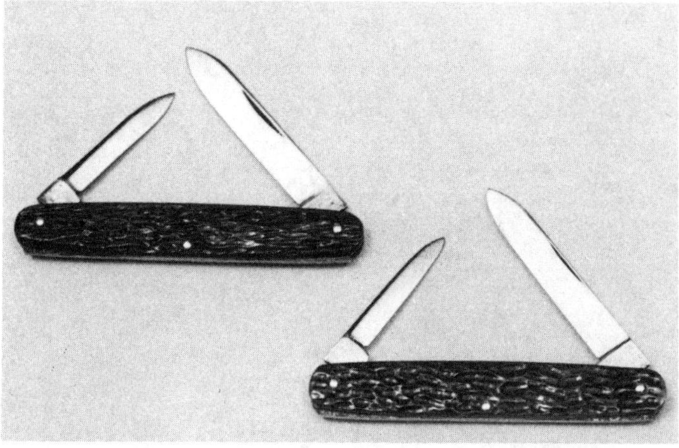

7433 Bone 3⅛" $45

Nr.	Handle	Size	Mint
S7434M	Marine Pearl Pyralin	3⅛	35
57434N	Blue & White Celluloid	3⅛	40
7434C	Cocobolo Celluloid	3⅛	45
7434G	Green Pearl Pyralin	3⅛	45
7434MB	Mottled Blue Pyralin	3⅛	45
7434MR	Mottled Red Pyralin	3⅛	45
74340	Onyx Celluloid	3⅛	45
7434P	Smoked Pearl Celluloid	3⅛	45
7434S	Tortoise Celluloid	3⅛	45
7434W	Ivory Celluloid	3⅛	45
7434X	Mottled Green Celluloid	3⅛	45
7434AC	Asst. Pyralin	3⅛	45
S7434C	Cocobolo Celluloid	3⅛	45
S7433	Bone	3⅛	45
S7434G	Green Pearl Pyralin	3⅛	45
S7434P	Smoked Pearl Celluloid	3⅛	45
S7434S	Tortoise Celluloid	3⅛	45
S7434W	Ivory Celluloid	3⅛	45
S7434X	Mottled Green Celluloid	3⅛	45
S7434AC	Celluloid	3⅛	45
7439GSIL	Nickel Silver	3⅛	35
7439GM	Metal	3⅛	35
F7444GGShac	Green Gold Plate	2⅛	225
F7444DSha	Black & Green Celluloid	2⅛	125
7444SS	Sterling Sliver	2⅞	135
744GG	Gold Plate	2⅞	250
744SSShac	Sterling Silver	2⅞	135
7444STG	Stag Celluloid	2⅞	125
F7444B	Black Celluloid	2⅞	110
F7444S	Tortoise Celluloid	2⅞	125
7444E	Black & Pearl Celluloid	2⅞	125
7444D	Black & Green Celluloid	2⅞	125
7444G	Green Jade Celluloid	2⅞	125
7444K	Cream & Brown Pyralin	2⅞	125
7444M	Marine Pearl Celluloid	2⅞	125
7444Q	Blue & White Celluloid	2⅞	125
7444S	Tortoise Celluloid	2⅞	125
7444AC	Asst. Celluloid	2⅞	125
7444K	Cream & Brown Pyralin	2⅞	110
7444R	Red Celluloid	2⅞	110
7444V	Black & White Celluloid	2⅞	110

434

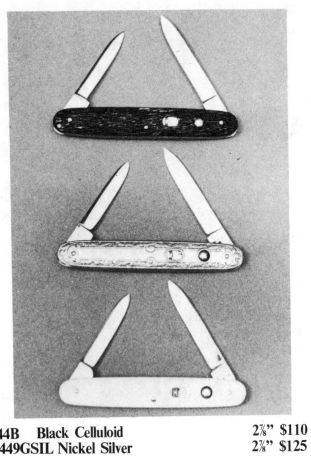

Nr.	Handle		Size	Mint
7444B	Black Celluloid		2⅞"	$110
F7449GSIL	Nickel Silver		2⅞"	$125
7444W	Ivory Celluloid		2⅞"	$125

Nr.	Handle	Size	Mint
8453T	Bone	3⅛	85
8456T	Mother Of Pearl	3⅛	85
8456B	Mother Of Pearl	3⅛	85
8456	Mother Of Pearl, Scissors	3⅛	85

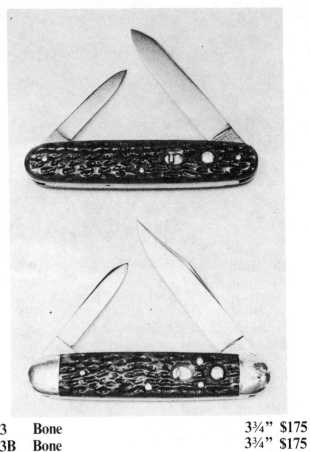

Nr.	Handle	Size	Mint
7503	Bone	3¾"	$175
7503B	Bone	3¾"	$175

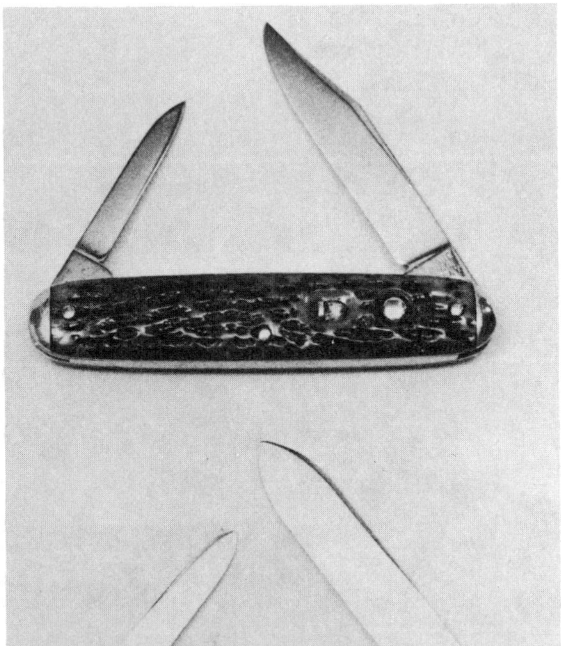

S7463	Bone	3⅝"	$125

7479GSIL	Silver	3⅛	35
7479GSIL	Silver Shackle	3⅛	35
7483T	Bone	3¼	50
07484W	Ivory Celluloid	3¼	45
7486	Mother Of Pearl	3¼	60
7484AC	Asst. Celluloid	3¼	50
SS7486	Mother Of Pearl	3¼	55
07494W	Ivory Celluloid	3⁷⁄₁₆	45
7494W	Ivory Celluloid	3⁷⁄₁₆	40

7503¾T	Bone	3¾"	$175
7504K	Cream & Brown Pyralin	3¾"	$150

Nr.	Handle	Size	Mint
7503T	Bone	3¾	175
7503¾B	Bone	3¾	200
7504GP	Gold Pearl Celluloid	3¾	150
7504HORN	Celluloid	3¾	150
75040	Onyx Celluloid	3¾	150
7504P	Smoked Pearl Celluloid	3¾	150
7504S	Tortoise Celluloid	3¾	150
7504W	Ivory Celluloid	3¾	150
7504X	Mottled Green Celluloid	3¾	150
7504AC	Asst. Celluloid	3¾	150
7504C	Cocobolo Celluloid	3¾	150
7504B	Black Celluloid	3¾	150
7504BRNZ	Bronze Celluloid	3¾	150
7504G	Green Pearl Celluloid	3¾	150
7504BT	Black Celluloid	3¾	150
7504CT	Cocobolo Celluloid	3¾	150
7504GT	Green Pearl Celluloid	3¾	150
7504KT	Cream & Brown Pyralin	3¾	150
7504PT	Smoked Pearl Celluloid	3¾	150
7504ST	Tortoise Celuloid	3¾	150
7504WT	Ivory Celluloid	3¾	150
7504CB	Cocobolo Celluloid	3¾	175
7504BB	Black Celluloid	3¾	175
7504PB	Smoked Pearl Celluloid	3¾	175
7504SB	Tortoise Celluloid	3¾	175
7504WB	Ivory Celluloid	3¾	175
7504¾PT	Smoked Pearl Celluloid	3¾	150
7504¾BT	Black Celluloid	3¾	150
7504¾CT	Cocobolo Celluloid	3¾	150
7504¾ST	Tortoise Celluloid	3¾	150
7504¾WT	Ivory Celluloid	3¾	150
7504¾S	Tortoise Celluloid	3¾	150
7504¾W	Ivory Celluloid	3¾	150
7504¾X	Mottled Green Celluloid	3¾	150
7504¾AC	Assorted Celluloid	3¾	150
7504¾K	Cream & Brown Pyralin	3¾	150
7504¾B	Black Celluloid	3¾	125
7504¾M	Marine Pearl Pyralin	3¾	125
7504¾G	Green Pearl Celluloid	3¾	150
7503¾	Bone	3¾	175
7504¾BP	Black Pearl Celluloid	3¾	150
7504¾BRNZ	Bronze Celluloid	3¾	150
7504¾C	Cocobolo Celluloid	3¾	150
7504¾GP	Gold Pearl Celluloid	3¾	150
7504¾Horn	Celluloid	3¾	150
7504¾K	Cream & Brown Pyralin	3¾	150
7504¾O	Onyx Celluloid	3¾	150
7504¾P	Smoked Pearl Celluloid	3¾	150
7504¾PB	Smoked Pearl Celluloid	3¾	175
7504¾BB	Black Celluloid	3¾	175
7504¾CB	Cocobolo Celluloid	3¾	175
7504¾SB	Tortoise Celluloid	3¾	175
7504¾WB	Ivory Celluloid	3¾	175
7506¾B	Mother Of Pearl	3¾	450
7506B	Mother Of Pearl	3¾	450

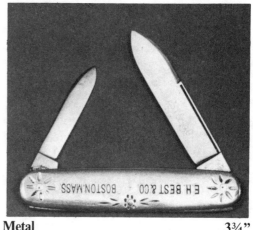

| 7529 | Metal | 3¾" | $40 |

Nr.	Handle	Size	Mint
7523B	Bone	3¾	200
7534¾C	Cocobolo Celluloid	3¾	200
7533B	Bone	3¾	200
C2534M	Marine Pearl Pyralin	3¹⁄₁₆	40

| C2533 | Bone, Flat Bolsters | 3¹⁄₁₆" | $50 |

| 2533 | Bone | 3¹⁄₁₆" | 60 |

C2534K	Pyralin	3¹⁄₁₆	40
C2534¾E	Celluloid	3¹⁄₁₆	45
C2534¾Q	Celluloid	3¹⁄₁₆	45
C2533¾SQ	Bone	3¹⁄₁₆	50
7554¾B	Black Celluloid	3¼	55

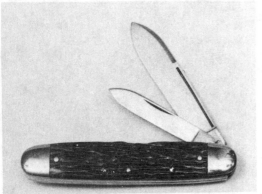

| 2563 | Bone | 3⅜" | $60 |

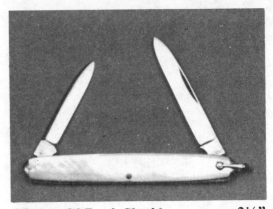

| 7606 | Mother Of Pearl, Shackle | 2¼" | $45 |

Nr.	Handle	Size	Mint
7606	Mother Of Pearl	2¼	45
7606	Mother Of Pearl	2¼	50
7609GM	Metal, Shackle	2¼	40
7609GM	Without shackle	2¼	40
E7609Gold	Gold Filled, Shackle	2¼	50
7609GSIL	Shac	2¼	40
C76099SSS	hac Corrugated Sterling Silver	2¼	50
7609	Gold Plate	2¼	50
7609SS	Sterling Silver	2¼	50

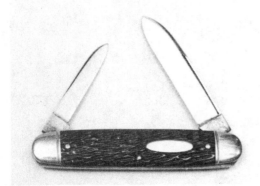

| 7563 | Bone | 3⅜" | $65 |

Nr.	Handle	Size	Mint
7564B	Black Celluloid	3⅜	50
SS2563	Bone	3⅜	65
SS2546AC	Asst. Celluloid	3⅜	55
2563¾	Bone	3⅜	60
07564W	Ivory Celluloid	3⅜	45
2564K	Cream with Brown Pyralin	3⅜	60
2564P	Smoked Pearl Celluloid	3⅜	60
2564AC	Assorted Celluloid	3⅜	60
2566	Mother Of Pearl	3⅜	75
7564¾S	Tortoise Celluloid	3⅜	60
7563¾	Bone	3⅜	60

| 2623 | Bone | 3½" | $75 |

2623¾	Clip Blades	3½	75
7623¾	Bone	3½	75
7624¾K	Cream & Brown Pyralin	3½	65

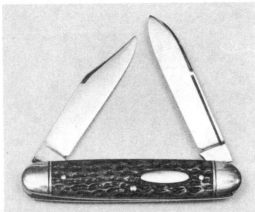

| 7573 | Bone | 3⅜" | $150 |

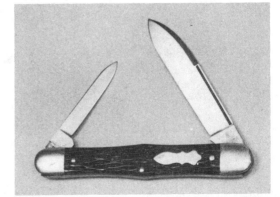

| 7633 | Bone | 3⅝" | $65 |

7604W	Ivory Celluloid	2¼	25
7604AC	Assorted Celluloid	2¼	30
7604	Ivory Celluloid	2¼	25
7604A	Shac Assorted Celluloid	2¼	30

SCHRADE CUTLERY

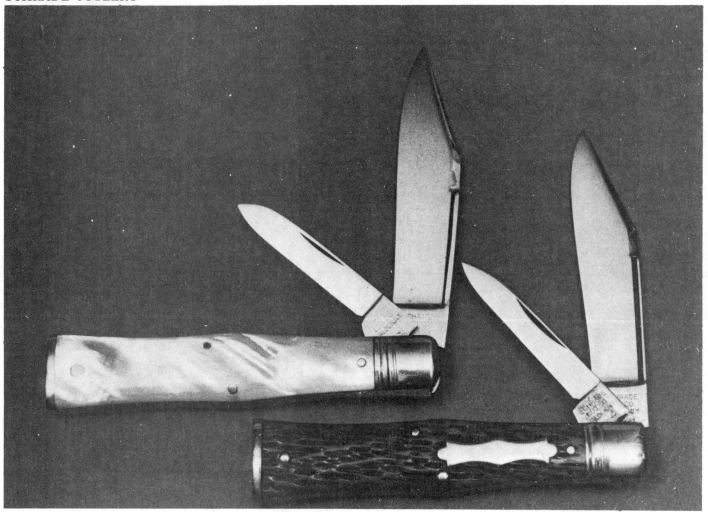

2646	Top: Pearl		4"	$650
2643	Bottom Bone		4"	$400

Nr.	Handle	Lgth.	Mint	Nr.	Handle	Lgth.	Mint
2643¾	Bone	4	275	7656	Mother of Pearl	3	50
7653T	Bone	3	45	R7663	Bone	3¹/₁₆"	60
7653	Bone	3	40	R7664E	Black & Pearl Celluloid	3¹/₁₆	50
7654W	Ivory Celluloid	3	30				
7654AC	Assorted Celluloid	3	35				
7654	HornT Celluloid	3	40				
7654AC	Assorted Celluloid	3	40				

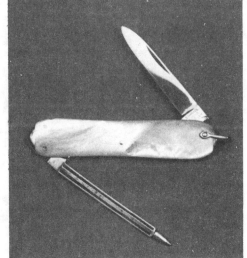

7656T   **Mother Of Pearl**   **3"**   **$50**

7663¼	**Bone**	**3¹/₈₁₆"**	**$100**
R7663⅛	Bone	3¹/₁₆	50
R7664¾B	Black Celluloid	3¹/₁₆	40
7664M	Marine Pearl Pyralin	2¹/₁₆	50
7663	Bone	3¹/₁₆	60

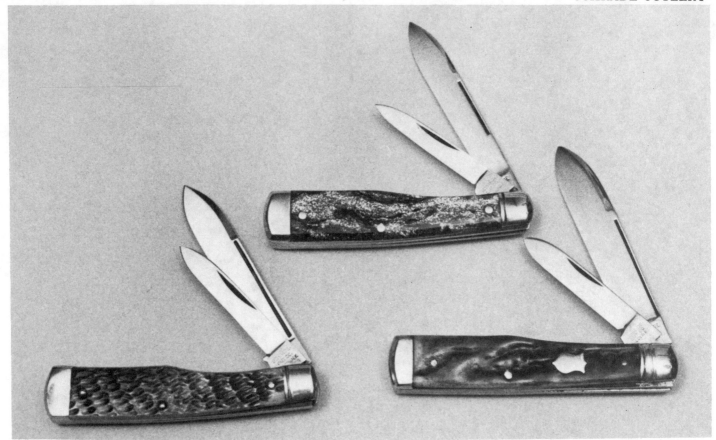

GUNSTOCK PATTERN			2694AC	Top: Christmas Tree		3"	$400
2693	Left: Bone	3"	$225	2693	Right: Genuine Stag	3"	$400

Nr.	Handle	Lgth.	Mint	Nr.	Handle	Lgth.	Mint
2694B	Black Celluloid	3	110	S7703B	Bone	2⅞	40
2694M	Marine Pearl Celluloid	3	110	S7706B	Mother Of Pearl	2⅞	45
2964AC	Asst. Celluloid	3	110	7703B	Bone	2⅞	45
				F7704WT	Ivory Celluloid	2⅞	30
				F7706T	Mother Of Pearl	2⅞	40
				7704WT	Ivory Celluloid	2⅞	30
				7704PT	Smoked Pearl Celluloid	2⅞	35
				7704ST	Celluloid	2⅞	35
				M7704GT	Green Jade Celluloid	2⅞	40
				M7703T	Bone	2⅞	40
				M7704MT	Marine Pearl Celluloid	2⅞	40
				M7704GT	Green Jade Celluloid, Shackle	2⅞	40

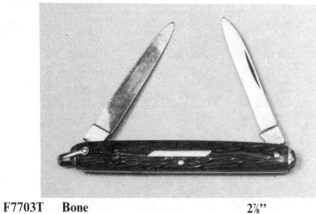

F7703T Bone   2⅞" $40

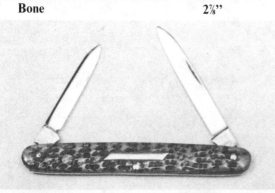

7703T Bone   2⅞" $40

7706T Mother Of Pearl   2⅞" $45

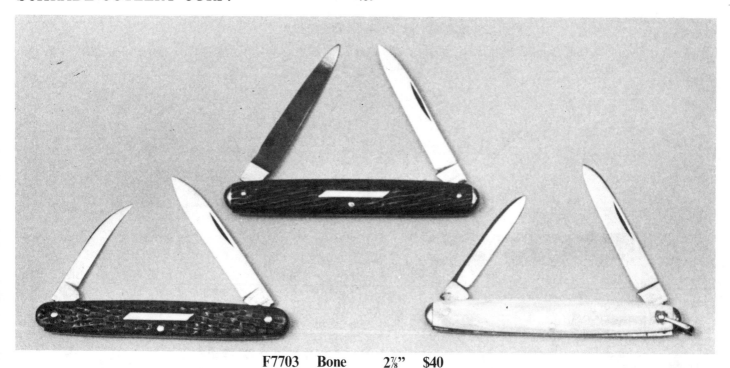

F7703 **Bone** 2⅞" **$40**

7703 **Bone** 2⅞" **$40**

7704MT **Marine Pearl Celluloid** 2⅞" **$35**

Nr.	Handle	Size	Mint
7706	Shackle, Mother Of Pearl	2⅞	40
M7709GOID	Without Shackle	2⅞	50
7709GSIL	Shackle, Nickel Silver	2⅞	25
7709GSIL	Nickel Silver	2⅞	25
M7719GM	Metal	2⅞	40
M7719GM	Shackle, Nickel Silver	2⅞	40
7719SS	Sterling Silver	2⅞	45
7719GSIL	Nickel Silver	2⅞	35

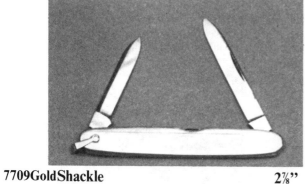

7709Gold **Shackle** 2⅞" **$50**

Nr.	Handle	Size	Mint
M7704NT	Celluloid, Shackle	2⅞	35
M7704NT	Striped Celluloid without shackle	2⅞	35
M7703T	Bone, Shackle	2⅞	40
M7704MT	Marine Pearl Pyralin	2⅞	30
F7706	Mother Of Pearl	2⅞	40
7706	Mother Of Pearl	2⅞	40
7704ST	Tortoise Shell, Celluloid, Shac	2⅞	40
7704ACT	Asst. Celluloid, Shackle	2⅞	40
7706T	Mother Of Pearl	2⅞	40
7704BT	Black Celluloid	2⅞	35
7704LT	Pearl Celluloid	2⅞	35
7704LT	Shackle, Nickle Silver	2⅞	35
7704MT	Marine Pearl Pyralin	2⅞	35
7704MT	Shackle, Silver	2⅞	35
SS7704BT	Black Celluloid	2⅞	35
SS7704LT	Pearl Celluloid	2⅞	35
SS704LT	Shackle, Nickle Silver	2⅞	35
SS7706T	Mother Of Pearl	2⅞	40
M7706B	Mother Of Pearl	2⅞	45
7706B	Mother Of Pearl Threaded Bols.	2⅞	50
7706T	Mother Of Pearl	2⅞	45

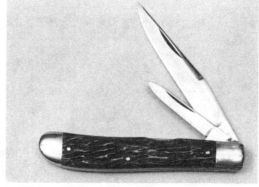

2723¾ **Plain Clip** 2⅞" **$45**

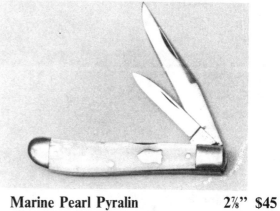

2724⅜ **Marine Pearl Pyralin** 2⅞" **$45**

Nr.	Handle	Size	Mint
2723⅜	Bone	2⅞	45
2724⅜K	Brown & Cream Pyralin	2⅞	45
2723	Spear Blade	2⅞	45

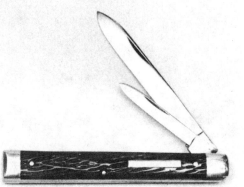

2733	**Bone**		**3¾" $175**
7743	Bone, Congress	3	55
7746	Mother Of Pearl	3	65
7744M	Marine Pearl Celluloid	3	45
7744K	Cream & Brown Pyralin	3	45
7749GS	Stag	3	65

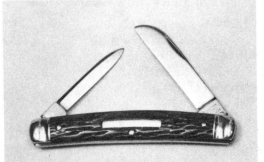

7753　Bone　　　　　3½" $65

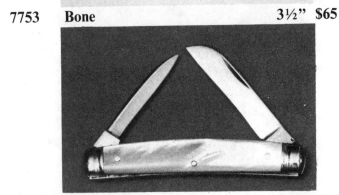

7756　Mother Of Pearl　　　3½" $75

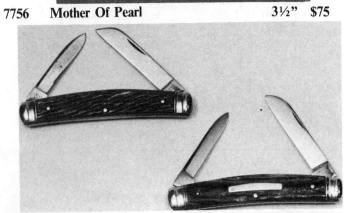

SS7753　Bone　　　　　3½" $65

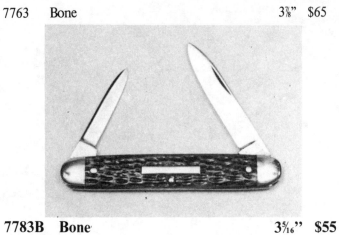

7763　Bone　　　　　　　3⅞" $65

7783B　Bone　　　　　3⁵⁄₁₆" $55

Nr.	Handle	Size	Mint
7784ACB	Assorted Celluloid	3⁵⁄₁₆	50
7786B	Pearl	3⁵⁄₁₆	65
SS7783B	Bone	3⁵⁄₁₆	50
SS7784ACB	Assorted Celluloid	3⁵⁄₁₆	45
SS7786B	Mother Of Pearl	3⁵⁄₁₆	60
7783¾B	Bone	3⁵⁄₁₆	55
7784PT	Smoked Pearl Celluloid	3⁵⁄₁₆	45
7783T	Bone	3⁵⁄₁₆	50
7784MT	Marine Pearl Pyralin	3⁵⁄₁₆	45
7784PPT	Persian Pearl Celluloid	3⁵⁄₁₆	45
7784T	Assorted Celluloid	3⁵⁄₁₆	45
7786T	Mother Of Pearl	3⁵⁄₁₆	50
7786	Mother Of Pearl	3⁵⁄₁₆	50

7793T　Bone　　　　　3¼" $65

7794¾MT	Marine Pearl Pyralin	3¼	60
7793¾B	Bone	3¼	55
7803¾	Bone	4	90

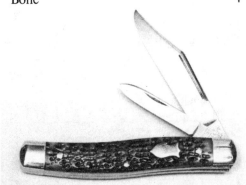

2813¾　Bone　　　　　4" $90

SCHRADE CUTLERY CORP.

7813 Genuine Stag (Germany) 4" $1,000

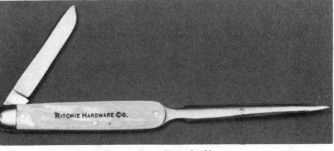

**L1824M Marine Pearl Pyralin; 3⅛"
Handle; 2⅞" Letter Opener 6" $45**

7813 Bone 4" $175

7843 Bone 4" $90

**S7814 Stg. Black Jigged Comp. 4" $300
Hawbaker Special, Improved Muskrat**

Nr.	Handle	Size	Mint
7812	Ebony	4	150
2814¾G	Green Pearl Celluloid	4	90
2814¾P	Smoked Pearl Celluloid	4	90
2813¾AC	Assorted Celluloid	4	90
2813	Bone	4	90
S7814¾Stg	Clip Blade	4	200

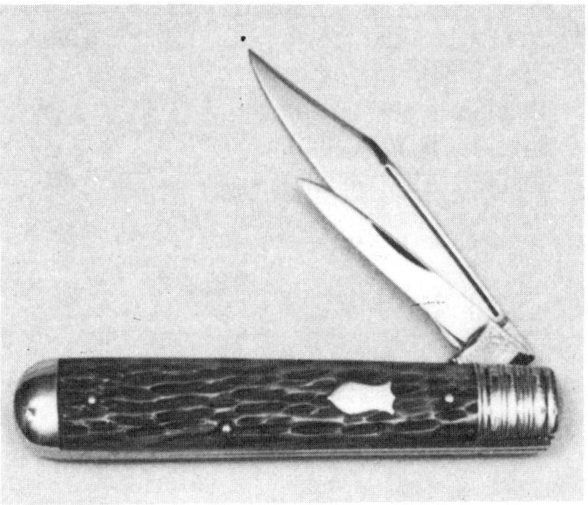

L2863¾ Bone 4½" $125

Nr.	Handle	Size	Mint
2863	Bone	4½	125
2863¾	Clip Pocket Blades	4½	125
07894W	Ivory Celluloid	3¾	45
7894½W	Ivory Celluloid	3¾	50

2903¾ Bone 3½" $65

2903	Bone	3¾	65
7903	Bone	3½	90
7904AC	Assorted Celluloid	3½	85
2904¾G	Green Pearl Celluloid	3½	55
2904¾AC	Assorted Celluloid	3½	55

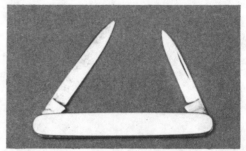

M7936 Nickle Silver Without Shackle   2½" $40

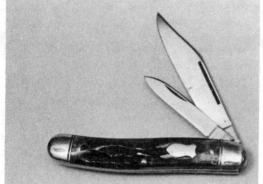

2909¾ Genuine Stag   3½" $75

M7936T Shackle, Mother Of Pearl   2½" $40

7913	Bone	3½	60
2919	Brass	3½	110
7923	Bone	3½	60
7924G	Green Pearl Pyralin	3½	60
7924AC	Assorted Celluloid	3½	60
7934BT	Black Celluloid	2½	30
7934WT	Ivory Celluloid	2½	30
7933T	Shackle, Bone	2½	35
7934BT	Shackle, Black Celluloid	2½	30
7934WT	Shackle, Ivory Celluloid	2½	30
7936T	Shackle, Mother Of Pearl	2½	40

Nr.	Handle	Size	Mint
M7936T	Shackle, Mother Of Pearl	2½	40
M7933T	Shackle, Bone	2½	35
M7936	Shackle, Nickle Silver Tip Bolster	2½	40

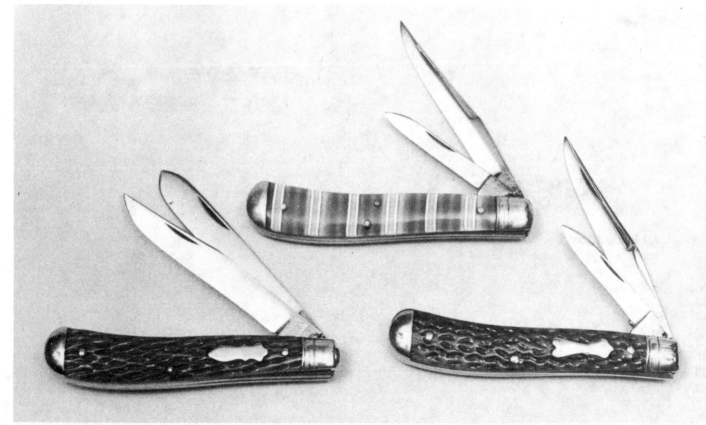

S2943¾ Bone 3⅞" $150   **2944¾J Pyralin 3⅞" $125**   **2943¾ Bone 3⅞" $110**

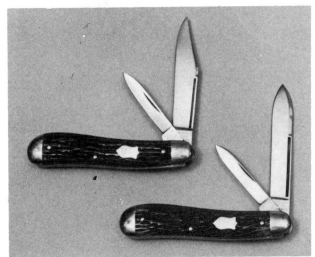

| 2953¾ | Bone | 3" | $65 |
| 2953 | Bone | 3" | $65 |

Nr.	Handle	Size	Mint
2954¾M	Marine Pearl Pyralin	3	65
2954¾P	Smoked Pearl Celluloid	3	65
2954¾AC	Assorted Celluloid	3	65
2956¾	Mother Of Pearl	3	75
2954AC	Assorted Celluloid	3	65

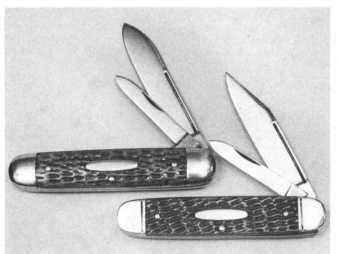

| R2973 | Bone | 4¼" | $150 |
| 2973¾ | Bone | 4¼" | $150 |

3053½	Bone	3⅝"	$165
C8083B	Bone	3	85
S8083B	Bone	3	60

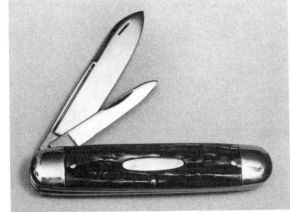

| 2973 | Genuine Stag | 4½" | $275 |

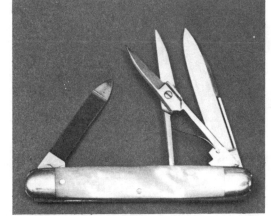

FS8086B Mother Of Pearl   3" $90

R7973	Bone	4½"	$250
R2974W	Ivory Celluloid	4¼	125
2974¾W	Ivory Celluloid	4¼	125

| 8083B | Bone | 3" | $80 |

Nr.	Handle	Size	Mint
8089GSB	Gen. Stag	3	90
8099GSIL	Nickel Silver	3 1/16	50

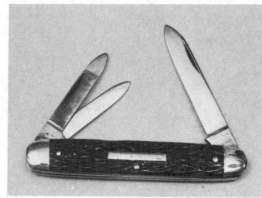

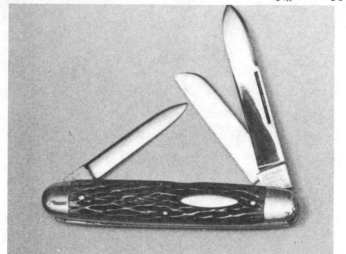

8143B	Bone	3⅛"	$85
8149GSB	Stag	3⅛	100
SL8146B	Mother Of Pearl	3⅛	90
8146	Mother Of Pearl	3⅛	90
8146T	Mother Of Pearl	3⅛	90
8143T	Bone	3⅛	80

8103	Bone	3⅛"	$75
8104P	Smoked Pearl Celluloid	3⅛	75
8103¼LB	Bone	3⅛	75
8104LBAC	Assorted Celluloid	3⅛	75
S8103	Bone	3⅛	55
S8104AC	Assorted Celluloid	3⅛	50
81043	Bone	4 5/16	150
71043	Bone	4 5/16	150
81004⅜Stg	Fibestos	3⅞	90
81016Sha	Mother Of Pearl	2½	50
8113B	Bone	3⅜	90
8113T	Bone	3⅜	90

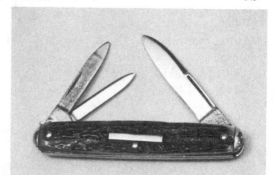

8149GST	Stag	3⅛"	$100
8163	Bone	3⅝	$125

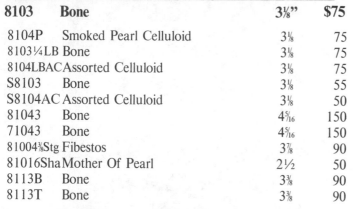

8114 B	Celluloid	3⅜"	$100
8114PB	Celluloid	3⅜	100
8114PT	Celluloid	3⅜	90
8114ST	Tortoise Celluloid	3⅜	90
8116	Mother Of Pearl	3⅜	90
8114W	Ivory Celluloid	3⅜	80
8116T	Mother Of Pearl	3⅜	90
8118T	Buffalo Horn	3⅜	90
8116B	Mother Of Pearl	3⅜	110
8118B	Buffalo Horn	3⅜	100
8133¾	Bone	3¼	90
8134¾KLB	Cream & Brown Pyralin	3¼	90

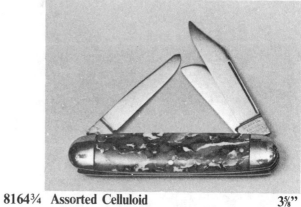

8164¾	Assorted Celluloid	3⅝"	$65
SS8173	Bone	3⅝	140

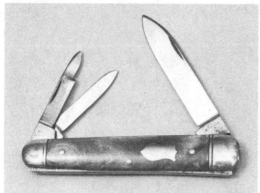

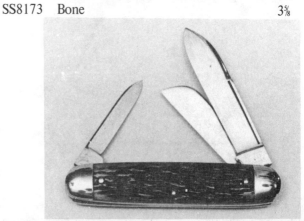

8173	Bone	3⅝"	$125

Nr.	Handle	Size	Mint
8172	Ebony	3⅝	100
8174GP	Gold Pearl Pyralin	3⅝	125
8174W	Ivory Celluloid	3⅝	110
8173¼	Bone	3⅝	125
S8174¼K	Cream & Brown Pyralin	3⅝	110
S8173¼	Bone	3⅝	125
8174¾X	Celluloid	3⅝	125
8173¾	Bone	3⅝	125
8174G	Green Pearl Pyralin	3⅝	125
8174¾W	Ivory Celluloid	3⅝	110
8176	Mother Of Pearl	3⅝	200
8179GS	Genuine Stag	3⅝	200
8182	Ebony	3⅝	100
8183	Bone	3⅝	125
8313T	Bone	3⅜	90
8313B	Silver Bolsters	3⅜	90
8316B	Mother Of Pearl	3⅜	110

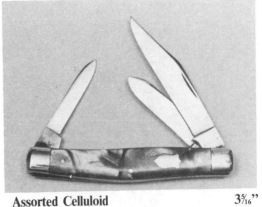

8344   **Assorted Celluloid**   3⁵⁄₁₆"   **$90**

2346   **Mother Of Pearl**   3⁵⁄₁₆"   **$200**

8323B   **Bone**   4"   **$175**

8354K   **Cream and Brown Pyralin**   3⁵⁄₁₆"   **$65**

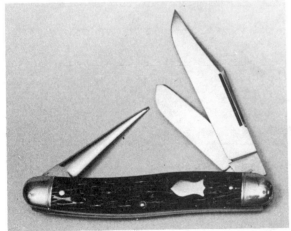

8323   **Bone**   3⅜"   **$125**

8324S	Tortoise Celluloid	3⁵⁄₁₆	125
8344K	Cream & Brown Pyralin	3⁵⁄₁₆	60
8343	Bone	3⁵⁄₁₆	65

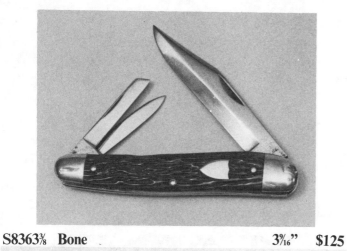

Nr.	Handle	Size	Mint
S836⅜B	Black Celluloid	3⁹⁄₁₆	75
8364⅜B	Black Celluloid	3⁹⁄₁₆	110
S8364⅜	Bone	3⁹⁄₁₆	125
8364¾B	Black Celluloid	3⁹⁄₁₆	75
SC8364⅜B	Pen Blade	3⁹⁄₁₆	75
S8374G	Green Pearl Pyralin	3⅝	125
S8374AC	Assorted Celluloid	3⅝	125
S8373¾	Bone	3⅝	125
S8374¾AC	Assorted Celluloid	3⅝	125

S8363⅜ Bone   3⁹⁄₁₆" **$125**

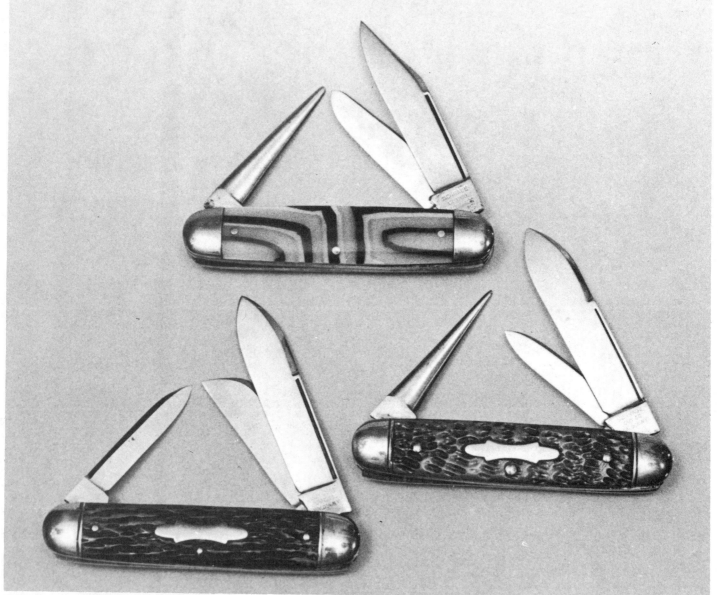

S8374¾ Top: Cream and Brown Pyralin   **3⅝" $125**

8373   Bottom: Bone   3⅝" **$125**   **S8373   Right: Bone (w/punch)**   3⅝" **$125**

Nr.	Handle	Size	Mint				
8384G	Green Pearl Pyralin	3⅝	125				
8384GP	Gold Pearl Pyralin	3⅝	125	8383	Bone	3⅝	125
8384AC	Assorted Celluloid	3⅝	125	8383¾	Bone Clip Blade	3⅝	125

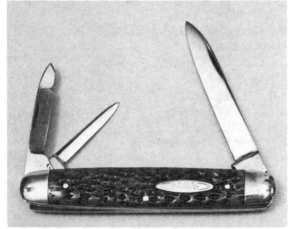

L8423B   Bone   3⅛" $80

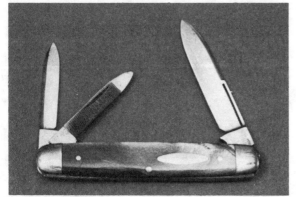

8424PB   Smoked Pearl Celluloid   3⅛" $80

8424T   Assorted Celluloid   3⅛" $120

Nr.	Handle	Size	Mint
8423T	Bone	3⅛	75
8426T	Mother Of Pearl	3⅛	90
M8423B	Bone	3⅛	60
M8426B	Mother Of Pearl	3⅛	65
L8424BP	Smoked Pearl Celluloid	3⅛	80
8424SqMB	Marine Pearl Celluloid	3⅛	65
8423B	Bone	3⅛	80
M8424PT	Smoked Pearl Celluloid	3⅛	55
M8423T	Bone	3⅛	60
M8426T	Mother Of Pearl	3⅛	65
8424¾MB	Marine Pearl	3⅛	90
8423¾B	Bone	3⅛	110
M8426	Mother Of Pearl	3⅛	65
8426B	Mother Of Pearl	3⅛	90
8443	Bone	3⅝	150

Nr.	Handle	Size	Mint
M9456T	Mother Of Pearl	3⅛	125
8463	Bone	3⅝	150
8476	Shackle, Mother Of Pearl	2¾	50
8476	Without Shackle	2¾	50
8479GM	Shackle, Metal	2¾	50
8479GM	Without Shackle	2¾	50
8479GSIL	Shackle, Nickel Silver	2¾	40

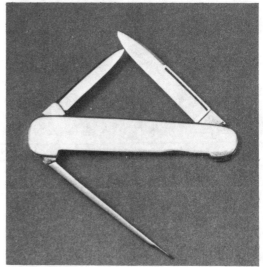

8479GSIL Nickel Silver   2¾" $40

8556⅜   Mother Of Pearl   3¼" $250

8554⅜B	Black Celluloid	3¼	75
8566	Mother Of Pearl	3⅜	150

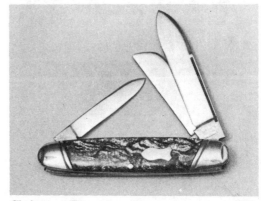

8564   **Christmas Tree**   3⅜" $200

Nr.	Handle	Size	Mint
8563	Bone	3⅜	110
8564AC	Assorted Pyralin	3⅜	110
8563¾	Clip Blade Bone	3⅜	110
8563¾AC	Clip Blade Bone	3⅜	110
8564¾AC	Assorted Pyralin	3⅜	110

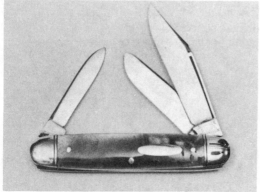

8574¾AP Abalone Pearl Pyralin   3⅜" $110

Nr.	Handle	Size	Mint
8573¾	Bone	3⅜	110
S8583	Bone	3⅜	110
8583	Bone	3⅜	110
8584Horn	Pyralin	3⅜	110
8584AC	Assorted Celluloid	3⅜	110
8584¾GP	Gold Pearl Pyralin	3⅜	80
8584¾K	Cream & Brown Pyralin	3⅜	80
8584¾M	Marine Pearl Celluloid	3⅜	80
8584¾R	Red Celluloid	3⅜	80
8584¾AC	Assorted Celluloid	3⅜	80
8584K	Cream & Brown Pyralin	3⅜	80
8584M	Marine Pearl Celluloid	3⅜	80
8584¾GP	Pyralin	3⅜	110
8483¾	Bone	3⅜	110
8593	Bone	3⅜	90
8594G	Pyralin	3⅜	90
8594¾X	Mottled Green Celluloid	3⅜	90
8604W	Ivory Celluloid	2¼	25
8604AC	Shackle, Assorted Celluloid	2¼	35

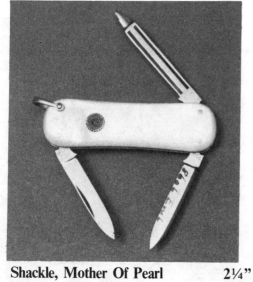

8606   Shackle, Mother Of Pearl   2¼" $50

Nr.	Handle	Size	Mint
8606	Mother Of Pearl	2¼	50
8604W	Ivory Celluloid	2¼	35
8604AC	Assorted Celluloid	2¼	40
S8606	Shackle, Mother Of Pearl	2¼	60
8609	Gold Plate	2¼	50
8609GM	Shackle, Metal	2¼	45
8609GM	Without Shackle	2¼	45
S8609GM	Shackle, Metal	2¼	50
8609SS	Shackle, Sterling Silver	2¼	50
8613LB	Bone	4	95
8614MLB	Marine Pearl Pyralin	4	75
8614YLB	Mottled Horn Celluloid	4	85
8614Y	Mottled Horn Celluloid	4	90
8614M	Marine Pearl Pyralin	4	80

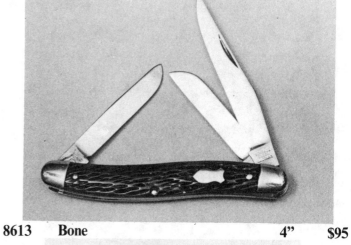

8613   Bone   4" $95

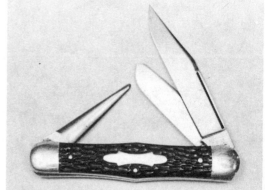

8623¾LB Bone   3½" $90
8624¾KLB Brown & Cream Pyralin   3½   80

C8633¾ Bone   3⅜" $125
SC8633¾ Bone, Clip Blade   3⅜   125

SCHRADE CUTLERY

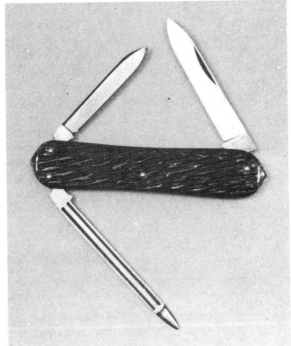

Nr.	Handle	Length	Mint
8666T	Mother Of Pearl	3	55
8666	Without Tips	3	50
8673	Bone	3	50
8676T	Mother Of Pearl	3	55

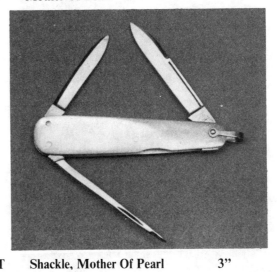

8676T	**Shackle, Mother Of Pearl**	**3"**	**$55**
8673T	Shackle, Bone	3	45
8676	Mother Of Pearl	3	55
8674GL	Shackle, Goldaleur Celluloid	3	45
8676	Shackle, Mother Of Pearl	3	55
8676GSil	Nickel Silver	3	40
8679GM	Shackle, Metal	3	45
8679GM	Without Shackle	3	45
8683T	Bone	3	50
8686	Mother Of Pearl	3	55
8683	Bone	3	50
8704MT	Marine Pearl Celluloid	2⅞	40
8706T	Mother Of Pearl	2⅞	50
8704¾BT	Black Celluloid	2⅞	50
8706B	Mother Of Pearl	2⅞	55
SS8729ET	Shackle, Metal	2⁹⁄₁₆	35
8729GSIL	Nickel Silver	2⁹⁄₁₆	45
8729SGIL	With Shackle	2⁹⁄₁₆	45
SS87291	Metal	2⁹⁄₁₆	45
SS87291	Metal, with Shackle	2⁹⁄₁₆	45
8729GM	Shackle, Metal	2⁹⁄₁₆	45
8729GM	Without Shackle	2⁹⁄₁₆	45
8729GOLD	Shackle, Gold Filled	2⁹⁄₁₆	50
8729GOLD	Without Shackle	2⁹⁄₁₆	50

8653T	**Bone**	**3"**	**$50**
Nr.	Handle	Lgth.	Mint
8653	Bone	3	45
8654W	Ivory Celluloid	3	35
8654AC	Assorted Celluloid	3	40
9754SqW	Ivory Celluloid	3	35
8654SqAC	Assorted Celluloid	3	40
8654MT	Marine Pearl Pyralin	3	45
8654GT	Green Pearl Celluloid	3	45
8654CT	Cocobolo Celluloid	3	45
8654FGKPT	Gold Pearl Celluloid	3	45
8654ST	Tortoise Celluloid	3	45
8654WT	Ivory Celluloid	3	40
8654ACT	Assorted Celluloid	3	45
8656T	Mother Of Pearl Shackle, with Emblem	3	60
8656T	Mother Of Pearl	3	50
8656T	Shackle, Nickel Silver	3	40
8656	Mother Of Pearl, with Emblem	3	60

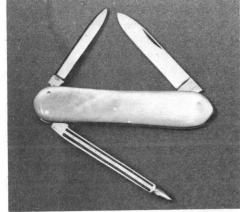

8656	**Mother Of Pearl**	**3"**	**$50**

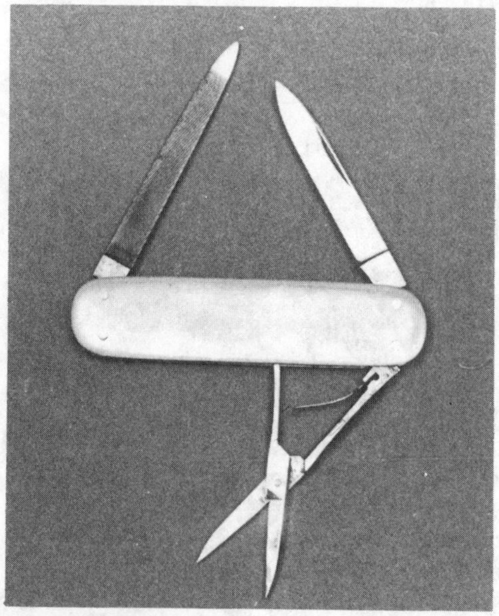

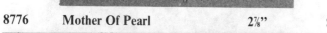

8776	**Mother Of Pearl**	**2⅞”**	**$60**

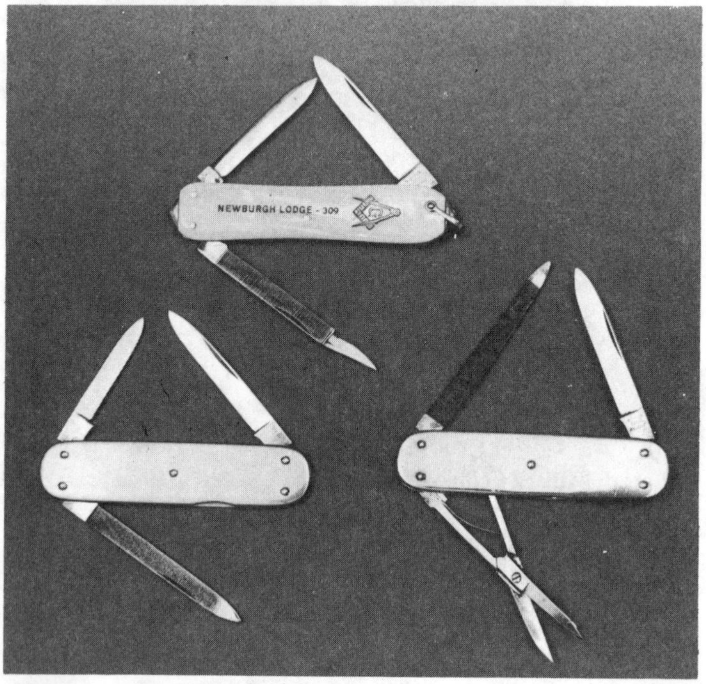

8654T	**Top: Mother of Pearl**	**2⅞”**	**$35**
F8776	**GSIL Left: Nickel Silver**	**2⅞”**	**$30**
SF8779	**GSIL Right: Nickel Silver**	**2⅞”**	**$40**

Nr.	**Handle**	**Length**	**Mint**
8779GM	Gun Metal	2⅞	40
8779GM	Metal	2⅞	50
8779GM	Shackle, Nickel Silver	2⅞	50
8786B	Mother Of Pearl	3 5/16	125
8783B	Bone Stag	3 5/16	110
8793⅛B	Bone, Wharncliffe	3¼	125
8794KT	Cream & Brown Pyralin	3¼	125

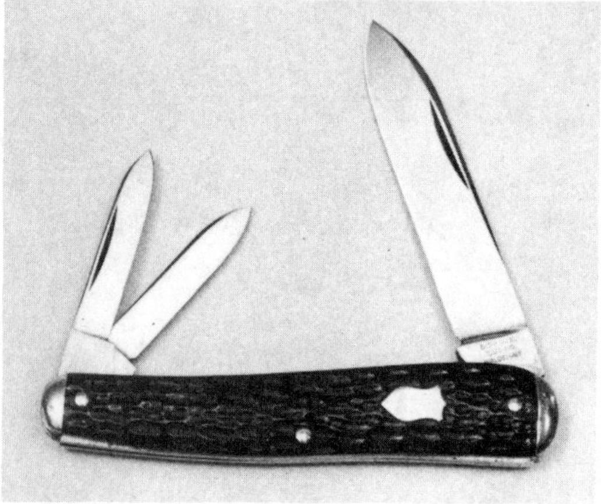

8793T	**Bone**	**3¼”**	**$125**

Nr.	**Handle**	**Length**	**Mint**
8803	Bone	4	95
M8806	Mother Of Pearl	4	200
8813	Bone	4	125

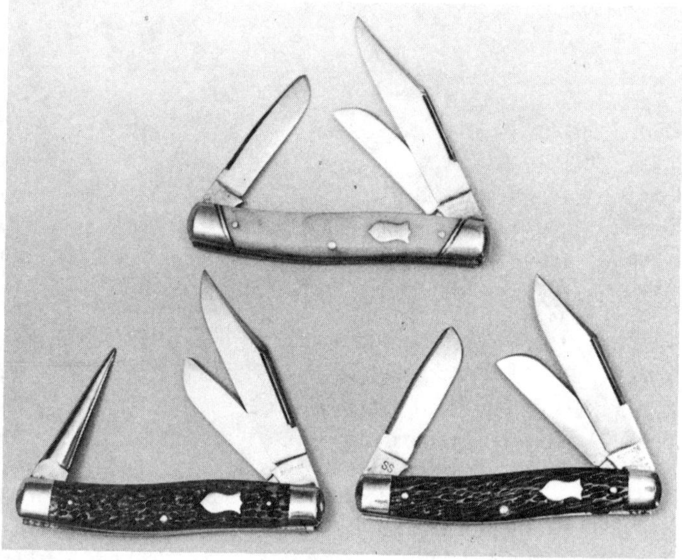

S08814NP	**Top: Opal Celluloid (Waterfall)**	**4”**	**$150**
8833	**Left: Bone**	**4”**	**$125**
SS8813	**Right: Bone**	**4”**	**$125**

8814P	Smoked Pearl Celluloid	4	125
8814G	Green Pearl Celluloid	4	125
8814GP	Gold Pearl Pyralin	4	125
8814X	Mottled Green Celluloid	4	125
8814AC	Assorted Celluloid	4	125
8823	Bone	4	95
8834K	Cream & Brown Pyralin	4	125
8834AP	Abalone Pearl Pyralin	4	125
8834	Horn Pyralin	4	125
08834AP	Pyralin, Slant Bolsters	4	135
08833	Bone	4	135
08834AC	Assorted Celluloid	4	135
S8374⅜R	Red Celluloid	3⅝	90
S8373⅜	Bone	3⅝	110
8853	Bone	3 5/16	65
8854K	Cream & Brown Pyralin	3 5/16	60
8853¼	Bone	3 5/16	65
8854¼K	Cream & Brown Pyralin	3 5/16	60

SCHRADE CUTLERY CORP.

451

Nr.	Handle	Size	Mint
8854¼M	Marine Pearl Celluloid	3⁵⁄₁₆	60
8854¼AC	Assorted Celluloid	3⁵⁄₁₆	60
8873	Bone	4	95

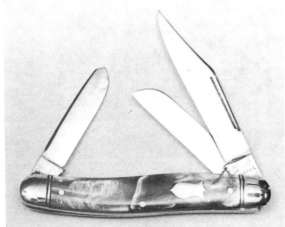

8874AC	**Assorted Celluloid**	**4"**	**$110**
8876	Mother Of Pearl	4	225
08883	Bone	4	140
8903	Pyralin	3½	75
8904K	Cream & Brown Pyralin	3½	75
8904P	Smoked Pearl Celluloid	3½	75
8904AC	Assorted Celluloid	3½	75

8913	**Bone**	**3½"**	**$75**
89.14	Horn Pyralin	3½	75
8914AP	Abalone Pearl Pyralin	3½	75
8914G	Green Pearl Pyralin	3½	75
894K	Cream & Brown Pyralin	3½	75
8914X	Mottled Green Celluloid	3½	75
8914AC	Assorted Pyralin	3½	75
8924GP	Green Pearl Pyralin	3½	75
8923	Bone	3½	85
8924AC	Assorted Pyralin	3½	75
8963	Bone	3⁹⁄₁₆	75
8964GP	Gold Pearl Pyralin	3⁹⁄₁₆	65
8964M	Marine Pearl Celluloid	3⁹⁄₁₆	60

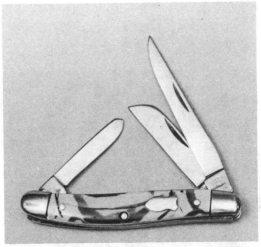

8964K	**Cream & Brown Pyralin**	**3⁹⁄₁₆"**	**$65**

8983	**Bone**	**3⁹⁄₁₆"**	**$110**

Nr.	Handle	Size	Mint
8984GP	Gold Pearl Pyralin	3⁹⁄₁₆	65
8984K	Cream & Brown Pyralin	3⁹⁄₁₆	65
8984M	Marine Pearl Celluloid	3⁹⁄₁₆	65
8984½GP	Gold Pearl Pyralin	3⁹⁄₁₆	65
8983¼	Bone	3⁹⁄₁₆	75
8984¼K	Cream & Brown Pyralin	3⁹⁄₁₆	65
8984¼M	Marine Pearl Celluloid	3⁹⁄₁₆	65
8993¼	Bone	3⁹⁄₁₆	75
8994¼GP	Gold Pearl Pyralin	3⁹⁄₁₆	65
8994¼K	Cream & Brown Pyralin	3⁹⁄₁₆	65
8994¼M	Marine Pearl Celluloid	3⁹⁄₁₆	65
8993	Bone	3⁹⁄₁₆	75
8994GP	Gold Pearl Pyralin	3⁹⁄₁₆	65
8994K	Cream & Brown Pyralin	3⁹⁄₁₆	65

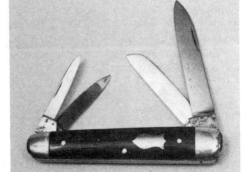

9112	**Ebony**	**3⅜"**	**$75**

Nr.	Handle	Size	Mint
9033	Bone	3⅝	125
9039GSIL	Nickel Silver	3⅝	125
9113B	Bone	3⅜	125
9116B	Mother Of Pearl	3⅜	140

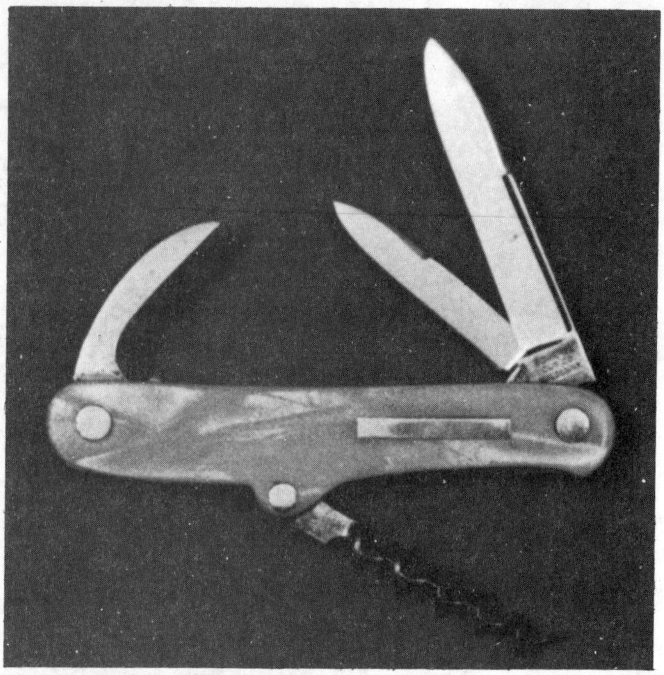

9124M Marine Pearl Pyralin 3¼" $150

9124B	Black Celluloid	3¼	150
9129GSIL	Nickel Silver	3¼	150
9134T	Bone	3¼	90
9144GLT	Goldaleur Celluloid	3⅛	90

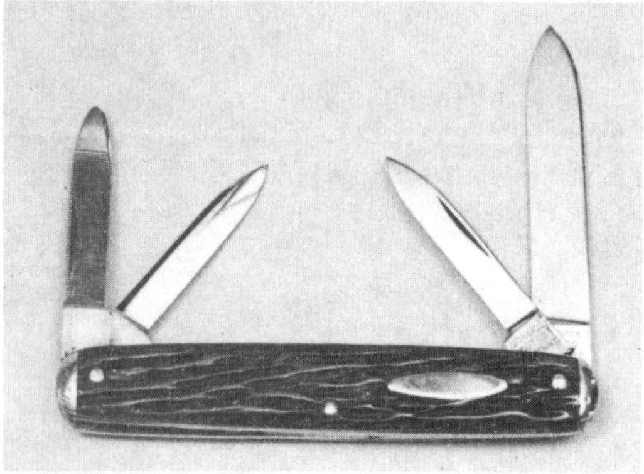

9143T Bone 3⅛" $120

9143B	Bone	3⅛	85
9144WT	Ivory Celluloid	3⅛	75
9146	Mother Of Pearl	3⅛	100
9144WB	Celluloid	3⅛	75
9146T	Mother Of Pearl	3⅛	100

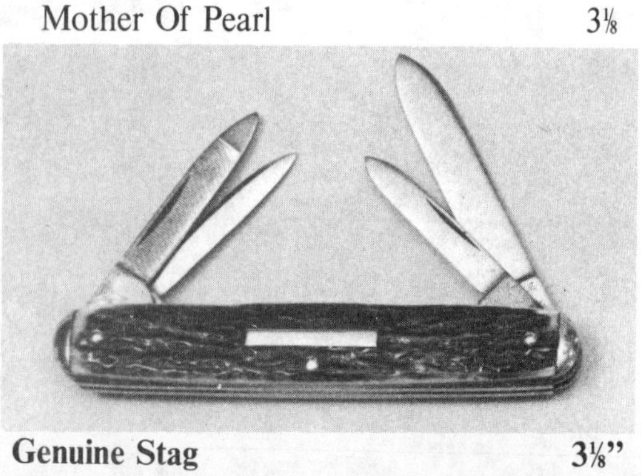

9149T Genuine Stag 3⅛" $155

9173 Bone 3⅝" $150

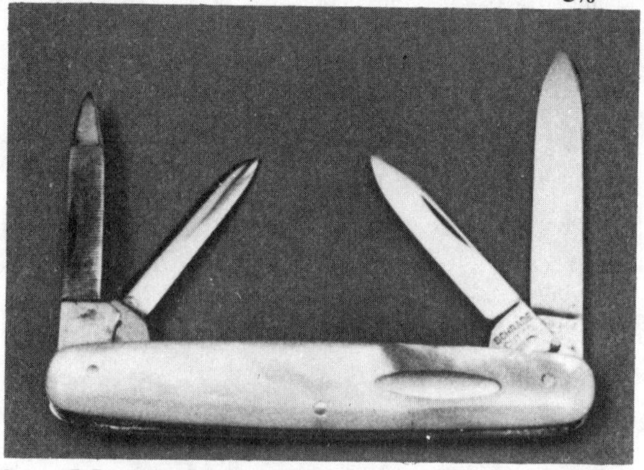

9426 Mother Of Pearl 3⅛" $90

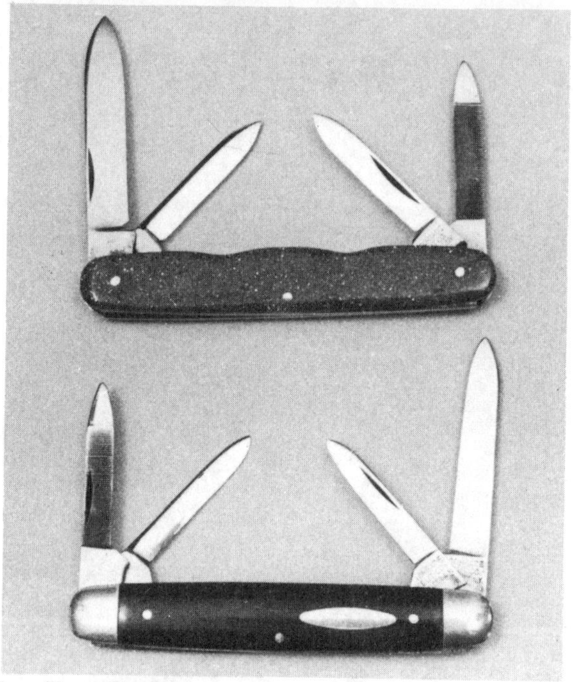

9426 Top: Goldaleur 3⅛" $75
P9428B Ebony 3⅛" $65

Nr.	Handle	Size	Mint
9426B	Mother Of Pearl	3⅛	90
9423B	Bone	3⅛	90
9424PB	Smoked Pearl Celluloid	3⅛	80
9426T	Mother Of Pearl	3⅛	90
9423T	Bone	3⅛	80
9463	Bone	3⅝	150

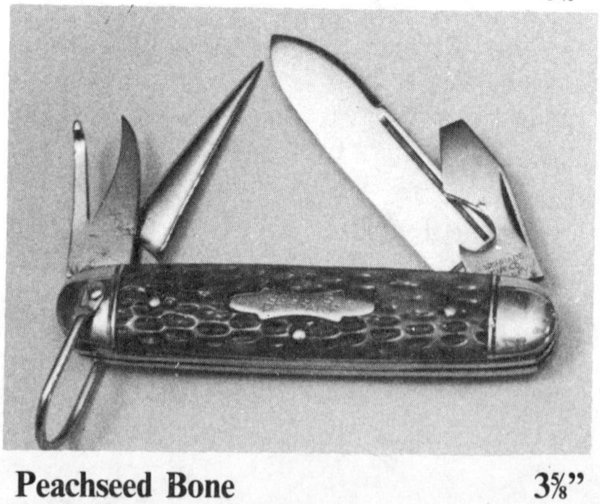

S9463 Peachseed Bone 3⅝" $150

9463SP Bone   3⅝" $150

Nr.	Handle	Size	Mint
D9463	Bone	3⅝	200
SD9463	Bone	3⅝	125
C9463¾	Bone	3⅝	150
9464US	Celluloid	3⅝	150
M9466	Mother Of Pearl	3⅝	225
9563	Bone	3⅜	125
9583	Bone	3⅜	125

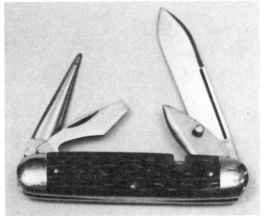

9593   **Bone**   3⅜" $150

Nr.	Handle	Size	Mint
9594US	Red-White-Blue Celluloid	3⅜	165
G9594US	Red-White-Blue Celluloid	3⅜	175
G9593	Bone	3⅜	150
P9594M	Marine Pearl Pyralin	3⅜	150
G9596	Mother Of Pearl	3⅜	225
9604W	Celluloid	2¼	40
9604AC	Shackle, Assorted Celluloid	2¼	40
9606	Shackle, Mother Of Pearl	2¼	60
9606	Mother Of Pearl	2¼	60
9604W	Ivory Celluloid	2¼	40
9604AC	Assorted Celluloid	2¼	45
9609	Gold Plate	2¼	60
9676T	Mother Of Pearl	3	125
9679SS	Solid Sterling Silver	3	85
9703B	Bone	2⅞	60
9706B	Mother Of Pearl	2⅞	70
9709GST	Stag	2⅞	60
9704GT	Green Jade Celluloid	2⅞	50
9704MT	Marine Pearl Celluloid	2⅞	50

Nr.	Handle	Size	Mint
9706T	Mother Of Pearl	2⅞	60
9736	Mother Of Pearl	2⅝	90
9736	Without Shackle	2⅝	90
9739GM	Shackle, Metal	2⅝	60
9739GM	Without Shackle	2⅝	60
9746	Mother Of Pearl	3	90

9743   **Bone**   3" $75

9753   **Bone**   3½" $125

F9753   **Bone**   3½" $125

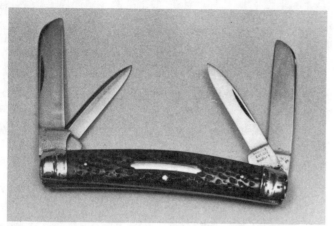

9763   Bone   3⅞" $125

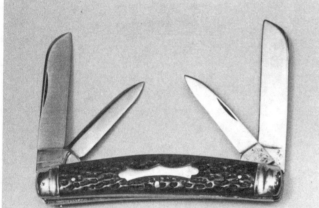

9773   Bone   3⅞" $350

Nr.	Handle	Size	Mint
9783T	Bone	3⁵⁄₁₆	80
9786T	Mother Of Pearl	3⁵⁄₁₆	90
9783B	Bone	3⁵⁄₁₆	90
9786B	Mother Of Pearl	3⁵⁄₁₆	110
9803LB	Bone	4	125
M9806	Mother Of Pearl	4	225
M9803	Bone	4	150

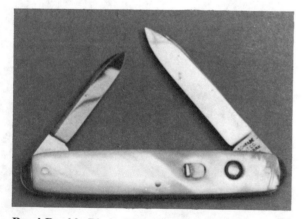

Gen. Pearl Double Blade Switch, 3⅜" Schrade Cut. Co. $325

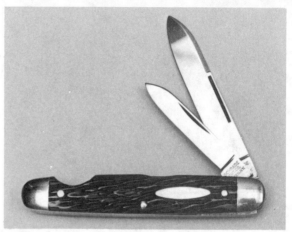

2 Bl. Easy Opener, Peachseed Bone, 3¼" Schrade Cut. Co., Walden, NY $125

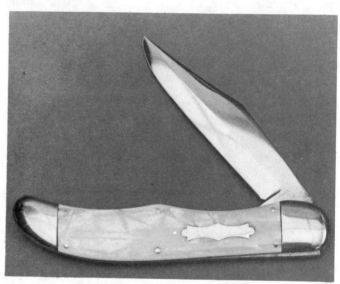

C.I. w/Sh., F/H, 5¼", Schrade Cut. Co., Walden, NY $175

WINCHESTER
TRADE MARK

Because of declining governmental contracts after WWI, Winchester made a decision to enter the pocket knife market. In order to do this they bought two companies, The Eagle Knife Company and Napanoch Knife Company. With the combined knowledge from both companies they began producing large numbers of pocket knives.

In the early 20's, Associated Simmons Hardware, owners of Walden Knife Company, merged with Winchester and at that time production of the Walden line was terminated. As with Remington, WWII halted the manufacturing of Winchester pocket knives never to resume again.

No.	Name, Handle	Lgth	Price
1050	Toothpick Asst. Celluloid	5	300
1051	Texas Jack Celluloid	4¼	300
1060	Texas Jack Celluloid	4⅛	220
1201	Jack Nickel Silver	3⅜	190

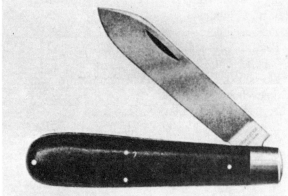

1605	**Cocobolo**	**3½"**	**$75**
1608	Cocobolo	3⅜	70
1610	Pruner, Cocobolo	4⅛	80
1611	Mariner's Knife, Cocobolo	3¼	80
1613	Maize, Cocobolo	3⅜	120
1614	Maize, Cocobolo	4⅛	90
1621	Budding, Ebony	4¾	135
1624	Maize	4	90
1632	Cocobolo	3⅜	85
1633	Pruner, Cocobolo	3⅜	90
1701	Barlow, Bone	3½	125
1703	Barlow, Bone	5	250
1704	Barlow, Stag	5	300
1785	Barlow, Bone	3½	140
1905	Jack, Stag	4½	150

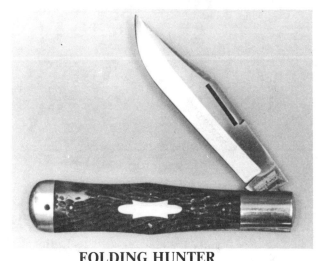

FOLDING HUNTER

1920	Bone		5⅜"	$1100

No.	Name, Handle	Lgth	Price
1921	Stag	3⅜	120
1922	Stag	3⅜	120
1923	Texas Jack, Stag	4⅛	200
1924	Powder Horn, Stag	4¼	320
1925	Jack, Stag	3½	300
1937	Texas Jack, Stag	3⅞	170
2028	Jack, Shell Celluloid	3⅜	170

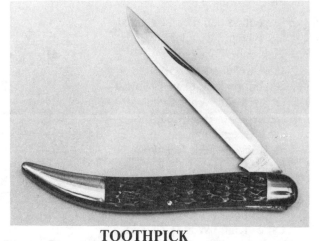

TOOTHPICK

1936	Brown Bone		5"	$350

No.	Name, Handle	Lgth	Price
2094	Jack, Celluloid	3⅜	200
2098	Jack, Celluloid	3⅜	180

1938   Brown Bone   3⅜" $125

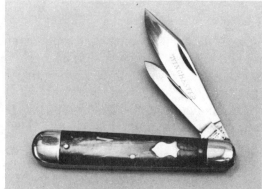

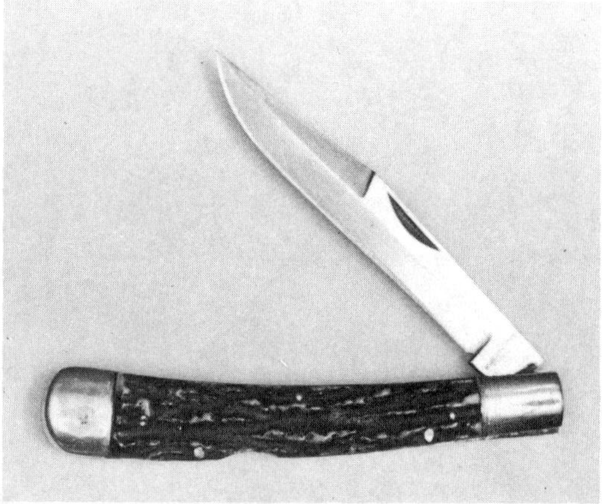

JACK

2099	Pink Celluloid	3⅜"	$150

No.	Name, Handle	Lgth	Price
2106	Jack, Blue Abalone Celluloid	3⅜	160
2107	Dog Leg, Gold Celluloid	2¾	130
2109	Sleeveboard, Gold Celluloid	2⅞	90
2110	Jack, Celluloid	3½	150
2111	Jack, Celluloid	3½	150
2112	Jack, Celluloid	3½	150
2113	Peanut, Celluloid	2¾	125
2114	Candle End, Celluloid	3	140
2115	Sleeveboard, Pearl Celluloid	2⅞	160
2116	Sleeveboard, Celluloid	3⅜	90
2117	Serpentine Jack, Black Celluloid	3⅛	175
2201	Senator, Nickel Silver	3¼	75
2202	Serpentine Jack, Smooth	3	80
2204	Senator, Nickel Silver	3⅛	75

LOCKBACK

1950   Stag   5¼" $1200

No.	Name, Handle	Lgth	Price
2037	Jack, Celluloid	3	100
2038	Jack, Pearl Celluloid	3	170
2039	Jack, Celluloid	3	100
2047	Equal End Jack, White Celluloid	4¼	250
2051	Senator, White Celluloid	2⅝	150
2052	Senator, Pearl Celluloid	2⅝	100
2053	Senator, Celluloid	2⅝	120
2054	Senator, Celluloid	3¼	75
2055	Senator, Celluloid	3¼	75
2057	Senator, Veriegated Celluloid	3⅜	110
2058	Senator, Blue Abalone Celluloid	3¼	100
2059	Senator, Celluloid	3¼	100
2067	Serpentine Pen, Pearl Celluloid	3	110
2068	Sleeveboard, Celluloid	3⅜	180
2069	Jack, Blue Celluloid	3⅜	170
2070	Jack, Celluloid	3½	125
2078	Serpentine Pen, Black Celluloid	3⅜	120
2079	Office Knife, White Celluloid	3⅜	100
2082	Sleeveboard, Pearl Celluloid	3	110
2083	Jack, Green Celluloid	3⅛	150
2084	Sleeveboard, Blue Celluloid	3⅜	160
2085	Serpentine Jack, Celluloid	3	130
2086	Dog Leg, Celluloid	2¾	130
2087	Serpentine Jack, Shell Celluloid	3	130
2088	Serpentine Pen, Grey Celluloid	3⅜	110
2089	Office Knife, White Celluloid	3¾	110
2090	Serpentine Pen, Celluloid	3	125

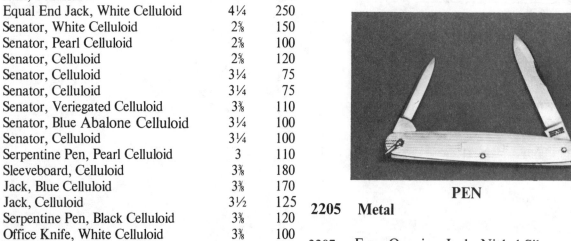

PEN

2205	Metal	3¼"	$125

2207	Easy Opening Jack, Nickel Silver	3⅜	160
2208	Jack, Nickel Silver	3⅜	160
2215	Jack, Nickel Silver	3½	80
2301	Senator, Pearl without bail	2¼	90
2302	Senator, Pearl with bail	2¼	90

WINCHESTER

457

SMALL SENATOR

No.	Name, Handle	Lgth	Price
2303	**Pearl**	2⅝"	**$110**
2306	Senator, Pearl	2⅝	100
2307	Senator, Pearl	2⅞	90
2308	Senator, Pearl	2⅞	90
2309	Senator, Pearl	3	120

WHARNCLIFFE

No.	Name, Handle	Lgth	Price
2312	**Pearl**	2⅞"	**$125**
2314	Serpentine Jack, Pearl	3	90
2316	Serpentine Jack, Pearl	3	150
2317	Serpentine Jack, Pearl	3	125
2320	Sleeveboard, Pearl	2⅞	90

PEN

No.	Name, Handle	Lgth	Price
2324	**Pearl**	3"	**$125**

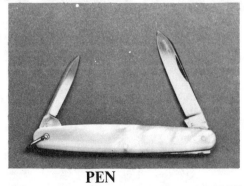

PEN

No.	Name, Handle	Lgth	Price
2330	**Pearl**	3¼"	**$125**

No.	Name, Handle	Lgth	Price
2331	Congress, Pearl	3¼	150
2335	Congress, Pearl	3¼	150
2337	Senator, Pearl	3¼	110
2338	Senator, Pearl	3¼	160
2344	Senator, Pearl	3¼	125
2345	Senator, Pearl	3¼	90
2346	Lobster, Pearl	3	110
2352	Jack, Pearl	3⅛	180
2356	Lobster, Pearl	3	110
2361	Dog Leg, Pearl	2¾	115
2363	Congress, Pearl	3	125
2366	Sleeveboard, Pearl	3⅜	125
2367	Sleeveboard, Pearl	3	90
2368	Sleeveboard, Pearl	3	90
2369	Senator, Pearl	2⅝	100
2374	Senator, Pearl	2⅞	90
2375	Senator, Pearl	2⅝	100
2376	Senator, Pearl	3	130
2377	Senator, Pearl	2⅝	150

DR.'S KNIFE

No.	Name, Handle	Lgth	Price
2380	**Pearl**	3¼"	**$325**
2603	Jack, Cocobolo	3⅜	160
2604	Jack, Cocobolo	3½	160
2605	Jack, Cocobolo	3⅜	200
2606	Jack, Cocobolo	3⅜	160

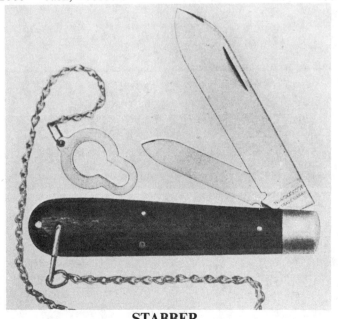

STABBER

No.	Name, Handle	Lgth	Price
2608	Cocobolo	3⅝"	**$125**

458

WINCHESTER

No.	Name, Handle	Lgth	Price	No.	Name, Handle	Lgth	Price
2610	Jack, Cocobolo	3⅜	175	2633	Premium Stockman, Ebony	3¼	120
2611	Serpentine Jack, Cocobolo	3	120	2635	Jack, Cocobolo	3½	125
2612	Jack, Cocobolo	3⅝	190	2636	Jack, Ebony	3½	120
2613	Jack, Cocobolo	3⅝	190	2638	Serpentine Jack, Cocobolo	3½	160
2614	Jack, Cocobolo	3⅜	190				

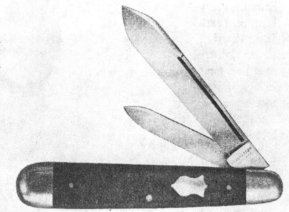

SLIM JACK

2627	**Cocobolo**	**3¼"**	**$125**
2629	Jack, Ebony	3½	180
2630	Jack, Ebony	3⅜	125

SLEEVEBOARD

2613	**Ebony**	**3⅜"**	**$110**

LIGHT PREMIUM STOCKMAN

2632	**Cocobolo**	**3⅜"**	**$110**

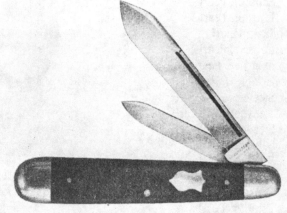

COKE BOTTLE

2640	**Ebony**	**3¾"**	**$200**
2641	Trapper, Cocobolo	3⅞	300
2649	Jack, Ebony	3¾	160
2660	Jack, Ebony	3½	160
2661	Jack, Ebony	3½	160
2662	Jack, Ebony	3½	160
2665	Jack, Ebony	3⅜	180
2666	Jack, Ebony	3⅜	75
2681	Electrician's Ebony	3¾	110

TEXAS JACK

2690	**Ebony**	**4½"**	**$225**
2701	Barlow, Bone	3½	225
2702	Barlow, Bone	3½	275

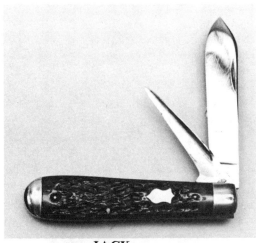

JACK

No.	Name, Handle	Lgth	Price
2703	**Brown Bone**	3½"	**$150**
2820	Jack, Bone	3⅜	90
2830	Senator, Stag	3¼	75
2840	Stag	2	100
2841	Stag	3	100
2842	Senator, Stag	3¼	125
2843	Stag	3⅜	160
2844	Jack, Stag	3¾	275
2845	Jack, Stag	3¾	230
2846	Premium Stockman, Stag	3¼	125

PEN

No.	Name, Handle	Lgth	Price
2847	**Brown Bone**	3¼"	**$125**
2848	Jack, Stag w/chain	3½	135
2849	Jack, Stag	3⅜	140
2850	Jack, Stag	3¾	285
2851	Gunstock Jack, Stag	3	350
2852	Serpentine Cattle, Stag	3	130

GUNSTOCK

No.	Name, Handle	Lgth	Price
2853	**Brown Bone**	3½"	**$400**

No.	Name, Handle	Lgth	Price
2853	Jack, Stag	3⅜	200
2854	Jack, Stag	3⅜	160
2855	Jack, Stag	3⅜	160
2856	Dog Leg, Stag	2¾	115
2857	Serpentine Jack, Stag	3⅛	135
2858	Serpentine Jack, Stag	3	90
2859	Sleeveboard, Stag	2⅞	90
2860	Sleeveboard, Stag	3¼	160
2861	Sleeveboard, Stag	3¼	160
2862	Sleeveboard, Stag	3⅜	100
2863	Congress, Stag	3¼	150
2864	Swell Center, Stag	3⅜	165
2865	Swell Center, Stag	3½	320
2866	Senator, Stag	2⅞	85
2867	Senator, Stag	3⅜	130
2868	Equal End Pen, Stag	3⅜	130
2869	Gunstock, Stag	3¾	230
2870	Gunstock, Stag	3¾	200
2871	Gunstock, Stag	3¾	225
2872	Gunstock, Stag	3¼	225

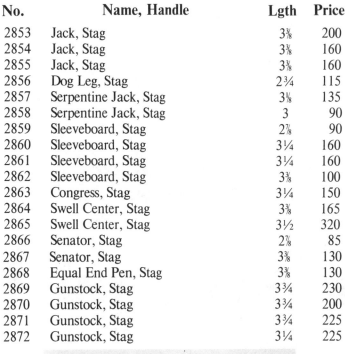

SMALL BARLOW

No.	Name, Handle	Lgth	Price
2873	**Brown Bone**	3½"	**$200**
2874	Jack, Stag	3½	160
2875	Premium Stockman, Stag	3¼	125

SMALL MUSKRAT

No.	Name, Handle	Lgth	Price
2876	**Brown Bone**	3¼"	**$300**
2878	Texas Jack, Stag	4¼	325
2879	Sleeveboard, Stag	4½	550
2880	Texas Jack, Stag	4½	400
2881	Texas Jack, Stag	4½	400
2901	Stag	3½	160

No.	Name, Handle	Lgth	Price
2958	Jack, Stag	3⅜	160
2959	Jack, Stag	3⅜	220
2961	Jack, Stag	3⅜	160
2962	Dog Leg, Stag	2¾	100
2963	Senator, Stag	3	125
2964	Jack, Stag	3⅜	150
2966	Jack, Stag	3⅜	225
2967	Swell Center, Stag	3⅞	350

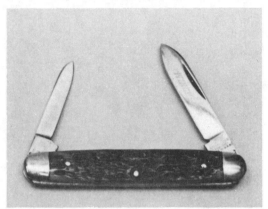

PEN

2902	**Bone**	2⅝"	**$90**
2903	Swell Center, Stag	3½	200
2904	Texas Jack, Stag	3⅞	375
2905	Texas Jack, Stag	4½	400
2907	Texas Jack, Stag	4½	400
2908	Swell Center, Stag	3⅝	175
2910	Lobster, Stag	3	100
2911	Jack, Stag	3½	160
2914	Sleeveboard, Stag	3⅜	180
2917	Serpentine Jack, Stag	3	130
2918	Serpentine Pen, Stag	3⅜	150
2921	Jack, Stag	3½	280
2923	Premium Stockman, Stag	4	200
2924	Congress, Stag	3	125
2925	Jack, Stag	3⅛	160
2928	Texas Jack, Stag	4	200
2930	Jack, Stag	3⅝	200
2931	Jack, Stag	3⅜	110
2932	Congress, Stag	3¼	150
2933	Sleeveboard, Stag	3	125
2934	Senator, Stag	3⅜	100
2938	Sleeveboard, Stag	3	150
2940	Jack, Stag	3⅝	215
2943	Sleeveboard, Stag	3⅜	100

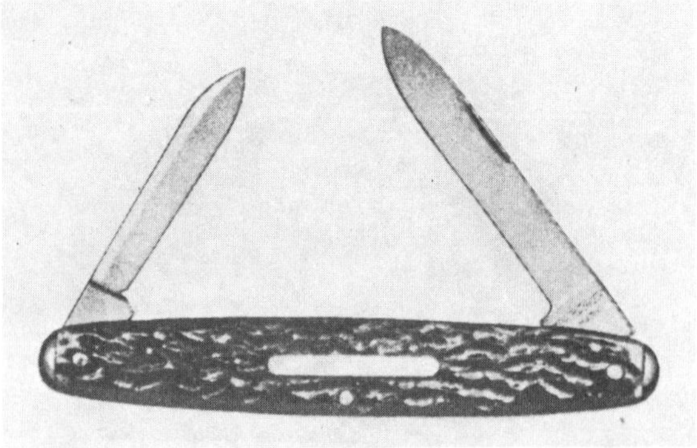

SWELL CENTER

2969	**Bone**	3⅞	**$250**
2973	Jack, Stag	3⅝	180
2974	Serpentine Jack, Stag	3½	160
2976	Texas Jack, Stag	4	200
2978	Dr.'s Knife, Stag	3⅜	320
2980	Cattle, Stag	3⅝	180

PEN

2981	**Brown Bone**	3¼"	**$110**
2982	Texas Jack, Stag	4	320
2983	Jack, Stag w/chain	3⅜	130
2988	Texas Jack, Stag	4	320
2990	Dog Leg, Stag	2¾	130

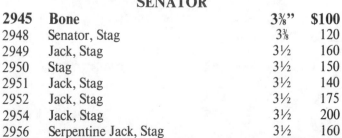

SENATOR

2945	**Bone**	3⅜"	**$100**
2948	Senator, Stag	3⅜	120
2949	Jack, Stag	3½	160
2950	Stag	3½	150
2951	Jack, Stag	3½	140
2952	Jack, Stag	3½	175
2954	Jack, Stag	3½	200
2956	Serpentine Jack, Stag	3½	160

PEANUT

2991	**Brown Bone**	2⅞"	**$140**

No.	Name, Handle	Lgth	Price
2992	Stag	3⅝	140
2993	Stag, Trapper Pen Blade	3⅞	375
2994	Jack, Stag	3⅝	160
2995	Jack, Stag	3⅝	200
2996	Congress, Stag	3¾	180
2997	Serpentine Pen, Stag	3⅜	160
2998	Jack, Stag	3⅜	140

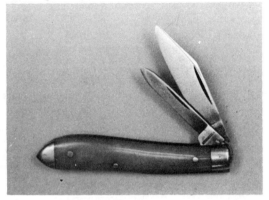

DOG LEG JACK
2999	**White Smooth Bone**	**3⅛"**	**$175**
2999	Serpentine Jack, Stag	3⅛	210
3001	Swell Ctr. Cattle, Pearl Celluloid	3½	280

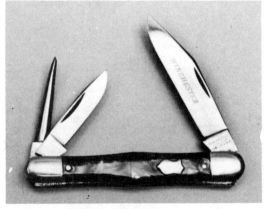

WHITTLER
3002	**Green Cell.**	**3¾"**	**$275**
3003	Prem. Stockman, Celluloid	3½	275
3005	Swell Ctr., Black Celluloid	3⅝	250
3006	Serpentine Pen, Black Celluloid	3⅜	250
3007	Prem. Stockman, Black Celluloid	4	280
3008	Cattle, White Celluloid	3⅝	300
3009	Cattle, White Celluloid	3⅝	280
3010	Swell Ctr. Cattle, Blue Abalone Cell.	3⅝	330
3014	Prem. Stockman, Pearl Celluloid	4	280
3015	Swell Ctr., Gold Celluloid	3⅝	260

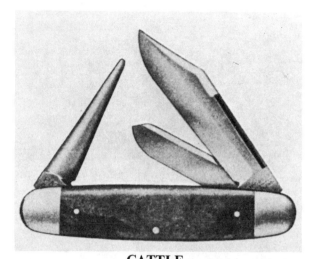

CATTLE
3016	**Celluloid**	**3¾"**	**$300**
No.	Name, Handle	Lgth	Price
3017	Prem. Stockman, Variegated Cell.	4	300
3018	Prem. Stockman, Celluloid	4	280
3019	Whittler, Red Celluloid	3½	280
3020	Whittler, Celluloid	3½	300

WHITTLER
3022	**Imi. Tortoise Shell**	**3¼"**	**$250**
3023	Whittler, Red Celluloid	3⅝	350
3024	Whittler, Celluloid	3⅝	350
3025	Prem. Stockman, Blue Abalone Cell.	3½	175
3026	Prem. Stockman, Variegated Cell.	3¼	275
3027	Prem. Stockman, Red Celluloid	3¼	215
3028	Prem. Stockman, Celluloid	3¼	210
3029	Prem. Stockman, Celluloid	3¼	210
3030	Senator, Blue Abalone Cell.	3⅜	210
3031	Senator, Grey Celluloid	3⅜	275
3033	Serpentine, Gold Celluloid	3	150
3034	Serpentine Cattle, Blue Abalone Cell.	3	150
3035	Gold Celluloid	3⅜	180
3036	Cattle, Celluloid	3⅜	150
3040	Whittler, Celluloid	3	175
3041	Senator, Celluloid	3	180
3042	Senator, Celluloid	3⅜	180
3043	Senator, Celluloid	3⅜	200
3044	Senator, Celluloid	3⅜	200
3045	Whittler, Celluloid	3¼	150
3046	Whittler, Celluloid	3¼	175
3047	Prem. Stockman, Celluloid	3½	150
3048	Prem. Stockman, Celluloid	4	200

No.	Name, Handle	Lgth	Price
3360	Bartenber, Pearl	3¼	200
3366	Whittler Senator, Pearl	3⅜	250
3370	Lobster, Pearl	3	125
3371	Lobster, Pearl	3	175
3373	Whittler Senator, Pearl	2⅞	165
3377	Sleeveboard, Pearl	3⅜	250
3378	Sleeveboard Whittler, Pearl	3	200
3379	Senator Whittler, Pearl	3	200
3380	Sleeveboard, Pearl	2¾	110
3381	Lobster, Pearl	3⅛	125

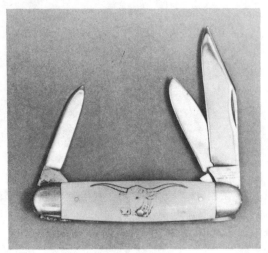

CATTLE KNIFE

| 3049 | Imi. White Bone | 3⅝" | $300 |

No.	Name, Handle	Lgth	Price
3331	Lobster, Pearl	3	125
3338	Sleeveboard, Pearl	3	110
3341	Cattle, Pearl	3⅜	225

WHITTLER

| 3345 | Pearl | 3¼' | $225 |

3347	Whittler, Pearl	3¼	250
3348	Prem. Stockman, Pearl	3¼	150
3349	Sleeveboard, Pearl	3	200
3350	Whittle Senator, Pearl	3¼	225
3352	Senator, Pearl	3½	260
3353	Senator, Pearl	2⅝	160

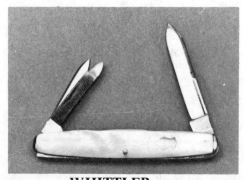

WHITTLER

| 3357 | Pearl | 3⅛" | $250 |

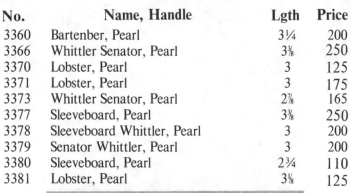

LOBSTER

| 3382 | Pearl | 3" | $150 |

3625	Cattle, Ebony	3⅝	150
3902	Swell Ctr., Stag	3½	300
3903	Swell Ctr., Stag Whittler, 3 backspring		800

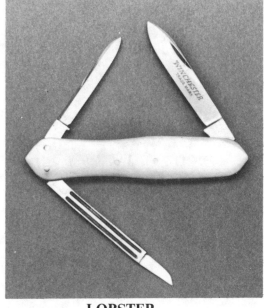

WHITTLER

| 3904 | Brown Bone | 3⅝" | $1000 |

3905	Swell Ctr. Cattle, Stag	3½	280
3906	Prem. Stockman, Stag	4	300
3907	Prem. Stockman, Stag	4	325
3908		3¾	275
3909	Senator, Stag	3⅜	250
3911	Senator Whittler, Stag	3	200

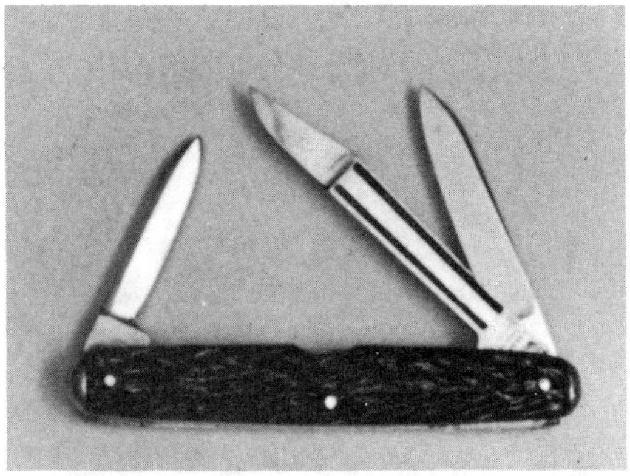

3914 Brown Bone 2¾" $125

No.	Name, Handle	Lgth	Price
3915	Swell Ctr. Cattle, Stag	3½	235

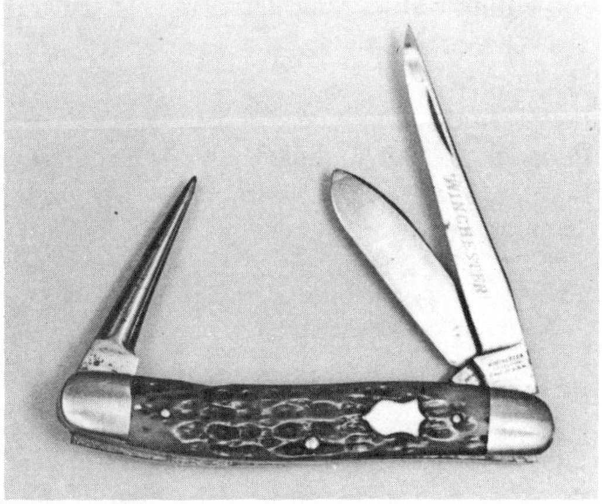

3916 Brown Bone 3½" $225

3917	Premium Stockman, Stag	3½	175
3924	Senator, Stag	3	200
3925	Swell Center, Stag	3⅜	320
3927	Serpentine Pen, Stag	3⅜	250
3928	Premium Stockman, Stag	4	250
3929	Congress, Stag	3¼	280
3931	Sleeveboard, Stag	3	140
3932	Senator, Stag	3⅜	180
3933	Senator, Stag	3⅜	250
3936	Cattle, Stag	3⅝	300
3938	Senator, Stag	3⅜	180
3939	Senator, Stag	3⅜	200

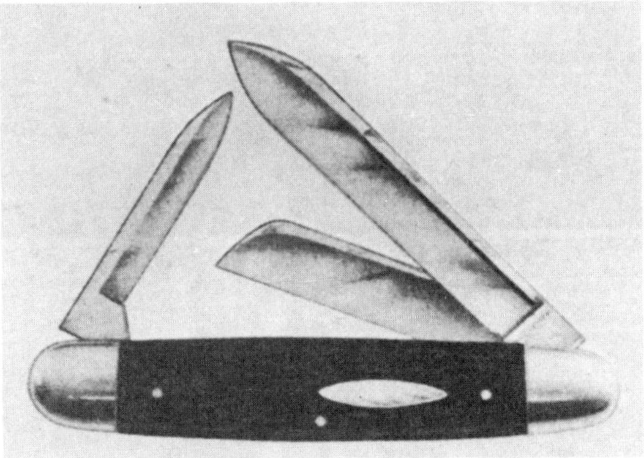

LIGHT CATTLE

3942 Bone 3⅜" $250

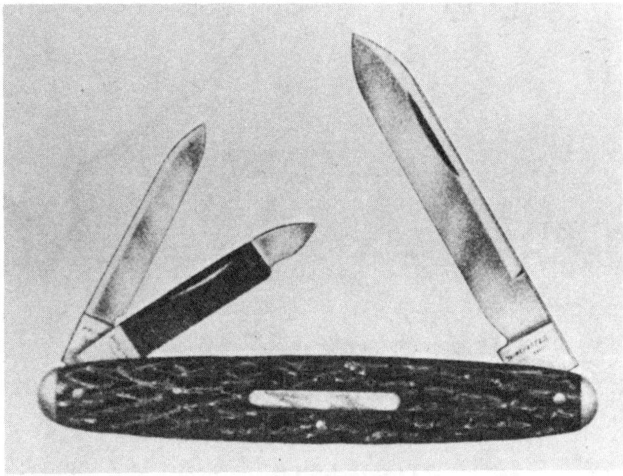

WHITTLER

3944 Bone 3¼" $250

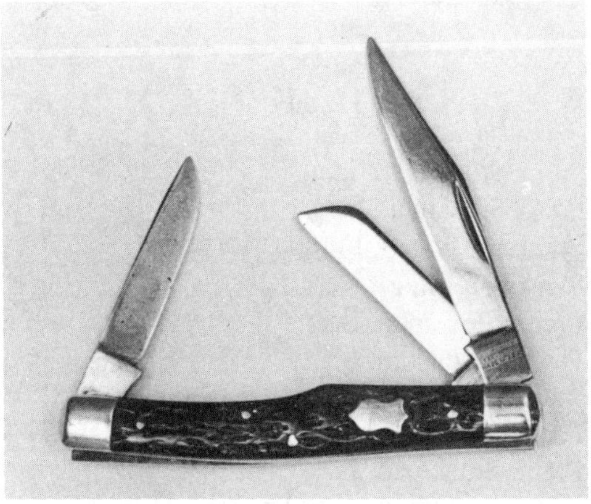

REVERSE GUNSTOCK

3948 Brown Bone 3⅝" $300

No.	Name, Handle	Lgth	Price
3949	Serpentine Cattle, Stag	3	150
3950	Cattle, Stag	3⅝	275
3951	Cattle, Stag	3⅝	275

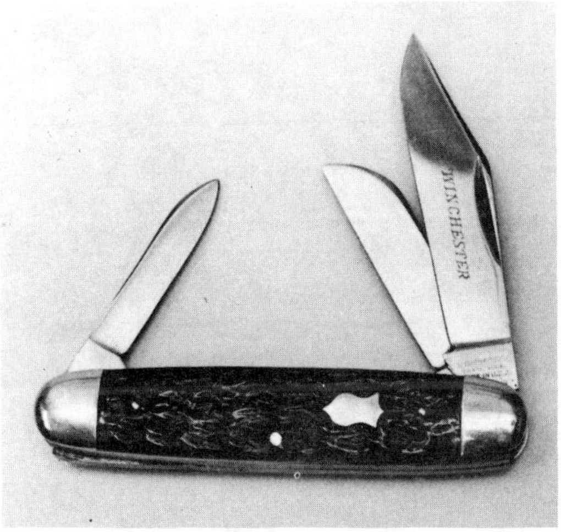

CATTLE

3952 Brown Bone 3¾" $250

3953	Bartender, Stag	3¼	175

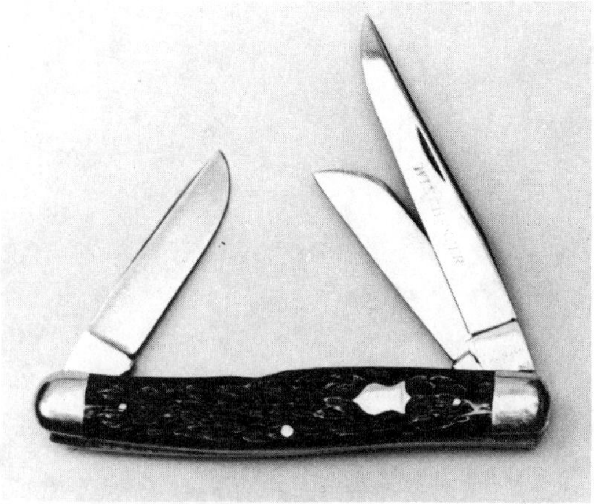

STOCKMAN

3959	**Brown Bone**	**4"**	**$250**

No.	Name, Handle	Lgth	Price
3960	Prem. Stockman, Stag	4	250
3961	Prem. Stockman, Stag	4	250
3962	Prem. Stockman, Buffalo Horn	4	320
3963	Stockman, Stag	4	225
3964	Prem. Stockman, Stag	4	225
3965	Prem. Stockman, Stag	3¼	175
3966	Prem. Stockman, Stag	3¼	150
3967	Prem. Stockman, Stag	3¼	200
3968	Prem. Stockman, Stag	3¼	250
3969	Prem. Stockman Whittler, Stag	3¼	250
3971	Swell Ctr., Stag	3⅝	280
3972	Swell Ctr., Stag	3⅝	320
3973	Cattle, Stag	3½	260
3975	Cattle, Stag	3⅜	250
3977	Cattle, Stag	3⅜	250

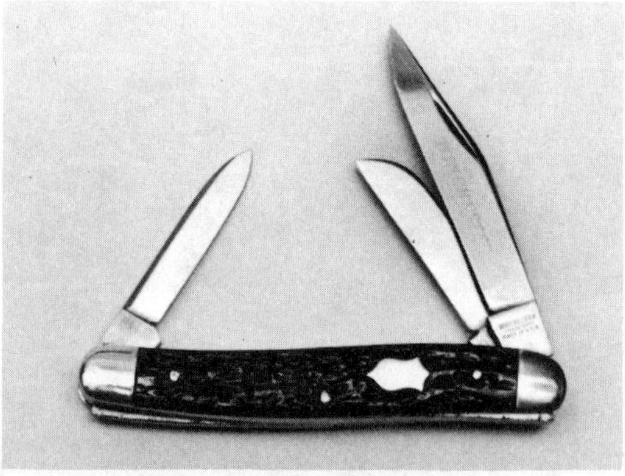

SERPENTINE STOCKMAN

3978	**Brown Bone**	**3¼"**	**$150**

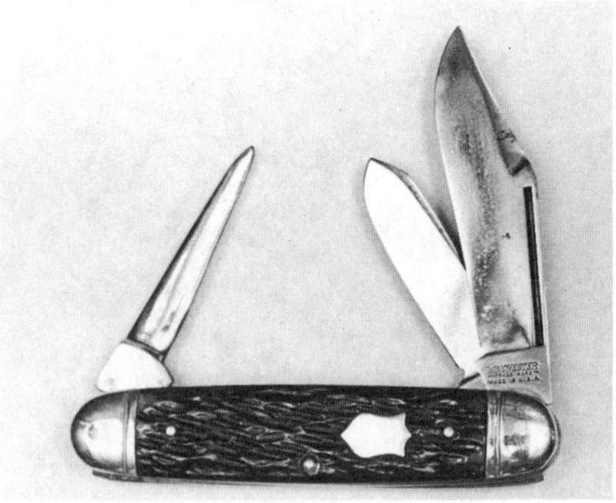

CATTLE

3979	**Brown Bone**	**3⅝"**	**$250**
3980	Serpentine Cattle, Stag	3	215
3991	Sleeveboard, Stag	3⅜	180
3992	Senator, Stag	3⅜	250
3993	Prem. Stockman, Stag	4	250
4001	Prem. Stockman, Celluloid	4	420
4301	Lobster, Pearl	2¾	225
4313	Senator, Pearl	3	250

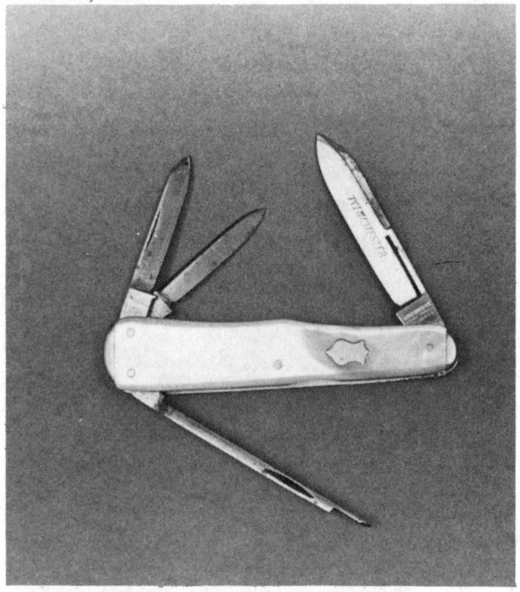

GUNSTOCK WHITTLER

4320	**Pearl**	**3⅛"**	**$250**
4340	Senator, Pearl	3¼	300
4341	Senator, Pearl	3¼	300

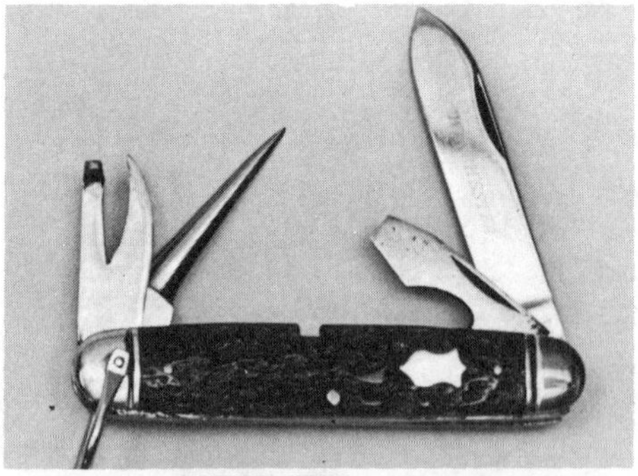

UTILITY

4901	**Brown Bone**	**3⅜"**	**$250**

No.	Name, Handle	Lgth	Price
4910	Stag	4	550
4918	Congress, Stag	3	230
4920	Lobster, Stag	3⅛	160
4930	Congress, Stag	3¼	300
4931	Congress, Stag	3½	300

SCOUT

| 4950 | Bone | | 3⅝" | $300 |

UTILITY

4950	**Brown Bone**		**3¾"**	**$275**
4951	Utility, Stag	3⅝	300	
4962	Prem. Stockman, Stag	4	300	
4963	Prem. Stockman, Stag	4	300	
4975	Bartender, Stag	3¼	210	
4990	Utility, Stag	3⅝	300	
4991	Utility, Stag	3½	250	

PREMIUM STOCKMAN

| 4961 | Bone | | 4" | $300 |

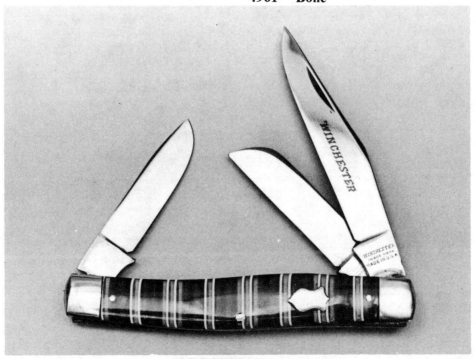

STOCKMAN

| 3018 | Candystripe | | 4" | $325 |

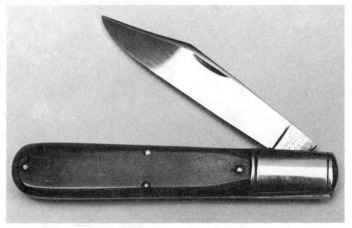

1703   Brown Bone 1 Bl.   5⅛"   Winchester USA $250
Daddy Barlow

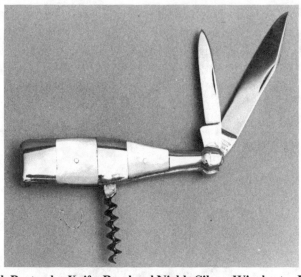

2 Bl. Bartender Knife, Pearl and Nickle Silver, Winchester USA, 3⅜", Very Rare $500

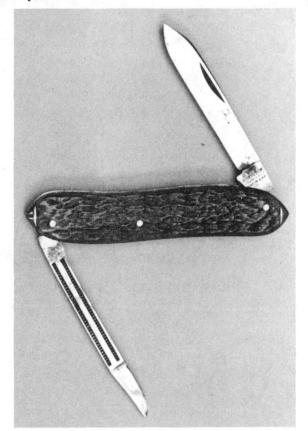

2910   Lobster, Bone   Winchester $135

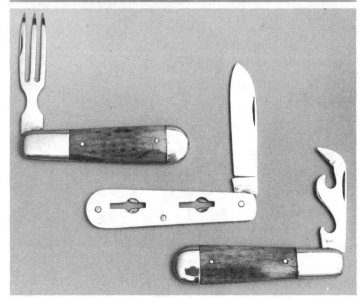

Winchester 3 Piece Hobo, Brown Bone,   3½", Rare $1200

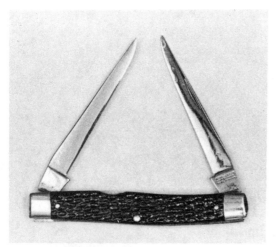

MUSKRAT

No Nr. Imi. Jigged Bone   4" $125

PEN

No Nr. Brown Bone   2⅝" $90

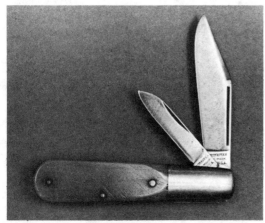

BARLOW

No Nr. Bone   3¼" $175

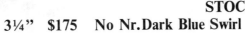

STOCKMAN

No Nr. Dark Blue Swirl   3⅜" $140

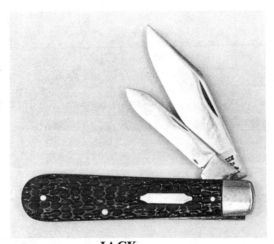

JACK

No Nr. Imitation Bone   3⅜" $90

STOCKMAN

No Nr. Imi. Black Bone   3⅞" $150

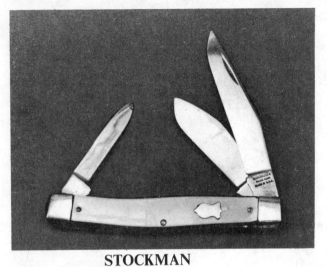

STOCKMAN

No Nr.Imi. Pearl   4" $200

No Nr.Imi. Bone   3⅜" $110

ADDITIONAL WINCHESTERS

See previous listings for more information.

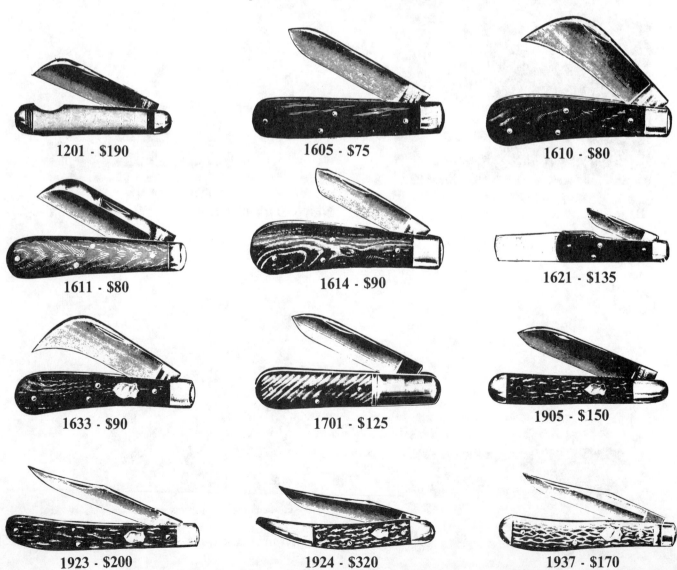

1201 - $190

1605 - $75

1610 - $80

1611 - $80

1614 - $90

1621 - $135

1633 - $90

1701 - $125

1905 - $150

1923 - $200

1924 - $320

1937 - $170

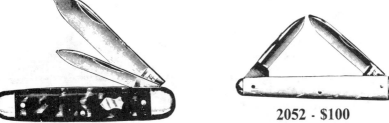

2028 - $170

2052 - $100

2055 - $75

2059 - $100

2070 - $125

2079 - $100

2082 - $110

2085 - $130

2089 - $110

2094 - $200

2110 - $150

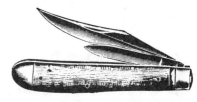

2113 - $125

2114 - $140

2116 - $90

2117 - $175

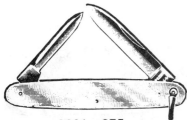

2201 - $75

2202 - $80

2204 - $75

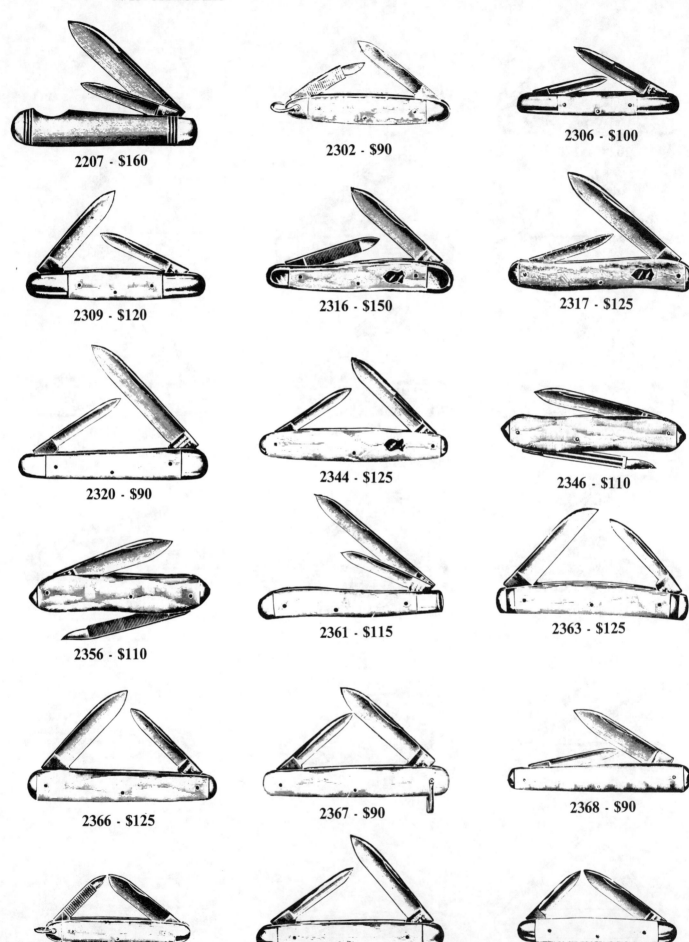

2207 - $160

2302 - $90

2306 - $100

2309 - $120

2316 - $150

2317 - $125

2320 - $90

2344 - $125

2346 - $110

2356 - $110

2361 - $115

2363 - $125

2366 - $125

2367 - $90

2368 - $90

2375 - $100

2376 - $130

2377 - $150

2612 - $190

2613 - $190

2608 - $125

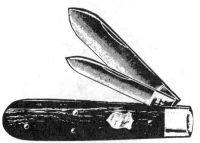

2614 - $190

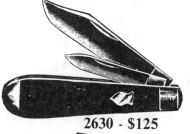

2630 - $125

2633 - $120

2635 - $125

2649 - $160

2660 - $160

2681 - $110

2830 - $75

2842 - $125

2844 - $275

2845 - $230

2846 - $125

2848 - $135

2849 - $140

2850 - $285

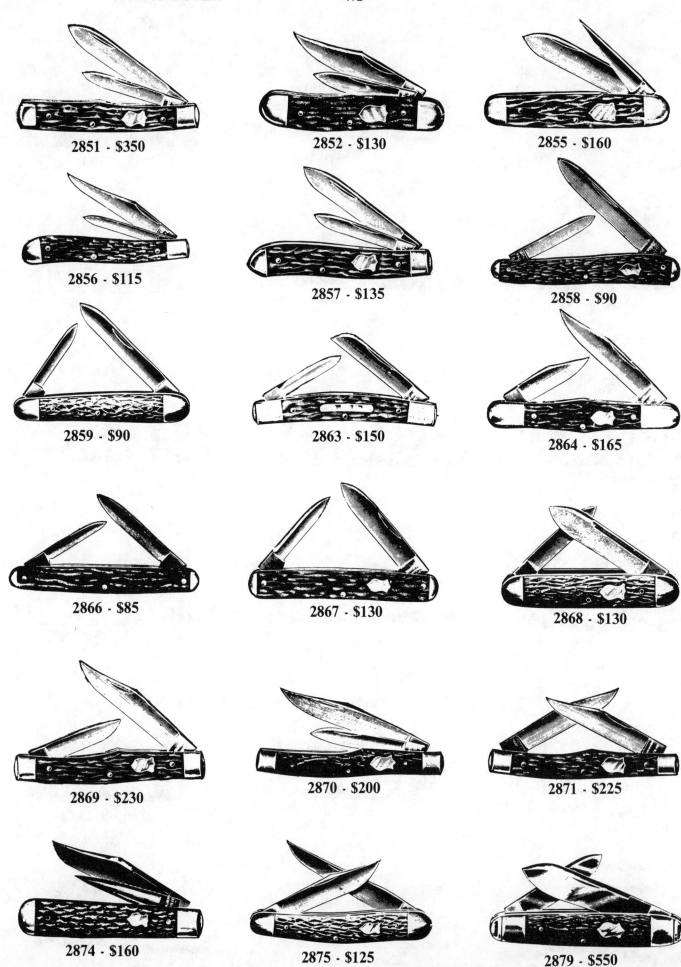

2851 - $350

2852 - $130

2855 - $160

2856 - $115

2857 - $135

2858 - $90

2859 - $90

2863 - $150

2864 - $165

2866 - $85

2867 - $130

2868 - $130

2869 - $230

2870 - $200

2871 - $225

2874 - $160

2875 - $125

2879 - $550

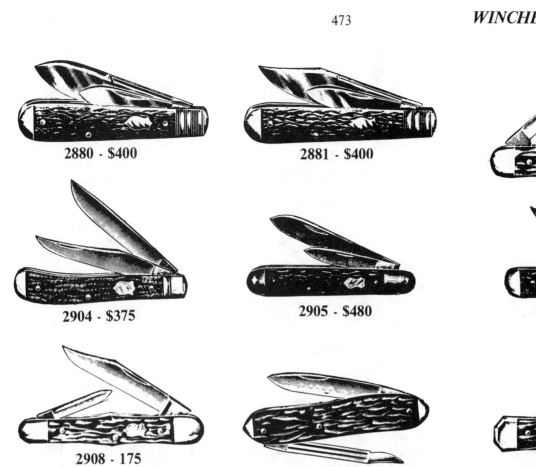

2880 - $400

2881 - $400

2903 - $200

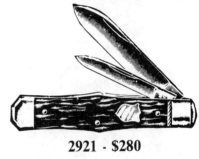

2904 - $375

2905 - $480

2907 - 400

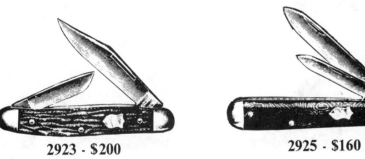

2908 - 175

2910 - $100

2921 - $280

2923 - $200

2925 - $160

2928 - $200

2932 - $150

2933 - $125

2934 - $100

2938 - $150

2945 - $100

2951 - $140

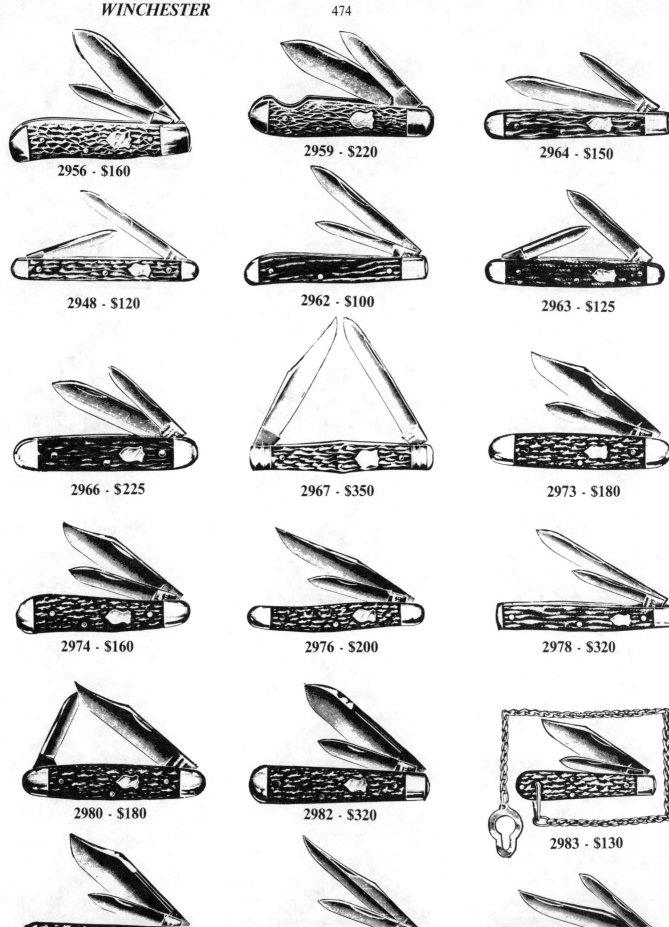

2956 - $160

2959 - $220

2964 - $150

2948 - $120

2962 - $100

2963 - $125

2966 - $225

2967 - $350

2973 - $180

2974 - $160

2976 - $200

2978 - $320

2980 - $180

2982 - $320

2983 - $130

2988 - $320

2990 - $130

2993 - $375

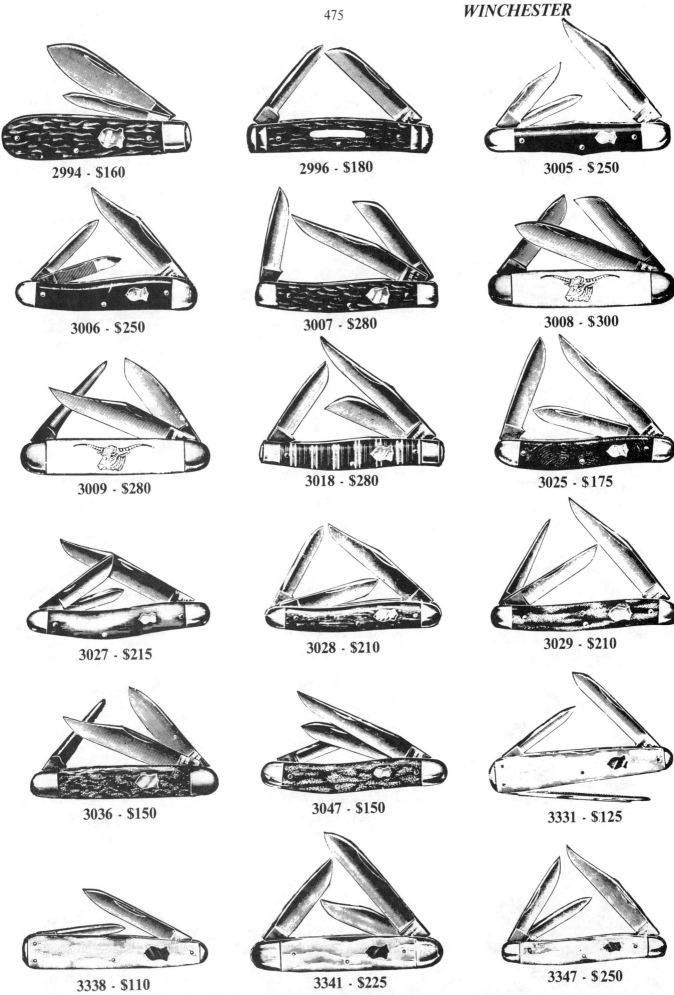

2994 - $160

2996 - $180

3005 - $250

3006 - $250

3007 - $280

3008 - $300

3009 - $280

3018 - $280

3025 - $175

3027 - $215

3028 - $210

3029 - $210

3036 - $150

3047 - $150

3331 - $125

3338 - $110

3341 - $225

3347 - $250

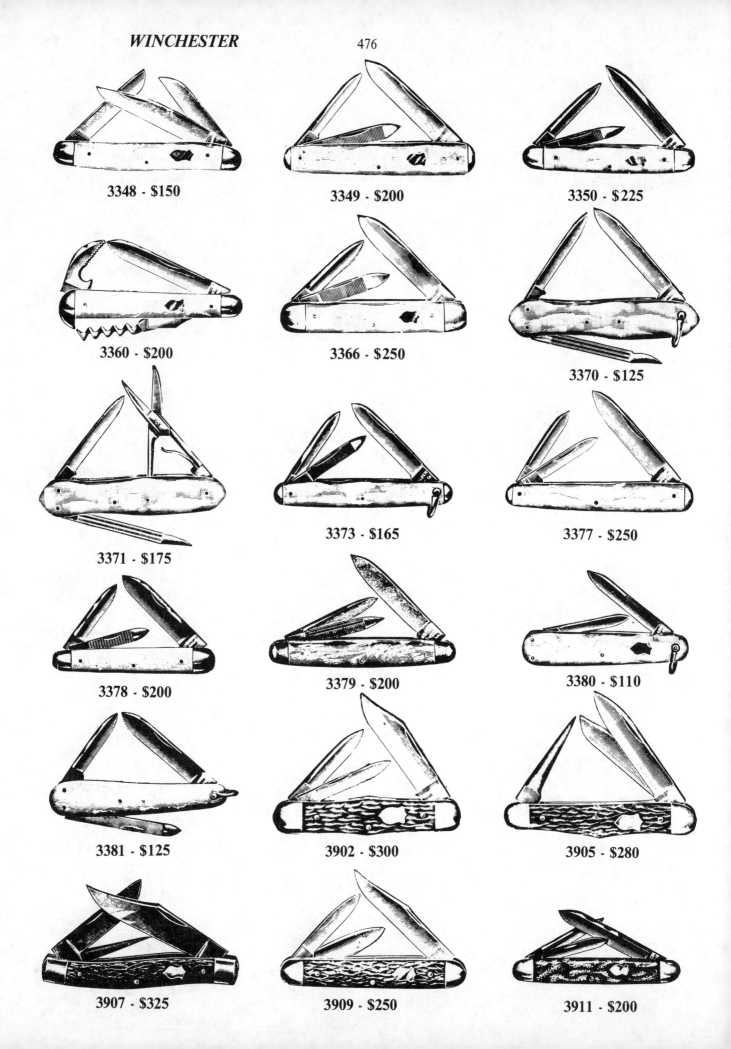

3348 - $150

3349 - $200

3350 - $225

3360 - $200

3366 - $250

3370 - $125

3371 - $175

3373 - $165

3377 - $250

3378 - $200

3379 - $200

3380 - $110

3381 - $125

3902 - $300

3905 - $280

3907 - $325

3909 - $250

3911 - $200

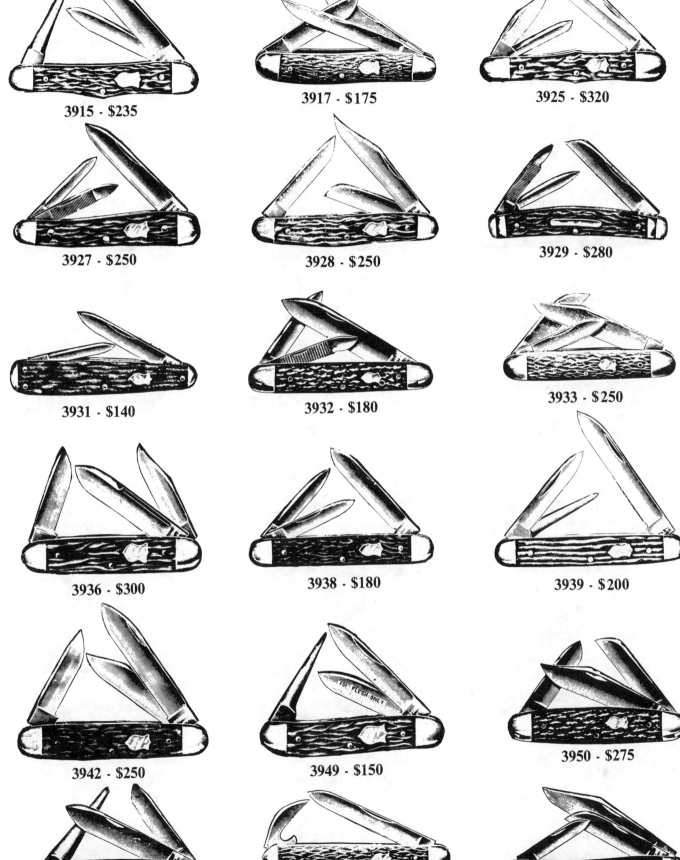

3915 - $235

3917 - $175

3925 - $320

3927 - $250

3928 - $250

3929 - $280

3931 - $140

3932 - $180

3933 - $250

3936 - $300

3938 - $180

3939 - $200

3942 - $250

3949 - $150

3950 - $275

3951 - $275

3953 - $175

3960 - $250

3961 - $250

3962 - $320

3964 - $225

3965 - $175

3966 - $150

3968 - $250

3969 - $250

3971 - $280

3972 - $320

3975 - $280

3977 - $250

3980 - $215

3991 - $180

3992 - $270

3993 - $250

4001 - $420

4301 - $225

4340 - $300

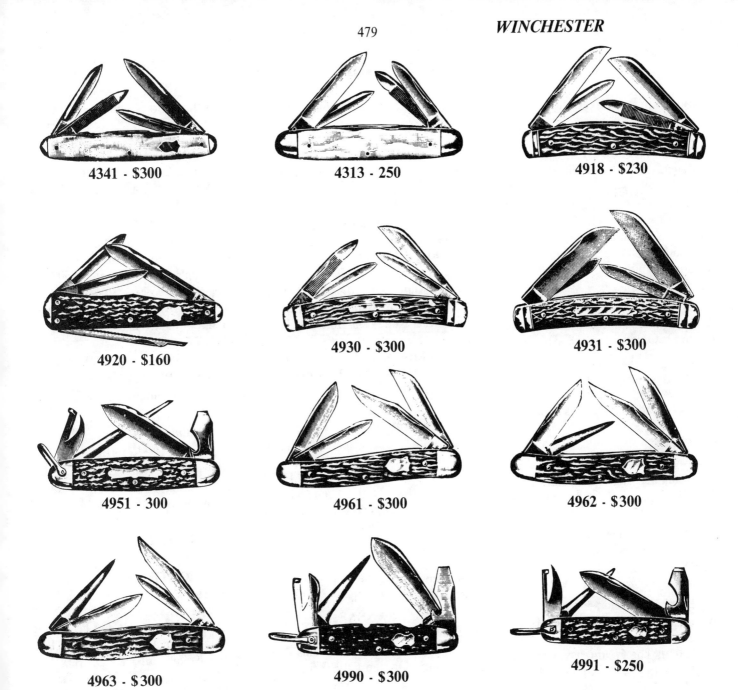

4341 - $300

4313 - 250

4918 - $230

4920 - $160

4930 - $300

4931 - $300

4951 - 300

4961 - $300

4962 - $300

4963 - $300

4990 - $300

4991 - $250

CLUBS

If your club is inadvertently omitted or is a newly formed club, please notify the author and it will be included in future editions.

ALABAMA
Wheeler Basin Knife Club, P. O. Box 346, Hartselle, AL 35640; **Circle City Cutlery,** Dothan, AL 36301; **Elk River Knife Collectors,** Rogerville, AL 35652; **Noccalula Knife Collectors Association,** Gadsden, AL 35902; **Sand Mountain Cutlery Club,** Albertville, AL 35905.

ARIZONA
Arizona Knife Collectors Club, P. O. Box 652, Glendale, AZ 85311.

CALIFORNIA
The Bay Area Knife Collectors Assoc., P. O. Box 5765, Berkeley, CA 94705; **Southern California Blades Knife Collectors Club,** P. O. Box 1140, Lomita, CA 90717.

CANADA
The Canadian Knife Collectors Club, 148 Islington Ave., Toronto, Ontario M8V 3B6 087.

COLORADO
Rocky Mountain Blade Collectors, P. O. Box 115, Louisville, CO 80027.

FLORIDA
Bold City Knife Club, 4652 Bankhead Ave., Jacksonville, FL 32207; **Gator Cutlery Club,** P. O. Box 11973, Tampa, FL 33680; **The Gold Coast Chapter,** 715 S. 46th Ave., Hollywood, FL; **Florida Knife Collectors Assoc.,** 3301 Delaware Ave., Titusville, FL 32780; **Leesburg Chapter F.K.C.A.** (Satellite of Florida Knife Collectors Assoc.), 3301 Delaware Ave., Titusville, FL.

GEORGIA
Flint River Knife Club, P. O. Box 1772, Forest Park, GA 30050; **Ocmulgee Knife Collectors,** P. O. Box 388, Gordon, GA 31031; **Three Rivers Knife Club,** Rt. 7, Box 783 Jones Mill Road N.E., Rome, GA 30161; **Peach State Cutlery Club,** 4661 Mahonia Way, Acworth, GA 30101; **Chattahoochee Cutlery Club,** Tucker, GA 30084; **Valdosta Knife Club,** Valdosta, GA 31601.

IDAHO
Idaho Knife Collectors Association, Boise, ID 83707.

ILLINOIS
American Edge Collectors Assoc., P. O. Box 2207, Hammond, IN 46323; **Soy Knife Collectors,** Box 1752, Decatur, IL 62525; **Jefferson County Custom Knife Club,** 709 Airport Road, Mt. Vernon, IL 62864; **The Bunker Hill Pocket Knife Collectors and Trade Club,** RR 2, Bunker Hill, IL 62014; **River to River Knife Club,** Marion, IL 62959; **St. Louis Area,** Greenville, IL 62246.

INDIANA
Northern Indiana Knife Club, 8911 Park Valley Ct., Hobart, Indiana; **Indiana Knife Collectors,** Anderson, IN 46011; **Evansville Knife Club (E.K.C.)** Evansville, IN 47710; **Michigan Knife Collectors Club,** South Bend, IN 46615; **Fort City Knife Collectors Club.**

IOWA
The Hawkeye Knife Collectors Club, Rt. 2, Box 46, Earlham, IA 50072.

KANSAS
Kansas Knife Collectors Club, Arkansas City, KS 67005; **High Plains Blade Collectors,** Garden City, KS 67846.

KENTUCKY
Central Kentucky Knife Club, P. O. Box 5049, Lexington, KY 40555; **Kentucky Cutlery Assoc.,** P. O. Box 58012, Louisville, KY 40258; **Eagle Creek Knife Club,** Owenton, KY 40359; **Yellow Banks Cutlery Club,** Owensboro, KY 42302; **Fort City Knife Collectors Club; King Coal Knife Club,** Madisonville, KY 42431; **Eastern Kentucky Cutlery Club,** Pikeville, KY 41501.

MARYLAND
Chesapeake Bay Knife Club, Inc. Baltimore, MD 21224.

MASSACHUSETTS
Northeast Cutlery Collectors Assoc., 19 North Central Ave., Wollaston, MA 02170.

MICHIGAN
Wolverine Knife Collectors Club, P. O. Box 52, Belleville, MI 48111; **Flint Edge Knife Club,** Flint, MI 48503; **The Great Lakes Knifecrafters Assoc.,** Mt. Clemens, MI 48045; **Anyone in the Saginaw Valley area:** Flushing, MI 48433.

MINNESOTA
North Star Blade Collectors, P. O. Box 20523, Bloomington, MN 55420.

MISSISSIPPI
Rebel Knife Club, Tupelo, MS 38801.

MISSOURI
Gateway Area Knife Club, P. O. Box 11058, Ferguson, MO 63135; **Kansas City Knife Club,** Rayton, MO 64133.

NEW YORK
KA-BAR Knife Collectors Club, Olena, NY 14760.

NORTH CAROLINA
Tar Heel Cutlery Club, 2730 Tudor Rd., winston-Salem, NC 27106; **North Carolina Cutlery Club,** 113 Powell Dr., Fuquay Varina, NC 27526; **Bechtler Mint Knife Club,** P. O. Box 149, Rutherfordton, NC 28139; **Trapper Knife Collectors Club,** Gastonia, NC 28052; **Albermarle Knife Club,** Albemarle, NC 28001; **Mountain Whittler Knife Club,** Asheville, NC 28816; **Kotton County Knife Collectors,** Charlotte, NC 28215; **The Gem Capital Knife Club,** Franklin, NC 28734; **The Catawba Valley Knife Club,** Morganton, NC 28655.

OHIO
Fort City Knife Collectors Club, P. O. Box 31396, Cincinnati, OH 45231; **Western Reserve Cutlery Assoc.,** P. O. Box 94, Doylestown, OH 44230.

OKLAHOMA
Sooner Knife Collectors Club, 1813 SW 30th, Moore, OK 73160.

OREGON
Oregon Knife Collectors Assoc., P. O. Box 246, Cheshire, OR 97419.

PENNSYLVANIA
Mason Dixon Knife Club, P. O. Box 196, Quincy,, PA 17247; Allegheny Mountain Knife Collectors Assoc., P. O. Box 23, Hunker, PA 15639; Eastern Pennsylvania Knife Collectors, Rt. 3, Box 433, Coopersburg, PA 18036; Keystone Blade Assoc., P. O. Box 46, Lewisburg, PA 17837; The Case Collectors Club, Bradford, PA 16701; The Delaware Valley Knife Collectors Club, Fallsington, PA 19054; Pocono Knife Club, Pocono Lake, PA 18347.

SOUTH CAROLINA
Palmetto Cutlery Club, P. O. Box 1177, Greer, SC 29651.

TENNESSEE
Music City Knife Collectors, P. O. Box 17134, Nashville, TN 37217; Tennessee Valley Blades Knife Club, P. O. Box 1223, Athens, TN 37303; Memphis Knife Collectors, 3550 Merritt St., Memphis, TN 38128; Smokey Mountain Knife Collectors, Box 1176, Maryville, TN 37801; Colonel Coon Knife Club, P. O. Box 1676, Dyersburg, TN 38025; Fight'n Rooster Cutlery Club, Box 936, Lebanon, TN 37087; Choo Choo Knife Club, North Chattanooga, TN 37343; East Tennessee Knife Collectors, Bristol, TN 37620; Hardeman County Knife Collectors Assoc., Hornsby, TN 38044; The Golden Circle Knife Club, Jackson, TN 38301; Middle Tennessee Knife Collectors Club, Murfreesboro, TN 37130.

TEXAS
Lone Star Knife Club, P. O. Box 8660, Waco, TX 76714; Gulf Coast Knife Club, P. O. Box 3323, Pasadena, TX 77501; Texas Knife Collectors Assoc., Box 4754, Austin, TX 78765; Permian Basin Knife Club, P. O. Box 5744, Midland, TX 79704; The West Texas Knife Club, Sweetwater, TX 79556.

VIRGINIA
Old Dominion Knife Collectors, 2403 Floraland Dr., NW, Roanoke, VA 24012; Northern Virginia Knife Collectors, Inc. P. O. Box 501, Falls Church, VA 22046; Military Knife and Bayonet Club, 1142 West Grace St., Richmond, VA 23220.

WASHINGTON
North West Knife Collectors, 1911 SW Campus Drive, Suite 271, Fed Way, WA 98023; The Cascade Blade Association, Redmond, WA 98052.

WEST VIRGINIA
Ohio Valley Knife Collectors, New Martinsville, WV 26155.

WISCONSIN
Badger Knife Club, 7024 West Wells St., Wauwatosa, WI 53213.

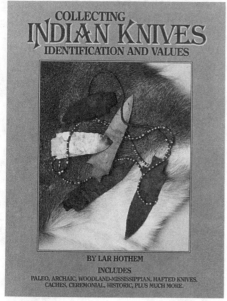
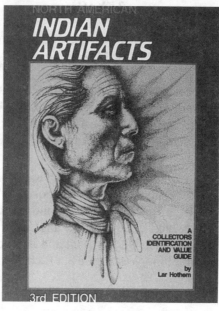
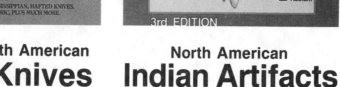